THE
OFFICIAL BOTTLE
PRICE LIST

Books by Ralph M. and Terry H. Kovel

The Official Bottle Price List
The Complete Antiques Price List
Know Your Antiques
American Country Furniture 1780–1875
A Directory of American Silver, Pewter and Silver Plate
Dictionary of Marks — Pottery and Porcelain

THE OFFICIAL BOTTLE PRICE LIST

by Ralph M. and Terry H. Kovel

ILLUSTRATED

CROWN PUBLISHERS, INC., NEW YORK

Second Printing Before Publication
©1971 by Crown Publishers, Inc.
Library of Congress Catalog Card Number: 79 — 171980

Printed in the United States of America
Published simultaneously in Canada by General Publishing
Company Limited

ACKNOWLEDGMENTS

To the following companies and collectors, etc., our special thanks for their help in obtaining the pictures of bottles for use in this book: Bill Agee; Vern Schrantz, Ball Brothers Co., Inc.; Richard A. Griebel, P. Ballantine & Sons; Robert Weisenberger, James Beam Distilling Co.; Mr. D'arcy, Black & White Scotch; John McKay, II, The Carter's Ink Co.; William K. Bass, Coca-Cola U.S.A.; J. Glennon Walsh, Ezra Brooks Distilling Co.; Robert J. Franklin, Dant-Old Charter; Walter H. Douglas, Dayton, Ohio; Arthur Palombo, Frankfort Distillers Co.; Mrs. Oswald G. Fritz; Thomas F. Wipperman, Glenmore Distilleries Co.; W. Dan Lemeshka, The Gorham Company; J. C. Malin, William Grant and Sons, Inc.; Arlene and Paul Greaser; Thomas H. McIntosh, H. J. Heinz Company; Mrs. Deborah Levine Herman; Cathy Horvitz; Tom Horvitz; William C. Handlan & Ted Simmons, Jack Daniel Distillery; C. J. McCarthy, Lestoil—Standard House Products, Inc.; Mr. and Mrs. Jack M. Levine, Cleveland, Ohio; Even G. Kulsveen, Lionstone Distilleries, Ltd.; Mrs. Ted Lux; J. M. Starke, McCormick Distilling Company; Bart Harris, Miller Brewing Co.; Ronald B. Field, Mogen David Wine Corporation; H. C. Bennett, National Distillers Products Co.; George Kraus, Old Style Colony Winery, Inc.; Jack F. Varick, Joseph Schlitz Brewing Co.; R. O. Parrish, Stitzel Weller—Old Fitzgerald & Cabin Still; Toledo Museum of Art; Rudolph Reifstahl and the Libbey bequest; Mr. Van Heher, Wheaton-Nuline. Special thanks must go to several people who gave help when it was needed the most. David Eisendrath and Gordon Bass helped with the color pictures. Bill Agee loaned us pictures from his book about bottles *Collecting the Cures*. To Debby Herman, Eleanor Ruf, and Norma Hannon an extra bit of appreciation for getting this all put together on time with as few mistakes as possible.

INTRODUCTION

Bottle collecting has become one of the top hobbies in the United States. Not only early historical flasks and figural bottles are collected, but also many types of modern bottles and reproductions. Bottle clubs and bottle shows have set the rules for this Official Bottle Price List. We have taken the terms from those in common usage and tried to organize the thousands of listings in easy-to-use form. Medicine bottles include all medicine or drugstore bottles, except those under the more specific headings of bitters or sarsaparilla. Modern liquor bottles are listed under the brand name if more than five of the bottles are in the collectible series. If you are not a regular at bottle shows, it may take a few tries to become accustomed to the method of listing. If you cannot find a bottle, try several related headings. For instance, hair dye is found under "household" bottles; many named bottles are found under "medicine," "food," "fruit jar," etc. If your fruit jar has several names, such as "Ball, Mason," look under "fruit jar, ball," or "fruit jar, mason."

The prices shown are in most cases the actual prices asked for bottles during the past year. A few bottles have been included to complete a listing. When this has been done, the prices are estimates based on known prices of the past two years. The estimated prices appear only for modern bottles in a series. Pre-World War I bottles are all listed at actual sale price.

Prices may vary in different parts of the country, so a range is given. Because of the idiosyncrasies of the computer, it was impossible to place a range of price on bottles that are illustrated. The price listed is an average.

Spelling is meant to help the collector. If the original bottle spelled the word "catsup" or "ketchup," that is the spelling that appears. If the period was omitted from "Dr." or the apostrophe from "Jones' sarsaparilla," that is the way it appears. A few bottles are included that had errors in the original spelling and that error is used in the list. "Whiskey" is used even if the bottle held Scotch or Canadian and should be spelled "whisky."

Every bottle illustrated in black and white is indicated by the word "illus." in the text. Every priced bottle pictured in color is indicated by the word "color" in the listing.

There are a very limited number of the color illustrated bottles shown without prices. They are so rare that no accurate prices are available. We thought the pictures should show the best ones to be an incentive to the collector. To guess at the price would be unfair to everyone.

At the end of the book, you will find a list of bottle clubs. It is as accurate as we could make it, but addresses and names change each month and new clubs are formed daily. The bibliography is for other books about bottles that might help you with your specialty.

We welcome any information about clubs, prices, or content for future books, but cannot give appraisals by mail. We have tried to be accurate, but we cannot be responsible if any errors in pricing appear.

NATIONAL BOTTLE CLUBS

Antique Bottle Collectors
Association
P.O. Box 467
Sacramento, California 95802

National Jim Beam Bottle &
Specialties Club
490 El Camino Real
Belmont, California 94002

BOTTLE CLUBS

A.B.C. of Colorado
Box 63
Denver, Colorado

A.B.C. of Hawaii
P.O. Box 591
Ewa, Hawaii 96706

A.B.C. of Jacksonville
27 S. 15th Street
Fernandina Beach, Florida

A.B.C. of Orange County
223 E. Ponona
Santa Ana, California 92707

A.B.C.A. of Florida
14301 S.W. 87th Avenue
Miami, Florida 33158

A.B.C.A. of Fresno
Steve Kincade
P.O. Box 1932
Fresno, California 93718

A.B.C.A. of Reno-Sparks
4965 Mason Road
Reno, Nevada 89500

A.B.C.A. of Sacramento, Inc.
Box 467
Sacramento, California

Alabama Bottle Collector's
Association
2713 Hanover Circle S.
Birmingham, Alabama

Alabama Bottle Collector's Society
1768 Hanover Circle
Birmingham, Alabama

Alamo Chapter A.B.C.A.
c/o Robert Duff
701 Castano Avenue
San Antonio, Texas 78209

Alamosa Bottle Collectors
c/o Mrs. Robert Russell
Route 2, Box 170
Alamosa, Colorado 81101

American Association of Perfume
Collectors
P.O. Box 55074
Houston, Texas 77055

Amethyst Bottle Club
3245 Military Avenue
Los Angeles, California

Anchorage Beam Club
5401 Chera Avenue
Anchorage, Alaska 99504

Antique Bottle & Glass Collectors
311 Avenue East
Snohomish, Washington 98290

Antique Bottle Club of Colorado
2555 S. Raleigh
Denver, Colorado 80219

Antique Bottle Club of Hawaii
c/o R. Elliot
P.O. Box 591
Ewa, Hawaii 96706

Antique Bottle Club of
Orange County
P.O. Box 10424
Santa Ana, California 92711

Antique Questers
172 Conners Avenue
Chico, California 95926

Apollo Beach A.B.C.A.
P.O. Box 3354
Apollo Beach, Florida 33570

Arizona Territory A.B.C.
P.O. Box 1221
Tucson, Arizona 85715

Arizona Treasures Unlimited
5506 W. McDowell Road
Phoenix, Arizona

Arnfalt Collectors Beam Club
Tony Arnfalt
New Richland, Minnesota 56072

Avon Bottle & Specialties Collectors
Southern California Division
9233 Mills Avenue
Montclair, California 91763

Avon Collectors Club
P.O. Box 1406
Mesa, Arizona 86201

Beam Club of Southern California
114 Coronado Terrace
Los Angeles, California 90026

Benton Beams & Antiques
MaBelle V. Bramlettle
Benton, California 93512

Bishop Belles & Beaux Bottle Club
P.O. Box 1475
Bishop, California

Bottle Collectors Association of
  Florida
14301 S.W. 8th Avenue
Miami, Florida

Bytown Bottle Collectors Club
820 Dundee Avenue
Ottawa 14, Ontario, Canada

Canal Zone B.C.A.
Box 2232
Balboa, Canal Zone

Capitol Bottle Collectors
207 West 18th
Olympia, Washington 98501

Catoctin Bottle Club
c/o Frank Joy
2106 Sunnybrook Drive
Frederick, Maryland 21701

Catskill Mountain Jim Beam
  Bottle Club
c/o William Gibbs
Six Gardner Avenue
Middletown, New York 10940

Cave City A.B.C.
Route 1, Box 155
Carlsbad, New Mexico 88220

Central & Midwestern States
  Beam & Specialties Club
c/o Elmer Collins
44 S. Westmore
Lombard, Illinois 60148

Central California Avon Bottle Club
5101 Stockton Boulevard
Sacramento, California 95820

Central Ohio Bottle Club
P.O. Box 19864
Columbus, Ohio 43219

Central South Oregon A.B.C.
708 South F. Street
Lakeview, Oregon 97630

Cherry Valley Beam &
  Specialties Club
Ruby Birch
P.O. Box 1193
Cherry Valley, California

Cheyenne A.B.C.
3520 Laramie Street
Cheyenne, Wyoming

Chico Antique Bottle Club
2559 White Avenue
Chico, California

Chief Solano Bottle Club
4-D Boynton Avenue
Suisun City, California

Colorado Beam Bottle &
  Specialties Club
530 Yellowstone Road
Colorado Springs, Colorado 80910

Curiosity Bottle Association
Box 103
Napa, California 94558

Dant "Americana" Bottle Club
J. W. Dant Distillers Co.
1290 Avenue of the Americas
New York, New York 10019

Decanter Club
Two Spring Street
Potsdam, New York 13676

Des Moines Jim Beam &
  Specialty Club
Edward Van Dyke
2417 48th Street
Des Moines, Iowa 50310

Dirigo Bottle Collector's Club
237 14th Street
Bangor, Maine 04401

Dixie Beam Bottle Club
C. B. Carter
Clarksville, Virginia 23927

Dover Foxcroft Bottle Club
c/o Wayne Champion
50 Church Street
Dover Foxcroft, Maine 04426

Eagle Valley Gophers
227 E. Long Street
Carson City, Nevada 39701

Eastern Monroe Country
  Bottle Club
c/o Bethlehem Lutheran Church
1767 Plank Road
Webster, New York

Em Tee Bottle Club
Box 62
Jerome, Idaho

Emerald Empire Bottle Club
Rattlesnake Creek Road
Dexter, Oregon 97431

Emmett Historical Bottle
  Association
108 Grove Street
Petoskey, Michigan 49770

Empire State Bottle & Specialty Club
William Bateman
East Main Street
Milford, New York 13807

Empire State Bottle Coll. Assn.
Jones Road, Box 274
Syracuse, New York 13209

Endless Mountain Antique
  Bottle Club
Bentley Creek, Pennsylvania

Erie Bottle Club
926½ West 29th Street
Erie, Pennsylvania 16508

Evergreen State Beam Bottle Club
1540 Maple Lane
Kent, Washington 98031

Eytown Bottle Collectors
c/o Don McKenzie
820 Dundee Avenue
Ottawa, Ontario, Canada

Ezra Brooks Bottle & Specialties Club
420 N. First Street
Kewanee, Illinois 61443

Ezra Brooks Specialties Club
636 W. Ivy Street
Glendale, California 91204

Ezra Brooks Specialties Club
4908½ Meridian Street
Los Angeles, California 90042

Fabulous Valley A.B.C.
Box 638
Osburn, Idaho 83849

Fallon Bottle Club
Tolas Place
Fallon, Nevada

Figural Bottle Association
The Bottle Stopper
Eagle, Wisconsin 53119

Finger Lakes B.C.A.
4742 Sweeney Road, R.D. 4
Cortland, New York 13045

First Canadian Bottle &
    Specialty Club
Doug Reid
1221 19th Avenue N.W.
Calgary 43, Alberta, Canada

First Chicago Bottle Club
1419 W. Fullerton
Chicago, Illinois 60614

Flint Hills Beam & Specialty Club
201 W. Pine
El Dorado, Kansas 67042

Foard C. Hobby Club
Box 625
Crowell, Texas 79227

Forks of the Delaware Bottle Club
J. H. Chidsey
1700 Butler Street
Easton, Pennsylvania 18042

Fort Wayne Bottle Club
Thurman Fuhrman
5622 Arbor Avenue
Fort Wayne, Indiana

Fort Wayne Historical Bottle Club
R.R. #1
Ossian, Indiana 46777

Foursome (Jim Beam)
H. G. Lewis, Sr.
1208 Azalea Drive
Longview, Texas

Friendly Jim's Beam Club
James Bradley, Sr.
508 Benjamin Franklin H. W. East
Douglassville, Pennsylvania 19518

Frontier Collectors
504 N.W. Bailey
Pendleton, Oregon 97801

Gem A.B.C., Inc.
306 Linden
Boise, Idaho

The Genesee Valley Bottle
    Collectors Assn.
28 Nettlecreek Road
Fairport, New York 14450

Georgia Bottle Club
Tom Zachary
2996 Pangborn Road
Decatur, Georgia 30033

Glass Bells of San Gabriel
518 W. Neuby Avenue
San Gabriel, California 91776

Glasshoppers Figural Bottle Assn.
Box 576
Lomita, California 90717

Gold Diggers A.B.C.
1958 So. Stage Road
Medford, Oregon 97501

Golden Gate Ezra Brooks Club
12517 San Pablo Avenue
Richmond, California 94805

Golden Gate Historical Bottle Society
1623 Sherman Street
Alameda, California

Granite State Bottle Club
c/o Alfred Davis
116 Academy Street
Laconia, New Hampshire 03246

Greater California Antique Bottle Club
P.O. Box 9262
Sacramento, California 95816

Greater St. Louis Area
   Beam Bottle Club
c/o Jack Huggins
103 Powder Mill Road
Belleville, Illinois

Green Mountain Bottle Club
c/o Fred Brown
School Street
Hartford, Vermont 05047

Gulf Coast Bottle & Jar Club
2221 Camille
Pasadena, Texas 77503

Hangtown Bottleers
366 Placerville Drive
Placerville, California 95667

Hawaii Beam Bottle & Specialty Club
Alberdene Little
2003 Kalia Road 23A
Honolulu, Hawaii 96815

The Heart of Illinois A.B.C.
105 Kerfoot Street
East Peoria, Illinois 61611

Hellgate A.B.C.
509 Westview Drive
Missoula, Montana

"High-Country" A.B.C.
221 Poncha Avenue, Box 324
Alamosa, Colorado

High Desert Bottle Hunters
P.O. Box 581
Ridgecrest, California 93555

Historical Bottle Diggers
Route 3, Box 204
Broadway, Virginia 22815

Hoosier Bottle Club
P.O. Box 33126
Indianapolis, Indiana 42603

Horsetooth A.B.C.A.
304 Ellen
Fort Collins, Colorado

Humboldt Antique Bottle Club Assn.
786 Dorothy Court
Arcata, Eureka, California

Huntsville Historical Bottle Club
113 Monto Sono Boulevard S.E.
Huntsville, Alabama

Illinois Bottle Club
416 East Webster
Griggsville, Illinois 62340

International Decanters Club
Opal Redman
101 E. Third Street
Dayton, Ohio 45402

Iowa Antique Bottleers
1506 Albia Road
Ottumwa, Iowa 52501

Iowa Bottleers
902 N. Johnson
Ottumwa, Iowa 52501

Islamorada Original
  Florida Keys Collector's Club
Ella Ellis
Box 386
Islamorada, Florida

Jersey Diggers Bottle Club
Belleplain Road
Leesburg, New Jersey 08327

Jim Beam Bottle Club
P.O. Box 103
Napa, California 94558

Jim Beam Bottle Club
c/o Al Cembura
139 Arlington
Berkeley, California

Jim Beam Bottle Club
P.O. Box 2178
San Leandro, California 94577

Jim Beam Collectors
107 Mohawk Drive
Barrackville, West Virginia 26559

Jim Beam Collectors Club
10 Lunt Road
Falmouth, Maine 04105

Jim's Gems
c/o Joe Dias
1241 Enslen Avenue
Modesto, California 95350

Joliet Bottle Club
c/o C. W. Sieber
12 E. Kenmore Avenue
Joliet, Illinois 60431

Juniper Hills Bottle Club
Route 1, Box 18
Valyermo, California 93563

J. V. Gunn Midwest
  Ezra Brooks Limited Bottle Club
Box 29198
Lincoln, Nebraska 68529

Kaye City Bottle Club
Route 1, Box 155
Carlsbad, New Mexico

Kelly Club
Mary Kelly
147 North Brainard Avenue
La Grange, Illinois 60525

Kim Club for Bottle Collectors
22000 Shaker Boulevard
Shaker Heights, Ohio 44122

Klickital B.C.A.
Goldendale, Washington

Larkin Bottle Club
Clarence Larkin
107 W. Grimes
Red Oak, Iowa 51566

Las Vegas Beam Club
1850 Las Vegas Boulevard
Las Vegas, Nevada 89030

Lewis & Clark B.C.A.
8435 S.W. 52nd Avenue
Portland, Oregon 97219

Lionstone Western Figural Club
P.O. Box 2275
Colorado Springs, Colorado 80901

Little Rock A.B.C.
5311 Halifax Drive
Little Rock, Arkansas 72209

Longhorn Bottle Club
4352 Normandy
Dallas, Texas

Los Angeles Historical Bottle Club
1524 Harding Avenue
Pasadena, California

Los Banos A.B.C.
635 Jefferson Avenue
Los Banos, California 93635

Marin County Bottle Club
c/o Jean Wyrick
31 Ridge Drive
San Raphael, California 94901

Marysville-Yuba City
    Antique Bottle Club
475 South Barrett Road
Yuba City, California 95991

Memphis A.B.C.
1070 Terry Circle
Memphis, Tennessee 38107

Memphis Bottle Collectors Club
3822 Macon Road
Memphis, Tennessee

Merrimack Valley Bottle Club
96 Elm Street
North Andover, Massachusetts 01845

Michigan Bottle Club
145 Spruce, Box 48
Hemlock, Michigan 48626

Middle Tennessee B.C.C.
2804 Belmont, Apt. 1
Nashville, Tennessee 37212

Mid-State A.B.C.A.
3400 East Grant Avenue
Orlando, Florida 32806

Milkbottles Only Organization (MOO)
Box 5456
Newport News, Virginia 23605

Milwaukee Jim Beam & A.B.C.
Box 56
6361 South 27th
Frankland, Wisconsin 53132

Milwaukee Jim Beam Club
3779 South 95th Street
Milwaukee, Wisconsin 53228

Mineral County, A.B.C.
Box 237
Hawthorne, Nevada

Miniature Bottle Mart
Lawrence Romanoff
1913 Sheridon Road
Highland Park, Illinois 60035

Minnesota First Antique Bottle Club
Box 254
Mound, Minnesota 55364

Mission Bells (Beams)
Fawn Rowe
1114 Coronado Terrace
Los Angeles, California 90026

Modalla Bottle Club
Route 1, Box 205
Muleno, Oregon

Modesto Old Bottle Club
MOBC
P.O. Box 1791
Modesto, California

Monterey Bay Beam Bottle &
    Specialty Club
R. W. Brugge, Jr.
P.O. Box 463
Aptos, California 95003

Mother Lode A.B.C. of
    Calaveras County
Route 1, Box 950
Sonora, California 95379

Mount Whitney Bottle Club
Keeler, California

Mt. Bottle Club
422 Orpheus
Encinitas, California

Napa-Solano Bottle Club
P.O. Box 554
Yountville, California 94559

National Early American Glass Club
31 Norwood Street
Sharon, Massachusetts

National Jim Beam Bottle &
 Specialties Club
490 El Camino Real
Belmont, California 94002

National Society of Powder Horn &
 Flask Collectors
202 W. 8th Street
Plainfield, New Jersey

Nebraska Antique Bottle &
 Collectors Club
1718 South 8th
Omaha, Nebraska 68108

Nevada Beam Club
Terry duPont III
The B-Lazy-?
Box 426
Fallon, Nevada 89406

New England B.C.A.
7a Broad Street
Lynn, Massachusetts 01902

New England Bottle Club
Box 472
Henniker, New Hampshire 03242

New England Collectors Club
Al Goodrich
Groveland, Massachusetts

North Alabama Bottle & Glass Club
P.O. Box 109
Decatur, Alabama 35601

North Jersey A.B.C.A.
P.O. Box 617
Westwood, New Jersey 07675

Northeastern A.B.C.
513 Curtis
Brush, Colorado 80723

Northeastern Bottle Collector Assn.
1 Keeler Street
Petaluma, California

Northern Colorado Antique
 Bottle Club
227 W. Beaver Avenue
Fort Morgan, Colorado 80701

Northern New York B.C.A.
Box 257
Adams Center, New York 13606

Northwest Beam & Specialties Club
Box 4365, Station B
Spokane, Washington 92202

Northwestern Bottle Club of
 Santa Rosa
1537 Beachwood Road
Santa Rosa, California

Northwestern Bottle Collectors Assn.
P.O. Box 1121
Santa Rosa, California 95402

Northwestern B.C.A.
10190 Martinelli Road
Forestville, California 95436

Nutmeg State Beam Club
Roy Schmidt
25 Meadowood Drive
Middletown, Connecticut 06457

Ohio Bottle Club
P.O. Box 585
Barberton, Ohio 44203

Oregon A.B.C.
c/o William Blackburn
Route 3, Box 23
Molalla, Oregon 97038

Oregon B.C.A.
Box 175
Aurora, Oregon

Original Florida Keys Collector Club
P.O. Box 386
Islamorada, Florida

Paradise Glasshoppers
6982 Skyway
Paradise, California 95969

Paul Bunyan Bottle Club
c/o Mrs. Francis Kearns
237 14th Street
Bangor, Maine 04401

Peaks & Plains A.B.C.
1525 Cheyenne Boulevard
Colorado Springs, Colorado

Pekin Bottle Collectors Assn.
P.O. Box 535
Pekin, Illinois 61554

Peninsula Bottle Club
P.O. Box 886
Belmont, California 94002

Pennsylvania Dutch
   Jim Beam Bottle Club
812 Pointview Avenue
Ephrata, Pennsylvania 17522

Petaluma Bottle & Antique Club
9773 Minn. Avenue
Cotati, California 94928

Pinetree Bottle Club
c/o Gene Swinger ,
79 School Street
South Portland, Maine 04100

Pioneer Fruit Jar Collectors Assn.
P.O. Box 175
Grand Ronde, Oregon 97347

Pocatello A.B.C.A.
Route 2
Inkon, Idaho 83245

The Prism Club, Figural
765 Brossard Drive
Thousand Oaks, California 91360

Queen Mary Jim Beam Specialty Club
Al Halpern
1802 Chanticleer Drive
Anaheim, California 92804

Richmond Area B.C.A.
3064 Forest Hills Avenue
Richmond, Virginia 23225

Rochester New York B.C.
7908 West Henrietta Road
Rush, New York 14543

Rock & Bottle Club
c/o Mrs. M. E. Boothe
Route 1
Fruitland, Idaho

Rocky Mountain Jim Beam Bottle &
   Specialty Club
George Hoeper
P.O. Box 12162
Alcott Station
Denver, Colorado 80212

Rogue Valley Bottlers
Yreka, California

St. Louis Antique Bottle Assn.
c/o Webster Groves Public Library
301 East Lockwood Boulevard
St. Louis, Missouri

San Antonio Antique Bottle Club
701 Castana Avenue
San Antonio, Texas 78209

San Bernardino County A.B.C.
P.O. Box 127
Bloomington, California 92316

San Bernardino County Historical
    Bottle Club
c/o Fontana Y.W.C.A.
17366 Merrill Avenue
Fontana, California 92335

San Diego Antique Bottle Club
P.O. Box 454
Julian, California

San Diego Bottle Club
P.O. Box 536
San Diego, California

San Jose Antique Bottle Club
1058 Timber Crest Drive
San Jose, California

San Jose Club
175 Mt. Charley Road
Los Gatos, California

San Luis Obispo Bottle Society
Route 1, Box 108
Templeton, California 93465

Santa Barbara Bottle Club
1825 Garden Street
Santa Barbara, California 93101

Santa Barbara Bottle Club
5381 Paseo Cameo
Santa Barbara, California 93105

Satuit A.B.C.
757 Country Way
North Scituate, Massachusetts

Sea Way Valley Beam &
    Decanter Club
RFD #2, c/o Dick Cook
Potsdam, New York 13676

Sequoia Antique Bottle Society
723 West Walnut
Visalia, California

Shasta Antique Bottle
    Collectors Assn.
Route 1, Box 3147A
Anderson, California

Skagit Glass & Bottle Club
Route 3, Box 110
Sedro Woolley, Washington 98248

Southeastern A.B.C.
2996 Pangborn Road
Decatur, Georgia 30033

Southeastern New England A.B.C.
656 Noank Road
Mystic, Connecticut 06355

Southern Nevada A.B.C.
2624 St. George Street
North Las Vegas, Nevada

Southern Oregon Bottle Collectors
503 South Main Street
Canyonville, Oregon 97417

Southwest Oklahoma A.B.C.
710 N. 31
Lawton, Oklahoma 73501

Southwestern Wyoming Avon Club
P.O. Box 1688
Rock Springs, Wyoming 82901

Suncoast A.B.C.
P.O. Box 12712
St. Petersburg, Florida 33733

Sussex County B.C.A.
Division Sussex County
   Historical Society
Newton, New Jersey 07860

Taft Antique Bottle Club
522 'E'' Street
Taft, California 93268

Teen Bottle Club
Route 1, Box 60-TE
Eureka, California 95501

Tehama County A.B.C.
Route 1, Box 775
Red Bluff, California 96080

Texas Longhorn Bottle Club
916 Riverwood Road
Dallas, Texas 75217

Tonopah A.B.C.
P.O. Box 545
Tonopah, Nevada 89049

Trenton Jim Beam Bottle Club
John Michalczyn
431 Rutgers Avenue
Trenton, New Jersey

Tulsa Oklahoma Bottle Club
5752 E. 25th Place
Tulsa, Oklahoma 74114

Twin Bridges Beam Bottle &
   Specialty Club
4 Michigan Road
Pennsville, New Jersey 08070

Upper Susquehanna Bottle Club
Box 183
Milford, New York 13807

Utah A.B.C.
23 Villa Drive
Clearfield, Utah

Utah Antique Bottle Society
4907 S. 2400-A
Roy, Utah

Utah Bottle Club
P.O. Box 15
Ogden, Utah 84402

Waldo County Bottlenecks Club
Head of the Tide
Belfast, Maine 04815

Washington B.C.A.
8319 49th Street East
Puyallup, Washington 98371

Washington State A.B.C.A.
1200 112 S.W.
Everett, Washington 98201

Washington State B.C.A.
12745 Phinney Avenue
North Seattle, Washington

Willits Bottle Club
c/o John Hathaway
Willits, California 95490

Yankee Bottle Club
c/o Kay Fox
Page Street
Keene, New Hampshire 03431

Ye Old Bottle Club
Gaastra, Michigan 49027

BIBLIOGRAPHY

Authors' Note

Most of the books not published privately and listed in the bibliography can be obtained at local bookstores. We list below the specialized shops that carry many books not normally stocked.

WHERE TO BUY BOOKS

Antique Publications
Emmitsburg, Maryland 21727

Hotchkiss House
89 Sagamore Drive
Rochester, New York 14617

Mid-America Book Company
Leon, Iowa 50144

Old Time Bottle Publishing Co.
611 Lancaster Drive N.E.
Salem, Oregon 97301

Ole Empty Bottle House
Box 136
Amador City, California 95601
    (Bottle Books)

The Little Glass Shack
3161 57th Street
Sacramento, California 95820

GENERAL

Adams, John P. *Bottle Collecting in New England.* New Hampshire Publishing Company, Somersworth, New Hampshire 03878, 1969. $3.95.

Bailey, Shirley R. *Bottle Town.* Privately printed, 1968. $3.50. (Order from author, 24 Westwood Terrace, Millville, New Jersey.)

Ballou, Hazel, and Alley, Kaylen. *The Beginners Book Collecting Jars and Bottles for Fun and Money.* Privately printed, 1966. $2.00. (Order from author, 1802 Margrave, Fort Scott, Kansas.)

Bates, Virginia T., and Chamberlain, Beverly. *Antique Bottle Finds in New England.* Privately printed, 1968. $3.95. (Order from William L. Bauhan, Inc., Noone House, Peterborough, New Hampshire.)

Beare, Nikki. *Bottle Bonanza: A Handbook for Glass Collectors.* Privately printed, 1965. $3.00. (Order from Hurricane House Publishers, Inc., 14301 S.W. 87th Avenue, Miami, Florida.)

Blumenstein, Lynn. *Bottle Rush U.S.A.* Salem, Oregon: Old Time Bottle Publishing Company. 1966. $4.25.

————. *Old Time Bottles Found in Ghost Towns.* Privately printed, 1966. $2.50.

————. *"Redigging the West" for Old Time Bottles.* Privately printed, 1966. $4.25.

Bressie, Wes & Ruby. *Ghost Town Bottle Price Guide.* Privately printed, 1966. $3.00. (Order from author, Route 1, Box 582, Eagle Point, Oregon.)

Colcleaser, Donald E. *Bottles of Bygone Days.* Privately printed, 1965. $2.00. (Order from author, P.O. Box 2006, Napa, California.)

————. *Bottles of Bygone Days, Part II.* Privately printed, 1966. $2.00.

————. *Bottles Yesterday's Trash Today's Treasures.* Privately printed, 1967. $3.75.

Davis, Marvin and Helen. *Antique Bottles.* Privately printed, 1967. $3.00. (Order from author, 2320 Highway 66, Ashland, Oregon 97520.)

————. *Bottles and Relics.* Privately printed, 1970. $4.50.

————. *Old Bottle Collecting for Fun & Profit.* Privately printed, 1966. $2.25.

————. *Pocket Field Guide for the Bottle Digger.* Privately printed, 1967. $2.00.

Devner, Kay. *At the Sign of the Mortar.* Privately printed, 1970. $2.75. (Order from author, 8945 E. 20th, Tucson, Arizona 85710.)

————. *Backward Through a Bottle.* Privately printed, 1964. $2.00.

Eastin, June. *Bottles West, Volume I.* Privately printed, 1965. $3.00. (Order from author, P.O. Box 703, Joshua Tree, California 92252.)

Ferraro, Pat and Bob. *A Bottle Collector's Book.* Privately printed, 1966. $3.00. (Order from author, Box 239, Lovelock, Nevada 89419.)

————. *The Past in Glass.* Privately printed, 1964. $3.00.

Fike, Richard E. *Guide to Old Bottles, Contents & Prices.* Privately printed, 1969. $2.75. (Order from author, 1135 Maxfield Drive, Ogden, Utah.)

————. *Guide to Old Bottles, Contents & Prices, Volume II.* Privately printed, 1969. $2.75.

————. *Handbook for the Bottle-ologist.* Privately printed, 1969. $2.75.

Freeman, Dr. Larry. *Grand Old American Bottles.* Watkins Glen, New York: Century House, 1964. $25.00.

Illinois Glass Company. *Old Bottle List Bonanza, Illustrated Catalogue & Price List*. Watkins Glen, New York: Century House, Americana Publishers.

Jones, May. *The Bottle Trail*. Privately printed, 1965. $2.25. (Order from author, P.O. Box 23, Nara Visa, New Mexico.)

————. *The Bottle Trail, Volume 2*. Privately printed, 1963. $2.25.

————. *The Bottle Trail, Volume 3*. Privately printed, 1963. $2.25.

————. *The Bottle Trail, Volume 4*. Privately printed, 1966. $2.25.

————. *The Bottle Trail, Volume 5*. Privately printed, 1965. $2.25.

————. *The Bottle Trail, Volume 6*. Privately printed, 1966. $2.25.

————. *The Bottle Trail, Volume 7*. Privately printed, 1967. $2.25.

————. *The Bottle Trail, Volume 8*. Privately printed, 1967. $2.25.

Kaufmann, Don and June. *Dig Those Crazy Bottles: A Handbook of Pioneer Bottles*. Privately printed, 1966. (Order from author, 3520 Laramie Street, Cheyenne, Wyoming.

Kendrick, Grace. *The Antique Bottle Collector*. Privately printed, 1964. $2.00. (Order from author, 485 West Fourth Street, Fallon, Nevada.)

————. *"The Mouth-Blown Bottle."* Privately printed, 1968. $6.95.

————. *Price Supplement to the Antique Bottle Collector*. Privately printed, 1965. $1.50.

Kenyon, Harry C. *Jersey Diggins, Volume 1*. Privately printed, 1969. $3.50. (Order from The Old Barn, Newfield, New Jersey.)

Kincade, Steve. *Early American Bottles and Glass*. Privately printed, 1964. $3.00. (Order from Clovis Printing Company, 619 Fifth Street, Clovis, California.)

Kovel, Ralph and Terry. *The Complete Antiques Price List*. New York: Crown Publishers, Inc., 1970. $5.95.

————. *Know Your Antiques*. New York: Crown Publishers, Inc., 1967. $7.95.

Leahy, Midge and Phil. *The Bottles of Leadville, Colorado*. Privately printed, 1967. $2.00. (Order from author, 4165 Stuart Street, Denver, Colorado.)

Lyons, Adrian D. *Your Friend's and My Friend's Bottle Book*. Privately printed, 1967. $3.00. (Order from author, The Mother Lode Bottle Shop, Maestown, California.)

Lyons, Bill and Jean. *Bottles from Bygone Days*. Privately printed, 1967. $4.25. (Order from author, Box 147, South Vienna, Ohio 45369.)

Maust, Don. *Bottle and Glass Handbook*. Uniontown, Pennsylvania: E. G. Warman Publishing Company, 1956. $3.00.

McConnell, Walter E. *Tri-State Bottles*. Privately printed, 1969. $3.00. (Order from author, R.D. #2, Box 116, Newton, New Jersey 07860.)

McKearin, George L. and Helen. *American Glass.* New York: Crown Publishers, Inc., 1959. $14.95.

————. *Two Hundred Years of American Blown Glass.* New York: Crown Publishers, Inc., 1950. $15.00.

Motter, Faye. *Stories in Bottles.* Privately printed, 1966. (Order from author, P.O. Box 37, Edina, Missouri.)

Munsey, Cecil. *The Illustrated Guide to Collecting Bottles.* New York: Hawthorn Books, Inc., 1970. $9.95.

Phillips, Helen V. *400 Old Bottles, Book #1.* Privately printed, 1967. (Order from author, 528 W. 5th Street, Cheyenne, Wyoming.)

Putnam, H. E. *Bottle Identification.* Privately printed, 1965. $2.50. (Order from author, P.O. Box 517, Jamestown, California.)

Putnam, P. A. *Bottled Before 1865.* Privately printed, 1968. $2.75. (Order from House of Putnam, P.O. Box 578, Fontana, California 92325.)

Rawlinson, Fred. *Old Bottles of the Virginia Peninsula, 1885–1941.* Privately printed, 1968. $4.30. (Order from FAR Publications, P.O. Box 5456, Newport News, Virginia 23605.)

Reed, Adele. *Bottle Talk.* Privately printed, 1966. $2.00. (Order from author, 272 Shepard Lane, Bishop, California 93514.)

————. *Old Bottles and Ghost Towns.* Privately printed, 1962. $2.00.

Sellari, Carlo and Dot. *Eastern Bottles Price Guide, Volume 1.* Privately printed, 1969. $4.50.

————. *Eastern Bottles Price Guide, Volume 2.* Privately printed, 1970. $4.50.

Tibbitts, John C. *How to Collect Antique Bottles.* Privately printed, 1969. $4.00.

————. *John Doe, Bottle Collector.* Privately printed, 1967. $4.00.

————. *1200 Bottles Priced.* Privately printed, 1970. $4.50. (Order from The Little Glass Shack, 3161 56th Street, Sacramento, California 95820.)

Tufts. James W. *The Manufacture and Bottling of Carbonated Beverages.* Frontier Book Company, Publisher, Fort Davis, Texas 79734, 1969. $3.50.

Umberger, Art and Jewel. *It's a Corker!* Privately printed, 1966. $3.00. (Order from author, 819 W. Wilson, Tyler, Texas 75701.)

Walbridge, William S. *American Bottles Old & New, 1607 to 1920.* Frontier Book Company, Publisher, Fort Davis, Texas 79734, 1969. $4.00.

Wood, Serry. *The Old Apothecary Shop.* Watkins Glen, New York: Century House, 1956. $2.00.

Yount, John T. *Bottle Collector's Handbook & Pricing Guide.* Educator Books, Inc., Drawer 32, San Angelo, Texas 76901, 1970. $3.95.

MODERN

Pictorial Bottle Review. *Collectors Edition Presents Beams, Avons, Ezra Brooks, Luxards, Garniers, Fancy and Figural Bottles.* B & K Enterprises, P.O. Box 42558, Los Angeles, California 90050, 1969.

Avon

Ahrendt, L. *Avon Bottle Collector's Guide.* Privately printed, $2.00. (Order from author, 5101 Stockton Road, Sacramento, California 95820.)

————. *Avon Powder Boxes, Plastics & Toys.* Privately printed, 1969. $2.00.

————. *Avon's California Perfume Company.* Privately printed, 1969. $3.00.

————. *Mini Miniatures of Avon.* Privately printed, 1969. $2.00.

Flowers, Bryant. *The Flowers Collection. Avn Guide.* Privately printed, 1970. $5.00 (Order from author, P.O. Box 1613, Pampa, Texas 79065.)

Hastin, Bud. *Avon Bottle Encyclopedia.* Privately printed, 1971. $8.95. (Order from author, Box 9868, Kansas City, Missouri 64134.)

Newson, Ralph W., and Lamalfa, Jean V. *Fun with Avon Old & New: Bottle Collectors Notebook.* Privately printed, 1969. $3.75. (Order from Arjay Specialties, Box 4371, Panorama City, California 91412.)

————. *Treasures of Avon.* Privately printed, 1969. $3.75.

Stuart, Lynn R. *Stuart's Book on Avon Collectables.* Privately printed, 1971. $4.20. (Order from author, P.O. Box 862, Gilbert, Arizona 85234.)

Texas Collector's. *Texas Collector's Guide.* Privately printed, 1970. $5.00. (Order from author, Box 1479, Pampa, Texas 79065.)

Western Collector. *Avon-2: A Western Collector Handbook & Price Guide.* 1971. $4.95. (Order from Western Collector Books, 511 Harrison Street, San Francisco, California 94105.)

————. *Western Collector's Handbook and Price Guide to Avon Bottles.* San Francisco, California: Western World Publishers, 1969. $3.95. (Order from Western Collector Books, 511 Harrison Street, San Francisco, California 94105.)

Beam

Cembura, Al, and Avery, Constance. *Jim Beam Bottles, 1970 1971 Identification and Price Guide.* Privately printed, 1970. $4.95. (Order from Al Cembura, 139 Arlington Avenue, Berkeley, California 94707.)

Bischoff

Avery, Constance and Leslie, and Cembura, Al. *Bischoff Bottles, Identification and Price Guide.* Privately printed, 1969. $4.75. (Order from Al Cembura, 139 Arlington Avenue, Berkeley, California 94707.)

Ezra Brooks

Western Collector. *Western Collector's Handbook and Price Guide to Ezra Brooks Decanters.* San Francisco, California: Western World Publishers, 1970. $4.95. (Order from Western Collector Books, 511 Harrison Street, San Francisco, California 94105.)

Garnier

Avery, Constance, and Cembura, Al. *Garnier Bottles.* Privately printed, 1970. $4.95. (Order from Al Cembura, 139 Arlington Avenue, Berkeley, California 94707.)

Schwartz, Jeri and Ed. *Just Figurals: A Guide to Garnier.* Privately printed, 1969. $4.25. (Order from author, 270 North Broadway, Yonkers, N.Y. 10701.)

Luxardo

Avery, Constance, and Cembura, Al. *Luxardo Bottles: Identification and Price Guide.* Privately printed, 1968. $4.75. (Order from Al Cembura, 139 Arlington Avenue, Berkeley, California 94707.)

BITTERS

Bartholomew, Ed. *1001 Bitters Bottles.* Bartholomew House, Publishers, Fort Davis, Texas 79734, 1970. $4.95.

Watson, Richard. *Bitters Bottles.* New York: Thomas Nelson & Sons, 1965. $10.00.

————. *Supplement to Bitters Bottles.* Camden, New Jersey: Thomas Nelson & Sons, 1968. $6.50.

CANDY CONTAINERS

Eikelberner, George, and Agadjanian, Serge. *American Glass Conainers.* Privately printed, 1967. $7.50. (Order from Serge Agadjanian, River Road, Belle Mead, New Jersey 08502.)

————. *More American Glass Candy Containers.* Privately printed, 1970. $6.00.

Matthews, Robert T. *Old Glass Candy Containers Price Guide.* Privately printed, 1966. $3.62. (Order from author, Glenelg, Maryland 21737.)

FIGURAL

Revi, Albert Christian. *American Pressed Glass and Figure Bottles.* New York: Thomas Nelson & Sons, 1964. $15.00.

Umberger, Jewel and Arthur L. *Collectible Character Bottles.* Privately printed, 1969. $12.50. (Order from Corker Book Company, 819 West Wilson, Tyler, Texas.)

Vincent, Pal. *The Moses Bottle.* Privately printed, 1969. $4.25. (Order from The Palabra Shop, Jct. Rtes. 26 and 122, Poland Spring, Maine 04274.)

Wearin, Otha D. *Statues That Pour: The Story of Character Bottles.* Denver, Colorado: Sage Books, 2679 South York Street, 1965. $6.00.

FLASKS

Barber, Edwin A. *Old American Bottles.* New York: David McKay Co., 1900. $3.50. (Reprint available from Frontier Book Co., Publisher, Fort Davis, Texas 79734.)

Van Rensselaer, Stephen. *Early American Bottles & Flasks.* Southampton, New York: Cracker Barrel Press, 1921. $3.00.

————. *Early American Bottles & Flasks — Revised.* Stratford, Connecticut, 1969. $15.00. (Order from J. Edmund Edwards, 61 Winton Place, Stratford, Connecticut 06497.)

FRUIT JARS

Bird, Douglas, and Corke, Marion and Charles. *A Century of Antique Canadian Glass Fruit Jars.* Privately printed, 1970. $6.95. (Order from Douglas Bird, 859 Valetta Street, London 74, Ontario, Canada.)

————. *North American Fruit Jar Index.* Privately printed, 1968. $6.00.

Burris, Ronald B. *An Illustrated Guide for Collecting Fruit Jars with Price Guide.* Privately printed, 1966. $1.75. (Order from author, 2941 Campus Drive, Visalia, California 93277.)

————. *Collecting Fruit Jars, Book #2, with Price Guide.* Privately printed, 1967. $2.00.

————. *More Collectable Jars, Book #3, with Price Guide.* Privately printed, 1968. $2.50.

Creswick, Alice, and Rodrigues, Arleta. *The Cresrod Blue Book of Fruit Jars.* Privately printed, 1969. $4.50. (Order from Cresrod Publishing Company, 0-8525 Kenowa SW, Grand Rapids, Michigan 49504.)

Harvest Publishing Company. *Harvest 2nd Fruit Jar Finders Price Guide.* Privately printed, 1970. $3.95. (Order from Harvest Publishing Company, Box 3015-M, Milwaukee, Wisconsin 53218.)

Rodrigues, Arleta, and Creswick, Alice. *A Collection of Yesterday's Fruit Jars from Great Aunt May's Cellar.* Privately printed, 1967. $6.50. (Order from Arleta Rodrigues, P.O. Box 2413, Castro Valley, California 94546.)

Schroeder, Bill. *1000 Fruit Jars Priced & Illustrated.* Privately printed, 1970. $3.95. (Order from author, Route 4, Paducah, Kentucky 42001.)

Toulouse, Julian Harrison. *A Collectors' Manual Fruit Jars.* Jointly published by Camden, New Jersey: Thomas Nelson & Sons, and Hanover, Pennsylvania: Everybody's Press, 1969. $15.00.

Umberger, Art and Jewel. *The Kitchen Cupboard: Fruit Jar Price Guide.* Privately printed, 1967. $3.00. (Order from author, 819 West Wilson, Tyler, Texas 75701.)

INKWELLS

Nelson, Lavinia, and Hurley, Martha. *Old Inks.* Privately printed, 1967. $5.00. (Order from "Old Inks," 22 Bryant Road, Nashua, New Hampshire.)

Walter, Leo G., Jr. *Walter's Inkwells of 1885: Book #1.* Privately printed, 1968. $3.75. (Order from Stagecoach Antiques, 443 West Market Street, Akron, Ohio 44303.)

MEDICINE

Agee, Bill. *Collecting the Cures.* Privately printed, 1969. $3.00. (Order from author, 1200 Melrose, Waco, Texas 76710.)

Bartholomew, Ed. *1200 Old Medicine Bottles with Prices Current.* Frontier Book Company, Fort Davis, Texas 79734, 1970. $3.95.

Devner, Day. *Patent Medicine Picture.* Privately printed, 1968. $2.50. (Order from author, 8945 East 20th, Tucson, Arizona 85710.)

Freeman, Dr. Larry. *The Medicine Showman.* Watkins Glen, New York: Century House, 1957. $4.00.

Jensen, Al and Margaret. *Old Owl Drug Bottles & Others.* Privately printed, 1968. $3.50. (Order from author, 783 Alice Avenue, Mountain View, California 94040.)

Penland, Belle. *Bottles, Corks & Cures.* Privately printed, 1963. $2.65. (Order from author, P.O. Box 118, Twain, California 95984.)

MILK

Rawlinson, Fred. *Make Mine Milk.* Privately printed, 1970. $3.85. (Order from FAR Publications, Box 5456, Newport News, Virginia 23605.)

Roth, Evelyn. *The Milky Way.* Privately printed, 1969. $2.50. (Order from author, 245 Shore Road, Ocean View, New Jersey 08230.)

MINIATURES

Snyder, Robert E. *Bottles in Miniature.* Privately printed, 1969. $4.00. (Order from author, 4235 West 13th, Amarillo, Texas 79106.)

————. *Bottles in Miniature, Volume II.* Privately printed, 1970. $4.75.

SARSAPARILLA

Shimko, Phyllis. *Sarsaparilla Bottle Encyclopedia.* Privately printed, 1969. $6.50. (Order from author, Box 117, Aurora, Oregon 97002.)

Umberger, Art and Jewel. *It's a Sarsaparilla! Price Guide.* Privately printed, 1968. $3.00. (Order from author, 819 W. Wilson, Tyler, Texas 75701.)

SODA AND MINERAL WATER

Fountain, John C., and Colcleaser, Donald. *Dictionary of Soda & Mineral Water Bottles.* Amador City, California: "Ole Empty Bottle House Publishing Company," 1968. P.O. Box 136. $3.75.

Lincoln, Gerald David. *Antique Blob Top Bottles, Central & Southern New England.* Privately printed, 1970. $3.25. (Order from author, 700 Berlin Road, Marlboro, Massachusetts 01752.)

Schmeiser, Alan. *Have Bottles Will Pop.* Privately printed, 1968. $6.95. (Order from author, Dixon, California 95620.)

WHISKEY AND BEER

Anderson, Sonja and Will. *Andersons' Turn-of-the-Century Brewery Dictionary.* Privately printed. $15.95. (Order from author, 1 Lindy Street, Carmel, New York 10512.

————. *Beers, Breweries & Breweriana.* Privately printed, 1969.

Fountain, John C., and Colcleaser, Donald. *Dictionary of Spirits and Whiskey Bottles.* Amador City, California: "Ole Empty Bottle House Publishing Company," 1969. P.O. Box 136. $3.75.

Howe, John. *A Whiskeyana Guide Antique Whiskey Bottles.* Privately printed, 1967. $3.00. (Order from author, 4894 Sandy Lane, San Jose, California 95124.)

Kauffman, Don and June. *The United States Brewers' Guide, 1630–1864.* Privately printed, 1967. $1.75. (Order from author, 3520 Laramie Street, Cheyenne, Wyoming 82001.)

Pewee Valley Press. *Decanter Collector's Guide.* Privately printed, 1970. $2.75. (Order from author, P.O. Box 248, Pewee Valley, Kentucky 40056.)

Silva, Bev and Joe. *Research on San Francisco Whiskey Bottles.* Privately printed, 1967. $2.00. (Order from author, 6829 Mayhews Lndg. Road, Newark, California 94560.)

Wilson, Bill and Betty. *Spirits Bottles of the Old West.* Privately printed, 1968. $10.00. (Order from Antiques & Hobby Publishing Company, Box 136, Amador City, California 95601.)

Newspapers of Interest to Bottle Collectors

Antique Monthly
P.O. Drawer 440
Tuscaloosa, Alabama 35401

Antique News
Box B
Marietta, Pennsylvania 17547

Antique Trader
Kewanee, Illinois 61443

Collector's News
Grundy Center, Iowa 50638

Collector's Weekly
Box 1119
Kermit, Texas 79745

Down East Glassman
P.O. Box 203
West Hartford, Connecticut 06107

Eastern Antiquity
1 Dogwood Drive
Washington, New Jersey 07882

The Gallery
3717 Mt. Diablo Boulevard
Lafayette, California 94549

Tri-State Trader
P.O. Box 90-DM
Knightstown, Indiana 46148

Western Antique Mart
P.O. Box 2171
Eugene, Oregon 97402

Antiques Journal
Babka Publishing Co.
Kewanee, Illinois 61443

Hobbies
Lightner Publishing Corp.
1006 South Michigan Avenue
Chicago, Illinois 60605

National Antiques Review
P.O. Box 619
Portland, Maine 04104

National Bottle Gazette
P.O. Box 36
Amador City, California 95601

Old Bottle Magazine
P.O. Box 243
Bend, Oregon 97701

Pictorial Bottle Review
B & K Enterprises, Inc.
P.O. Box 42558
Los Angeles, California 90050

Relics
P.O. Box 3668
1012 Edgecliff Terrace
Austin, Texas 78704

Spinning Wheel
511 Harrison Street
San Francisco, California 94105

Western Collector
511 Harrison Street
San Francisco, California 94105

THE
OFFICIAL BOTTLE
PRICE LIST

Ezra Brooks,
Grandfather's Clock, 1970

Ezra Brooks, West Virginia
Mountaineer, 1971

Jack Daniel,
Hip Flask, Silver Top

Ezra Brooks,
Golden Rooster, 1969

Jack Daniel's
No. 7 Decanter

Ezra Brooks, White Turkey, 1971

Ezra Brooks, Indianapolis Race Car, 1970

Ezra Brooks, Ticker Tape, 1970

Ezra Brooks, Distillery, 1970

Whiskey, Early Times,
Prohibition, Can

Whiskey, Early Times,
Prohibition, Bottle

Whiskey, Old Tucker
Reserve, Prohibition

Ezra Brooks,
Gold Eagle, 1971

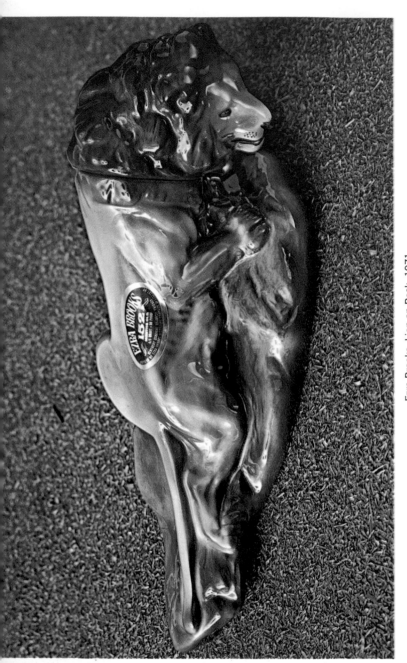

Ezra Brooks, Lion on Rock, 1971

Whiskey, Flora
Temple Harness Trot

Whiskey, Booz, E. C.,
Old Cabin

Whiskey,
James Kane

Whiskey,
Gibbons

Flask, Mc Kearin G V,
Success to the Railroad

DANT

Front row: Ringnecked Pheasant, Bobwhite, Prairie
Chicken, Chukar Partridge.

Back row: Ruffed Grouse, Woodcock, Mountain Quail,
California Quail.

Dickel, Powder Horn

A CENTURY OF PROGRESS,1833-1933,BUILDING,CLEAR,SCREW CAP....	9.50
A.H.BULL EXTRACT OF SARSAPARILLA,OPEN PONTIL................	34.00
ACID,BLOWN IN MOLD,GLASS STOPPER,AQUA......................	2.50
ACID,BLOWN IN MOLD,7 1/4 IN. TALL,AMBER....................	2.25
ACID,BLOWN IN MOLD,11 1/4 IN. TALL,AQUA....................	3.00
ACID,GREEN.. 2.00 TO	3.00
ALE,THREE MOLD,BLACK GLASS,IMPROVED PONTIL.................	8.00
AMANA COLONIES,DIE SCHWESTER,THE SISTER....................	14.95
AMBER,JEN-SAL,MARKED O-750,9 IN............................	2.50
ANDERSON BROS.,E.ST.LOUIS,ILL.,CLEAR.......................	2.50
ANDERSONS DERMADOR...	8.00
ANTEDILUVIAN,ETCHED,AMBER..................................	4.00
APOTHECARY JAR,PAUL MASSON.................................	14.90
APOTHECARY,S.C.DISPENSARY,PINT,PALM TREE,CLEAR.............	20.00
APOTHECARY,S.C.DISPENSARY,QUART,PALM TREE,CLEAR............	20.00
APOTHECARY,S.C.DISPENSARY,ROUND............................	30.00
APOTHECARY,S.C.DISPENSARY,1/2 PINT,PALM TREE,CLEAR.........	20.00
APOTHECARY,BLOWN IN MOLD,BROWN.............................	3.00
APOTHECARY,BRITISH,GILT HAND LETTERS.......................	8.00
APOTHECARY,BROWN,WHITE & GOLD PORCELAIN LABEL,STOPPER,PAIR..	7.50
APOTHECARY,DRUGSTORE,AMBER.................................	4.50
APOTHECARY,DRUGSTORE,BLUE..................................	4.00
APOTHECARY,DRUGSTORE,CLEAR.................................	8.00
APOTHECARY,DRUGSTORE,GOLD..................................	4.00
APOTHECARY,DRUGSTORE,GREEN.................................	4.00
APOTHECARY,DRUGSTORE,PONTIL................................	6.00
APOTHECARY,ENGLISH,GOLD & RED CENTER MEDALLION,CLEAR.......	9.00
APOTHECARY,GLASS INSERT,STOPPER,R.BENZ CO.,6 1/2 IN.HIGH....	5.00
APOTHECARY,GOLD & WHITE PORCELAIN LABELS,GLASS STOPPER,
  7 IN.TALL...	9.50
APOTHECARY,GROUND GLASS CLOSURE............................	4.00
APOTHECARY,MEASURING SCALE,AMBER...........................	3.00
APOTHECARY,SET OF 6,LABELS,BROWN...........................	30.00
APOTHECARY,SQUARE,AMBER,QUART,LABEL........................	10.00
APOTHECARY,STOPPER,LABELED,PONTIL,8 IN.....................	8.50
APOTHECARY,3 PIECE MOLD,COBALT BLUE........................	35.00
AQUAS DE MONDARIZ,THREE PART MOLD,GREEN....................	8.00
ARMANETTI,HARRY HOFFMAN....................................	11.95
AROMATIC SCHNAPPS,SCHIEDAM,UDOLPHOWOLLE,AMBER..............	22.00
ASHBURTON,BITTERS..	21.00
ASHBURTON,DECANTER,QUART...................................	28.00
ATOMIZER,BLUE TO CLEAR CUTTING,OVERLAY,4 1/2 IN............	14.00
ATOMIZER,GALLE,CAMEO GLASS,PURPLE LEAVES & FLORAL,ORANGE....	195.00
ATOMIZER,GALLE,CAMEO GLASS,PURPLE LEAVES & FLORAL,WHITE.....	175.00
ATOMIZER,PATE DE VERRE,SIGNED A.WALTER NANCY...............	200.00
ATOMIZER,PATE DE VERRE,4 1/2 IN. HIGH......................	201.00
ATOMIZER,ROSALINE,7 IN. HIGH...............................	111.00
ATWOODS GENUINE PHYSICAL,DUG,FIVE STAR.....................	35.00

AVON STARTED IN 1886 AS THE CALIFORNIA PERFUME COMPANY.
IT WAS NOT UNTIL 1929 THAT THE NAME AVON WAS USED. IN
1939 IT BECAME THE AVON PRODUCTS, INC. EACH YEAR AVON
SELLS MANY FIGURAL BOTTLES FILLED WITH COSMETIC
PRODUCTS. CERAMIC, PLASTIC, AND GLASS BOTTLES ARE MADE
IN LIMITED EDITIONS.

AVON,AFTER SHAVE FOAM............................... 18.00 TO	18.50
AVON,AFTER SHAVE SAMPLE,1957,FULL..........................	4.95
AVON,AFTER SHAVE,SILVER LABEL,1951.........................	4.95
AVON,AFTER SHAVE,WOODEN CAP................................	12.50
AVON,AFTER SHOWER COLOGNE FOR MEN,FULL & BOXED.............	7.95
AVON,AFTER SHOWER FOAM,SILVER WITH BLACK CAP,1965..........	15.50
AVON,AFTER SHOWER POWDER,BLACK & WHITE.....................	8.00
AVON,AFTER SHOWER,BLACK,1957...............................	10.00

```
AVON,AFTER SHOWER,FLASK,1959.................................        45.0(
AVON,AFTER SHOWER,8 OZ.,1959.................................        19.5(
AVON,ALPINE FLASK...................... 15.00 TO                     62.5(
AVON,ALPINE FLASK,FULL & BOXED...............................        55.0(
AVON,ALPINE FLASK,1966.......................................        37.5(
AVON,AMERICAN BEAUTY FRAGRANCE JAR,1912......................       135.0(
AVON,AMERICAN BEAUTY ROSE FRAGRANCE JAR......................        25.0(
AVON,ANGEL,FULL & BOXED......................................         4.5(
AVON,ANGEL,1968....................................... 2.50 TO       4.5(
AVON,ANGELS,GILT.............................................         7.45
AVON,ANGLER POWDER SACHET,FULL & BOXED,1969..................         4.5(
AVON,ANGLER,FULL & BOXED............................. 4.00 TO         7.5(
AVON,ANGLER,1969.............................................         4.49
AVON,ANTISEPTIC BOTTLE.......................................        10.00
AVON,APOTHECARY JAR,FULL & BOXED,1966........................        20.00
AVON,APOTHECARY JAR,1966............................. 8.75 TO        17.5(
AVON,APPLE BLOSSOM COLOGNE,6 OZ.,1936............... 75.00 TO        90.00
AVON,APPLE BLOSSOM TOILET WATER,1935.........................        40.00
AVON,ARIEL FACE POWDER BOX,FULL,1940................ 20.00 TO        39.50
AVON,ARIEL PERFUME,1 OZ.,1935................................        70.00
AVON,ASTRINGENT,1939.........................................        24.00
AVON,ATTENTION COLOGNE,6 OZ.,1947................... 75.00 TO        80.00
AVON,ATTENTION POWDER SACHET.................................        18.00
AVON,ATTENTION POWDER SACHET,1937............................        12.50
AVON,ATTENTION TOILET WATER,BOXED............................        31.00
AVON,AWARD,ELUSIVE,BLOUSE,PURSE,SCARF,CUFF LINKS.............        60.00
AVON,AWARD,HONOR NECKLACE,1966...............................        10.00
AVON,AWARD,MARBLE BASE GOLD STATUE,1958......................        75.00
AVON,AWARD,MARBLE BASE GOLD STATUE,1959......................        70.00
AVON,AWARD,PEARL PIN.........................................        11.50
AVON,AWARD,PERFUME GLACE NECKLACE,1966.......................        24.00
AVON,AWARD,SAPPHIRE PIN......................................        17.50
AVON,AWARD,SILVER BOWL,12 IN.,EMBLEM IN BOTTOM...............        45.00
AVON,AWARD,STOCKHOLDERS CHRISTMAS............................        35.00
AVON,AWARD,WHITE GINGER PERFUME GLACE,1967...................        14.50
AVON,BAA BAA BLACK SHEEP,1955................................        50.00
AVON,BALLAD PERFUME................................. 75.00 TO       100.00
AVON,BALLAD PERFUME,1 DRAM...................................        22.00
AVON,BARBER BOTTLE................................. 15.00 TO         25.00
AVON,BARBER,WITH CONTENTS....................................        26.00
AVON,BAROMETER,FULL CONTENTS,1969............................         5.00
AVON,BATH BOUQUET SET,FULL & BOXED...........................        22.50
AVON,BATH GALEE..............................................         3.50
AVON,BATH OIL FOR MEN........................................        12.50
AVON,BATH SEASONS,SALT & PEPPER,3 COLORS,1968................         4.00
AVON,BATH SEASONS,SALT & PEPPER,1967................ 2.60 TO         6.00
AVON,BATH SEASONS,1967.......................................         4.50
AVON,BATH URN,CRUET,MILK GLASS,1963................. 6.50 TO        14.00
AVON,BATH URN,1962,ROSE BUD..................................         4.95
AVON,BATH URN,1964..........................................          6.00
AVON,BATH URN,1965..........................................          5.95
AVON,BATH URN,1967..........................................          3.95
AVON,BAY RUM JUG.................................... 4.25 TO         12.00
AVON,BAY RUM JUG,1963........................................        10.00
AVON,BAY RUM KEG.................................... 9.00 TO         12.50
AVON,BAY RUM KEG,1965........................................        10.00
AVON,BAY RUM TALC............................................        12.00
AVON,BAYBERRY SOAP...........................................         8.00
AVON,BEAUTY BASKET,1947......................................        70.00
AVON,BEAUTY DUST.................................... 20.00 TO        25.00
AVON,BEEHIVE,FOAM,3 BOTTLES,1952.............................       100.00
AVON,BEEHIVE,SILK & HONEY,METAL,AMBER,1969.......... 3.00 TO         4.00
AVON,BELL,DINNER,1968........................................         4.95
AVON,BELL,SCHOOL,1965............................... 7.50 TO        18.00
AVON,BIG ROCKER,FULL.........................................        49.95
```

```
AVON,BIRD FEEDER & KIT,FULL & BOXED.........................         5.95
AVON,BIRDFEEDER BUBBLE BATH,FULL & BOXED....................         3.00
AVON,BIRTHDAY CAKE,1951...........................100.00 TO   150.00
AVON,BLUE BLAZER AFTER SHAVE,FULL & BOXED.......... 18.50 TO    19.95
AVON,BLUE BLAZER AFTER SHAVE,1965.................. 16.00 TO    17.00
AVON,BLUE BLAZER SET WITH PIN,FULL & BOXED..................    50.00
AVON,BLUE BLAZER SET WITH TIE TAC,FULL & BOXED..............    65.00
AVON,BLUE BLAZER TALC,1965..................................     8.00
AVON,BLUE BLAZER,DOUBLE CAP.................................    20.00
AVON,BLUE LOTUS CREAM LOTION,PLASTIC........................     1.00
AVON,BOAT,BRASS TOP,WITH CONTENTS...........................     6.00
AVON,BOAT,SILVER COLOR......................................     8.00
AVON,BODY POWDER FOR MEN....................................     6.00
AVON,BODY POWDER WITH CHAMOIE PUFF,FULL & BOXED.............    10.00
AVON,BOLERO................................................    39.50
AVON,BOOK,CLASSIC,1969.....................................     3.50
AVON,BOOK,FIRST EDITION,1967....................... 3.00 TO     6.00
AVON,BOOK,LIGHT AMBER.......................................     5.00
AVON,BOOT,AMBER,GOLD TOP,1965...................... 3.00 TO     5.00
AVON,BOOT,AMBER,SILVER TOP,1965.................... 4.95 TO     7.00
AVON,BOOT,GREEN,SILVER TOP..................................     6.00
AVON,BOOT,MAJORETTE,1967....................................     3.95
AVON,BOOT,SPRAY,1967.......................................     2.75
AVON,BOWLING PIN,VIGORATE,1960.............................     9.00
AVON,BOXING GLOVES,PAIR,1968...............................    18.00
AVON,BRACELET,CHARM,5 CHARMS...............................    20.00
AVON,BRAVE AFTER SHAVE SKIN CONDITIONER FOR MEN.............     2.00
AVON,BRIGHT NIGHT BEAUTY DUST..............................    13.00
AVON,BRIGHT NIGHT COLOGNE,4 OZ.................... 11.00 TO    15.00
AVON,BRIGHT NIGHT CREAM SACHET,FULL & BOXED.................     5.75
AVON,BRIGHT NIGHT CREAM SACHET,1952........................     3.50
AVON,BRIGHT NIGHT ESSENCE DE FLEURS,1957...................     8.50
AVON,BRIGHT NIGHT PERFUME......................... 25.00 TO    50.00
AVON,BRIGHT NIGHT PERFUME,1/2 OZ..................125.00 TO   150.00
AVON,BRIGHT NIGHT PERFUME,3 DRAMS.................125.00 TO   150.00
AVON,BRIGHT NIGHT POWDER BOX...............................    10.00
AVON,BRIGHT NIGHT POWDER SACHET................... 6.00 TO    12.00
AVON,BRIGHT NIGHT SPRAY MIST...............................    16.00
AVON,BRIGHT NIGHT TOILET WATER,FULL & BOXED.................    17.50
AVON,BROCADE BEAUTY DUST,1968..............................     5.00
AVON,BROCADE COLOGNE MIST,PLASTIC..........................     1.00
AVON,BROWN MANICURE TRAY,1967..............................     7.50
AVON,BROWN PLASTIC BOAT....................................     2.50
AVON,BUBBLE BATH,1952......................................    16.50
AVON,BUD VASE COLOGNE,1968........................ 2.95 TO     5.95
AVON,BUD VASE,FULL & BOXED,RUBY............................     3.60
AVON,BUD VASE,MILK GLASS,HAND,1969................ 2.50 TO     5.00
AVON,BUREAU ORGANIZER BOTTLE,LEATHER,1965..................     8.00
AVON,BUREAU ORGANIZER,1965........................ 28.00 TO    32.00
AVON,BUTTERFLY SOAP SET....................................     7.75
AVON,BUTTONS & BOWS COLOGNE,1963.................. 4.00 TO     9.00
AVON,CADDY AFTER SHAVE,1968....................... 10.00 TO    15.00
AVON,CADILLAC,GOLD,1969....................................     5.00
AVON,CALIFORNIA PERFUME CO.,CLEAR..........................    25.00
AVON,CALIFORNIA PERFUME CO.,FRUIT FLAVOUR,1905.............    45.00
AVON,CALIFORNIA PERFUME CO.,RECTANGULAR,AMETHYST...........     4.00
AVON,CALIFORNIA PERFUME COMPANY AWARD PIN,1933.............    50.00
AVON,CALIFORNIA PERFUME COMPANY BAY RUM,1937...............    25.00
AVON,CALIFORNIA PERFUME COMPANY CONC.EX.VANILLA,2 OZ.,1915.    75.00
AVON,CALIFORNIA PERFUME COMPANY CREAM SHAVING STICK,1907...    45.00
AVON,CALIFORNIA PERFUME COMPANY FACE LOTION..........ILLUS..   100.00
AVON,CALIFORNIA PERFUME COMPANY FACE POWDER................    20.00
AVON,CALIFORNIA PERFUME COMPANY FRUIT FLAVOR BOTTLE,1905...    42.50
AVON,CALIFORNIA PERFUME COMPANY PERFECTION LEMON...........    50.00
AVON,CALIFORNIA PERFUME COMPANY POLISH REMOVER.............    30.00
```

AVON, CALIFORNIA PERFUME COMPANY FACE LOTION

```
AVON, CAMEO COMPACT..............................................     9.00
AVON, CAMEO CREAM SACHET, 1962..................................     5.00
AVON, CAMEO SOAP, 1962..........................................    10.00
AVON, CANDLE....................................................     7.50
AVON, CANDLE, MILK GLASS, 1964....................... 6.50 TO      10.00
AVON, CANDLE, POWDER SACHET, AMBER..............................     9.95
AVON, CANDLE, POWDER SACHET, FROSTED............................    10.00
AVON, CANDLE, POWDER SACHET, GOLD, GREEN BAND...................    10.50
AVON, CANDLE, POWDER SACHET, RED................................     9.95
AVON, CANDLE, RED, 1964............................. 10.00 TO      15.00
AVON, CANDLE, 1965, AMBER.......................................     7.50
AVON, CANDLEHOLDER, EMBOSSED, FOOTED, AMBER, 1965....... 10.00 TO  16.50
AVON, CANDLEHOLDER, EMBOSSED, FOOTED, RED, 1965......... 10.00 TO  15.00
AVON, CANDLEHOLDER, EMBOSSED, MILK GLASS, 1965......... 10.00 TO   15.00
AVON, CANDLEHOLDER, FLUTED, BLUE, GOLD BAND, 1967........ 9.00 TO  12.00
AVON, CANDLEHOLDER, FLUTED, FLORAL, GOLD, 1966.......... 8.00 TO   10.00
AVON, CANDLEHOLDER, FLUTED, GOLD, GREEN BAND............ 8.00 TO   10.00
AVON, CANDLEHOLDER, GOLD, 1969..................................     6.00
AVON, CANDLEHOLDER, GOLDEN APPLE, 1968................. 4.00 TO     7.50
AVON, CANDLEHOLDER, METALLIC GOLD, RED, 1967........... 6.00 TO     9.00
AVON, CANDLEHOLDER, RED, FULL & BOXED, 1964.....................    12.95
AVON, CANDLEHOLDER, REGENCE, GREEN, GOLD, 1967......... 12.50 TO   15.00
AVON, CANDLEHOLDER, REGENCE, TALL, BLUE, 1968......... 12.00 TO    15.00
AVON, CANDLEHOLDER, REGENCE, TALL, GREEN, 1968........ 12.00 TO    15.00
AVON, CANDLEHOLDER, REGENCE, TALL, OLIVE, 1968........ 12.00 TO    14.00
AVON, CANDLEHOLDER, SILVER APPLE, 1968..........................    20.00
AVON, CANDLEHOLDER, TALL, REGENCE, FULL & BOXED, 1968...........     8.95
AVON, CANDLEHOLDER, WASSAIL BOWL, 1969..........................     6.95
AVON, CANDLEHOLDER, WHITE & GOLD, 1966..........................     7.95
AVON, CANDLEHOLDER, 1ST CHRISTMAS, GOLD, 1967......... 12.50 TO    15.00
AVON, CANDLESTICK COLOGNE, FULL & BOXED.........................     4.50
AVON, CANDLESTICK, AMBER............................. 9.95 TO      11.00
AVON, CANDLESTICK, GOLD BAND, MILK GLASS.............. 12.00 TO    15.00
AVON, CANDLESTICK, SILVER, PAIR, 1966................ 25.00 TO     30.00
AVON, CANDLESTICK, SILVER, 1ST ISSUED 1966........... 8.00 TO      14.00
AVON, CANNON, DEFENDER, AMBER, 1966.................. 11.00 TO     18.00
AVON, CANNON, FULL & BOXED......................................    20.00
AVON, CAPITOL DECANTER, 1970, FULL & BOXED......................     3.50
AVON, CAPTAIN'S CHOICE, 1965......................... 6.00 TO      10.00
AVON, CAR, CADILLAC, GOLD, 1969.................................     5.00
AVON, CAR, DEUSENBERG, 1970......................... 3.60 TO        4.50
AVON, CAR, ELECTRIC CHARGER, 1970................... 2.00 TO        3.00
AVON, CAR, PACKARD, FULL & BOXED................................     4.50
AVON, CAR, STERLING SIX, 1968....................... 2.50 TO        7.00
AVON, CAR, STRAIGHT EIGHT, 1969..................... 3.00 TO        4.00
AVON, CAR, TOURING T................................ 4.00 TO        6.50
AVON, CAR, VOLKSWAGEN, 1970.....................................     2.50
```

```
AVON,CARRIAGE,EMBOSSED,2 OZ.....................................  15.00
AVON,CASEY'S LANTERN,AMBER,1966..................... 15.00 TO    25.00
AVON,CASEY'S LANTERN,GREEN,1966.................................  22.50
AVON,CASEY'S LANTERN,RED,1966...................... 17.00 TO    22.50
AVON,CAT ON A BASKET,SACHET.....................................   4.00
AVON,CERAMIC FRAGRANCE JAR,PINK.................................  55.00
AVON,CHARISMA AWARD,(PIN,EARRINGS & BRACELET)..................  15.00
AVON,CHARISMA COLOGNE,1968......................................   5.00
AVON,CHARISMA NECKLACE,BRACELET & EARRINGS......................  20.00
AVON,CHRISTMAS ANGEL,1968........................... 2.50 TO     4.50
AVON,CHRISTMAS CANDLE,FULL & BOXED,1967............. 7.50 TO     9.00
AVON,CHRISTMAS COLOGNE,1969.....................................   3.00
AVON,CHRISTMAS ORNAMENT,EMBOSSED,INDENTED SIDE,BLUE,1968....     4.00
AVON,CHRISTMAS ORNAMENT,EMBOSSED,INDENTED SIDE,GOLD,1968....     4.00
AVON,CHRISTMAS ORNAMENT,EMBOSSED,INDENTED SIDE,GREEN,1968...     4.00
AVON,CHRISTMAS ORNAMENT,EMBOSSED,INDENTED SIDE,RED,1968.....     4.00
AVON,CHRISTMAS ORNAMENT,RED.....................................   4.00
AVON,CHRISTMAS ORNAMENT,SET OF 4,1968...........................  11.00
AVON,CHRISTMAS ORNAMENT,SET OF 4,1969...........................   6.00
AVON,CHRISTMAS ORNAMENT,SWAGS,GOLD,1967............. 4.00 TO     6.00
AVON,CHRISTMAS ORNAMENT,SWAGS,GREEN,1967............ 4.00 TO     6.00
AVON,CHRISTMAS ORNAMENT,SWAGS,PURPLE,1967........... 4.00 TO     6.00
AVON,CHRISTMAS ORNAMENT,SWAGS,RED,1967.............. 4.00 TO     6.00
AVON,CHRISTMAS ORNAMENT,SWAGS,SILVER,1967........... 4.00 TO     6.00
AVON,CHRISTMAS ORNAMENT,2 COLORS,1969...........................   5.00
AVON,CHRISTMAS RECORD,1968......................................   4.95
AVON,CHRISTMAS TREE,GOLD,1968....................... 4.00 TO     5.00
AVON,CHRISTMAS TREE,GREEN,1968..................................   2.50
AVON,CHRISTMAS TREE,RED,1968....................................   2.50
AVON,CHRISTMAS TREE,SILVER,1968.................................   2.50
AVON,CLASSIC COLOGNE,SWIRL,1969.................................   3.00
AVON,CLASSIC DECANTER,GODDESS BATH OIL,1969......... 3.75 TO     5.00
AVON,CLASSIC DECANTER,1969......................................   3.00
AVON,CLASSICS BOOK,CLEAR,1969...................................   3.50
AVON,CLASSICS BOOK,COLOGNE,4 OZ..................... 3.95 TO     5.00
AVON,CLOCK,DAYLIGHT SAVING TIME,1968................ 3.00 TO     6.00
AVON,CLOVER LEAF TRAY............................... 6.00 TO     9.00
AVON,COCONUT OIL SHAMPOO,1 PINT,1939............................  17.95
AVON,COLOGNE FOR MEN,FULL,1959..................................  11.95
AVON,COPPER PENNY,1970..........................................   4.00
AVON,COTILLION BEAUTY DUST,EMPTY,1954............... 8.00 TO    14.95
AVON,COTILLION BEAUTY DUST,FULL & BOXED.........................   3.95
AVON,COTILLION COLOGNE,1940.....................................  15.00
AVON,COTILLION CREAM LOTION,FULL & BOXED,1954..................  17.95
AVON,COTILLION CREAM LOTION,4 1/2 OZ.,CLEAR.....................   7.00
AVON,COTILLION CREAM LOTION,4 1/2 OZ.,FROSTED...................   8.00
AVON,COTILLION CREAM SACHET,FROSTED JAR.........................  10.00
AVON,COTILLION POWDER BOX,1960..................................   6.50
AVON,COTILLION POWDER SACHET,1952................... 10.00 TO    12.50
AVON,COTILLION POWDER SACHET,1957...............................   7.00
AVON,COTILLION SACHET,1937......................................  14.00
AVON,COTILLION SACHET,1951......................................   6.00
AVON,COTILLION SACHET,1962,FULL & BOXED.........................   2.00
AVON,COTILLION TALC,FROSTED.....................................  11.00
AVON,COTILLION TALC,4 1/2 OZ.,1951,FROSTED......................   6.00
AVON,COTILLION TOILET WATER,2 OZ.,1951..........................  11.50
AVON,COURTING LAMP,FULL & BOXED.................................   5.00
AVON,COVERED WAGON,FULL & BOXED.................................   3.60
AVON,CRANBERRY SHAKER............................... 3.00 TO     4.00
AVON,CREAM HAIR LOTION,1956,SILVER LABEL........................   8.00
AVON,CREAM HAIR LOTION,2 OZ.,1960...............................   3.00
AVON,CREAM SACHET,1960..........................................  10.00
AVON,CREAM,1937.................................................   7.50
AVON,CRIMSON CARNATION TOILET WATER.............................  12.00
AVON,CRUET DECANTER,EMBOSSED SIDES & BASE,CLEAR,1966........    11.00
```

```
AVON,CRUET,BATH URN,MILK GLASS,1963.................. 6.50 TO    14.00
AVON,CRYSTAL BEAUTY DUST,1966.................................   16.00
AVON,CRYSTAL COLOGNE,FULL & BOXED.............................    6.95
AVON,CRYSTAL GLORY TOP........................................    3.00
AVON,CRYSTAL GLORY,1961.............................. 6.50 TO   12.00
AVON,CUP,DEMITASSE,BLUE & WHITE,1968................. 4.00 TO    6.00
AVON,CUP,DEMITASSE,RED & YELLOW,1969..........................    5.00
AVON,DAISIES WON'T TELL BUBBLE BATH,1962......................    7.00
AVON,DAISIES WON'T TELL COLOGNE,2 OZ.,1962....................    5.00
AVON,DAISY COLOGNE,GLASS BAND,1958............................    8.00
AVON,DAISY PIN,1969...........................................    6.00
AVON,DECANTER,MALLARD,GREEN,1967..................... 6.00 TO    7.00
AVON,DECISIONS,DECISIONS,8 OZ.,1965................. 17.50 TO   23.00
AVON,DECISIONS,FULL & BOXED......................... 24.95 TO   30.00
AVON,DECISIONS,1/2 SIZE.......................................   23.00
AVON,DEFENDER,STAND,CANNON,AMBER,1966............... 11.00 TO   18.00
AVON,DELUXE PRE-SHAVE LOTION,FULL & BOXED.....................   19.95
AVON,DEMI CUP,FULL & BOXED,BLUE,1968................ 4.00 TO    6.00
AVON,DEODORANT,2 OZ.,FULL & BOXED,1959........................    5.00
AVON,DEW KISS,1960............................................    2.00
AVON,DEW KISS,1967............................................    1.00
AVON,DINNER BELL,1968.........................................    4.95
AVON,DOLLARS & SCENTS,CONTENTS,1966...........................   25.00
AVON,DOLLARS & SCENTS,1966.......................... 16.00 TO   23.50
AVON,DOLPHIN DECANTER,FROSTED,1968.................. 4.00 TO   10.00
AVON,DOLPHIN,FULL & BOXED.....................................    6.00
AVON,DRESSING TABLE CAMEO,CREAM SACHET,BLUE,1962..............   10.00
AVON,DRESSING TABLE CAMEO,CREAM SACHET,PINK,1962..............   10.00
AVON,DUCK,FULL & BOXED,1967......................... 8.00 TO    9.00
AVON,DUCK,MALLARD,DECANTER,1967..................... 6.00 TO    7.00
AVON,DUELING PISTOL,FULL & BOXED,1966.........................   25.00
AVON,DUESENBERG CAR................................. 3.60 TO    4.50
AVON,EASTER BASKET-YOUNG HEARTS...............................   75.00
AVON,EIFFEL TOWER,FULL & BOXED................................    3.50
AVON,ELECTRIC CHARGER,FULL & BOXED,1970............. 2.50 TO    3.00
AVON,ELEGANTE BEAUTY DUST,1956................................   13.00
AVON,ELEGANTE COLOGNE,4 OZ.,1956..............................   10.00
AVON,ELEGANTE PERFUME.........................................   25.00
AVON,ELEGANTE PERFUME,1/2 OZ.,1957..................125.00 TO  150.00
AVON,ELEGANTE PERFUME,3 DRAMS,1957..................125.00 TO  150.00
AVON,ELEGANTE POWDER SACHET,1956.................... 6.50 TO   11.00
AVON,ELEGANTE TOILET WATER,2 OZ.FULL IN ORIGINAL BOX.........   30.00
AVON,ELUSIVE BEAUTY DUST CREAM SACHET,1970....................    4.00
AVON,EVENING LIGHTS PURSE.....................................   25.00
AVON,EXCALIBUR COLOGNE,1969...................................    4.00
AVON,EXCALIBUR,FULL CONTENTS,1969.............................    5.00
AVON,FAIR LADY SET,FULL & BOXED,1939..........................  125.00
AVON,FAIR LADY SET,1939.......................................  100.00
AVON,FAN ROCKER,SEA SHELL,1962...................... 3.00 TO    5.00
AVON,FIRST CHRISTMAS CANDLE,1967................... 12.00 TO   15.00
AVON,FIRST CLASS MALE,FULL & BOXED,1955.......................   20.00
AVON,FIRST EDITION,BOOK,CLEAR,1967.................. 3.00 TO    6.00
AVON,FIRST EDITION,FULL & BOXED,1967................ 4.50 TO    6.00
AVON,FLAME BOTTLE.............................................    2.50
AVON,FLAME BOTTLE,METAL LEAF BASE.............................    9.50
AVON,FLASK AFTER SHOWER,1959..................................   40.00
AVON,FLASK,ALPINE,1966.............................. 15.00 TO   62.50
AVON,FLAT TOP ROCKER PERFUME,1 OZ.,FULL & BOXED,1959.........   65.00
AVON,FLAT TOP ROCKER,1/2 OZ.,1963.............................    4.00
AVON,FLING COLOGNE,1969.......................................     .75
AVON,FLORAL TRIO,1965.........................................   15.00
AVON,FLOWER FANTASY,1963......................................    8.50
AVON,FLOWERTIME COLOGNE,1951..................................   15.00
AVON,FLOWERTIME TALC,1951........................... 20.00 TO   21.00
AVON,FLOWERTIME TOILET WATER,2 OZ.,1951............. 12.50 TO   20.00
```

```
AVON,FLUFF PUFF,FULL & BOXED.......................................      5.00
AVON,FOOTBALL HELMET,BLUE STRIPE,1968................... 4.50 TO         6.45
AVON,FOOTBALL HELMET,BLUE,FULL & BOXED,1968.......... 7.50 TO           9.00
AVON,FOOTBALL HELMET,FULL & BOXED,1968............... 7.50 TO          19.00
AVON,FOOTBALL HELMET,PLAIN,1968...................... 5.00 TO           6.45
AVON,FOOTBALL HELMET,SHINY GOLD,FULL & BOXED....... 17.50 TO           19.50
AVON,FOOTBALL HELMET,SHINY GOLD,1968............... 15.00 TO           19.00
AVON,FOOTBALL,TOY..................................................      9.50
AVON,FORE & AFTER SET,2 BOTTLES,FULL & BOXED.....................      15.00
AVON,FOREVER SPRING BODY POWDER,1951,FULL........................      10.00
AVON,FOREVER SPRING COLOGNE,4 OZ.,1951............... 13.00 TO         18.00
AVON,FOREVER SPRING CREAM SACHET,1951................ 6.00 TO          9.00
AVON,FOREVER SPRING CREAM SACHET,1957............................       8.50
AVON,FOREVER SPRING PERFUME.......................... 16.00 TO         25.00
AVON,FOREVER SPRING PERFUME,1/2 OZ.,1951............125.00 TO        150.00
AVON,FOREVER SPRING PERFUME,3 DRAMS.................125.00 TO        150.00
AVON,FOREVER SPRING POWDER SACHET,1951............... 6.50 TO         11.00
AVON,FOREVER SPRING TOILET WATER WITH BLUE BIRD,FULL & BOXED          18.00
AVON,FOUR A.AFTER SHAVE,1965.....................................      20.00
AVON,FOX HUNT COLOGNE,1966.......................................      10.00
AVON,FOX HUNT SET,FULL,1966......................................      25.00
AVON,FRAGRANCE BELL,1965.........................................       5.00
AVON,FRAGRANCE CHEST,RED LID,1967................... 10.00 TO         25.00
AVON,FRAGRANCE CHEST,SILVER LID,1966.............................      25.00
AVON,FRAGRANCE FLING BOTTLE,CLEAR,1968...........................       1.00
AVON,FRAGRANCE JAR,CERAMIC.......................................      50.00
AVON,FRAGRANCE JAR,RUBBER,1957...................................      40.00
AVON,FRAGRANCE ORNAMENT,3,FULL & BOXED,1965......... 35.00 TO         45.00
AVON,FRAGRANCE TOUCH,FULL & BOXED,HAND,1969......................       5.00
AVON,FRAGRANCE TRIO,FANCY STOPPER,1969...........................      15.00
AVON,FRAGRANCE TRIO,GOLD LEAF DESIGN,1966........................       5.00
AVON,FRENCH FROSTING................................. 2.00 TO          3.00
AVON,FRENCH PERFUME,1 OZ.........................................      27.00
AVON,FURNITURE POLISH............................................       8.00
AVON,FUTURA EXCALIBUR COLOGNE FIGURE.............................      12.00
AVON,FUTURA,1969.................................... 12.00 TO         18.00
AVON,GARDEN OF FRAGRANCE,1948....................................      75.00
AVON,GARDEN OF LOVE POWDER SACHET,1937...........................      12.50
AVON,GARDEN OF LOVE POWDER SACHET,1945,FULL & BOXED..........      15.00
AVON,GARDEN OF LOVE SACHET,1943..................................      18.00
AVON,GARDENIA,1951..............................................      39.50
AVON,GAVEL,FULL & BOXED..........................................      15.00
AVON,GAVEL,1967..................................... 7.50 TO         10.00
AVON,GENTLEMAN'S COLLECTION,3 BOTTLES,1968.......................      10.00
AVON,GENTLEMAN'S COLOGNE,2 OZ.,1968..............................       2.50
AVON,GENTLEMEN'S COLLECTION,FULL & BOXED,RED,1968................      18.00
AVON,GEORGE WASHINGTON DECANTER,FULL & BOXED,1970................       2.70
AVON,GLOBE,MAN'S WORLD,1969......................... 3.00 TO          5.00
AVON,GODDESS,CLASSIC BATH OIL,1969.................. 3.75 TO          5.00
AVON,GOLD BOX,1940..............................................      58.00
AVON,GOLD BOX,1948..............................................      75.00
AVON,GOLD BOX,1957..............................................      85.00
AVON,GOLD CADILLAC,1969.........................................       5.00
AVON,GOLD VANITY,1967...........................................      16.50
AVON,GOLDEN ANGEL,FULL & BOXED,1968.............................       4.50
AVON,GOLDEN ANGEL,1968.............................. 2.50 TO          4.50
AVON,GOLDEN APPLE................................... 4.00 TO          7.50
AVON,GOLDEN APPLE,FULL & BOXED,1968.............................       6.00
AVON,GOLDEN APPLE,1968..........................................       6.00
AVON,GOLDEN HEIRLOOM,JEWEL BOX,1968.............................      20.00
AVON,GOLDEN LEAF PERFUME,1/2 OZ.................................      20.00
AVON,GOLDEN LEAF PIN,FULL & BOXED...............................       3.95
AVON,GOLDEN PROMISE BODY POWDER,1950............................      20.00
AVON,GOLDEN PROMISE COLOGNE,4 OZ................................      20.00
AVON,GOLDEN PROMISE COLOGNE,1951.................... 15.00 TO         20.00
```

```
AVON,GOLDEN PROMISE PERFUME,1/2 OZ...................125.00 TO  150.00
AVON,GOLDEN PROMISE PERFUME,3 DRAMS..................125.00 TO  150.00
AVON,GOLDEN PROMISE PERFUME,1951...............................  25.00
AVON,GOLDEN PROMISE POWDER SACHET,1947.........................  10.00
AVON,GOLDEN PROMISE POWDER SACHET,1952,FULL & BOXED...........   12.50
AVON,GOLDEN PROMISE POWDER SACHET,1954.........................  15.00
AVON,GOLDEN PROMISE TOILET WATER,FULL & BOXED.................   20.00
AVON,GOLDEN TOPAZ,1 OZ.,FULL & BOXED.......................... 125.00
AVON,GREEK GODDESS.............................................  7.00 TO   10.00
AVON,GREEK GODDESS POWDER SACHET,FULL & BOXED................    5.50
AVON,GREEK GODDESS,1969.......................................  3.75 TO    5.00
AVON,GUN,WITH CASE,DUELING PISTOL,1966........................   25.00
AVON,HAND LOTION,1951.........................................    6.00
AVON,HAND,MILK GLASS,FRAGRANCE TOUCH,1969.............  2.50 TO    5.00
AVON,HANDS,TOUCH OF BEAUTY,SOAP,1969..........................    4.00
AVON,HANSEL-GRETEL SOAP & HOUSE,1964..........................    3.50
AVON,HAPPY HOURS,3 BOTTLES,1958...............................   25.00
AVON,HEART....................................................   37.50
AVON,HEART,FAN TOP............................................    7.95
AVON,HEARTS ON A PIN CUSHION,1966................... 30.00 TO   40.00
AVON,HEARTS,THREE ON TRAY,1964................................   14.00
AVON,HEAVEN LIGHT FACE POWDER,DEMONSTRATOR ARTIST'S PALETTE.    18.50
AVON,HELMET,BLUE STRIPE,1968.........................  4.50 TO    6.45
AVON,HELMET,FOOTBALL,PLAIN,1968......................  5.00 TO    6.45
AVON,HELMET,SHINY GOLD............................... 15.00 TO   19.00
AVON,HELMET,SHINY GOLD,FULL & BOXED,1968............. 17.50 TO   19.50
AVON,HER PRETTINESS FOUNTAIN,1970.............................    2.00
AVON,HERE'S MY HEART BEAUTY DUST..............................    4.00
AVON,HERE'S MY HEART BEAUTY DUST,FULL & BOXED.................    3.95
AVON,HERE'S MY HEART COLOGNE MIST,1958,EMPTY..................    4.95
AVON,HERE'S MY HEART LOTION,1958,FULL & BOXED.................    5.00
AVON,HERE'S MY HEART PERFUME.........................125.00 TO  150.00
AVON,HERE'S MY HEART PERFUME OIL,1965.........................   10.00
AVON,HERE'S MY HEART POWDER SACHET............................    6.00
AVON,HERE'S MY HEART POWDER SACHET,GLASS......................    4.50
AVON,HERE'S MY HEART POWDER SACHET,PLASTIC....................    4.50
AVON,HONOR AWARD,1966.........................................   18.00
AVON,HOUSE OF CHARM...........................................   55.00
AVON,HOUSE OF CHARM,FULL & BOXED,1954.........................   75.00
AVON,ICE CREAM SODA,PRETTY PEACH,1966............... 12.50 TO   15.00
AVON,ICICLE,FLACON PERFUME,1967......................  2.50 TO    3.50
AVON,INDIAN HEAD PENNY,FULL & BOXED,COPPER,1970...............    2.50
AVON,INKWELL,FULL & BOXED,1969................................    5.00
AVON,INKWELL,1969.............................................    5.00
AVON,INSECT REPELLENT,1950....................................    8.00
AVON,ISLAND LIME,FULL & BOXED,1966............................    6.95
AVON,ISLAND LIME,GREEN,1966...................................   12.00
AVON,ISLAND LIME,YELLOW,1967..................................    8.00
AVON,ISLAND LIME,1968.........................................    4.00
AVON,IT'S A BLAST,FULL & BOXED................................    5.25
AVON,JASMINE BATH OIL.........................................    2.50
AVON,JASMINE BATH SALTS,1937..................................   27.00
AVON,JASMINE TOILET WATER,FULL & BOXED........................   18.00
AVON,JEWEL COLLECTION,FULL & BOXED,1964............. 37.50 TO   55.00
AVON,JEWELED SOMEWHERE POWDER SACHET..........................    8.00
AVON,JUG,BAY RUM,1963................................  4.25 TO   12.00
AVON,JUST TWO,BLACK & CLEAR,BOXED,1965............... 57.50 TO   65.00
AVON,JUST TWO,CLEAR,1965......................................   18.00
AVON,JUST TWO,FULL & BOXED,1965...............................   75.00
AVON,KEEPSAKE CREAM SACHET,FULL & BOXED.......................    2.70
AVON,KEG,BAY RUM.....................................  9.00 TO   12.50
AVON,KEY NOTE,FULL & BOXED,1967...................... 11.50 TO   12.50
AVON,KEY NOTE,1967............................................    8.00
AVON,KING PIN,1969...................................  2.00 TO    3.00
AVON,KING PINS,SET OF 10,1969.................................   26.00
```

```
AVON,LACE MY SHOE,PLASTIC.........................................      4.95
AVON,LADY BELLE,STYROFOAM BELL,2 PERFUMES,FULL & BOXED......     70.00
AVON,LADY SLIPPER SOAP,1965.......................................     10.00
AVON,LADY SLIPPER,SOAP & PERFUME SET,FULL & BOXED...........      3.60
AVON,LANTERN,CASEY'S,AMBER,1966...................... 15.00 TO     25.00
AVON,LANTERN,CASEY'S,FULL & BOXED,AMBER...................     34.95
AVON,LANTERN,CASEY'S,FULL & BOXED,RED,1966...................     34.95
AVON,LANTERN,CASEY'S,GREEN,1966...................................     22.50
AVON,LANTERN,CASEY'S,RED,1966........................ 17.00 TO     22.50
AVON,LAVENDER & LACE,1970.........................................      5.00
AVON,LAVENDER POWDER SACHET,FULL............... 4.50 TO      6.00
AVON,LAVENDER POWDER SACHET,FULL & BOXED............ 7.95 TO      8.50
AVON,LAVENDER SACHET,1/2 FULL.....................................      5.00
AVON,LAVENDER SACHET,1962.........................................      6.95
AVON,LEAD PENCIL.................................................      2.50
AVON,LEISURE HOURS,FULL & BOXED..................................      4.50
AVON,LEMON VELVET BEAUTY DUST,PLASTIC,1969.....................      1.00
AVON,LEMONOL SLICES,1967.........................................     14.95
AVON,LEMONOL SOAP,3,EMBOSSED,BOXED..............................     16.00
AVON,LIPSTICK,PLASTIC BOX,OLD BRASS SAMPLE.....................      8.00
AVON,LOOKING GLASS COLOGNE,FULL & BOXED........................      2.70
AVON,LOTION LOVELY,FULL,1964.....................................      9.95
AVON,LOTION LOVELY,1964..........................................      7.50
AVON,LOVEBIRD,FULL & BOXED.......................................      5.00
AVON,LOVEBIRD,FULL & BOXED,1969..................................      3.50
AVON,LOVEBIRD,1969............................................ 5.00 TO      6.00
AVON,LOVEBIRD,1970..............................................      4.25
AVON,LUSCIOUS PERFUME,1939.......................................    100.00
AVON,MACHINE OIL.................................................     10.00
AVON,MALLARD DUCK DECANTER,1967...................... 6.00 TO      7.00
AVON,MALLARD,FULL & BOXED............................. 8.00 TO      9.00
AVON,MAN'S BOOT,GOLD TOP,1965........................ 3.00 TO      5.00
AVON,MAN'S BOOT,SILVER TOP,1965...................... 4.95 TO      7.00
AVON,MAN'S WORLD,FULL & BOXED,1969...............................      5.00
AVON,MAN'S WORLD,GLOBE,1969.......................... 3.00 TO      5.00
AVON,MAPLE FLAVORING,FULL & BOXED................................     20.00
AVON,MAROON BOXING GLOVE,LEFT HAND,1968........................     13.00
AVON,MASTER ORGANIZER,FULL & BOXED..............................     17.50
AVON,MEDALLION,GOLD,1886-1962....................................     15.00
AVON,MEN'S AFTER SHOWER,8 OZ.,GOLD FOIL........................     50.00
AVON,MEN'S BARBER BOTTLE,1963........................ 15.00 TO     25.00
AVON,MENDING CEMENT..............................................      8.00
AVON,MERRIMENT COLOGNE,FULL & BOXED,1955.......................     25.00
AVON,MICKEY MOUSE,1969...........................................      4.49
AVON,MILK CAN,FULL & BOXED.......................................      6.00
AVON,MILK GLASS CANDLEHOLDER,1964.................... 6.50 TO     10.00
AVON,MILK GLASS CRUET,BATH URN,1963.................. 6.50 TO     14.00
AVON,MINIATURE GRANDFATHER'S CLOCK,AWARD AVON EMBLEM ON
   PENDULUM.....................................................     50.00
AVON,MISS LOLLYPOP BOOT,1968.....................................      7.50
AVON,MISS LOLLYPOP COLOGNE MIST,1968............................     10.00
AVON,MISS LOLLYPOP CREAM SACHET,1968............................      4.00
AVON,MISS LOLLYPOP PERFUME ROLLETTE,FULL & BOXED.............      1.50
AVON,MISS LOLLYPOP SPRAY,PLASTIC,PINK,1968........... 6.00 TO      7.50
AVON,MOTHERS HELPER BLUE IRON...................................     10.00
AVON,MOTHICIDE..................................................     10.00
AVON,MOTHICIDE PERFECTION,1938...................................     15.00
AVON,MOTHICIDE,RED..............................................     10.00
AVON,MOUSE,PETITE,FULL & BOXED...................................      4.50
AVON,NAIL O CUTICLE CREAM,1937-38................................      5.00
AVON,NEARNESS BEAUTY DUST,PLASTIC................................      9.95
AVON,NEARNESS BEAUTY DUST,1956...................................      9.50
AVON,NEARNESS BEAUTY DUST,1956,EMPTY.............................     14.95
AVON,NEARNESS BEAUTY DUST,1959...................................      8.50
AVON,NEARNESS BODY POWDER,FROSTED GLASS,1956..................     14.00
```

```
AVON,NEARNESS BODY POWDER,FROSTED,EMPTY.....................    24.95
AVON,NEARNESS COLOGNE MIST,1956............................    17.50
AVON,NEARNESS COLOGNE MIST,1958............................    20.00
AVON,NEARNESS COLOGNE,4 OZ.,EMPTY..........................    24.95
AVON,NEARNESS CREAM SACHET,1956............................     6.95
AVON,NEARNESS PERFUME......................................    25.00
AVON,NEARNESS PERFUME,1/2 OZ.,1955.........................    75.00
AVON,NEARNESS PERFUME,1 DRAM,1956..........................     8.50
AVON,NEARNESS PERFUME,3 DRAMS..............................    75.00
AVON,NEARNESS POWDER SACHET................... 8.00 TO       10.00
AVON,NEARNESS POWDER SACHET,FULL & BOXED...................    12.95
AVON,NEARNESS POWDER SACHET,1956...........................    12.00
AVON,NEARNESS TOILET WATER.................................    16.00
AVON,NEARNESS TOILET WATER,1956............................    15.00
AVON,NEARNESS TOILET WATER,1965............................    14.00
AVON,NECKLACE,BLACK STONE,1966.............................     7.50
AVON,NECKLACE,STONE,BLACK..................................    12.00
AVON,NEST EGG SOAP & SPONGE,1967...........................     7.95
AVON,OCCUR BEAUTY DUST,FULL & BOXED........................     3.95
AVON,OCCUR BEAUTY DUST,1964................................     3.00
AVON,OCCUR PERFUME,1 OZ.,1964..............................    19.95
AVON,OCCUR POWDER SACHET...................................     5.00
AVON,OCCUR POWDER SACHET,FULL & BOXED......................    10.95
AVON,OPENING PLAY HELMET,BLUE STRIPE,1968........... 4.50 TO    6.45
AVON,OPENING PLAY HELMET,PLAIN,1968................. 5.00 TO    6.45
AVON,OPENING PLAY HELMET,SHINY GOLD,1968........... 15.00 TO   19.00
AVON,ORCHARD BLOSSOM COLOGNE,1935..........................    85.00
AVON,OWL & 1ST ADDITION BOOK...............................     2.75
AVON,OWL PIN,1968................................... 4.00 TO   10.00
AVON,OWL,WISE CHOICE AFTER SHAVE,AMBER,1969................     3.00
AVON,PACKARD ROADSTER,FULL & BOXED.........................     4.50
AVON,PADDLE'N BALL,1963....................................     7.00
AVON,PAID STAMP,FULL & BOXED...............................     3.50
AVON,PARADE DRESS,3 PIECE SET,1951.........................    45.00
AVON,PATTERNS RING,FULL & BOXED,1969.......................     6.00
AVON,PEACH BASKET SACHET,EMPTY,1965.................. 3.95 TO    5.00
AVON,PEACH SODA.................................... 12.50 TO   15.00
AVON,PENCIL CADDY..........................................     9.00
AVON,PENNY ARCADE,FULL & BOXED,1951........................    40.00
AVON,PERFECTION BLACK WALNUT,1/2 OZ.,1939..................    25.00
AVON,PERFECTION EXTRACT,C.P.C.,1/2 OZ.............. 12.50 TO   20.00
AVON,PERFECTION EXTRACT,C.P.C.,2 OZ................ 20.00 TO   25.00
AVON,PERFECTION EXTRACT,C.P.C.,4 OZ........................    40.00
AVON,PERFECTION FLAVOR.....................................    17.00
AVON,PERFECTION FURNITURE POLISH...........................    18.50
AVON,PERFECTION MAPLE FLAVOR,2 OZ.,1939....................    25.00
AVON,PERFECTION MOTHICIDE,FULL.............................    18.50
AVON,PERFECTION POWDER CLEANER.............................     8.00
AVON,PERFECTION SAVORY COLOGNE,4 OZ.,1939..................    25.00
AVON,PERFUME GLACE,FULL & BOXED,1967................ 9.50 TO   25.00
AVON,PERFUME GLACE,1967....................................     6.00
AVON,PERFUME,1 DRAM,1948...................................     4.00
AVON,PERFUME,1 DRAM,1959...................................     1.00
AVON,PERFUME,1/2 OZ.,BRASS LEAVES,1966.............. 7.95 TO   17.00
AVON,PERFUME,1/2 OZ.,1969,TALL RIBBED CLEAR TOP,FULL & BOXED    8.50
AVON,PERFUME,1 OZ.,MADE IN FRANCE,1963............. 30.00 TO   35.00
AVON,PERSIAN WOOD BEAUTY DUST...................... 6.00 TO   10.00
AVON,PERSIAN WOOD BEAUTY DUST,1956,RED.....................     8.50
AVON,PERSIAN WOOD BEAUTY DUST,1957,EMPTY...................     9.95
AVON,PERSIAN WOOD COLOGNE,1956.............................     5.00
AVON,PERSIAN WOOD CREAM LOTION,1961,FULL & BOXED...........    17.95
AVON,PERSIAN WOOD POWDER SACHET,PLASTIC,1961...............     4.50
AVON,PERSIAN WOOD POWDER,RED...............................     7.50
AVON,PETI-FLEUR COLOGNE,1969...............................     2.50
AVON,PETTIPOINT GLACE......................................    11.00
```

```
AVON,PICTURE FRAME COLOGNE,FULL & BOXED............. 4.50 TO    6.50
AVON,PILLBOX PERFUME GLACE,1967,FULL & BOXED................    6.95
AVON,PIN,5 PEARLS IS A PLUS STAR WITH DIAMOND,CHAIN.........   40.00
     AVON, PIN BOTTLE, SEE ALSO AVON, BOWLING PIN
AVON,PINCUSHION................................... 15.00 TO    35.00
AVON,PINCUSHION,FULL & BOXED...................... 39.50 TO    44.95
AVON,PINE BATH OIL,1957...........................            10.00
AVON,PINE BATH SALTS,1951.........................            10.00
AVON,PINE BATH SALTS,1952.........................            12.00
AVON,PIPE DREAM,AMBER PIPE,1967................... 12.00 TO    15.00
AVON,PIPE,FULL & BOXED............................ 15.00 TO    17.00
AVON,PISTOLS,DUELING,WITH CASE,20 PACES,1966....... 25.00 TO   39.95
AVON,PONY POST,SHORT,1968......................... 4.00 TO     6.00
AVON,PONY POST,TALL,GREEN,1966...................... 6.00 TO    8.50
AVON,POOL PADDLER'S SOAP,BOXED,1959...............            12.00
AVON,POTBELLY STOVE,FULL & BOXED..................             2.50
AVON,PRE-ELECTRIC SHAVE,SILVER LABEL..............             8.00
AVON,PRESIDENT AWARD COMPACT......................            15.00
AVON,PRETTY ME DOLL,1969..........................             4.00
AVON,PRETTY PEACH BEAUTY DUST,1965................             8.00
AVON,PRETTY PEACH COLOGNE MIST,SODA,1965........... 12.50 TO   15.00
AVON,PRETTY PEACH CREAM SACHET,1965............... 3.95 TO     5.00
AVON,PRETTY PEACH TALC,1965.......................             7.00
AVON,PUMP,BLACK,1968..............................             5.00
AVON,PUMP,FULL & BOXED,1968.......................             5.00
AVON,PYRAMID OF FRAGRANCE,BOXED,1969.............. 7.95 TO    15.00
AVON,PYRAMID OF FRAGRANCE,FULL & BOXED............            12.50
AVON,QUAINTANCE COLOGNE,4 OZ......................            13.00
AVON,QUAINTANCE COLOGNE,1951...................... 15.00 TO   16.50
AVON,QUAINTANCE CREAM LOTION......................            13.00
AVON,QUAINTANCE DIARY.............................            80.00
AVON,QUAINTANCE DIARY WITH PERFUME,VELVET,GREEN...           125.00
AVON,QUAINTANCE PERFUME...........................            25.00
AVON,QUAINTANCE PERFUME,1/2 OZ....................125.00 TO   150.00
AVON,QUAINTANCE PERFUME,3 DRAMS...................125.00 TO   150.00
AVON,QUAINTANCE POWDER SACHET..................... 7.00 TO    10.00
AVON,QUAINTANCE TALC..............................            13.00
AVON,RAPTURE BEAUTY DUST,FULL & BOXED,1965........             3.95
AVON,RAPTURE BEAUTY DUST,1965.....................             3.00
AVON,RAPTURE PIN,AWARD............................            10.00
AVON,RAPTURE POWDER SACHET,FULL & BOXED,1964......            11.95
AVON,RAPTURE RHAPSODY SET,FULL & BOXED,1964.......            39.95
AVON,RAPTURE RHAPSODY TRAY WITH BOTTLES,1965......            18.50
AVON,RAPTURE RHAPSODY,1964........................            35.00
AVON,RED CANDLE,1964.............................. 10.00 TO   15.00
AVON,RED LANTERN,CASEY'S,1966..................... 17.00 TO   22.50
AVON,REFRESHING HOURS,1962........................             5.00
AVON,REGENCE CANDLE,SHORT,GREEN,GOLD,1967......... 12.00 TO   15.00
AVON,REGENCE CANDLE,TALL,BLUE,1968................ 12.00 TO   15.00
AVON,REGENCE CANDLE,TALL,GREEN,1968............... 12.00 TO   15.00
AVON,REGENCE MIRROR...............................             7.00
AVON,REGENCE PERFUME,1/2 OZ.......................            15.00
AVON,REGENCE PERFUME,1 OZ.,1968................... 25.00 TO   35.00
AVON,REGENCE SET..................................            18.50
AVON,REGENCY BEAUTY DUST..........................             4.00
AVON,RENAISSANCE TRIO,1966........................             4.00
AVON,RICH MOISTURE CREAM..........................             2.00
AVON,RIVIERA COLOGNE,DECANTER,FULL & BOXED,PAIR,1968.........  12.00
AVON,RIVIERA DECANTER,1968........................ 6.00 TO     7.95
AVON,RIVIERA,FULL & BOXED,1968....................             9.25
AVON,ROCKER,FAN,SEA SHELL,1962.................... 3.00 TO     5.00
AVON,ROSE DEMI-CUP,1969...........................             5.00
AVON,ROSE FRAGRANCE CERAMIC,1943..................            55.00
AVON,ROSE FRAGRANCE CERAMIC,1952..................            30.00
AVON,ROSE FRAGRANCE JAR,FROSTED STOPPER,1952......            22.50
```

```
AVON,ROSE FRAGRANCE JAR,1937.................................           40.00
AVON,ROSE GERANIUM SOAP SET,1966............................            7.00
AVON,ROSE GERANIUM TALC.....................................            4.50
AVON,ROUND TOP ROCKER,FAN,1962..............................            3.00
AVON,ROYAL JASMINE BATH SALTS,8 OZ.,1957....................           24.50
AVON,ROYAL ORB,1965.............................. 18.00 TO             25.00
AVON,ROYAL VASE DECANTER,FULL & BOXED,1970..................            4.00
AVON,ROYAL VASE DECANTER,FULL,1970..........................            3.95
AVON,RUBBER FOOTBALL,1967...................................            7.95
AVON,SABER..................................................            4.00
AVON,SACHET JAR.............................................            1.00
AVON,SALT & PEPPER,GREEN FLOWER,1967........................            6.00
AVON,SALT & PEPPER,PINK FLOWERS,1968........................            4.00
AVON,SANTA CLAUS CHIMNEY....................................           10.00
AVON,SCHOOL BELL,FULL & BOXED,1960..........................           14.95
AVON,SCHOOL BELL,1965............................... 7.50 TO           18.00
AVON,SCIMITAR,FULL & BOXED,1968.................... 10.00 TO           17.50
AVON,SCIMITAR,GOLD & RED,1968...................... 7.25 TO            10.00
AVON,SCIMITAR,SILVER........................................           24.50
AVON,SEA GARDEN BATH FOAM,1948..............................            3.00
AVON,SEA HORSE,FULL & BOXED.................................            4.00
AVON,SEA SHELL,FAN ROCKER,1962.................... 3.00 TO             5.00
AVON,SHAKER,CRANBERRY GLASS,FULL & BOXED........... 3.00 TO            4.00
AVON,SHAVING CHOICE,1967....................................            4.00
AVON,SHAVING TIME,FULL & BOXED..............................            4.50
AVON,SHINY GOLD HELMET,FULL & BOXED............... 17.50 TO            19.50
AVON,SHINY GOLD HELMET,1968...................... 15.00 TO            19.00
AVON,SHOE WHITE.............................................            8.00
AVON,SILK'N HONEY BEEHIVE,FULL & BOXED,1969.................            5.95
AVON,SILVER BATH FOAM,FULL & BOXED..........................           12.00
AVON,SILVER BATH OIL,FULL & BOXED...........................           12.00
AVON,SILVER BOOT,1965............................. 4.95 TO             7.00
AVON,SILVER CANDLESTICK,1966...................... 8.00 TO            14.00
AVON,SILVER DUESENBERG,FULL & BOXED............... 3.60 TO             4.50
AVON,SILVER TOP BOOT,1965......................... 4.95 TO             7.00
AVON,SILVER VANITY SHOWCASE,1964................. 11.00 TO            22.50
AVON,SIX CAR,STERLING............................. 2.50 TO             7.00
AVON,SKIN SO SOFT ROSE BUD VASE,FULL & BOXED,1968...........           13.00
AVON,SKIN SO SOFT,1966......................................            2.50
AVON,SMART MOVE,PLASTIC.....................................           12.50
AVON,SNAIL PERFUME,FULL & BOXED,1968.............. 3.95 TO             7.00
AVON,SNAIL PERFUME,1968........................... 3.50 TO             5.00
AVON,SNOOPY,MILK GLASS MUG,1969.............................            2.00
AVON,SODA,PRETTY PEACH,1966...................... 12.50 TO            15.00
AVON,SOLID GOLD CADILLAC,1969...............................            5.00
AVON,SOMEWHERE BEAUTY DUST,PINK,PLASTIC,1963................            7.00
AVON,SOMEWHERE COLOGNE MIST,PINK,PLASTIC,1961...............            9.00
AVON,SOMEWHERE COLOGNE,2 OZ.,PINK,1963......................            6.95
AVON,SOMEWHERE CREAM LOTION,1963............................           10.00
AVON,SOMEWHERE CREAM LOTION,1963,FULL & BOXED...............           14.95
AVON,SOMEWHERE CREAM SACHET,PINK,GLASS,JEWELED,1961.........            3.95
AVON,SOMEWHERE PERFUME,1 OZ.,RHINESTONES AROUND BOTTOM......           65.00
AVON,SOMEWHERE PERFUME,1 OZ.,1961...........................          125.00
AVON,SOMEWHERE POWDER SACHET,FULL & BOXED,1963...... 9.95 TO          12.95
AVON,SOMEWHERE POWDER SACHET,JEWELED TOP....................            4.00
AVON,SOMEWHERE POWDER SACHET,PINK,1961......................            4.75
AVON,SOMEWHERE POWDER SACHET,SQUARE,1967....................            8.00
AVON,SOMEWHERE POWDER SACHET,1966...........................           12.00
AVON,SONNET TOILET WATER,1940...............................           40.00
AVON,SPICY AFTER SHAVE LOTION,CLEAR GLASS,1967..............            2.00
AVON,SPIRIT OF ST.LOUIS,FULL & BOXED........................            6.00
AVON,SPLASH & SPRAY,GOLD SWIRL,CLEAR,1968.......... 14.00 TO          17.00
AVON,SPORTS RALLY TALC,1965.................................            5.00
AVON,SPRAY ESSENCE,FULL & BOXED,1966........................            7.95
AVON,SSS DECANTER,1964........................... 14.00 TO            18.00
```

```
AVON,SSS DECANTER,1965...............................  12.50 TO    15.00
AVON,STAGECOACH AFTER SHAVE,1960.............................     10.00
AVON,STAGECOACH,EMBOSSED,2 OZ.,1960................  15.00 TO    18.00
AVON,STAGECOACH,EMBOSSED,4 OZ.,1960................  18.00 TO    21.00
AVON,STAGECOACH,EMBOSSED,5 OZ.,1960..........................     20.00
AVON,STAGECOACH,8 OZ.........................................     15.00
AVON,STAGECOACH,1960,EMBOSSED AFTER SHOWER,8 OZ.............     25.00
AVON,STEER HORNS,WESTERN CHOICE,FULL & BOXED.......  17.50 TO    20.00
AVON,STEER HORNS,WESTERN CHOICE,1967................  14.50 TO    16.00
AVON,STEIN,6 OZ.,SILVER,1968.......................   3.75 TO    90.00
AVON,STEIN,8 OZ.,SILVER,1965.......................   5.50 TO    12.00
AVON,STERLING SIX CAR,1968.........................   2.50 TO     7.00
AVON,STOCKHOLDERS CHRISTMAS ORNAMENT,1959...........  50.00 TO    75.00
AVON,STRAIGHT EIGHT CAR,1969.......................   3.00 TO     4.00
AVON,STRAWBERRIES'N CREAM,FULL & BOXED,1970.................      2.95
AVON,STRAWBERRY FAIR SOAP....................................      4.00
AVON,STRUCTURED FOR MEN,1969,FULL & BOXED....................      9.95
AVON,SUN LOTION,1951.........................................      9.00
AVON,SWAN LAKE COLOGNE.......................................     23.00
AVON,SWEET AS HONEY,BEEHIVE,1952................... 100.00 TO   125.00
AVON,SWINGER GOLF BAG,FULL & BOXED,1969......................      3.45
AVON,SWINGER,FULL & BOXED,1969...............................      4.50
AVON,SWIRL,COLOGNE,CLASSIC,1967..............................      3.00
AVON,TALC FOR MEN,1962.......................................      6.00
AVON,TALC,GREEN..............................................      4.00
AVON,TALL PONY POST................................   6.00 TO     8.50
AVON,TELEPHONE,AVON CALLING,FULL & BOXED,1969.......   5.95 TO     6.95
AVON,TELEPHONE,1969................................   5.25 TO     7.00
AVON,TEMPLE OF LOVE,BOXED....................................     11.50
AVON,TEMPLE OF LOVE,HOLDER & SACHET..........................     15.95
AVON,THAT'S FOR ME,FULL & BOXED..............................     45.00
AVON,THREE HEARTS ON CUSHION,1966..................  30.00 TO    40.00
AVON,THREE HEARTS ON GLASS TRAY,EMPTY,1964...................     14.00
AVON,THREE HEARTS ON GLASS TRAY,FULL,1964....................     15.95
AVON,TIC-TOC-TIGER,1968......................................      3.00
  AVON, TO A WILD ROSE, SEE AVON, WILD ROSE
AVON,TOPAZE BEAUTY DUST,FULL & BOXED.........................      3.95
AVON,TOPAZE COLOGNE,1960.....................................      1.50
AVON,TOPAZE COLOGNE,1964.....................................     18.00
AVON,TOPAZE CREAM LOTION,EUROPEAN............................      3.50
AVON,TOPAZE GEM PERFUME,GLASS STOPPER........................    100.00
AVON,TOPAZE PERFUME,1 OZ.,1960...............................    125.00
AVON,TOPAZE PERFUME,1959.....................................     75.00
AVON,TOPAZE POWDER SACHET,FULL & BOXED,1964..................     11.95
AVON,TOPAZE TALC,1960........................................      6.00
AVON,TORPEDO CHRISTMAS ORNAMENT..............................     45.00
AVON,TOUCH OF BEAUTY,FULL & BOXED,HANDS,1969.................      4.00
AVON,TOURING T,FULL & BOXED,1969...................   4.00 TO     6.00
AVON,TOWN PUMP,CONTENTS,BOX,1968.............................      5.00
AVON,TOWN PUMP,1968..........................................      5.00
AVON,TOY FOOTBALL............................................      9.50
AVON,TRAILING ARBUTUS,1940...................................     40.00
AVON,TRIANGLE,BALLAD,GARDEN OF LOVE,COTILLION & PERFUME.....     70.00
AVON,TRIBUTE LEGENDARY HERO,WARRIOR,BLUE & SILVER,1967......      9.00
AVON,TRIBUTE LEGENDARY HERO,WARRIOR,FROSTED,1968.............      4.00
AVON,TRIBUTE,TALC FOR MEN,BLUE CAN,1963......................     15.00
AVON,TWENTY PACES,PISTOLS,FULL & BOXED,1966.........  25.00 TO    39.95
AVON,TWO LOVES,FULL & BOXED...................................      8.00
AVON,UNFORGETABLE HEIRLOOM,1956....................  30.00 TO    35.00
AVON,UNFORGETABLE HEIRLOOM,1965....................  25.00 TO    26.50
AVON,UNFORGETABLE PERFUME OIL,1964,FULL & BOXED..............      5.00
AVON,UNFORGETABLE POWDER SACHET,GOLD,PINK,1965...............      6.00
AVON,UNFORGETABLE SOAP,BOXED,1966............................      8.00
AVON,URN,CRUET,MILK GLASS,1963.....................   6.50 TO    14.00
AVON,VANITY SHOWCASE,1964..........................  11.00 TO    22.50
```

```
AVON,VIGORATE AFTER SHAVE,FROSTED,1960.....................      6.00
AVON,VIGORATE,CYLINDER,1959................................     45.00
AVON,VIKING HORN,FULL & BOXED,1966.................. 14.95 TO   17.95
AVON,VIKING HORN,1966............................... 9.00 TO   15.00
AVON,VOLKSWAGEN,FULL & BOXED,1970..........................      2.50
AVON,WARRIOR HEAD,TRIBUTE,BLUE & SILVER,1967...............      9.00
AVON,WARRIOR HEAD,TRIBUTE,FROSTED,1968.....................      4.00
AVON,WARRIOR,CONTENTS.4 OZ.................................      2.50
AVON,WARRIORS,EUROPEAN,RIBBED,CLEAR,1969...................     16.00
AVON,WASSAIL BOWL,FULL & BOSED,1969........................      6.95
AVON,WASSAIL BOWL,1969.............................. 6.95 TO    8.50
AVON,WATCH,DAYLIGHT SAVING TIME,1968................ 3.00 TO    6.00
AVON,WEATHER OR NOT,BAROMETER,1969.................. 5.00 TO    7.00
AVON,WESTERN CHOICE,STEER HORNS,PAIR,1967.......... 14.50 TO   16.00
AVON,WHITE GINGER & BUBBLE BATH,PLASTIC...................      1.00
AVON,WHITE GINGER,1967....................................      2.00
AVON,WHITE MOIRE COLOGNE,6 OZ.,1947................ 75.00 TO   80.00
AVON,WHITE MOIRE POWDER SACHET,1948.......................     13.00
AVON,WILD COUNTRY DUSTING POWDER FOR MEN,1967,FULL & BOXED..     4.95
AVON,WILD ROSE BEAUTY DUST,FULL & BOXED,1960..............      3.95
AVON,WILD ROSE BEAUTY DUST,1955...........................     13.00
AVON,WILD ROSE COLOGNE....................................      3.00
AVON,WILD ROSE COLOGNE,EMBOSSED ROSE ON CAP,BLUE..........     25.00
AVON,WILD ROSE COLOGNE,2 OZ.,1964.........................      4.50
AVON,WILD ROSE COLOGNE,4 OZ.,FULL & BOXED.................     11.95
AVON,WILD ROSE CREAM LOTION,1958..........................      6.00
AVON,WILD ROSE CREAM SACHET...............................     13.00
AVON,WILD ROSE CREAM SACHET,3 CORNER,1952.................      8.50
AVON,WILD ROSE POWDER SACHET..............................      4.50
AVON,WILD ROSE SPONGE WITH SOAP,1959......................      5.00
AVON,WILD ROSE TALC,CARDBOARD BODY POWDER,1952............     10.00
AVON,WILD ROSE TOILET WATER...............................     10.00
AVON,WILD ROSE,DEMI CUP,BLUE,RED,FULL & BOXED....... 4.00 TO    6.00
AVON,WINDJAMMER,PAINTED LABEL,1968........................      6.00
AVON,WINDJAMMER,PAPER LABEL,1968..........................      7.50
AVON,WISE CHOICE,OWL,1969.................................      3.00
AVON,WISE OWL,1969,FULL & BOXED...........................      5.00
AVON,WISHING BEAUTY DUST,1965.............................      8.50
AVON,WISHING BEAUTY DUST,1965,FULL........................     14.95
AVON,WISHING COLOGNE,GOLD LETTERING,CLEAR.......... 10.00 TO   11.00
AVON,WISHING DATE BOOK,1964...............................     25.00
AVON,WISHING POWDER................................ 5.00 TO    7.50
AVON,WISHING TOILET WATER,FULL & BOXED,1945...............     35.00
AVON,WITCH HAZEL,CUT GLASS STOPPER,1925...................    150.00
AVON,YOUNG HEARTS COLOGNE,1954............................     20.00
AYER'S CHERRY PECTORAL,OPEN PONTIL........................     11.00
AYER'S HAIR VIGOR,COBALT BLUE,STOPPER,7 IN................     18.00
AZTEC GOD,GREEN,CERAMIC...................................     17.00
BABY,BRONZE,EMBOSSED ON FRONT,GRADUATED ON BACK...........      4.00
BABY,DATED 1894...........................................      3.50
BABY,NURSING,EMPIRE,TABLESPOON & OUNCE,AMETHYST...........      3.00
BABY,NURSING,HAPPY........................................      2.50
BABY,NURSING,TAPERED,OVAL,3 OZ.,CLEAR.....................      2.50
BABY,NURSING,THERMOLAC MFG.CO.,BOSTON,MASS.,PAT.JUNE 20,
  1911....................................................     35.00
BABY,NURSING,1-8 OZ.,GRADUATED SCALE,AMETHYST.............      8.00
BABY,NURSING,1-8 OZ.,GRADUATED SCALE,CLEAR................      8.00
BABY,SEATED,KISS SNOOKUMS,5 IN............................     18.50
BABY'S,EMBOSSED DOGS,8 OZ.................................      4.50
BABY'S,KITTENS............................................      6.00
BACCARAT,COLOGNE,ARTIST SIGNED,HEAVY CUT..................     45.00
BACCARAT,DECANTER,BULBOUS,SIGNED,CA.1896,ETCHED,CLEAR.....     66.00
BACCARAT,DECANTER,SIGNED & NUMBERED,STOPPER...............    101.00
BACCARAT,DECANTER,12 IN. HIGH,ETCHED BANDS OF SWANS,FLUTE
  CUT....................................................     41.00
```

```
BACCARAT,PERFUME,BULBOUS,SILVER SWIRL........................    26.00
BACCARAT,PERFUME,BULBOUS,SWIRL RIB,AMBER.....................    41.00
BACCARAT,PERFUME,CRANBERRY & CLEAR...........................    26.00
BACCARAT,PERFUME,GUERLAIN,4 1/2 IN. HIGH.....................    16.00
BACCARAT,PERFUME,LEAF DESIGN,SIGNED,CRANBERRY STRIPE.........    36.00
BACCARAT,PERFUME,SIGNED,STOPPER,CLEAR........................    22.00
BACCARAT,PERFUME,SIGNED,STOPPER,RUBINA.......................    21.00
BALLANTINE,DUCK...............................ILLUS.. 12.00 TO  18.50
BALLANTINE,FISHERMAN..........................ILLUS.. 13.00 TO  22.00
BALLANTINE,FISHERMAN,SEATED..................................    15.00
BALLANTINE,GOLF BAG...........................ILLUS.. 11.95 TO  18.50
BALLANTINE,KNIGHT,SILVER......................ILLUS.. 13.00 TO  19.95
BALLANTINE,KNIGHT,SCOTTISH...................................    13.00
BALLANTINE,MALLARD DUCK......................................     9.95
BALLANTINE,OLD CROW CHESSMAN.................................    11.95
BALLANTINE,ZEBRA..............................ILLUS.. 13.00 TO  14.00
BALLAST,ROUND BOTTOM,BLOB TOP,AQUA...........................     4.50
BANFI EIFFEL TOWER...........................................     4.50
BANFI ELK-HEAD...............................................    15.95
BANK,BEAR,CLEAR..............................................     3.50
BANK,CLOWN,CLEAR.............................................     2.00
BANK,ELEPHANT,CLEAR..........................................     3.50
BANK,KITTEN,CLEAR............................................     3.50
BANK,LINCOLN,A.B.M...........................................     2.00
BANK,PIGGY,CLEAR.............................................     3.50
BAR,CREMED ABRICOT,ENAMELED,10 PANELS........................    30.00
BAR,CUT GLASS,QUART,PLAIN,CLEAR..............................    25.00
BAR,ENAMELED NELSON'S ROCK CORN WHISKEY......................    15.00
BAR,FANCY,PLAIN RIB BOTTOM,CLEAR.............................    12.00
BAR,HERDON,EMBOSSED,CLEAR....................................    15.00
BAR,RYE,LIGHT AMETHYST.......................................    18.00
BAR,WHISKEY,STRAIGHT-SIDED,MASSACHUSETTS.....................    17.50
```

BARBER BOTTLES WERE USED AT EITHER THE BARBERSHOP OR
THE HOME.   THEY HELD HAIR TONIC.   THESE SPECIAL, FANCY
BOTTLES WERE POPULAR IN THE LAST HALF OF THE NINETEENTH
CENTURY.

```
BARBER,AMBER,PRESSED GLASS,STOPPER...........................    22.50
BARBER,AMETHYST,ENAMEL FLORAL................................    40.00
BARBER,APPLE GREEN,PAINTED FLOWERS,HAND-BLOWN,PEWTER STOPPER     25.00
BARBER,BACCARAT,BLUE SWIRL...................................    21.00
BARBER,BAY RUM,AMBER.........................................     3.50
BARBER,BAY RUM,LADY IN BLUE,COLOGNE,LADY IN PINK,PEWTER TOP,
  PAIR.......................................................    75.00
BARBER,BAY RUM,RING TOP,MILK GLASS...........................    25.00
BARBER,BAY RUM,WATER,WHITE FROSTED GLASS,PAIR,MATCHING JAR..    23.50
BARBER,BAY RUM,WITCH HAZEL,NO STOPPERS,CLAMBROTH,PAIR.......    24.00
BARBER,BLOWN,ENAMEL DECOR,BLUE...............................    71.00
BARBER,BLOWN,ENAMEL DECOR,BULBOUS BASE,LONG NECK,BLUE.......    39.00
BARBER,BLOWN,ENAMEL TRIM,AMETHYST............................    81.00
BARBER,BLOWN,ROLLED RIM BASE,PEWTER SHAKER TOP,RUBY.........    36.00
BARBER,BRISTOL,ENAMEL DECOR,5 IN. HIGH,YELLOW & BLUE........    29.00
BARBER,BROWN,SATIN GLASS,CRYSTAL STOPPER.....................    22.00
BARBER,CAMPHOR,LIBBEY-OWENS,STOPPER..........................    16.00
BARBER,CLAMBROTH.............................................     6.00
BARBER,CLEAR,MILK GLASS STOPPER..............................     4.50
BARBER,CLEAR,PANELED DESIGN,ROUGH PONTIL,CIRCA 1864,PAIR....    35.00
BARBER,COBALT,ENAMEL TRIM....................................    30.00
BARBER,COBALT,SILVER SWAG DECOR IN FLEUR-DE-LIS SHAPE,
  6 1/2 IN...................................................    30.00
BARBER,CRANBERRY FLASH,STOPPER...............................    23.50
BARBER,CRANBERRY,OPALESCENT SWIRL,STOPPER....................    16.00
BARBER,CRANBERRY,WHITE LOOPINGS,SATIN,PEWTER STOPPER,
```

BALLANTINE, DUCK

BALLANTINE, FISHERMAN

BALLANTINE,
GOLF BAG

BALLANTINE,
KNIGHT, SILVER

BALLANTINE, ZEBRA

```
     10 3/4 IN.................................................    85.00
BARBER,CRUDE LIP,ROUGH PONTIL,ENAMELED FLOWERS,AMETHYST.....    50.00
BARBER,CUT GLASS,PETALS,STOPPER............................    26.00
BARBER,ENAMEL DECOR,AMETHYST,PAIR..........................    55.00
BARBER,FLASHED IRIDESCENT,ENAMELED FLORAL,MAROON-CRANBERRY..    22.50
BARBER,FLORAL DESIGN,MILK GLASS............................    25.00
BARBER,FLUTED INSIDE,SMOOTH OUTSIDE,ENAMEL DECOR,COBALT BLUE    46.00
BARBER,FOUR SIDES,TWO OVAL,AMBER SATIN.....................    22.50
BARBER,GREEN,ENAMEL DECOR..................................    40.00
BARBER,GREEN,PASTEL FLORAL,RAISED WHITE ENAMEL.............    25.00
BARBER,GREEN,WHITE ENAMEL LATTICE & DAISIES,HAND-BLOWN......    35.00
BARBER,H.MICHELSEN,BAY RUM,FIFTH,AMETHYST..................     6.00
BARBER,H.MICHELSEN,BAY RUM,FIFTH,CLEAR.....................     6.00
BARBER,HOBNAIL.............................................     5.00
BARBER,HOBNAIL,WHITE BALL STOPPER,6 1/2 IN.HIGH,OPALESCENT..    13.00
BARBER,HOLZHAUER,AMBER.....................................    15.00
BARBER,INVERTED THUMBPRINT,ENAMEL,ROUGH PONTIL,AMBER........    50.00
BARBER,INVERTED THUMBPRINT,ENAMEL,ROUGH PONTIL,GREEN........    50.00
BARBER,MARKED WATER,STERLING SILVER DECOR,MILK GLASS........    14.00
BARBER,MARY GREGORY,MARKED BAY RUM,ENAMEL,AMETHYST..........    50.00
BARBER,MILK GLASS..........................................    16.00
BARBER,MILK GLASS,OCTAGONAL SHAPE..........................    20.00
BARBER,MILK GLASS,PORCELAIN STOPPER........................    12.50
BARBER,MILK GLASS,RING TOP,ROUND,SUNKEN PANEL..............    20.00
BARBER,MILK GLASS,6 SIDED LADIES LEG.......................    22.50
BARBER,OCTAGON SHAPE,MILK GLASS,WHITE......................    21.00
BARBER,OPALESCENT HOBNAIL,6 1/2 IN. HIGH,WHITE BALL STOPPER.    13.00
BARBER,OPALESCENT SWIRL,STOPPER,CRANBERRY..................    16.00
BARBER,OPAQUE,PEWTER STOPPER...............................    10.00
BARBER,PEWTER STOPPER,RIBBED,SIGNED N WAPLER,COBALT BLUE,
     PAIR..................................................    27.00
BARBER,PONTIL,ENAMELED TRIM,AMETHYST.......................    80.00
BARBER,PONTIL,ENAMELED TRIM,BLUE...........................    70.00
BARBER,RIBBED,OPEN PONTIL,BLOWN,COBALT.....................    32.00
BARBER,ROUGH PONTIL,ENAMELED FLOWER,CRANBERRY GLASS.........    15.00
BARBER,RUBY BLOWN,ROLLED RIM BASE,PEWTER SHAKER TOP.........    36.00
BARBER,SANDWICH GLASS,AMETHYST.............................   116.00
BARBER,SPANISH LACE,BLUE...................................    26.00
BARBER,SPANISH LACE,VASELINE...............................    38.00
BARBER,SPANISH LACE,8 IN. HIGH,CRANBERRY...................    56.00
BARBER,SWIRLED RIB PATTERN,INVERTED THUMBPRINT BASE,AMBER...    62.50
BARBER,TOILET WATER,6 PANELS,LADY LEG NECK,MILK GLASS.......    25.00
BARBER,WITCH HAZEL,STERLING SILVER DECOR,MILK GLASS.........    14.00
BARCLAY PATENT SPIRAL GROOVE...............................     5.00
BARDENHEIERS WINE,VINES & GRAPE CLUSTERS,BROWN,1930.........     4.00
     BARREL, SEE ALSO FOOD, BARREL
BARREL,DESIGNED BY ISAAC NEWTON PIERCE,DATED 1865,PRESSED
     GLASS.................................................    15.00
BARREL,FOOD CONTAINER,JOSHUA WRIGHT,PHILA.,AQUA,
     10 1/2 IN.TALL........................................    37.50
BARREL,GREEN,6 HOOPS ON TOPS & BOTTOM,MARKED LAM A & F,
     1/2 GAL...............................................    15.00
BARREL,PICKLE,EMERALD GREEN,8 IN...........................    15.00
BARREL,PICKLE,EMERALD GREEN,9 3/4 IN.......................    25.00
BARSOTTINI,ALPINE PIPE...........................5.95 TO      8.00
BARSOTTINI,ANTIQUE AUTO....................................     5.99
BARSOTTINI,ANTIQUE BOURBON CERAMIC.........................    14.95
BARSOTTINI,ANTIQUE CARRIAGE................................     5.99
BARSOTTINI,APOLLO..........................................    14.95
BARSOTTINI,ARCH OF TRIUMPH.......................11.00 TO     12.75
BARSOTTINI,AUGUSTINE MONK..................................    11.95
BARSOTTINI,BARREL ON WAGON.................................    16.95
BARSOTTINI,CANDLESTICK.....................................    11.00
BARSOTTINI,CANNON..........................................    17.95
BARSOTTINI,CARRIAGE LAMP...................................     8.00
```

```
BARSOTTINI,CLOCK......................................  9.90 TO   22.00
BARSOTTINI,CLOCK WITH CHERUB..................................   14.95
BARSOTTINI,CLOWN......................................  3.95 TO    6.00
BARSOTTINI,COLISEUM...........................................    9.45
BARSOTTINI,DONKEY.............................................    6.00
BARSOTTINI,DUELING PISTOL,BROWN...............................    7.00
BARSOTTINI,DUELING PISTOL,GREEN...............................    7.00
BARSOTTINI,EIFFEL TOWER...............................  5.95 TO    8.00
BARSOTTINI,ELEPHANT...........................................    6.00
BARSOTTINI,ELKS HEAD..................................  9.40 TO   20.00
BARSOTTINI,FATHER JOHN........................................   12.00
BARSOTTINI,FLORENTINE CANNON..................................   10.00
BARSOTTINI,FLORENTINE STEEPLE.................................    8.00
BARSOTTINI,FRUIT BASKET.......................................    7.95
BARSOTTINI,GALLIANO CARABINIERE...............................   14.95
BARSOTTINI,GIRAFFE............................................   18.00
BARSOTTINI,HEIDE..............................................   15.00
BARSOTTINI,HORSE..............................................   10.95
BARSOTTINI,HORSE HEAD.........................................   14.00
BARSOTTINI,IMPERIAL CANNON,METAL..............................   12.90
BARSOTTINI,LAMPLIGHTER................................ 20.95 TO   23.00
BARSOTTINI,LEANING TOWER......................................    7.50
BARSOTTINI,LITTLE BACCHUS.....................................   10.55
BARSOTTINI,LOVEBIRDS.................................. 11.95 TO   17.00
BARSOTTINI,LUCKY DICE.........................................    9.25
BARSOTTINI,MANDOLIN...........................................    8.00
BARSOTTINI,MEZZOTINT..........................................    9.00
BARSOTTINI,MODEL A ROADSTER...................................    6.00
BARSOTTINI,MONASTERY CASK.....................................   17.45
BARSOTTINI,MONK IN BARREL.....................................   10.95
BARSOTTINI,MONK WITH CUP......................................   10.95
BARSOTTINI,MONK WITH WINE JUG.................................   13.00
BARSOTTINI,OWL................................................   12.95
BARSOTTINI,PISTOL,BROWN.......................................    5.95
BARSOTTINI,PISTOL,GREEN.......................................    5.95
BARSOTTINI,PISTOL,LABEL,LINED BOX.............................   15.00
BARSOTTINI,RABBIT WITH CARROT.................................   10.95
BARSOTTINI,RENNAISSANCE.......................................    8.30
BARSOTTINI,ROADSTER...........................................    5.95
BARSOTTINI,ROMAN COLISEUM.....................................   10.00
BARSOTTINI,ROMAN TRIBUNE......................................   13.40
BARSOTTINI,ROMAN URN..........................................    9.00
BARSOTTINI,ROOSTER.................................... 12.75 TO   14.00
BARSOTTINI,SANTA CLAUS........................................   10.95
BARSOTTINI,TIVOLI CLOCK............................... 20.95 TO   23.00
BARSOTTINI,TRIBUNE.................................... 10.95 TO   13.40
BARSOTTINI,WAGON WITH BARREL..................................   21.00
BARSOTTINI,WILLIAM TELL.......................................   15.00
BARSOTTINI,WISE WINKING OWL...................................   12.95
BAVARIAN BREWING CO.,COVINGTON,KY.,BROWN......................    3.50
```

BEAM BOTTLES ARE MADE AS CONTAINERS FOR THE KENTUCKY
STRAIGHT BOURBON MADE BY THE JAMES BEAM DISTILLING
COMPANY. THE BEAM CERAMICS WERE FIRST MADE IN 1953.
EXECUTIVE SERIES BOTTLES STARTED IN 1955. REGAL CHINA
SPECIALTIES WERE STARTED IN 1955 AND POLITICAL FIGURES
IN 1956. CUSTOMER SPECIALTIES WERE FIRST MADE IN 1956,
TROPHY SERIES IN 1957, STATE SERIES IN 1958.
   BEAM, SEE ALSO WHISKEY, BELL SCOTCH

```
BEAM,AGNEW,REGAL CHINA,1970...........................ILLUS..2,850.00
BEAM,ALASKA PURCHASE,CENTENNIAL,1966................. 24.00 TO   27.95
BEAM,ALASKA STAR,STATE,1958......................... 80.00 TO   95.00
BEAM,ALASKA STAR,STATE,1964,1965..............................   73.00
```

```
BEAM,AMERICAN GOTHIC,COLLECTOR'S EDITION,1968................          2.00
BEAM,AMVETS,1970.......................................  8.95 TO      13.00
BEAM,ANNIV.WHITE FOX,REGAL SPECIALTY,1969.......... 45.95 TO          70.00
BEAM,ANTIOCH CENTENNIAL,1967.......................  8.95 TO          15.88
BEAM,ANTIQUE TRADER,REGAL SPECIALTY,1968............  5.95 TO          6.95
BEAM,ARISTIDE BRUANT,COLLECTOR'S EDITION..................            2.50
BEAM,ARIZONA GRAND CANYON........................... 18.00 TO         22.95
BEAM,ARIZONA,POWELL EXPOSITION,1969......................             6.00
BEAM,ARIZONA,STATES,1968............................  5.95 TO         11.00
BEAM,ARMANETTI,BACCHUS.............................. 29.95 TO         39.95
BEAM,ARMANETTI,FIRST AWARD,1969..................... 14.00 TO         15.95
BEAM,ARMANETTI,VASE,CUSTOMER SPECIALTY,1968........ 10.00 TO          13.95
BEAM,ARTIST BEFORE EASEL,COLLECTOR'S EDITION,1966..........           2.50
BEAM,ASHTRAY,CHINA,IVORY........................... 32.00 TO          35.00
BEAM,ASHTRAY,POLITICAL,PAIR,1956.........................            31.00
BEAM,ASHTRAY,REGAL CHINA SPECIALTY,1955..................            27.50
BEAM,ASHTRAY,STATE TAX STAMP,IVORY.......................            37.50
BEAM,ASHTRAY,4 LABELS,1955,IVORY.........................            36.50
BEAM,AU CAFE,COLLECTOR'S EDITION,1970....................             2.50
BEAM,BASEBALL,CENTENNIAL,1969,1970..................  5.95 TO         10.00
BEAM,BEAMEISTER,IMPORT..............................  1.95 TO         2.50
BEAM,BING CROSBY,29TH REGAL CHINA,1970..............  6.95 TO         11.00
BEAM,BLACK CANASTA,NOT AUTHENTIC BEAM...............  8.95 TO         19.50
BEAM,BLACK HORSE,TROPHY,1967,REISSUE ............... 17.50 TO         21.50
BEAM,BLACK KATZ CAT,CUSTOMER SPECIALTY,1968..............            19.95
BEAM,BLUE BOY,COLLECTOR'S EDITION,1966..............  7.50 TO         9.50
BEAM,BLUE CHERUB,EXECUTIVE,1960.....................100.00 TO        130.00
BEAM,BLUE DAISY,REGAL CHINA SPECIALTY,1967..........  5.95 TO         7.95
BEAM,BLUE DELFT,GLASS SPECIALTY,1963................  3.50 TO         6.00
BEAM,BLUE FOX,BIRTHDAY,RENNIE,1967..................150.00 TO        230.00
BEAM,BLUE JAY,TROPHY SERIES,1969....................  8.00 TO         8.95
BEAM,BLUE SLOT MACHINE,HAROLD'S CLUB,1967........... 14.95 TO         17.45
BEAM,BOATING PARTY,COLLECTOR'S EDITION,1970..............             2.00
BEAM,BOY WITH CHERRIES,COLLECTOR'S EDITION,1969..........             3.00
BEAM,BOY,BLUE,COLLECTOR'S EDITION,1966..............  7.50 TO         9.50
BEAM,BROADMOOR,REGAL CHINA SPECIALTY,1968............ILLUS..          9.00
BEAM,BRONTE JUG,MINIATURE,1970,BEAM IMPORT...............             1.75
BEAM,BRONTE JUG,3/4 QUART,1970,BEAM IMPORT...............             7.50
BEAM,BRONTE,FLAGON,12 OZ.,1970,BEAM IMPORT...............            11.50
BEAM,BROWN HEAD KENTUCKY,STATE SERIES,1967......... 18.00 TO         23.00
BEAM,BUFFALO HUNT,COLLECTOR'S EDITION,1968...............             2.00
BEAM,CABLE CAR,GREEN,REGAL CHINA,1968,1969..........  3.50 TO         5.95
BEAM,CAL-NEVA,CASINO SERIES,RENO,1969.............. 12.00 TO         14.00
```

BEAM,AGNEW,
REGAL CHINA,1970

BEAM,BROADMOOR,
REGAL CHINA
SPECIALTY,1968

```
BEAM,CALIFORNIA MISSION,CLUB SERIES,1970............  42.50 TO    50.00
BEAM,CAMEO BLUE,GLASS SPECIALTY,1965,SHEPHERD.......   3.50 TO     6.00
BEAM,CANASTA,BLACK,NOT AUTHENTIC BEAM...............   8.95 TO    19.50
BEAM,CANNON,GLASS SPECIALTY,1970....................   5.25 TO     6.00
BEAM,CARDINAL,TROPHY SERIES,1968....................  29.95 TO    41.00
BEAM,CAT,BURMESE,YELLOW EYES,TROPHY SERIES,1967..............    12.00
BEAM,CAT,SIAMESE,BLUE EYES,TROPHY SERIES,1967...............     12.00
BEAM,CAT,TABBY,BLUE EYES,TROPHY SERIES,1967........  10.95 TO    12.00
BEAM,CENTENNIAL,ALASKA PURCHASE,1966................  24.00 TO    27.95
BEAM,CENTENNIAL,ANTIOCH.............................   8.95 TO    15.99
BEAM,CENTENNIAL,BASEBALL,1969,1970..................   5.95 TO    10.00
BEAM,CENTENNIAL,CHEYENNE,WYOMING,1967...............   9.95 TO    15.00
BEAM,CENTENNIAL,CIVIL WAR,NORTH,1961................  37.00 TO    43.50
BEAM,CENTENNIAL,CIVIL WAR,SOUTH,1961................  39.00 TO    44.50
BEAM,CENTENNIAL,ELKS,1968,CLUB......................   7.00 TO    14.00
BEAM,CENTENNIAL,LARAMIE,1968........................ILLUS..       6.00
BEAM,CENTENNIAL,LOMBARD,ILLINOIS,1969...............   6.00 TO     7.95
BEAM,CENTENNIAL,POWELL EXPEDITION,1970..............   7.50 TO     8.00
```

BEAM,CENTENNIAL,LARAMIE,1968

```
BEAM,CENTENNIAL,PREAKNESS,1970......................   9.95 TO    14.50
BEAM,CENTENNIAL,RENO,1968-69........................   6.00 TO     7.95
BEAM,CENTENNIAL,SAN DIEGO PORTOLA TREK,1969,GLASS...........     5.00
BEAM,CENTENNIAL,SAN DIEGO,1968,CHINA................   4.95 TO     6.95
BEAM,CENTENNIAL,SANTA FE,1960.......................195.00 TO   215.00
BEAM,CENTENNIAL,ST.LOUIS ARCH,1964..................  24.00 TO    29.95
BEAM,CENTENNIAL,ST.LOUIS ARCH,1967..................  22.50 TO    24.95
BEAM,CHERUB,BLUE,EXECUTIVE SERIES,1960..............  80.00 TO   100.00
BEAM,CHERUB,GRAY,EXECUTIVE SERIES,1958..............130.00 TO   166.00
BEAM,CHERUB,LAVENDER,ZIMMERMAN,1968,1969............   6.95 TO     8.75
BEAM,CHERUB,SALMON,ZIMMERMAN,1968,1969......................     7.50
BEAM,CHEYENNE,CENTENNIAL,1967.......................   9.95 TO    15.00
BEAM,CHURCHILL DOWNS,PINK ROSES,REGAL SPECIALTY,1969,1970...     9.95
BEAM,CHURCHILL DOWNS,RED ROSES,REGAL,1969...........  12.95 TO    15.95
BEAM,CHURCHILL DOWNS,RED ROSES,REGAL,1970...........  12.95 TO    15.95
BEAM,CIVIL WAR,NORTH,CENTENNIAL,1961................  37.00 TO    43.50
BEAM,CIVIL WAR,SOUTH,CENTENNIAL,1961................  39.00 TO    44.50
BEAM,CLEAR CRYSTAL SCOTCH,GLASS SPECIALTY,1967......   4.00 TO    11.95
BEAM,CLEAR CRYSTAL,BOURBON,GLASS,1966...............   2.95 TO     4.95
BEAM,CLEOPATRA,RUST,GLASS SPECIALTY,1962............   3.50 TO     6.95
BEAM,CLEOPATRA,YELLOW,GLASS SPECIALTY,1962..........  14.00 TO    16.95
BEAM,CLUB,CALIFORNIA MISSION,1970...................ILLUS..      50.00
BEAM,CLUB,DENVER,1970...............................            99.50
BEAM,CLUB,ELKS,1968,1969............................   7.00 TO    14.00
BEAM,CLUB,FOX,BLUE,RENNIE,1967......................150.00 TO   230.00
```

```
BEAM,CLUB,FOX,GOLD,GOLDIE,1969......................105.00 TO   200.00
BEAM,CLUB,FOX,WHITE,1969............................. 45.95 TO    70.00
BEAM,CLUB,ROCKY MOUNTAIN,1970.........................ILLUS..    40.00
BEAM,CLUB,YUMA RIFLE CLUB............................ 38.00 TO    44.95
BEAM,COCKTAIL SHAKER,GLASS SPECIALTY,1953...........  4.50 TO     9.00
BEAM,COFFEE WARMER,BLACK & GOLD NECK,1956...........  4.50 TO     7.50
BEAM,COFFEE WARMER,PLASTIC NECKBAND,1954............ 11.00 TO    14.95
BEAM,COLLECTOR'S EDITION,VOL.I,1966.................             34.00
BEAM,COLLECTOR'S EDITION,VOL.II,1967................             24.00
BEAM,COLLECTOR'S EDITION,VOL.III,1968...............             22.00
BEAM,COLLECTOR'S EDITION,VOL.IV,1969................             20.00
BEAM,COLLECTOR'S EDITION,VOL.V,1970.................             20.00
BEAM,COLORADO,STATE SERIES,1959..................... 30.00 TO    50.00
BEAM,COVERED WAGON,HAROLD'S CLUB,1969,1970..........  6.95 TO    18.00
BEAM,CRYSTAL,CLEAR,BOURBON,GLASS,1966...............  2.95 TO     4.95
BEAM,CRYSTAL,EMERALD,GLASS SPECIALTY,1968...........  3.00 TO     4.50
BEAM,CRYSTAL,OPALINE,GLASS SPECIALTY,1969...........              4.50
BEAM,CRYSTAL,RUBY,GLASS SPECIALTY,1967..............  3.00 TO     7.95
BEAM,CUSTOMER SPECIALTY,ARMANETTI,1969...............ILLUS..    15.00
```

BEAM,CLUB,CALIFORNIA   BEAM,CLUB,   BEAM,CUSTOMER SPECIALTY,
MISSION,1970   ROCKY MOUNTAIN,1970   ARMANETTI,1969

```
BEAM,CUSTOMER SPECIALTY,SLOT,BLUE,1967...............ILLUS..    15.00
BEAM,DAISY,BLUE,CHINA SPECIALTY,1967................  5.95 TO     7.95
BEAM,DANCING SCOT,MUSICAL.............................ILLUS..    45.00
BEAM,DANCING SCOT,SHORT,GLASS SPECIALTY,1963........ 30.00 TO    49.95
BEAM,DANCING SCOT,TALL,GLASS SPECIALTY,1964-70......  7.95 TO    11.50
BEAM,DEL WEBB MINT 400,REGAL CHINA,1970............. 15.95 TO    39.50
BEAM,DELFT ROSE,GLASS SPECIALTY,1963................  8.00 TO     9.00
BEAM,DELFT,BLUE,1963................................  3.50 TO     6.00
BEAM,DENVER CLUB,RUSH TO THE ROCKIES,1970........... 25.00 TO    27.00
BEAM,DOE,TROPHY SERIES,1963.........................             35.00
BEAM,DOE,TROPHY SERIES,1967,REISSUE................. 30.00 TO    36.00
BEAM,DOE,1963,LIGHT HEAD............................             36.50
BEAM,DOG,TAX STAMP,1959.............................             72.50
BEAM,DOG,TROPHY SERIES,1959......................... 54.95 TO    72.50
BEAM,DUCK & GEESE,GLASS,1955........................             10.00
BEAM,DUCK,STATE TAX STAMP,1957......................             45.00
BEAM,DUCK,TROPHY SERIES,1957........................ 30.00 TO    45.00
BEAM,EAGLE,TROPHY SERIES,1965....................... 15.95 TO    17.95
    BEAM, ELEPHANT, SEE BEAM, POLITICAL
BEAM,ELKS CLUB,CENTENNIAL,1968......................  7.00 TO    14.00
BEAM,EMERALD CRYSTAL.................................  3.00 TO     4.50
BEAM,EMILE ZOLA,COLLECTOR'S EDITION,1969............              2.50
```

```
BEAM,EXECUTIVE,CHALICE,GOLD,1961...............................      67.00
BEAM,EXECUTIVE,CHERUB,BLUE,1960.....................  80.00 TO    100.00
BEAM,EXECUTIVE,CHERUB,GRAY,1958....................130.00 TO    166.00
BEAM,EXECUTIVE,FLOWER BASKET,1962.............................      50.00
BEAM,EXECUTIVE,GOLD DIAMOND,1964...................  46.50 TO     50.00
BEAM,EXECUTIVE,GOLDEN CHALICE,1961.................  70.00 TO     82.50
BEAM,EXECUTIVE,MAJESTIC,CASE,1966.............................      40.00
BEAM,EXECUTIVE,MAJESTIC,1966.......................  33.50 TO     38.00
BEAM,EXECUTIVE,MARBLED FANTASY,1965................  70.00 TO     80.00
BEAM,EXECUTIVE,PRESIDENT,1968..........................ILLUS..     12.00
```

BEAM,
CUSTOMER
SPECIALTY,
SLOT,BLUE,
1967

BEAM,
DANCING
SCOT,
MUSICAL

BEAM,EXECUTIVE,
PRESIDENT,1968

```
BEAM,EXECUTIVE,PRESIDENTIAL,CASE,1968.........................      14.95
BEAM,EXECUTIVE,PRESTIGE,CASE,1967.............................      24.00
BEAM,EXECUTIVE,PRESTIGE,1967.......................  19.75 TO     21.50
BEAM,EXECUTIVE,ROYAL DI MONTE,1957.................  71.00 TO     80.00
BEAM,EXECUTIVE,ROYAL GOLD DIAMOND,1964.............  46.50 TO     50.00
BEAM,EXECUTIVE,ROYAL GOLD,ROUND,1956...............140.00 TO    160.00
BEAM,EXECUTIVE,ROYAL PORCELAIN,1955................175.00 TO    225.00
BEAM,EXECUTIVE,ROYAL ROSE,1963.....................  48.00 TO     54.00
BEAM,EXECUTIVE,SOVEREIGN,CASE,1969............................      14.95
BEAM,EXECUTIVE,SOVEREIGN,1969......................  11.00 TO     12.00
BEAM,EXECUTIVE,TAVERN SCENE,1959...................  65.00 TO     95.00
BEAM,EXECUTIVE,1970................................  15.00 TO     20.00
BEAM,FIRST NATIONAL BANK OF CHICAGO,1964....................2,250.00
BEAM,FISH,GOLD SPECKLED HIGHLIGHTS............................    350.00
BEAM,FISH,STATE TAX STAMP,1957................................     45.00
BEAM,FISH,TROPHY SERIES,1957.......................  36.00 TO     45.00
BEAM,FLORIDA SHELL,BRONZE,STATE SERIES,1968-69......   5.95 TO      8.00
BEAM,FLORIDA SHELL,MOTHER-OF-PEARL,STATE,1968.......   5.45 TO      8.00
BEAM,FLORIDA SHELL,MOTHER-OF-PEARL,STATE,1969.......   5.45 TO      8.00
BEAM,FLORIDA SHELLS,PAIR......................................     25.00
BEAM,FLOWER BASKET,EXECUTIVE,1962.............................     50.00
BEAM,FOREMOST,BLACK,GOLD,CUSTOMER,1956.............120.00 TO    135.00
BEAM,FOREMOST,GRAY,GOLD,1956.......................115.00 TO    119.00
BEAM,FOREMOST,GREEN,GOLD,AUTHENTICITY LETTER,1956..........5,000.00
BEAM,FOREMOST,PINK SPECKLED,1956...................275.00 TO    293.00
BEAM,FOX,BLUE,CLUB SERIES,1967.....................150.00 TO    230.00
BEAM,FOX,GOLD,CLUB SERIES,1969.....................105.00 TO    200.00
BEAM,FOX,GREEN,TROPHY SERIES,1965..................  48.00 TO     60.00
BEAM,FOX,GREEN,TROPHY SERIES,1967..................  45.00 TO     50.00
BEAM,FOX,WHITE,CLUB SERIES,1969....................  45.95 TO     70.00
BEAM,FRANKLIN MINT,1970............................  10.95 TO     12.50
```

```
BEAM,FRUIT BASKET,COLLECTOR'S EDITION,1969...................           3.00
BEAM,GARE SAINT LAZARE,COLLECTOR'S EDITION,1970.............           2.50
BEAM,GENIE,SMOKED CRYSTAL,GLASS,1964.................. 4.00 TO           9.50
BEAM,GEORGE GISZE,COLLECTOR'S EDITION,1967.................           2.00
BEAM,GERMANY,REGAL CHINA SPECIALTY,1970............. 10.95 TO          16.00
BEAM,GOLD FOX,GOLDIE,CLUB SERIES,1969......................          130.00
BEAM,GOLDEN CHALICE,EXECUTIVE,1961................. 70.00 TO          82.50
BEAM,GOLDEN GATE,CUSTOMER SPECIALTY,1969........... 85.00 TO          99.50
BEAM,GOLDEN NUGGET,CUSTOMER SPECIALTY,1969........ 95.00 TO          99.50
BEAM,GRAND CANYON,REGAL CHINA SPECIALTY,1969....... 17.50 TO          32.90
BEAM,GRAY CHERUB,EXECUTIVE SERIES,1958.....................          150.00
BEAM,GRAY HORSE,TROPHY SERIES,1967.........................           21.50
BEAM,GRAY SLOT,REGAL CHINA,1968.................... 4.95 TO           6.95
BEAM,GRECIAN,GLASS,1961............................ 3.50 TO           7.50
BEAM,GREEN FOX,TROPHY SERIES,1965................. 48.00 TO          60.00
BEAM,H.C.OF RENO..........................................          149.95
BEAM,HAROLD'S CLUB COVERED WAGON,1969.............. 6.95 TO          18.00
BEAM,HAROLD'S CLUB MAN IN A BARREL NO.1,1957.......395.00 TO         426.00
BEAM,HAROLD'S CLUB MAN IN A BARREL NO.2,1958.......286.00 TO         295.00
BEAM,HAROLD'S CLUB NEVADA,GRAY,1963................171.00 TO         185.00
BEAM,HAROLD'S CLUB NEVADA,SILVER,1964..............180.00 TO         200.00
BEAM,HAROLD'S CLUB PINWHEEL,1965................... 91.00 TO         110.00
BEAM,HAROLD'S CLUB SILVER OPAL,GLASS,1957.......... 20.00 TO          24.95
BEAM,HAROLD'S CLUB SLOT MACHINE,1967,BLUE.......... 14.95 TO          17.45
BEAM,HAROLD'S CLUB VIP,EXECUTIVE,1967..............106.00 TO         112.50
BEAM,HAROLD'S CLUB VIP,EXECUTIVE,1968.............. 60.00 TO         110.00
BEAM,HAROLD'S CLUB VIP,EXECUTIVE,1969..............100.00 TO         175.00
BEAM,HAROLD'S CLUB,GRAY SLOT,1968.................. 4.95 TO           6.95
BEAM,HAROLD'S CLUB,GRAY,1963.......................171.00 TO         185.00
BEAM,HAROLD'S CLUB,SILVER,1964.....................180.00 TO         200.00
BEAM,HARRAH'S,GRAY,1963...................................          460.00
BEAM,HARRY HOFFMAN,REGAL CHINA,1969,1970........... 6.95 TO          10.95
BEAM,HARVEY'S LAKE TAHOE,GLASS,CUSTOMER,1969........ 9.95 TO          12.00
BEAM,HAULING IN THE GILL NET,COLLECTOR'S EDITION,1968.......           2.50
BEAM,HAWAII,STATE SERIES,1959...................... 72.50 TO          78.00
BEAM,HAWAII,STATE SERIES,1967...................... 45.00 TO          55.00
BEAM,HEMISFAIR,REGAL CHINA SPECIALTY,1968.......... 14.00 TO          17.50
BEAM,HORSE,BLACK,1962..................................... 25.00
BEAM,HORSE,BLACK,1967.............................. 17.50 TO          21.50
BEAM,HORSE,BROWN,1962.....................................           25.00
BEAM,HORSE,BROWN,1967.....................................           21.50
BEAM,HORSE,GRAY,1962......................................           25.00
BEAM,HORSE,GRAY,1967......................................           21.50
BEAM,HORSE,WHITE,1962.....................................           25.00
BEAM,HORSESHOE CLUB,CUSTOMER SPECIALTY,1969........ 9.95 TO          14.00
BEAM,IDAHO,STATE SERIES,1963....................... 65.00 TO          77.50
BEAM,ILLINOIS,STATE SERIES,1968.................... 7.95 TO          11.00
BEAM,INDIAN MAIDEN,COLLECTOR'S EDITION,1968................           2.50
BEAM,INDIANAPOLIS 500,CHINA SPECIALTY,1970......... 10.50 TO          15.00
BEAM,JESTER,COLLECTOR'S EDITION,1967......................           2.00
BEAM,JEWISH BRIDE,COLLECTOR'S EDITION,1970................           2.00
BEAM,JUG,GREEN,REGAL CHINA SPECIALTY,1965.......... 6.00 TO           9.95
BEAM,JUG,OATMEAL,REGAL CHINA SPECIALTY,1966........ 50.00 TO          65.00
BEAM,JUG,TURQUOISE,REGAL CHINA SPECIALTY,1966....... 4.50 TO           6.00
BEAM,KANSAS,STATE SERIES,1960,1961................. 65.00 TO          74.90
BEAM,KATZ CAT,BLACK,CUSTOMER SPECIALTY,1968........ 19.95 TO          31.95
BEAM,KATZ CAT,YELLOW,CUSTOMER SPECIALTY,1967....... 24.95 TO          29.00
BEAM,KENTUCKY COLONEL,REGAL CHINA,1970............. 10.95 TO          13.50
BEAM,KENTUCKY DERBY,PINK ROSES............................           9.95
BEAM,KENTUCKY DERBY,RED ROSES...................... 12.95 TO          15.95
BEAM,KENTUCKY,BLACK HEAD,STATE SERIES,1967......... 13.95 TO          15.95
BEAM,KENTUCKY,BROWN HEAD,STATE SERIES,1967......... 18.00 TO          23.00
BEAM,KENTUCKY,WHITE.......................................           16.95
   BEAM, KITTEN, SEE BEAM, CAT
BEAM,LARAMIE,1968,CENTENNIAL....................... 5.00 TO           6.00
```

```
BEAM,LAS VEGAS GOLDEN GATE,1969.....................  85.00 TO    99.50
BEAM,LAS VEGAS GOLDEN NUGGET,1969...................  95.00 TO    99.50
BEAM,LAS VEGAS,REGAL CHINA,1969.....................   5.95 TO     7.95
BEAM,LAUGHING CAVALIER..............................               2.50
BEAM,LILAC,LOMBARD,1969,CENTENNIAL..................   6.00 TO     7.95
BEAM,LOMBARD LILAC,CENTENNIAL.......................   6.00 TO     7.95
BEAM,MAINE,MAINE TAX STAMP..........................              15.00
BEAM,MAINE,1970.....................................   9.95 TO    16.50
BEAM,MAJESTIC,EXECUTIVE,1966........................  33.50 TO    38.00
BEAM,MAN IN BARREL NO.1,1957........................ 395.00 TO   426.00
BEAM,MAN IN BARREL NO.2,1958........................ 296.00 TO   295.00
BEAM,MAN ON A HORSE,COLLECTOR'S EDITION,1967........               2.00
BEAM,MANTIOWOC SUBMARINE,REGAL CHINA,1970...........   5.95 TO    11.50
BEAM,MARBLED FANTASY,EXECUTIVE,1965.................  70.00 TO    80.00
BEAM,MARDI GRAS,COLLECTOR'S EDITION,1966............               2.50
BEAM,MARINA CITY,CUSTOMER SPECIALTY,1962............  39.95 TO    48.00
BEAM,MARK ANTONY,GLASS SPECIALTY,1962...............  19.00 TO    22.00
BEAM,MINIATURE......................................               1.95
BEAM,MINT 400,DEL WEBB,CHINA SPECIALTY,1970.........  15.95 TO    39.50
BEAM,MISSION CLUB...................................  25.00 TO    50.00
BEAM,MONTANA,STATE SERIES,1963......................  95.00 TO   104.95
BEAM,MOUNT RUSHMORE,SOUTH DAKOTA,STATE,1970.........   5.00 TO    11.95
BEAM,MUNDUS ROSE,IMPORT.............................   1.95 TO     3.95
BEAM,MUSICIANS ON WINE CASK,REGAL CHINA,1964........  10.95 TO    13.00
BEAM,NEBRASKA,STATE SERIES,1967.....................  11.00 TO    15.50
BEAM,NEVADA,STATE SERIES,1963,1964..................  65.00 TO    88.50
BEAM,NEW HAMPSHIRE,STATE SERIES,1967,1968...........   9.95 TO    12.95
BEAM,NEW JERSEY BLUE,STATE SERIES,1963,1964.........  95.00 TO   110.00
BEAM,NEW JERSEY GOLD,STATE SERIES,1963,1964.........  65.00 TO    75.00
BEAM,NEW JERSEY GRAY,STATE SERIES,1963,1964.........  95.00 TO   110.00
BEAM,NEW JERSEY YELLOW,STATE SERIES,1963,1964.......  65.00 TO    75.00
BEAM,NEW MEXICO.....................................   5.95 TO    10.50
BEAM,NEW YORK WORLD'S FAIR,REGAL CHINA,1964.........  27.50 TO    32.00
BEAM,NIGHT WATCH,COLLECTOR'S EDITION,1967...........               2.00
BEAM,NORTH DAKOTA,STATE SERIES,1964.................  79.95 TO    85.00
BEAM,NUGGET,GOLDEN,CUSTOMER SPECIALTY,1969..........  95.00 TO    99.50
BEAM,NURSE & CHILD,COLLECTOR'S EDITION,1967.........   3.00 TO     5.95
BEAM,OATMEAL JUG,REGAL CHINA SPECIALTY,1966.........  50.00 TO    65.00
BEAM,OHIO,STATE SERIES,1966.........................  12.50 TO    17.50
BEAM,OLD PEASANT,COLLECTOR'S EDITION,1970...........               2.50
BEAM,OLYMPIAN,GLASS,1960............................   4.50 TO     7.00
BEAM,ON THE TERRACE,COLLECTOR'S EDITION,1966........   4.95 TO     6.95
BEAM,ON THE TRAIL,COLLECTOR'S EDITION,1968..........               3.00
BEAM,OPALINE CRYSTAL,GLASS SPECIALTY,1969...........               4.50
BEAM,OREGON,STATE SERIES,1959.......................  29.95 TO    49.50
BEAM,PAUL BUNYAN....................................  10.95 TO    15.95
BEAM,PENNSYLVANIA,STATE SERIES,1967.................   5.95 TO    11.00
BEAM,PENNY THE POODLE,TROPHY,1970...................               9.00
BEAM,PHEASANT,TROPHY SERIES,1960....................              18.95
BEAM,PHEASANT,TROPHY SERIES,1961....................              19.50
BEAM,PHEASANT,TROPHY SERIES,1963....................              15.95
BEAM,PHEASANT,TROPHY SERIES,1966....................              16.00
BEAM,PHEASANT,TROPHY SERIES,1967....................              15.00
BEAM,PHEASANT,TROPHY SERIES,1968....................              15.95
BEAM,PIN BOTTLE,FIFTH,WOODEN STOPPER,1949-55........   8.95 TO    10.95
BEAM,PIN BOTTLE,PINT,WOODEN STOPPER,1952............   5.50 TO     9.00
BEAM,PIN BOTTLE,1949................................               3.50
BEAM,PIN BOTTLE,1950................................               3.50
BEAM,PIN BOTTLE,1951................................               3.50
BEAM,PIN BOTTLE,1952................................               3.50
BEAM,PIN BOTTLE,1953................................               3.50
BEAM,PIN BOTTLE,1954................................               3.50
BEAM,PIN BOTTLE,1955................................               3.50
BEAM,PIN BOTTLE,1956................................               3.50
BEAM,PIN BOTTLE,1957................................               3.50
```

```
BEAM,PIN BOTTLE,1958................................................    3.50
BEAM,PIN BOTTLE,1959................................................    3.50
BEAM,PIN BOTTLE,1960................................................    3.50
BEAM,PIN BOTTLE,1962................................................    3.50
BEAM,PIN BOTTLE,1963................................................    3.50
BEAM,PIN BOTTLE,1964................................................    3.50
BEAM,PIN BOTTLE,1965................................................    3.50
BEAM,PIN BOTTLE,1966................................................    3.50
BEAM,PIN BOTTLE,1967................................................    3.50
BEAM,PIN BOTTLE,1968................................................    3.50
BEAM,PIN BOTTLE,1969................................................    3.50
BEAM,PINCH..........................................................   15.00
BEAM,PINK ROSES,CHURCHILL DOWNS,REGAL SPECIALTY,1969,1970...         9.95
BEAM,PINWHEEL,CUSTOMER SPECIALTY,1965.............. 91.00 TO       110.00
BEAM,POLITICAL,ASHTRAY,PAIR,1956................... 31.00 TO        35.00
BEAM,POLITICAL,BOXERS,PAIR,1964.................... 29.95 TO        31.00
BEAM,POLITICAL,CAMPAIGNERS,PAIR,1960............... 25.00 TO        35.00
BEAM,POLITICAL,CLOWNS,PAIR,1968.................... 14.00 TO        15.00
BEAM,POLITICAL,DONKEY,ASHTRAY,1956..................................   16.00
BEAM,POLITICAL,DONKEY,BOXER,1964....................................   16.00
BEAM,POLITICAL,DONKEY,CAMPAIGNER,1960...............................   16.00
BEAM,POLITICAL,DONKEY,CLOWN,1968....................................   10.00
BEAM,POLITICAL,ELEPHANT,ASHTRAY,1956................................   16.00
BEAM,POLITICAL,ELEPHANT,BOXER,1964..................................   15.00
BEAM,POLITICAL,ELEPHANT,CAMPAIGNER,1960.............................   16.00
BEAM,POLITICAL,ELEPHANT,CLOWN,1968..................................   10.00
BEAM,POLITICAL,1956,ELEPHANT & DONKEY,PAIR......... 31.00 TO        35.00
BEAM,POLITICAL,1960,ELEPHANT & DONKEY,PAIR......... 25.00 TO        35.00
BEAM,POLITICAL,1964,ELEPHANT & DONKEY,PAIR......... 29.00 TO        31.00
BEAM,POLITICAL,1968,ELEPHANT & DONKEY,PAIR......... 14.00 TO        15.00
BEAM,PONDEROSA,REGAL CHINA SPECIALTY,1969..........  5.95 TO        13.90
BEAM,PONY EXPRESS,REGAL CHINA SPECIALTY,196........  5.95 TO        11.00
BEAM,POODLE,GRAY,TROPHY SERIES,1970................  9.50 TO        14.50
BEAM,POODLE,WHITE,TROPHY SERIES,1970...............  9.50 TO        14.50
BEAM,PORTOLA TREK,SAN DIEGO,GLASS,CENTENNIAL,1969...........         5.00
BEAM,POWELL EXPEDITION,CENTENNIAL,1969.............  7.50 TO         8.00
BEAM,PREAKNESS,CENTENNIAL,1970.....................  9.95 TO        14.50
BEAM,PRESIDENTIAL,EXECUTIVE,1968................... 11.00 TO        14.00
BEAM,PRESSED CRYSTAL BOURBON,1967..................  2.95 TO         4.95
BEAM,PRESSED CRYSTAL EMERALD,1968..................  3.00 TO         4.50
BEAM,PRESSED CRYSTAL RUBY,1967.....................  3.00 TO         7.95
BEAM,PRESSED CRYSTAL SCOTCH,1969....................................    4.00
BEAM,PRESTIGE,EXECUTIVE,1967....................... 19.75 TO        21.00
BEAM,PRIMA DONNA,RENO,CUSTOMER SPECIALTY,1969...... 12.00 TO        15.00
BEAM,PUSSY WILLOW..................................  7.00 TO         9.50
BEAM,PYREX COFFEE WARMER,BLACK HANDLE,1956.........  4.50 TO         7.50
BEAM,PYREX COFFEE WARMER,GOLD CORD,1954............ 11.00 TO        14.95
BEAM,PYREX COFFEE WARMER,GOLD HANDLE,1956..........  4.50 TO         7.50
BEAM,PYREX COFFEE WARMER,RED CORD,1954............. 11.00 TO        12.95
BEAM,QUEEN MARY GOLD FOX,1969.....................105.00 TO       200.00
BEAM,RAM CALENDAR,1958..............................................    2.00
BEAM,RAM THERMOMETER...............................  3.50 TO        24.95
BEAM,RAM,TROPHY SERIES,1958........................ 77.50 TO       120.00
BEAM,RED ROSES,CHURCHILL DOWNS..................... 12.95 TO        15.95
BEAM,REDFIN SUBMARINE,REGAL CHINA,1970..............ILLUS..         8.00
BEAM,REDWOOD,REGAL CHINA SPECIALTY,1967............  9.95 TO        16.50
BEAM,REGAL CHINA,CABLE CAR,1968.....................ILLUS..         5.00
BEAM,REGAL CHINA,CHURCHILL DOWNS,1970...............ILLUS..        10.00
BEAM,REGAL CHINA,RUIDOSO DOWNS,1968.................ILLUS..         6.00
BEAM,REGAL CHINA,TEXAS HEMISFAIR,1968...............ILLUS..        15.00
BEAM,REGAL CHINA,1955,ASHTRAY,IVORY.................................   27.50
BEAM,REGAL CHINA,1962,SEATTLE WORLD'S FAIR......... 27.50 TO        34.00
BEAM,REGAL CHINA,1964,NEW YORK WORLD'S FAIR........ 27.50 TO        32.00
BEAM,REGAL CHINA,1964,WINE CASK.................... 10.95 TO        13.00
BEAM,REGAL CHINA,1965,JUG,GREEN....................  6.00 TO         9.95
```

BEAM,
REDFIN SUBMARINE,
REGAL CHINA, 1970

BEAM, REGAL CHINA, CABLE CAR, 1968

BEAM, REGAL CHINA, CHURCHILL DOWNS, 1970

BEAM, REGAL CHINA,
RUIDOSO DOWNS, 1968

BEAM, REGAL CHINA,
TEXAS HEMISFAIR, 1968

```
BEAM,REGAL CHINA,1966,JUG,OATMEAL................... 50.00 TO    65.00
BEAM,REGAL CHINA,1966,JUG,TURQUOISE...................  4.50 TO     6.00
BEAM,REGAL CHINA,1967,DAISY,BLUE.....................  5.95 TO     7.95
BEAM,REGAL CHINA,1967,REDWOOD........................  9.95 TO    16.50
BEAM,REGAL CHINA,1967,YOSEMITE.......................  5.95 TO    13.95
BEAM,REGAL CHINA,1968,ANTIQUE TRADER.................  5.95 TO     6.95
BEAM,REGAL CHINA,1968,BROADMOOR HOTEL................  6.95 TO     9.95
BEAM,REGAL CHINA,1968,CABLE CAR......................  3.50 TO     5.95
BEAM,REGAL CHINA,1968,HEMISFAIR...................... 14.00 TO    17.50
BEAM,REGAL CHINA,1968,PONY EXPRESS...................  5.95 TO    11.00
BEAM,REGAL CHINA,1968,RUIDOSO........................  4.95 TO     7.50
BEAM,REGAL CHINA,1968,SLOT,GRAY......................  5.50 TO     6.00
BEAM,REGAL CHINA,1969,GRAND CANYON................... 17.50 TO    32.90
BEAM,REGAL CHINA,1969,HARRY HOFFMAN..................  6.95 TO    10.95
BEAM,REGAL CHINA,1969,KENTUCKY DERBY,PINK ROSES.............    9.95
BEAM,REGAL CHINA,1969,KENTUCKY DERBY,RED............. 12.95 TO    15.95
BEAM,REGAL CHINA,1969,LAS VEGAS......................  5.95 TO     7.95
BEAM,REGAL CHINA,1969,PONDEROSA......................  5.95 TO    13.90
BEAM,REGAL CHINA,1969,THAILAND.......................  7.00 TO     9.00
BEAM,REGAL CHINA,1970,AMVETS.........................  8.95 TO    13.00
BEAM,REGAL CHINA,1970,BELL,SCOTCH....................  5.95 TO    11.00
BEAM,REGAL CHINA,1970,BING CROSBY....................  7.00 TO    10.00
BEAM,REGAL CHINA,1970,GERMANY........................ 10.95 TO    16.00
BEAM,REGAL CHINA,1970,KENTUCKY COLONEL............... 10.95 TO    13.50
BEAM,REGAL CHINA,1970,MANITOWAC SUBMARINE............  5.95 TO    11.50
BEAM,REGAL CHINA,1970,MINT 400....................... 15.95 TO    39.50
BEAM,REGAL CHINA,1970,RUSH TO THE ROCKIES............ 25.00 TO    27.00
BEAM,REGAL CHINA,1970,SHRINERS.......................  6.95 TO    10.95
BEAM,RENO HORSESHOE CLUB,1969........................  9.95 TO    14.00
BEAM,RENO PRIMA DONNA,1969........................... 12.00 TO    15.00
BEAM,RENO,CAL-NEVA CLUB,1969......................... 12.00 TO    14.00
BEAM,RENO,CENTENNIAL,1968,1969.......................  6.00 TO     7.95
BEAM,RICHARD'S NEW MEXICO,CUSTOMER,1967..............  6.75 TO     8.25
BEAM,ROBIN,TROPHY SERIES,1969........................  7.00 TO    10.95
BEAM,ROCKY MOUNTAIN CLUB,1970........................ 39.95 TO    75.00
BEAM,ROSE DELFT,GLASS SPECIALTY,1963.................  8.00 TO     9.00
BEAM,ROYAL CRYSTAL,GLASS SPECIALTY,1959..............  5.95 TO     8.50
BEAM,ROYAL DI MONTE,EXECUTIVE,1957................... 71.00 TO    80.00
BEAM,ROYAL EMPEROR,GLASS SPECIALTY,1958..............  4.50 TO     8.95
BEAM,ROYAL GOLD DIAMOND,EXECUTIVE,1964............... 46.50 TO    50.00
BEAM,ROYAL GOLD ROYAL,EXECUTIVE,1956.................140.00 TO   160.00
BEAM,ROYAL OPAL,GLASS SPECIALTY,1957.................  6.95 TO    15.00
BEAM,ROYAL PORCELAIN,EXECUTIVE,1955..................175.00 TO   225.00
BEAM,ROYAL RESERVE,GLASS SPECIALTY,1953-70...........  3.95 TO     6.50
BEAM,ROYAL ROSE,EXECUTIVE,1963....................... 48.00 TO    54.00
BEAM,RUDOLPH,RED NOSED REINDEER,TROPHY,1963...................    5.00
BEAM,RUIDOSO DOWNS,REGAL CHINA,1968,1969.............  4.95 TO     7.50
BEAM,RUSH TO THE ROCKIES,REGAL CHINA,1970............ 25.00 TO    27.00
BEAM,SALUTE TO SPIRO AGNEW,1970.......................... 2,850.00
BEAM,SAN DIEGO,CENTENNIAL,1968.......................  4.95 TO     6.95
BEAM,SANTA FE,CENTENNIAL,WEAK GOLD,1960.................... 190.00
BEAM,SANTA FE,CENTENNIAL,1960............................. 215.00
BEAM,SANTA FE,GOOD GOLD,1960.............................. 225.00
BEAM,SCOTCH BELL,REGAL CHINA SPECIALTY,1970..........  5.95 TO    11.00
BEAM,SCOTCH CRYSTAL,CLEAR............................  4.00 TO    11.95
BEAM,SEATTLE WORLD'S FAIR,REGAL CHINA,1962........... 27.50 TO    34.00
BEAM,SHORT DANCING SCOT,GLASS SPECIALTY,1963........ 30.00 TO    49.95
BEAM,SHRINER,REGAL CHINA SPECIALTY...................  6.95 TO    10.95
BEAM,SLOT MACHINE,BLUE,HAROLD'S CLUB................. 14.95 TO    17.95
BEAM,SLOT MACHINE,GRAY,REGAL CHINA,1968,1969.........  5.50 TO     6.00
BEAM,SMOKED CRYSTAL,GENIE,GLASS,1964.................  4.00 TO     9.50
BEAM,SMOKED CRYSTAL,GLASS SPECIALTY,1964.............  4.00 TO     9.50
BEAM,SOLDIER & GIRL,COLLECTOR'S EDITION,1967.........  3.00 TO     4.95
BEAM,SOUTH CAROLINA,STATE SERIES,1970................  9.95 TO    16.00
BEAM,SOUTH DAKOTA,MT.RUSHMORE,STATE,1969,1970........  5.00 TO    11.95
```

```
BEAM,SOUTHERN CALIFORNIA MISSION.................... 50.00 TO  110.00
BEAM,SOVEREIGN,EXECUTIVE,1969...................... 11.00 TO   12.00
BEAM,SPACE NEEDLE,SEATTLE WORLD'S FAIR,1962........ 27.50 TO   34.00
BEAM,ST.LOUIS ARCH,CENTENNIAL,1964................. 24.00 TO   29.95
BEAM,ST.LOUIS ARCH,1967............................ 22.50 TO   24.95
BEAM,STATE,ALASKA STAR,1958........................ 80.00 TO   95.00
BEAM,STATE,ALASKA STAR,1964-65.....................          73.00
BEAM,STATE,ARIZONA,1968-69.........................  5.95 TO   11.00
BEAM,STATE,COLORADO,1959........................... 30.00 TO   50.00
BEAM,STATE,FLORIDA SHELL,BRONZE,1968...............  5.95 TO    8.00
BEAM,STATE,FLORIDA SHELL,PEARL,1968................  5.95 TO    8.00
BEAM,STATE,HAWAII,1959............................. 72.50 TO   78.00
BEAM,STATE,HAWAII,1967............................. 45.00 TO   55.00
BEAM,STATE,IDAHO,1963.............................. 65.00 TO   77.50
BEAM,STATE,ILLINOIS,1968...........................  7.95 TO   11.00
BEAM,STATE,KANSAS,1960-61.......................... 64.00 TO   74.90
BEAM,STATE,KENTUCKY,BLACK HEAD,1967................ 13.95 TO   15.95
BEAM,STATE,KENTUCKY,BROWN HEAD,1967................ 18.00 TO   23.00
BEAM,STATE,MAINE,1970..............................          15.00
BEAM,STATE,MONTANA,1963............................ 95.00 TO  104.95
BEAM,STATE,NEBRASKA,1967........................... 11.00 TO   15.50
BEAM,STATE,NEVADA,1963............................. 65.00 TO   88.50
BEAM,STATE,NEW HAMPSHIRE,1967......................  9.95 TO   12.95
BEAM,STATE,NEW JERSEY,BLUE,1963.................... 95.00 TO  110.00
BEAM,STATE,NEW JERSEY,GRAY......................... 95.00 TO  110.00
BEAM,STATE,NEW JERSEY,YELLOW,1963.................. 65.00 TO   75.00
BEAM,STATE,NORTH DAKOTA,1965....................... 79.95 TO   85.00
BEAM,STATE,OHIO,1966............................... 12.50 TO   17.50
BEAM,STATE,OREGON,1959............................. 29.95 TO   49.50
BEAM,STATE,PENNSYLVANIA,1967.......................ILLUS..   11.00
BEAM,STATE,SOUTH CAROLINA,1970.....................  9.95 TO   16.00
BEAM,STATE,SOUTH DAKOTA,MOUNT RUSHMORE.............  5.00 TO   11.95
BEAM,STATE,WEST VIRGINIA,1963......................120.00 TO  135.00
BEAM,STATE,WYOMING,1965............................ 70.00 TO   75.00
BEAM,SUBMARINE,REDFIN,1970.........................  5.95 TO   11.95
BEAM,SUNFLOWERS,COLLECTOR'S EDITION,1969...........           2.00
BEAM,TABBY CAT,1967................................ 10.95 TO   12.00
BEAM,TALL DANCING SCOT,GLASS,1964-1970.............  7.95 TO   11.50
BEAM,TALL SCOT WITH DANCING COUPLE.................          995.00
BEAM,TAVERN SCENE,EXECUTIVE,1959................... 65.00 TO   95.00
BEAM,TEXAS HEMISFAIR,REGAL CHINA,1968.............. 14.00 TO   17.50
BEAM,THAILAND,REGAL CHINA SPECIALTY,1969...........  7.00 TO    9.00
BEAM,THE BALCONY,COLLECTOR'S EDITION,1969..........           2.50
BEAM,THE GUITARIST,COLLECTOR'S EDITION,1969........           3.00
BEAM,THE JUDGE,COLLECTOR'S EDITION,1969............           2.00
BEAM,THE KENTUCKIAN,COLLECTOR'S EDITION,1968.......           2.00
BEAM,THE SCOUT,COLLECTOR'S EDITION,1968............           3.00
BEAM,TITUS AT THE WRITING DESK,COLLECTOR'S EDITION,1970.....  2.50
BEAM,TOMBSTONE TERRITORY...........................  8.95 TO   14.95
BEAM,TROPHY,BLUE JAY,1969..........................  8.00 TO    8.95
BEAM,TROPHY,BURMESE CAT,1967.......................          12.00
BEAM,TROPHY,CARDINAL,1968..........................ILLUS..   40.00
BEAM,TROPHY,DOE,1963............................... 30.00 TO   36.00
BEAM,TROPHY,DOE,1967............................... 30.00 TO   34.00
BEAM,TROPHY,DOG,1959............................... 54.95 TO   72.50
BEAM,TROPHY,DUCK,1957.............................. 30.00 TO   45.00
BEAM,TROPHY,EAGLE,1965............................. 15.95 TO   17.50
BEAM,TROPHY,FISH,1957.............................. 36.00 TO   45.00
BEAM,TROPHY,FOX,GREEN,1965......................... 48.00 TO   60.00
BEAM,TROPHY,FOX,GREEN,1967......................... 45.00 TO   50.00
BEAM,TROPHY,HORSE,BLACK,1962.......................          25.00
BEAM,TROPHY,HORSE,BLACK,1967....................... 17.50 TO   21.50
BEAM,TROPHY,KENTUCKY CARDINAL,1968................. 29.95 TO   41.00
BEAM,TROPHY,PHEASANT,1960..........................          19.00
BEAM,TROPHY,PHEASANT,1961..........................          19.50
```

```
BEAM,TROPHY,PHEASANT,1966.........................................    16.00
BEAM,TROPHY,POODLE,GRAY,1970........................... 9.50 TO     14.50
BEAM,TROPHY,POODLE,WHITE,1970..........................ILLUS..     12.00
BEAM,TROPHY,RAM,1958................................ 77.50 TO    120.00
BEAM,TROPHY,ROBIN,1969.............................. 7.00 TO     10.95
BEAM,TROPHY,SIAMESE CAT,1967.....................................    12.00
BEAM,TROPHY,TABBY CAT,1967......................... 10.95 TO     12.00
BEAM,TROPHY,WOODPECKER,1969......................... 7.95 TO     10.95
BEAM,TURQUOISE JUG,1966............................. 4.50 TO      6.00
BEAM,VIP,HAROLD'S CLUB,1967........................106.00 TO    112.50
BEAM,VIP,HAROLD'S CLUB,1968........................100.00 TO    110.00
BEAM,VIP,HAROLD'S CLUB,1969........................100.00 TO    175.00
BEAM,WEST VIRGINIA,STATE SERIES,1963...............120.00 TO    135.00
```

BEAM,STATE,
PENNSYLVANIA,1967

BEAM,TROPHY,
CARDINAL,1968

BEAM,
TROPHY,POODLE,
WHITE,1970

```
BEAM,WHISTLER'S MOTHER,COLLECTOR'S EDITION,1960...............     8.50
BEAM,WHITE ASHTRAY..............................................    27.50
BEAM,WHITE FOX,REGAL SPECIALTY,1969................. 45.95 TO     70.00
BEAM,WHITE HEAD KENTUCKY........................................    16.95
BEAM,WHITE HORSE,1962..........................................    25.00
BEAM,WINE CASK,REGAL CHINA SPECIALTY,1964........... 10.95 TO     13.00
BEAM,WOODPECKER,TROPHY SERIES,1969.................. 7.95 TO     10.95
BEAM,WORLD'S FAIR,HEMISFAIR,1968.................... 14.00 TO     17.50
BEAM,WYOMING,STATE SERIES,1965...................... 70.00 TO     75.00
BEAM,YELLOW KATZ CAT................................ 24.95 TO     29.00
BEAM,YOSEMITE,REGAL CHINA SPECIALTY,1967............ 5.95 TO     13.95
BEAM,YUMA RIFLE CLUB,1968........................... 38.00 TO     44.95
BEAM,ZIMMERMAN BLUE BEAUTY,1969,1970.............................    20.00
BEAM,ZIMMERMAN BLUE DAISY,1967...................... 5.95 TO      7.95
BEAM,ZIMMERMAN CHERUB,LAVENDER,1968,1969............ 6.95 TO      8.75
BEAM,ZIMMERMAN CHERUB,SALMON,1968,1969..........................     7.50
BEAM,ZIMMERMAN TWO HANDLED JUG,1965.................125.00 TO    135.00
BEAM,ZIMMERMAN,GLASS,1969,1970..................................     8.00
BEAM,ZOUAVE,COLLECTOR'S EDITION,1969............................     2.50
BEEF TONIC,RECTANGULAR PANELED CORNERS,7 IN.....................     6.00
BEEFEATER,FIBER STATUE..........................................    20.00
BEEFEATER,FIGURAL..............................................    13.00
BEEFEATER,YOEMAN...............................................    27.50
```

BEER WAS BOTTLED IN ALL PARTS OF THE UNITED STATES BY
THE TIME OF THE CIVIL WAR. STONEWARE AND THE STANDARD

BEER BOTTLE SHAPE OF THE 1870'S ARE INCLUDED IN THIS
CATEGORY.

BEER,AB,AQUA.. 1.00
BEER,A.B.C.BOHEMIAN,AMERICAN BREWING CO...................... 10.00
BEER,A.B.G.M. CO.,IN CIRCLE,AQUA................................ 6.00
BEER,A.B.G.M. CO.,OPALESCENT,AMBER.............................. 6.00
BEER,ALE,PLAIN POTTERY,BROWN & WHITE........................... 4.00
BEER,ALE,PLAIN POTTERY,WHITE.................................... 4.00
BEER,ALE,PLAIN,QUART,KICK UP PONTIL,APPLIED TOP,BLUE.......... 20.00
BEER,ALE,PLAIN,8 PANELS,GRAPHITED PONTIL,GREEN................ 25.00
BEER,ALE,TURN MOLD,10 IN. TALL,OLIVE GREEN..................... 3.00
BEER,ANHEUSER-BUSCH BEER CONSUMERS B.B.S.,CROWN,AMBER......... 3.50
BEER,ANHEUSER-BUSCH BEER CONSUMERS,CROWN,AMBER................ 3.50
BEER,ARLINGTON BOTTLING CO.,BLOB TOP,AMBER..................... 5.00
BEER,ARNAS,ROUND,AMBER... 3.00
BEER,BEADLESTON & WOERZ,EXCELSIOR EMPIRE BREWERY,AQUA......... 4.00
BEER,BIMAL,EMBOSSED.. 1.00
BEER,BLATZ MILWAUKEE,OLIVE..................................... 4.00
BEER,BLOB TOP,EMBOSSED.............................. 1.75 TO   2.00
BEER,BLOB TOP,PINT,AMBER....................................... 2.00
BEER,BLOB TOP,QUART,AMBER...................................... 2.00
BEER,BOURNE 30 DENBY EMBOSSED ON BOTTOM....................... 12.50
BEER,BROWN,8 1/2 IN. TALL...................................... 2.00
BEER,BUDWEISER,EMBOSSED,MOUTHBLOWN,AQUA....................... 9.00
BEER,C.B.CO.MONO,CHATTANOOGA,TENN.,11 1/4 IN.TALL,AMBER..... 4.00
BEER,C.CONRAD & CO.,ORIGINAL BUDWLESE,AQUA................... 12.00
BEER,CAL. BOTTLING CO.,AMBER....................... 5.00 TO   6.00
BEER,CAMBRINUS BOTTLING CO.,AMBER.................. 5.00 TO   6.00
BEER,CARLINGS,DATED 1940,ROUND BOTTOM......................... 3.00
BEER,CHAMPAGNE,BLOWN IN MOLD,AQUA................. 2.50 TO   3.50
BEER,CHAS SEILER,MILWAUKEE,BLOB TOP,AQUA...................... 6.00
BEER,CHRISTIAN MOERLEIN BREWING CO.,CINCINNATI,AQUA.......... 3.00
BEER,CLAUS WREDEN BREWING CO.,AMBER............... 5.00 TO   6.00
BEER,COBALT... 22.00
BEER,CONNECTICUT BREWERIES CO.,BLUE GREEN..................... 3.00
BEER,CONNECTICUT BRIDGEPORT,CONN.,REGISTERED,BLUE GREEN..... 4.00
BEER,CROCKERY,OLD JUG LAGER,NASHVILLE,TENN.,CREAM............ 8.00
BEER,DIEHL & LORD,BLOB TOP,CREAM ALE,SQUAT,AMBER............. 35.00
BEER,DU BOIS,BLOWN IN MOLD,BROWN............................... 3.00
BEER,EL DORADO BREWING CO.,AMBER.................. 5.00 TO   6.00
BEER,EMBOSSED... 3.00
BEER,EMBOSSED SEMINUDE,AQUA.................................... 2.50
BEER,EMBOSSED,BI-MOLD... 2.00
BEER,EMBOSSED,BLOB TOP,AMBER.................................. 1.00
BEER,ETCHED... 9.00
BEER,FRANK JONES BREWING CO.,11 1/2 IN. TALL,AMBER........... 2.00
BEER,G-B-S,ARROW,PORCELAIN WIRE TOP,ROUND,CLEAR.............. 3.00
BEER,G.F.BURKHARDT,BLOWN IN MOLD,AMBER......................... 7.00
BEER,GALVESTON BREWING CO.,ROUND,AQUA......................... 4.00
BEER,GENTLEMAN,A BREWING CO.,PURE MALT & HOPS,ROUND,AMBER... 8.00
BEER,GEO.CH.GEMUNDEN,LAGER BEER,BLOB TOP,8 IN. TALL.......... 12.00
BEER,GERMAN,WIRE HATNESS,PORCELAIN TOP......................... 2.00
BEER,GERMANIA BREWING CO.,CHARLESTON,S.C.,CROWN,AQUA......... 350.00
BEER,GREEN,PEWTER BANDS & HANDLE,PORCELAIN CLAMP ON TOP..... 50.00
BEER,HARRISON BOTTLING CO.,BLOWN IN MOLD,CLEAR............... 4.00
BEER,HAUCK,THE JOHN BREWING CO.,ROUND,AMBER.................. 5.00
BEER,HAUCK,THE JOHN BREWING CO.,ROUND,CLEAR.................. 6.00
BEER,HEUSTIS',E.M.,ROUND,NOT TO BE SOLD,REG.,AQUA........... 4.00
BEER,HOHMAN & BARTLETT SCHLITZ,BLOWN IN MOLD,BROWN.......... 3.50
BEER,HOSTER,COLUMBUS,OHIO,GLOBE EAGLE,GREEN................. 13.00
BEER,IMPERIAL QUART,AQUA...................................... 6.50
BEER,INDEPENDENT BR'G ASS'N,AMBER............................. 6.00
BEER,INDIANAPOLIS BREWING,DANCING GIRL,PINT,AMBER........... 10.50
BEER,JAMES RAY,XX ALE,BLOB TOP,AQUA.......................... 25.00
BEER,JOHN RAPP & SON,AMBER........................ 4.00 TO   5.00

```
BEER,JOHN RYAL,ALE,XXX STAR,1866,BLUE.........................   20.00
BEER,JOHN RYAN,XX PORTER & ALE PHILAD,1866,BLUE..............   20.00
BEER,KANSAS CITY BREWERY,16 OZ.,EMBOSSED,AMBER..............    9.50
BEER,LEIMAN,BLOB TOP........................................    4.00
BEER,LIMP ST.LOUIS IN EMBOSSED SHIELD.......................    5.00
BEER,LION BREWERY LTD.,AMBER........................ 8.00 TO   10.00
BEER,MALT IRON ALE,CROWN....................................    3.50
BEER,MALTINE MFG.CO.,AMBER..................................    3.00
BEER,MILK GLASS,9 IN........................................   14.00
BEER,MILK GLASS,13 IN.......................................   15.00
BEER,MILLER BECKER CO.,PINT,AQUA,12 IN..............ILLUS..    2.00
BEER,MILLER,BOCK,1917,CLEAR,12 1/2 OZ...............ILLUS..    8.00
BEER,MILLER,EMBOSSED...............................ILLUS..    8.00
BEER,MILLER,1902,BROWN,12 OZ.......................ILLUS..   12.00
BEER,MILLER,1910,CLEAR,12 OZ.......................ILLUS..    8.00
BEER,MILLER,1911,12 OZ.............................ILLUS..    8.00
BEER,MILLER,1919,12 OZ.............................ILLUS..    9.00
BEER,MILLER,1929,BROWN,12 OZ.......................ILLUS..    9.00
BEER,MOEHLIEN GERST BREWING CO.,OLD JUG LAGER,POTTERY,PINT..   10.00
BEER,MUTUAL BREWING CO.,CROWN,AMBER.........................    4.00
BEER,N.J.,BLOB TOP,EMBOSSED.................................    3.50
BEER,NEBRASKA BREWING CO.,AMBER.............................    8.00
BEER,NEBRASKA BREWING CO.,RED AMBER.........................    8.00
BEER,OLD ENGLISH,APPLIED LIP,SCREW IN STOPPER,AQUA..........    5.00
BEER,PABST,AQUA............................................    3.00
BEER,PABST,MILWAUKEE,TRADE MARK,AMBER.......................    4.00
BEER,PALMEDO BREWING CO.,S.C.,AQUA..........................    4.00
BEER,PLAIN,8 3/4 IN. HIGH,AMBER.............................    4.00
BEER,PLAIN,11 1/4 IN. TALL,BLUE.............................    4.00
BEER,PLAIN,11 1/4 IN. TALL,GREEN............................    4.00
BEER,PLAIN,11 1/2 IN.TALL,AMBER.............................    4.00
BEER,PLAIN,11 3/4 IN. TALL,BLUE.............................    4.00
BEER,POTTERY ALE,BROWN,TAN.......................... 3.00 TO    4.00
BEER,POTTERY,ALE.................................... 2.00 TO    3.00
BEER,POTTERY,OATMEAL EFFECT,GLAZE,CREAM.....................    5.00
BEER,QUART,RUBY RED................................. 7.00 TO   18.00
BEER,REGISTERED HB,HOLIHAN BROS.,BLOWN IN MOLD,AQUA.........    2.00
BEER,REGISTERED,HOHMAN & BARTLETT,BLOWN IN MOLD,AMETHYST....    3.50
BEER,REGISTERED,HOHMAN & BARTLETT,BLOWN IN MOLD,CLEAR.......    3.50
BEER,REGISTERED,MASSACHUSETTS BREWERIES CO.,GREEN...........    2.50
BEER,ROCHESTER BREWERY,WHITTLED,AMBER.......................    6.00
BEER,ROYAL RUBY RED,QUART...................................    7.50
BEER,ROYAL RUBY SCHLITZ,LABEL,7 OZ..........................   25.00
BEER,ROYAL RUBY,QUART,RED...................................    6.00
BEER,ROYAL RUBY,8 OZ........................................   14.00
BEER,RUBBER STOPPER.........................................     .75
BEER,RUBY RED,12 OZ................................. 9.50 TO   12.00
BEER,RUBY,QUART............................................   20.00
BEER,S.R.ERVEN,PHILADELPHIA,SQUAT,GREEN.....................   20.00
BEER,SCHLITZ,AMBER.........................................    3.00
BEER,SQUAT,OVAL VINAL,PAT.APR.19,1869,AMBER.................    5.00
BEER,ST.HELENA BOTTLING CO.,AMBER................... 5.00 TO    6.00
BEER,STROH BREWING CO.,AQUA......................... 5.00 TO    6.00
BEER,TAHOE,TAHOE BEER,FAMOUS AS THE LAKE SINCE 1862.........    4.95
BEER,THREE MOLD............................................    1.75
BEER,THREE PART MOLD,EMPRINE PORTAL,DARK OLIVE..............   12.00
BEER,THREE PART MOLD,KICK UP,CRUDE TOP,DARK OLIVE...........   12.00
BEER,THREE-PIECE MOLD,DARK OLIVE AMBER......................    3.00
BEER,TURN MOLD,COBALT BLUE..................................   18.00
BEER,TURN MOLD,8 1/2 IN. TALL,AMBER.........................    4.00
BEER,VICTORIA BREWING CO.,VICTORIA B.C.,NOT TO BE SOLD......    7.50
BEER,VICTORIA BREWING,RED AMBER.............................    5.50
BEER,WEISS,BLOWN IN MOLD,WHITTLE,AMBER......................    8.00
BEER,WEISS,SYRACUSE,AMBER...................................    7.50
BEER,WINE TYPE,CROWN TOP,MILK GLASS.........................   12.00
```

BEER,MILLER BECKER CO.,
PINT,AQUA,12 IN

BEER,MILLER,
EMBOSSED

BEER,
MILLER,1919,
12 OZ

BEER,MILLER,
1911,12 OZ

BEER,MILLER,BOCK,
1917,CLEAR,
12 1/2 OZ

BEER,MILLER,
1910,CLEAR,
12 OZ

BEER,MILLER,1902,
BROWN,12 OZ

BEER,MILLER,1929,
BROWN,12 OZ

```
BEER,WIRE HATNESS,PORCELAIN TOP,AMBER......................      2.00
BEER,11 1/4 IN. TALL,GREEN................................      3.00
BEER,11 1/2 IN. TALL,BROWN................................      3.00
BELLOWS,18TH CENTURY ...............................COLOR..     XX.XX
BENNINGTON,BOOK,C.1850..............................COLOR..     XX.XX
BENNINGTON,BOOT...........................................     75.00
BENNINGTON,COACHMAN,C.1846-1858.....................COLOR..     XX.XX
BENNINGTON,COACHMAN,DATE 1849.............................    250.00
BENNINGTON,FLASK,BOOK,UNMARKED............................     65.00
BENNINGTON,JUG,VERMONT,BIRD DECOR,1 GAL...................     35.00
BININGER TYPE,IRON PONTIL,RED AMBER,RING NECK.............     20.00
BINOCULAR,FULL SIZE,BLACK.................................      5.00
```

```
     BISCHOFF COMPANY HAS MADE FANCY DECANTERS SINCE IT WAS
     FOUNDED IN 1777 IN TRIESTE, ITALY.  THE MODERN
     COLLECTIBLE BISCHOFF BOTTLES HAVE BEEN IMPORTED TO THE
     UNITED STATES SINCE ABOUT 1950.  GLASS, PORCELAIN, AND
     STONEWARE DECANTERS AND FIGURALS ARE MADE.
BISCHOFF,AFRICAN HEAD,CERAMIC,1962.................. 16.00 TO   19.00
BISCHOFF,ALPINE PITCHER,PORCELAIN,1969....................     11.00
BISCHOFF,AMBER FLOWERS DECANTER,GLASS,1952......... 30.00 TO   35.00
BISCHOFF,AMBER LEAVES DECANTER,GLASS,1952.......... 30.00 TO   35.00
BISCHOFF,AMPHORA,MAJOLICA,1950............................     25.00
BISCHOFF,AMPHORA,2 HANDLED,1950...........................     25.00
BISCHOFF,AQUA & GOLD DECANTER,WATER SCENE,1956............     50.00
BISCHOFF,AQUA & SILVER DECANTER,GONDOLA,1954..............     33.00
BISCHOFF,ASHTRAY,MINIATURE,CERAMIC,1962.............. 4.00 TO   4.50
BISCHOFF,BELL HOUSE,CERAMIC,1960..........................     30.00
BISCHOFF,BELL TOWER,CERAMIC,1959..........................     30.00
BISCHOFF,BLACK CAT,GLASS,1969.............................     30.00
BISCHOFF,BOY,CHINESE,CERAMIC,1962.........................     40.00
BISCHOFF,BOY,SPANISH,CERAMIC,1961.................. 30.00 TO   40.00
BISCHOFF,CAMEO PITCHER DECANTER,CERAMIC,1962..............     20.00
BISCHOFF,CANDLESTICK,ANTIQUE,GLASS,1958...................     18.00
BISCHOFF,CANDLESTICK,FRUIT,CERAMIC,1964...................     22.00
BISCHOFF,CANDLESTICK,GOLD,GLASS,1958......................     18.00
BISCHOFF,CHARIOT URN,2 COMPARTMENTS,CERAMIC,1966..........     25.00
BISCHOFF,CHRISTMAS TREE DECANTER,1957.....................     55.00
BISCHOFF,CLOWN,BLACK HAIR,CERAMIC,1963....................     41.00
BISCHOFF,CLOWN,RED HAIR,CERAMIC,1963......................     41.00
BISCHOFF,COBALT BLUE & GOLD DECANTER,GONDOLA,1956.........     50.00
BISCHOFF,COBALT BLUE & SILVER DECANTER,1954........ 40.00 TO   45.00
BISCHOFF,CORONET DECANTER,AMBER GLASS,1952......... 32.00 TO   37.50
BISCHOFF,DACHSHUND,GLASS,1966.............................     31.90
BISCHOFF,DEER,CERAMIC,1969................................     22.00
BISCHOFF,DOG,ALABASTER GLASS,1969.........................     30.00
BISCHOFF,DUCK BOTTLE,GLASS,1964...........................     45.00
BISCHOFF,EGYPTIAN ASHTRAY,CERAMIC,1961....................      7.95
BISCHOFF,EGYPTIAN DANCER PITCHER,CERAMIC,1961.............     22.00
BISCHOFF,EGYPTIAN DECANTER,2 HANDLED,2 COMPARTMENTS,1960...     30.00
BISCHOFF,EGYPTIAN MAN VASE,CERAMIC,1961...................     25.00
BISCHOFF,EGYPTIAN MUSICIAN PITCHER,2 MUSICIANS,CERAMIC,1963.   19.00
BISCHOFF,EGYPTIAN PITCHER,3 MUSICIANS,1959......... 25.00 TO   30.00
BISCHOFF,EMERALD DECANTER,ROSES,1952......................     45.00
BISCHOFF,FESTIVAL,JEWELED VASE DECANTER,1957..............     50.00
BISCHOFF,FISH BOTTLE ASHTRAY,CERAMIC,1961.................     20.00
BISCHOFF,FISH BOTTLE,GLASS,1964...........................     32.00
BISCHOFF,FISH,RUBY,GLASS,1969.............................     30.00
BISCHOFF,FLORAL CANTEEN,CERAMIC,1969......................     18.00
BISCHOFF,FLOWER DECANTER,GOLD,PINK,BLUE,GREEN FLOWERS,1956..   50.00
BISCHOFF,FLOWERS DECANTER,RUBY,1953.......................     35.50
BISCHOFF,FRUIT CANTEEN,CERAMIC,1969.......................     18.00
BISCHOFF,FRUIT PLATE,CERAMIC,1966.................. 25.00 TO   39.90
```

```
BISCHOFF,GEESE DECANTER,AMBER,1952..........................    26.00
BISCHOFF,GEESE DECANTER,RUBY,1952...........................    26.00
BISCHOFF,GIRL,CHINESE,CERAMIC,1962..........................    40.00
BISCHOFF,GIRL,SPANISH,CERAMIC,1961................. 30.00 TO    40.00
BISCHOFF,GOLD DUST & GREEN DECANTER,1958....................    42.50
BISCHOFF,GOLD DUST DECANTER,GLASS,1958......................    38.00
BISCHOFF,GRAPES DECANTER,RUBY,1953..........................    35.50
BISCHOFF,GRECIAN VASE DECANTER,CERAMIC,1969.................    11.00
BISCHOFF,GREEN & SILVER DECANTER,1954.............. 30.00 TO    35.00
BISCHOFF,GREEN STRIPED DECANTER,1958........................    35.00
BISCHOFF,JUNGLE SCENE,AMBER,GLASS,1952......................    34.00
BISCHOFF,JUNGLE SCENE,RUBY,GLASS,1952.......................    34.00
   BISCHOFF, KAMOTSURU, SEE KAMOTSURU
   BISCHOFF, KORD, SEE KORD
BISCHOFF,LAVENDER & GOLD DECANTER,ROSES,1954................    25.00
BISCHOFF,LAVENDER & SILVER DECANTER,DAISIES,1954............    33.00
BISCHOFF,MASK,CERAMIC,GRAY,1963.................... 16.00 TO    21.00
BISCHOFF,NIGERIAN MASK,1963........................ 16.00 TO    21.00
BISCHOFF,OIL & VINEGAR CRUETS,CERAMIC,BLACK,WHITE,1959......    22.50
BISCHOFF,OPALINE,AQUA GLASS DECANTER,1957.......... 45.00 TO    50.00
BISCHOFF,PLATE,FRUIT,CERAMIC,1966.................. 25.00 TO    39.90
BISCHOFF,PORCELAIN DECANTER,GOLD TRIM,1953......... 18.00 TO    20.00
BISCHOFF,RED BELL SHAPED DECANTER,1957......................    45.00
BISCHOFF,RED ROSE DECANTER,HANDPAINTED FLOWERS,1957.........    50.00
BISCHOFF,ROOSTER ASHTRAY,CERAMIC,1962.......................     7.95
BISCHOFF,ROSE DECANTER,GOLD,1952............................    25.00
BISCHOFF,ROSE DECANTER,GREEN,1954...........................    30.00
BISCHOFF,ROSE DECANTER,PINK,1953............................    27.50
BISCHOFF,RUBY ETCHED DECANTER,GLASS,1953....................    35.00
BISCHOFF,RUBY ETCHED DECANTER,1952..........................    32.00
BISCHOFF,SENORITA,SPANISH GIRL,1961................ 30.00 TO    40.00
BISCHOFF,SILVER SPOTTED ASHTRAY,1958........................     6.00
BISCHOFF,SILVER SPOTTED DECANTER,1958.......................    35.00
BISCHOFF,STRIPED DECANTER,1958..............................    35.00
BISCHOFF,STRIPED RED,ASHTRAY,GLASS,1958.....................     4.50
BISCHOFF,TOPAZ & GOLD DECANTER,1955.........................    26.00
BISCHOFF,TOPAZ & SILVER DECANTER,1955.......................    40.00
BISCHOFF,TOPAZ BASKET DECANTER,1958................ 30.00 TO    35.00
BISCHOFF,VASE,GOLD,PAINTED FLOWERS,1955.....................    16.00
BISCHOFF,VASE,MODERN,CERAMIC,BLACK & GOLD,1959..............    35.00
BISCHOFF,VENETIAN DECANTER,BLUE,1953........................    25.00
BISCHOFF,VENETIAN DECANTER,GREEN,1953.......................    25.00
BISCHOFF,VENETIAN DECANTER,VIOLET,1953......................    25.00
BISCHOFF,WATCHTOWER,CERAMIC,1960............................    23.00
BISCHOFF,WEDDING PROCESSION VASE,CERAMIC,MEDIEVAL FIGURES,
   1962....................................................    25.00
BISCHOFF,WHITE & YELLOW VASE,1959...........................    20.00
BISCHOFF,WHITE PITCHER,GOLD HANDLE,1960.....................    22.00
BISCHOFF,WHITE SWAGS,JEWELED VASE DECANTER,1957.............    50.00
BISCHOFF,WILD GEESE DECANTER,RUBY,GLASS,1952................    26.00
BISCHOFF,WILD GEESE PITCHER,CERAMIC,1969....................    26.00
BISSO,SOPHIA................................................    22.00
```

BITTERS BOTTLES HELD THE FAMOUS 19TH-CENTURY MEDICINE
CALLED BITTERS. IT WAS OFTEN OF SUCH A HIGH ALCOHOL
CONTENT THAT THE USER FELT HEALTHIER WITH EACH SIP.
THE WORD BITTERS MUST BE EMBOSSED ON THE GLASS OR A
PAPER LABEL MUST BE AFFIXED FOR THE COLLECTOR TO CALL
THE BOTTLE A BITTERS BOTTLE. MOST DATE FROM
1840 TO 1900.
   BITTERS, SEE ALSO SARSAPARILLA

```
BITTERS,A.S.HOPKINS UNION,CONTENTS,LABELS,AMBER.............    20.00
BITTERS,A.SCHREINER N.O.,A NEW ORLEANS BOTTLE,AQUA..........    15.00
```

```
BITTERS,ABBOTT,MINIATURE,PEWTER STOPPER,LABEL................    10.00
BITTERS,ABBOTT'S,MACHINE MADE,AMBER..........................     6.00
BITTERS,AFRICAN STOMACH,AMBER................................    30.00
BITTERS,AFRICAN STOMACH,ROUND,SPRUANCE STANLEY & CO.,AMBER..    30.00
BITTERS,ALPINE HERB,TT & CO.,AMBER...........................    40.00
BITTERS,AMER PICON PHILLIPPEVILLE,BITTER IN CENTER,GREEN....    10.00
BITTERS,AMERICAN LIFE,AMBER..................................   250.00
BITTERS,ANGOSTURA BARK,EAGLE LIQUOR DISTILLERIES,AMBER......    40.00
BITTERS,ARABIAN,CRUDE........................................    25.00
BITTERS,AROMATIC ORANGE,AMBER................................   150.00
BITTERS,ATWOOD'S GENUINE,AQUA................................     9.00
BITTERS,ATWOOD'S GENUINE,AQUA................................    16.00
BITTERS,ATWOOD'S JAUNDICE......................... 3.00 TO      8.00
BITTERS,ATWOOD'S JAUNDICE,BIMAL..............................     5.50
BITTERS,ATWOOD'S JAUNDICE,BLOWN IN MOLD,12 SIDES,AQUA.......     6.00
BITTERS,ATWOOD'S JAUNDICE,CIRCA 1915,AMBER...................     4.00
BITTERS,ATWOOD'S JAUNDICE,CIRCA 1915,AQUA....................     4.00
BITTERS,ATWOOD'S JAUNDICE,CORK TOP,AQUA......................     4.00
BITTERS,ATWOOD'S JAUNDICE,FORM.BY MOSES ATWOOD,SCREW TOP,
   AQUA......................................................     2.00
BITTERS,ATWOOD'S JAUNDICE,FORM.BY MOSES ATWOOD,SCREW TOP,
   CLEAR.....................................................     2.00
BITTERS,ATWOOD'S JAUNDICE,FORMERLY BY MOSES ATWOOD,AQUA.....     6.00
BITTERS,ATWOOD'S JAUNDICE,FORMERLY BY MOSES ATWOOD,CLEAR....     6.00
BITTERS,ATWOOD'S JAUNDICE,FORMERLY MOSES ATWOOD,GEORGETOWN,
   CORK......................................................     4.00
BITTERS,ATWOOD'S JAUNDICE,MACHINE MADE,AQUA..................     3.00
BITTERS,ATWOOD'S JAUNDICE,MACHINE MADE,CLEAR.................     3.00
BITTERS,ATWOOD'S JAUNDICE,MACHINE MADE,12 SIDES,AQUA 3.00 TO     4.50
BITTERS,ATWOOD'S JAUNDICE,MOSES ATWOOD...............COLOR..    XX.XX
BITTERS,ATWOOD'S JAUNDICE,MOSES ATWOOD ON PANELS,AQUA.......     8.00
BITTERS,ATWOOD'S JAUNDICE,MOSES ATWOOD ON PANELS,CLEAR......     8.00
BITTERS,ATWOOD'S JAUNDICE,MOSES ATWOOD ON PANELS,PONTIL,AQUA    12.00
BITTERS,ATWOOD'S JAUNDICE,MOSES ATWOOD ON PANELS,PONTIL,
   CLEAR.....................................................    12.00
BITTERS,ATWOOD'S JAUNDICE,ORIGINAL...........................     6.00
BITTERS,ATWOOD'S JAUNDICE,SCREW TOP..........................     3.00
BITTERS,ATWOOD'S QUININE TONIC,..............................    30.00
BITTERS,ATWOOD'S,BITTERS-TEN.................................    10.00
BITTERS,ATWOOD'S,LABEL.......................................     4.00
BITTERS,ATWOOD'S,ORIGINAL....................................     5.00
BITTERS,AVAN HOBOKEN,OLIVE GREEN.............................    40.00
BITTERS,B-BAR,PORCELAIN SPOUT,ENGRAVED.......................    11.75
BITTERS,BARTO'S GREAT GIN,AMBER..............................    50.00
BITTERS,BAXTER,DR.MANDRAKE,LORD BROS.,12 PANELS,AMBER.......    20.00
BITTERS,BAXTER,DR.MANDRAKE,LORD BROS.,12 PANELS,CLEAR.......    10.00
BITTERS,BAXTER'S MANDRAKE.....................................     6.00
BITTERS,BEGG'S DANDELION,FLASK SHAPE,AMBER...................    30.00
BITTERS,BELL COCKTAIL,LADY'S LEG,KICK UP,AMBER..............    50.00
BITTERS,BELLE OF ANDERSON,PINT...............................    95.00
BITTERS,BIG BILL BEST,PARTIAL LABEL..........................   175.00
BITTERS,BIG BILL BEST,SQUARE,TAPERED,AMBER...................   125.00
   BITTERS, BISMARCK, SEE BITTERS, MULLER'S
BITTERS,BITTERQUELLE.............................. 4.00 TO     17.00
BITTERS,BITTERQUELLE,APPLIED COLLAR,OLIVE GREEN,9 IN........     6.00
BITTERS,BITTERQUELLE,CORK STOPPER,METAL RING,KING SOLOMONS..    55.00
BITTERS,BITTERQUELLE,GREEN...................................     6.50
BITTERS,BITTERQUELLE,OLIVE...................................     8.00
BITTERS,BITTERQUELLE,SAXLEHNERS JANOS,PLAIN,GREEN...........     6.00
BITTERS,BITTERQUELLE,SAXLEHNERS JANOS,WHITTLE,GREEN.........     6.00
BITTERS,BITTERQUELLE,WHITTLED,ROUND,GREEN....................     6.00
BITTERS,BOERHAVES HOLLAND,UMBERGER...........................    65.00
BITTERS,BOKER'S,AMBER........................................    40.00
BITTERS,BONPLAUNDS FEVER & AGUE REMEDY,OPEN PONTIL..........    12.00
BITTERS,BOSTON MALT,ROUND,GREEN................... 25.00 TO    35.00
```

```
BITTERS,BOURBON WHISKEY...................................    85.00
BITTERS,BOURBON WHISKEY,BRIGHT PUCE.......................   140.00
BITTERS,BOURBON WHISKEY,CLARET............................   145.00
BITTERS,BOURBON WHISKEY,PUCE..............................   175.00
BITTERS,BROPHYS...........................................    45.00
BITTERS,BROWN'S CELEBRATED INDIAN HERB..............COLOR..   XX.XX
BITTERS,BROWN'S INDIAN QUEEN,AMBER..................ILLUS..  225.00
BITTERS,BROWN'S INDIAN QUEEN,REDDISH AMBER................   250.00
BITTERS,BROWN'S IRON...................... 18.00 TO    31.00
BITTERS,BROWN'S IRON BITTERS,SQUARE,CRUDE MOLD,AMBER.......    20.00
BITTERS,BROWN'S IRON,HONEY AMBER..........................    35.00
BITTERS,BURDOCK BLOOD,AQUA................. 10.00 TO    12.00
BITTERS,BURDOCK BLOOD,CLEAR...............................    13.00
BITTERS,BURDOCK BLOOD,EMBOSSED............................    18.00
BITTERS,BURDOCK BLOOD,SCREW TOP,MACHINE MADE,SQUARE,AQUA....     3.00
BITTERS,BURDOCK BLOOD,TORONTO,ONT.,CLEAR..................     4.00
BITTERS,C.W.ABBOTT & CO.,AMBER..................... 5.00 TO     6.00
BITTERS,C.W.ABBOTTS,ROUND,AMBER...........................     7.00
BITTERS,C.W.ROBACK,BARREL,AMBER...........................   135.00
    BITTERS, CABIN, SEE ALSO BITTERS, DRAKE'S PLANTATION
BITTERS,CABIN,DR.PETZOLDS,AMBER...........................   125.00
```

BITTERS,BROWN'S INDIAN QUEEN,AMBER

```
BITTERS,CABIN,HOLTZERMANN,AMBER...............................   120.00
BITTERS,CABIN,OLD HOMESTEAD WILD CHERRY,AMBER.................   145.00
BITTERS,CABIN,OLD HOMESTEAD,AMBER.............................   150.00
BITTERS,CAHPIN & CORE SOUR MASH 1847,BARREL,GOLDEN AMBER....    60.00
BITTERS,CALDWELL'S HERB,GRAPHITE..............................   185.00
BITTERS,CALDWELL'S HERB,GREAT TONIC,TAPERED,AMBER............   200.00
BITTERS,CALDWELL'S,IRON PONTIL................................   196.00
BITTERS,CALIFORNIA FIG........................................    55.00
BITTERS,CALIFORNIA FIG,LABEL..................................    50.00
BITTERS,CANTON,LADY'S LEG,ROUND,AMBER.........................    35.00
BITTERS,CAPITOL,AQUA..........................................    28.00
BITTERS,CAPITOL,GREEN.........................................    35.00
BITTERS,CARMELITE,KIDNEY & LIVER,N.Y.,AMBER...................    40.00
BITTERS,CARMELITE,KIDNEY & LIVER,N.Y.,OLIVE...................    40.00
BITTERS,CARONI,PINT,GREEN..................... 10.00 TO    15.00
BITTERS,CHAPIN & GORE BARREL,INSIDE SCREW TOP,AMBER.........    45.00
BITTERS,CLARK'S CORDIAL,EMBOSSED LASH'S BITTERS CO.,CLEAR...    12.00
BITTERS,CLARK'S MANDRAKE COMPOUND,AQUA........................    33.00
BITTERS,CLARK'S ONLY 25 CENTS,SHERRY WINE ON FRONT,AQUA.....    30.00
BITTERS,CLARK'S SHERRY WINE,AQUA.................. 35.00 TO    88.00
BITTERS,CLARK'S SHERRY WINE,CLEAR................. 25.00 TO    35.00
BITTERS,CLARK'S VEGETABLE,ONLY 75 CENTS,AQUA.................   135.00
```

```
BITTERS,COCO MARIANI PARIS,WHITTLED,GREEN...................          8.00
BITTERS,COLE BROS.................................. 23.00 TO         65.00
BITTERS,COLE BROS.VEGETABLE,AQUA.................... 12.00 TO        25.00
BITTERS,COLUMBO PEPTIC............................. 23.00 TO         35.00
BITTERS,COLUMBO PEPTIC,NEW ORLEANS,L.A.,SQUARE,AMBER.........        35.00
BITTERS,CONGRESS & EMPIRE SPRING CO.........................        18.00
BITTERS,CONGRESS & EMPIRE,LOG CABIN,PINT,EMERALD.............        14.50
BITTERS,CRAIG'S KIDNEY & LIVER CURE COMPANY.................        70.00
BITTERS,CUMBERLAND,AMBER....................................       150.00
BITTERS,CURTIS & PERKINS WILD CHERRY,CRUDE,OPEN PONTIL,AQUA.        45.00
BITTERS,DAMIANA,AQUA........................................        51.00
BITTERS,DAMIANA,BAJA,CALIFORNIA,BLUE............... 35.00 TO         45.00
BITTERS,DAMIANA,LEWIS HESS MFG.................... 30.00 TO          35.00
BITTERS,DAMIANA,QUART,AQUA..................................        35.00
BITTERS,DANDELION XXX,CLEAR.................................        66.00
BITTERS,DEVIL CERT,CLEAR....................................        18.00
BITTERS,DEWITT'S STOMACH,BLOWN IN MOLD,BROWN................         7.00
BITTERS,DEWITT'S STOMACH,SQUARE,AMBER.......................        37.50
BITTERS,DOYLE'S HOP................................ 22.00 TO         24.00
BITTERS,DOYLE'S HOP BITTERS,AMBER.................. 21.00 TO         40.00
BITTERS,DOYLE'S HOP,AMBER,1872,9 1/2 IN.TALL....... 20.00 TO         30.0C
BITTERS,DOYLE'S HOP,QUART,AMBER.............................        22.00
BITTERS,DOYLE'S HOP,3 SIDED ROOF,1872,AMBER.................        12.00
BITTERS,DR.A.H.SMITHS OLD STYLE,AMBER.......................        40.00
BITTERS,DR.AYER'S,AMETHYST..................................        51.00
BITTERS,DR.BAXTER'S MANDRAKE........................ 4.00 TO         11.00
BITTERS,DR.BAXTER'S MANDRAKE BITTERS,12 SIDED,AMBER.........         6.00
BITTERS,DR.BAXTER'S MANDRAKE,BIMAL,AQUA.....................         9.00
BITTERS,DR.BAXTER'S MANDRAKE,BLUE.................. 10.00 TO         15.00
BITTERS,DR.BAXTER'S MANDRAKE,CLEAR.................. 8.00 TO          9.00
BITTERS,DR.BAXTER'S MANDRAKE,12 SIDED,WHITE.................        12.50
BITTERS,DR.BAXTER'S MANDRAKE,12 SIDES,AQUA......... 10.00 TO         12.50
BITTERS,DR.BELL'S BLOOD PURIFYING,6 STAR,QUART,AMBER........       110.00
BITTERS,DR.BOYCE'S TONIC....................................        40.00
BITTERS,DR.BOYCE'S TONIC BITTERS,PINT,AQUA..................        32.00
BITTERS,DR.BOYCES TONIC,AQUA,PINT...........................        32.00
BITTERS,DR.BULL'S...........................................        12.00
BITTERS,DR.C.W.ROBACK'S STOMACH,CINCINNATI,O.,AMBER.........       125.00
BITTERS,DR.C.W.ROBACK'S STOMACH,OLIVE AMBER..........ILLUS..       125.00
BITTERS,DR.DRAKES,AMBER.....................................        42.00
BITTERS,DR.FISCH,AMBER......................................       165.00
BITTERS,DR.FISCH,AMBER,FISH SHAPE....................ILLUS..       165.00
BITTERS,DR.FISCH'S,AMBER....................................        20.00
BITTERS,DR.FISCH'S,REDDISH AMBER............................       160.00
BITTERS,DR.FISCH'S,WILLIAMSBURG CLAY................ 1.00 TO          7.50
BITTERS,DR.FLINT'S QUAKER...................................        55.00
BITTERS,DR.FLINT'S QUAKER,AQUA..............................        19.00
BITTERS,DR.FLINTS QUAKER,AQUA...............................        25.00
BITTERS,DR.FLINTS QUAKER,EMBOSSED...........................        25.00
BITTERS,DR.FORMANECK'S BITTER WINE,ROUND,AMBER..............         8.00
BITTERS,DR.GEO.PIERCE'S INDIAN RESTORATIVE,AQUA.... 20.00 TO         26.00
BITTERS,DR.GILMORE'S,AMBER..................................        86.00
BITTERS,DR.GOODHUES,SALEM,MASS.,AQUA........................        95.00
BITTERS,DR.HANLEY'S ROOT & HERB,AQUA........................        32.00
BITTERS,DR.HARTER'S WILD CHERRY,AMBER.......................        30.00
BITTERS,DR.HARTER'S WILD CHERRY,AMBER,8 IN...........ILLUS..        25.00
BITTERS,DR.HARTER'S WILD CHERRY,APPLIED LIP.................        35.00
BITTERS,DR.HARTER'S WILD CHERRY,DAYTON,OHIO.................        25.00
BITTERS,DR.HARTER'S WILD CHERRY,MINIATURE,BROWN.............        18.00
BITTERS,DR.HARTER'S WILD CHERRY,RECTANGULAR,AMBER...........        25.00
BITTERS,DR.HARTER'S,SAMPLE SIZE.............................        35.00
BITTERS,DR.HARTER'S,WILD CHERRY,PINT........................        40.00
BITTERS,DR.HARTSHORN'S JAUNDICE,EMBOSSED....................         2.75
BITTERS,DR.HOOFLAND'S GERMAN TONIC................. 26.00 TO         32.00
BITTERS,DR.HOOFLAND'S GERMAN,AQUA...........................        75.00
```

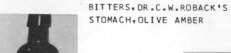

BITTERS, DR.C.W.ROBACK'S
STOMACH, OLIVE AMBER

BITTERS, DR.FISCH,
AMBER, FISH SHAPE

BITTERS, DR.HARTER'S
WILD CHERRY,
AMBER, 8 IN

BITTERS,DR.HOOFLAND'S GERMAN,OPEN PONTIL....................	30.00
BITTERS,DR.HOOFLAND'S,PINT,AQUA.........................	4.00
BITTERS,DR.HOPKIN'S UNION STOMACH,AMBER....................	39.00
BITTERS, DR.HOSTETTER, SEE ALSO BITTERS, DR.J.HOSTETTER	
BITTERS,DR.J.G.B.SIEGERT & HIJOS,ANGOSTURA BITTERS,ROUND,	
GREEN...	3.00
BITTERS,DR.J.G.B.SIEGERT & HIJOS,3 MOLD,GREEN....... 6.00 TO	10.00
BITTERS,DR.J.HOSTETTER'S STOMACH BITTERS............. 7.50 TO	10.00
BITTERS,DR.J.HOSTETTER'S STOMACH,AMBER............. 10.00 TO	22.00
BITTERS,DR.J.HOSTETTER'S STOMACH,BLOWN IN MOLD,AMBER........	8.00
BITTERS,DR.J.HOSTETTER'S STOMACH,GOLDEN AMBER..............	5.00
BITTERS,DR.J.HOSTETTER'S STOMACH,GREEN........... 85.00 TO	90.00
BITTERS,DR.J.HOSTETTER'S STOMACH,MACHINE MADE,SQUARE,AMBER..	5.00
BITTERS,DR.J.HOSTETTER'S STOMACH,MACHINE MADE,SQUARE,GREEN..	6.00
BITTERS,DR.J.HOSTETTER'S STOMACH,MISSPELLED NAME............	12.00
BITTERS,DR.J.HOSTETTER'S STOMACH,OLIVE.....................	50.00
BITTERS,DR.J.HOSTETTER'S STOMACH,QUART,AMBER...............	12.00
BITTERS,DR.J.HOSTETTER'S STOMACH,SQUARE,AMBER..............	12.00
BITTERS,DR.J.HOSTETTER'S STOMACH,SQUARE,GREEN..............	25.00
BITTERS,DR.J.HOSTETTER'S STOMACH,1860,RED AMBER............	10.00
BITTERS,DR.J.HOSTETTER'S,AMBER..................... 12.00 TO	35.00
BITTERS,DR.J.HOSTETTER'S,BUBBLES,BLACK........... 95.00 TO	100.00
BITTERS,DR.J.HOSTETTER'S,BUBBLES,OLIVE GREEN...............	40.00
BITTERS,DR.J.HOSTETTER'S,TAPERED COLLAR...................	12.00
BITTERS,DR.J.HOSTETTER'S,90 PERCENT LABELS................	13.00
BITTERS,DR.J.HUNTINGTONS GOLDEN TONIC,SIX STAR,NO.182,AMBER.	69.95
BITTERS,DR.J.SWEETS,EMBOSSED.............................	35.00
BITTERS,DR.JACOBS.......................................	85.00
BITTERS,DR.KAUFMANN'S,LABEL.............................	30.00
BITTERS,DR.LANGLEY'S ROOT & HERB........................	23.00
BITTERS,DR.LANGLEY'S ROOT & HERB BITTERS,REVERSED 99........	28.00
BITTERS,DR.LANGLEY'S ROOT & HERB, AQUA....................	65.00
BITTERS,DR.LANGLEY'S ROOT & HERB,BOSTON,PINT,AQUA..........	20.00
BITTERS,DR.LANGLEY'S ROOT & HERB,CLEAR............. 25.00 TO	35.00
BITTERS,DR.LANGLEY'S ROOT & HERB,EMBOSSED..................	40.00
BITTERS,DR.LANGLEY'S ROOT & HERB,IRON PONTIL,AQUA..........	50.00
BITTERS,DR.LANGLEY'S ROOT & HERB,OPEN PONTIL,WHITTLED.......	32.50
BITTERS,DR.LANGLEY'S ROOT & HERB,WHITTLED,PONTIL,AQUA.......	45.00
BITTERS,DR.LANGLEY'S,99 UNION ST.,SHORT NECK................	10.00
BITTERS,DR.LION'S STOMACH,AMBER,10 IN.,LABEL.........ILLUS..	25.00

```
BITTERS,DR.LOEW'S CELERY STOMACH............................   125.00
BITTERS,DR.LYFORD'S,AQUA....................................    76.00
BITTERS,DR.M.M.FENNER'S CAPITOL,QUART,AQUA..................    60.00
BITTERS,DR.MANLY HARDY'S JAUNDICE,AQUA......................    45.00
BITTERS,DR.PETZOLDS GENUINE GERMAN,RED AMBER................   125.00
BITTERS,DR.RATTINGEUS,EMBOSSED L.G.CO. BOTTOM,AMBER.........    56.00
BITTERS,DR.S.M.GOULD BOTANIC,INDIANS ON LABEL,1/2 GAL.,AQUA.    15.00
BITTERS,DR.S.S.FITCH,APPLIED FLANGED LIP,ROUGH PONTIL,AQUA..    20.00
BITTERS,DR.SAWENS..........................................    45.00
BITTERS,DR.SAWENS LIFE INVIGORATING........................    25.00
BITTERS,DR.SIMS............................................    90.00
BITTERS,DR.SOLOMONS GREAT INDIAN,AQUA......................    65.00
BITTERS,DR.STANLEY'S SOUTH AMERICAN INDIAN,AMBER...........    50.00
BITTERS,DR.STEPHEN JEWITT'S BITTERS,RINDGE,N.H.,OLIVE AMBER.   200.00
BITTERS,DR.STEWARTS TONIC,EMBOSSED,LABEL...................     35.00
BITTERS,DR.SWEETS..........................................    60.00
BITTERS,DR.THOMAS HALL'S CALIFORNIA PEPSIN WINE.............    18.00
BITTERS,DR.VON HOFF'S MINT CURACAO,AMBER...................     45.00
BITTERS,DR.VON HOPF'S,AMBER........................ 30.00 TO    50.00
BITTERS,DR.WALKER'S CALIFORNIA VINEGAR,AQUA................      8.00
BITTERS,DR.WARNERS GERMAN HOP..............................    40.00
BITTERS,DR.WARREN'S OLD QUAKER,RECTANGULAR,AQUA.............    25.00
BITTERS,DR.WARREN'S QUAKER.................................     25.00
  BITTERS, DRAKE'S PLANTATION, SEE ALSO BITTERS, CABIN
BITTERS,DRAKE'S PLANTATION..........................COLOR..     XX.XX
BITTERS,DRAKE'S PLANTATION BITTERS.................. 35.00 TO   45.00
BITTERS,DRAKE'S PLANTATION X,AMBER.........................    40.00
BITTERS,DRAKE'S PLANTATION 1860,AMBER...............ILLUS..     35.00
BITTERS,DRAKE'S PLANTATION,CITRON YELLOW...................     61.00
BITTERS,DRAKE'S PLANTATION,FOUR LEG........................    35.00
BITTERS,DRAKE'S PLANTATION,4 LOG,AMBER.....................    42.00
BITTERS,DRAKE'S PLANTATION,5 LOG.................... 38.00 TO   95.00
BITTERS,DRAKE'S PLANTATION,6 LOG...........................    35.00
BITTERS,DRAKE'S PLANTATION,6 LOG,AMBER.....................    40.00
BITTERS,DRAKE'S PLANTATION,6 LOG,X BITTERS.................     45.00
BITTERS,DRAKE'S 1860 PLANTATION X-3,STEP ROOF,AMBER........     50.00
BITTERS,DRAKE'S 1860 PLANTATION,6 LOGS,PAT.1862,CITRON......    50.00
BITTERS,DRAKE'S 1860 PLANTATION,6 LOGS,PAT.1862,GREEN.......    50.00
BITTERS,DRAKE'S 1860 PLANTATION,6 LOGS,PAT.1862,OLIVE GREEN.    50.00
BITTERS,DRAKES PLANTATION,AMBER,LABEL......................    40.00
```

BITTERS,DR.LION'S STOMACH,
AMBER,10 IN.,LABEL

BITTERS,DRAKE'S PLANTATION
1860,AMBER

```
BITTERS,DRAKES 1860 PLANTATION X,AMBER.............. 27.50 TO     40.00
BITTERS,DRAKES 1860 PLANTATION X,GREEN.......................     6.00
BITTERS,DUG ABBOTS,AMBER.....................................     2.75
BITTERS,E.E.HALL'S................................... 85.00 TO   105.00
BITTERS,E.J.ROSE'S MAGADOR...................................    60.00
BITTERS,E.BAKER'S PREMIUM 6 STAR,AQUA........................    65.00
BITTERS,E.BAKER'S PREMIUM,EMBOSSED,CLEAR.....................    65.00
BITTERS,EAGLE ANGOSTURA......................................    45.00
BITTERS,EAGLE ANGOSTURA BARK,EAGLE LIQUOR DISTILLERIES,AMBER     55.00
BITTERS,EAST INDIA,OMAHA,NEB.................................    50.00
BITTERS,ELECTRIC BRAND............................... 20.00 TO   21.00
BITTERS,ELECTRIC BRAND LAXATIVE,AMBER........................     5.00
BITTERS,ELECTRIC BRAND,AMBER......................... 18.00 TO   30.00
BITTERS,ELECTRIC BRAND,EMBOSSED..............................    16.00
BITTERS,ELECTRIC BRAND,QUART,AMBER...........................    18.00
BITTERS,ELECTRIC BRAND,H.E.BUCKLEN & CO.,CHICAGO,ILL.,AMBER.     20.00
BITTERS,ELECTRIC BRAND,LABELS................................    15.00
BITTERS,ELECTRIC BRAND,MACHINE MADE,AMBER....................    14.00
BITTERS,EMERSON EXCELSIOR BOTANIC,BY E.H.BURNS,AUGUSTA,MAINE     12.00
BITTERS,ERNST L.ARP & KIEL,BLUE...................... 25.00 TO   30.00
BITTERS,EXCELSIOR...........................................    105.00
BITTERS,FENNER'S CAPITAL,LABEL,AQUA..........................    25.00
BITTERS,FER-KINA GALENO,BEER TYPE,MACHINE MADE,BROWN........    16.00
BITTERS,FERRO-CHINA BISLERI,MILANO,WHITTLE MOLD,OLIVE.......    15.00
BITTERS,FERRO-CHINA-BISLERI,FULL,LABEL,GREEN................    12.00
BITTERS,FERRO-CHINA-BISLERI,WHITTLED,GREEN..................    22.50
BITTERS,FERRO-CHINA-VESUVIO,AMBER...........................    12.50
BITTERS,FERRO-CHINA,TIGER STAMP.............................    10.00
BITTERS,FISH...........................................COLOR..    XX.XX
BITTERS,FISH,AMBER...............................140.00 TO      180.00
BITTERS,FISH,GOLDEN AMBER...................................   175.00
BITTERS,FISH,REDDISH AMBER..................................   160.00
BITTERS,FISH,VARIANT........................................   125.00
BITTERS,FISH,W.H.WARE PAT.1866,AMBER........................    85.00
BITTERS,FLINT'S QUAKER,QUART,AQUA...........................    25.00
BITTERS,FLORA TEMPLE,PINT,AMBER.............................   175.00
BITTERS,FORESTINE BLOOD BITTERS,WAX-SEALED,PAPER LABEL......   125.00
BITTERS,GARRY OWEN,STRENGTHENING,AMBER......................    50.00
BITTERS,GENUINE BULL WILD CHERRY............................   110.00
BITTERS,GERMAN HOP BITTERS,1872,AMBER.......................    25.00
BITTERS,GERMAN HOP,EMBOSSED.................................    55.00
BITTERS,GLOBE TONIC,AMBER...................................    65.00
BITTERS,GOFF'S HERB BITTERS,BIMAL,AQUA......................     7.00
BITTERS,GOFF'S HERB,EMBOSSED,AQUA...........................     7.50
BITTERS,GRANDFATHER'S STOMACH BITTERS,GAL...................     3.00
BITTERS,GRANDFATHER'S STOMACH BITTERS,QUART.................      .75
BITTERS,GREAT WESTERN TONIC,AMBER...........................    96.00
BITTERS,GREELEY'S BOURBON,AMBER.............................   150.00
BITTERS,GREELEY'S BOURBON,PUCE...................145.00 TO      150.00
BITTERS,GREELEYS BURBONE,BARREL,PUCE........................   165.00
BITTERS,GREELY'S BOURBON,BARREL,PUCE........................   160.00
BITTERS,GREER'S ECLIPSE,AMBER........................ 65.00 TO  115.00
BITTERS,H.E.BUCKNER & CO. ELECTRIC BITTERS,AMBER............    18.00
BITTERS,HALL'S,BARREL,AMBER.................................    95.00
BITTERS,HALL'S,BARREL,LIGHT AMBER...........................    65.00
BITTERS,HALL'S,E.E.HALL,ORANGE AMBER........................    60.00
BITTERS,HALL'S,ESTABLISHED 1842,CITRON......................   700.00
BITTERS,HALLS,BARREL,AMBER..................................   120.00
BITTERS,HARTWIG KANTOROWICZ,HORSESHOE,POSEN,HAM,MILK GLASS..    71.00
BITTERS,HARTWIG KANTOROWICZ,MILK GLASS,BACKWARDS Z..........    65.00
BITTERS,HARTWIG'S CELEBRATED ALPINE.........................   150.00
BITTERS,HARTWIG'S CELEBRATED ALPINE,GOLD AMBER..............   135.00
BITTERS,HARTWIG'S PARIS,MILK GLASS..........................    95.00
BITTERS,HENRY'S MT.CIDER,GREEN..............................   175.00
BITTERS,HESPEREDIAN BAGLEY,BARREL,AMBER.....................    50.00
```

```
BITTERS,HI HI,AMBER.................................. 85.00 TO    .
BITTERS,HIGHLAND BITTERS & SCOTCH TONIC,GREEN...............   750.00
BITTERS,HIGHLAND,BARREL,DARK AMBER..........................   295.00
BITTERS,HILL'S HOREHOUND IRISH MOSS,CLEAR...........ILLUS..      6.00
BITTERS,HOLTZERMANN'S PATENT STOMACH,AMBER........125.00 TO    140.00
BITTERS,HOME,A.JACKSON & CO.,PROPRIETORS...................    150.00
BITTERS,HORSESHOE,WILLIAMSBURG CLAY................. 1.00        2.75
   BITTERS, HOSTETTER, SEE BITTERS, DR.J.HOSTETTER
BITTERS,HUA-UNDERBERG, 12 1/2 IN............................    35.00
BITTERS,HUNYADI JANOS SACLEHNER BITTERQUELLE,WHITTLE MOLD...     6.00
BITTERS,IMPERIAL,KIDNEY,LIVER,NERVE,BLOOD & STOMACH,AMBER...    60.00
BITTERS,INDIAN RESTORATIVE..................................    35.00
BITTERS,INDIAN RESTORATIVE,EMBOSSED.........................    25.00
BITTERS,INDIAN SAGWA.......................................      7.00
BITTERS,IRON BITTERS,EMBOSSED..............................     27.00
BITTERS,ITALIAN,QUART,AQUA.................................     15.00
BITTERS,J.A.GILKA,RED AMBER....................... 15.00 TO     20.00
BITTERS,JAUNDICE,NEW ENGLAND...............................      5.00
BITTERS,JEWETTS,WHITTLED,OPEN PONTIL,AQUA..................     70.00
BITTERS,JOHN BULL CEDRON,AMBER.............................    200.00
BITTERS,JOHN WYETH'S & BROS.,PHILADELPHIA,FULL,EMBOSSED.....    20.00
BITTERS,KAISER WHLHELM,AMBER...............................    125.00
BITTERS,KAISER WHLHELM,CLEAR TURNING PURPLE................     76.00
BITTERS,KELLY'S CABIN,1870,AMBER...........................    350.00
BITTERS,KELLY'S OLD CABIN,AMBER............................    400.00
BITTERS,KELLY'S OLD CABIN,1863,AMBER...............ILLUS..     400.00
BITTERS,KENNEDYS EAST INDIA,CLEAR..........................     22.00
BITTERS,KILMER'S AUTUMN LEAF EXTRACT,LABEL & BOX...........     11.00
BITTERS,KIMBALL'S JAUNDICE,OLIVE AMBER.....................    250.00
BITTERS,KING SOLOMON'S,AMBER...................... 90.00 TO    110.00
BITTERS,KING'S,25 CENT,AQUA................................     55.00
BITTERS,L.ROSE & CO.,EMBOSSED ROSES,AQUA...................     10.00
BITTERS,LACOUR'S,AMBER.....................................    200.00
BITTERS,LACOURS,LIGHT APPLE GREEN..........................    500.00
BITTERS,LACOURS,YELLOW GREEN...............................    550.00
BITTERS,LADY LEG,REED'S,AMBER..............................     60.00
BITTERS,LADY'S LEG,DUG AT FT.STAMBAUGH.....................     55.00
BITTERS,LADY'S LEG,GREEN.......................... 40.00 TO     75.00
BITTERS,LADY'S LEG,IRON PONTIL,GREEN.......................    150.00
BITTERS,LADY'S LEG,MILLS,EMBOSSED,A.M.GILMAS SOLE PROPRIETOR   200.00
```

BITTERS,HILL'S HOREHOUND
IRISH MOSS,CLEAR

BITTERS,KELLY'S OLD CABIN,
1863,AMBER

```
BITTERS,LADY'S LEG,PLAIN,ROUND,AMBER........................      45.00
BITTERS,LASH'S ABM,AMBER....................................       4.00
BITTERS,LASH'S BITTERS CO.,CLEAR............................       4.95
BITTERS,LASH'S KIDNEY & LIVER,AMBER................. 12.00 TO     40.00
BITTERS,LASH'S,AMBER............................... 11.00 TO     20.00
BITTERS,LASH'S,CONTENTS,SEAL & LABELS INTACT,AMBER..........      20.00
BITTERS,LASH'S,FULL,LABEL...................................      10.00
BITTERS,LASH'S,N.Y.,ROUND,AMBER.............................      10.00
BITTERS,LASH'S,N.Y.,ROUND,AMETHYST..........................      10.00
BITTERS,LASH'S,N.Y.,ROUND,CLEAR.............................      10.00
BITTERS,LASH'S,NATURAL TONIC LAXATIVE,AMBER.................      12.00
BITTERS,LASH'S,ROUND,CORDOL BUTTER,AMBER....................       8.00
BITTERS,LASH'S,ROUND,CORDOL BUTTER,AMETHYST.................       8.00
BITTERS,LASH'S,ROUND,CORDOL BUTTER,CLEAR....................       8.00
BITTERS,LASH'S,SAN FRANCISCO,ROUND,AMBER....................      18.00
BITTERS,LASHE'S BITTERS CO.,HILLS IRISH MOSS,CLEAR..........      12.50
BITTERS,LASHER'S BITTER,CLEAR...............................       4.00
BITTERS,LEAK'S KIDNEY & LIVER,AMBER.........................      61.00
BITTERS,LEIPZIGER BURGUNDER WEIN............................      25.00
BITTERS,LEOTRIC,PINT,GHOST LETTERS,TRADEMARK................      17.00
BITTERS,LEVOK'S STOMACH,AMBER...............................      75.00
BITTERS,LIPPMAN'S GERMAN,REVERSE N.Y. & SAVANNAH,GA.,AMBER..      41.00
BITTERS,LITTHAUER STOMACH,MILK GLASS...............125.00 TO    136.00
BITTERS,MALT BITTERS CO.,AMBER..................... 35.00 TO     45.00
  BITTERS, MANDRAKE, SEE BITTERS, DR.BAXTER
BITTERS,MARSHALL'S,AMBER....................................      45.00
BITTERS,MC KEEVER'S ARMY,CIVIL WAR DRUM SHAPE,AMBER.........     475.00
BITTERS,MISHLER'S HERB,AMBER................................      32.50
BITTERS,MIST OF THE MORNING.................................     225.00
BITTERS,MORNING STAR,TAPERED,AMBER..................150.00 TO    200.00
BITTERS,MOULTONS OLOROSA,TRADE MARK,AQUA....................     175.00
BITTERS,MOUNTAIN HERB & ROOT................................      15.00
BITTERS,MULLER'S GENUINE BISMARCK,AMBER.....................      75.00
BITTERS,NATIONAL,EAR OF CORN,DATED 1857,AMBER...............     230.00
BITTERS,NATIONAL,EAR OF CORN,OLIVE YELLOW...................     300.00
BITTERS,NIGHTCAP,TRIANGULAR,LIGHT AMETHYST..................      75.00
BITTERS,O'LEARYS............................................      90.00
BITTERS,OLD DR.TOWNSENDS CELEBRATED STOMACH,JUG,AMBER.......      75.00
BITTERS,OLD HOMESTEAD WILD CHERRY,GOLDEN AMBER..............     166.00
BITTERS,OLD HOMESTEAD,CABIN,AMBER...........................     100.00
BITTERS,OLD JERSEY..........................................       2.75
BITTERS,OLD SACHEM BITTERS & WIGWAM TONIC...........165.00 TO    175.00
BITTERS,OLD SACHEM,BARREL,AMBER.............................     100.00
BITTERS,OLD SACHEM,RED AMBER................................     165.00
BITTERS,OLD SACHEM,YELLOW...................................     165.00
BITTERS,OLD TIMES STOMACH,WITH PEPSIN,GAL...................       4.00
BITTERS,ORANGE,CROCK,LABEL..................................      30.00
BITTERS,OSWEGO,25 CENT,AMBER................................      65.00
BITTERS,OX BLOOD,SQUARE,CORK................................      29.00
BITTERS,OX BLOOD,SQUARE,CORK,CONTENTS.......................      29.00
BITTERS,OXYGENATED,AQUA,8 IN........................ILLUS..      50.00
BITTERS,OXYGENATED,OPEN PONTIL..............................      50.00
BITTERS,PAINE'S CELERY COMPOUND,AMBER............... 3.50 TO      9.00
BITTERS,PAINE'S CELERY COMPOUND,CLEAR.......................      12.00
BITTERS,PENNS FOR THE LIVER,SQUARE,BEVELED EDGE,AMBER.......      40.00
BITTERS,PEPSIN CALISAYA,DR.RUSSELL MED.CO.,RECTANGULAR,GREEN      20.00
BITTERS,PEPSIN CALISAYA,EMERALD GREEN.............. 48.00 TO     65.00
BITTERS,PEPSIN,R.W.DAVIS DRUG CO.,GREEN............. 65.00 TO     95.00
BITTERS,PERRINE'S,APPLE.....................................      95.00
BITTERS,PERUVIAN,AMBER............................. 25.00 TO     30.00
BITTERS,PHOENIX,OLIVE GREEN.................................     225.00
BITTERS,PINEAPPLE,AMBER.....................................     150.00
BITTERS,PINEAPPLE,BAR DESPENSER,BLOWN IN MOLD,AMBER.........     140.00
BITTERS,PLOW'S SHERRY,EMBOSSED,AMBER........................     370.00
BITTERS,POLO CLUB STOMACH...................................      46.00
```

BITTERS,OXYGENATED,AQUA,8 IN

```
BITTERS,POND'S EXTRACT,1846................................    6.00
BITTERS,POND'S KIDNEY & LIVER.............................   15.00
BITTERS,POND'S,LABEL......................................   35.00
BITTERS,POND'S,SQUARE,AMBER...............................   20.00
BITTERS,POOR MAN'S FAMILY,AQUA.................... 15.00 TO   45.00
BITTERS,PRICKLEY ASH BITTERS CO.,AMBER............ 29.00 TO   45.00
BITTERS,PRICKLEY ASH CO.,BEVELED CORNERS..................   35.00
BITTERS,PRICKLEY ASH CO.,MACHINE MADE,BEVELED CORNERS.....   12.00
BITTERS,PURDY'S COTTAGE,OPALESCENCE.......................   75.00
BITTERS,PURDY'S COTTAGE,YELLOW AMBER......................  175.00
   BITTERS, QUAKER, SEE BITTERS, DR.FLINT
BITTERS,RAMSEY'S TRINIDAD,BITTERS ON BOTTOM...............   75.00
BITTERS,RAMSEY'S TRINIDAD,ROUND,OLIVE.....................   45.00
BITTERS,READS AMERICAN,PIG SHAPE,AMBER....................    8.00
BITTERS,RED JACKET,BENNET & PIETERS,AMBER.................   42.50
BITTERS,RED JACKET,MONHEIMER & CO.,AMBER..................   52.50
   BITTERS, REED'S, SEE ALSO BITTERS, LADY LEG
BITTERS,REED'S 1870,GILT EDGE,TONIC BITTERS...............   30.00
BITTERS,REX BITTERS COMPANY,ROUND,AMBER,EMBOSSED..........   25.00
BITTERS,REX KIDNEY & LIVER BITTERS,AMBER..................   10.00
BITTERS,REX KIDNEY & LIVER,AMBER,EMBOSSED.................   25.00
BITTERS,REX KIDNEY & LIVER,CONTENTS,LABEL.................   45.00
BITTERS,ROBACK'S,BARREL...................................  125.00
BITTERS,ROBACK'S,C.W.,DR.,STOMACH,BARREL SHAPE,20 RIBS,BROWN 30.00
BITTERS,ROEHLING & SHULTZ,AMBER................... 35.00 TO   50.00
BITTERS,ROHER'S...........................................  135.00
BITTERS,ROTTERDAM,AVAN HOBOKEN,GREEN......................   40.00
BITTERS,ROYAL PEPSIN STOMACH,STOPPER,AMBER........ 70.00 TO   90.00
BITTERS,ROYAL PEPSIN STOMACH,99 PERCENT LABEL.............   45.00
BITTERS,ROYAL PEPSIN,ACID BATHED..........................   51.00
BITTERS,RUSH'S BUCHU & IRON,A.H.FLANDERS,M.D.,N.Y.,PINT,AQUA 15.00
BITTERS,RUSH'S,AMBER.............................. 28.50 TO   30.00
BITTERS,RUSS' ST.DOMINGO..................................   70.00
BITTERS,S.B.GOFF'S,HERB BITTERS,AQUA......................   10.00
BITTERS,S.O.RICHARDSON'S..................................   30.00
   BITTERS, S.T.DRAKE'S, SEE BITTERS, DRAKE'S
BITTERS,SALMON'S PERFECT STOMACH BITTERS..................   65.00
BITTERS,SANBORN'S KIDNEY & LIVER VEGETABLE LAXATIVE.......   70.00
BITTERS,SARASINA STOMACH,SIX STAR,AMBER...................  110.00
BITTERS,SAXLEHNER BITTERQUELLE............................   10.50
BITTERS,SAXLEHNER'S BITTERQUELLE,GREEN............. 5.00 TO    7.00
BITTERS,SAXLEHNER'S BITTERQUELLE,HUNYAD,JANOS,CIRCA 1900,
   GREEN..................................................    5.00
BITTERS,SAZERAC AROMATIC,LADY'S LEG,1/2 SIZE,AMBER........  375.00
BITTERS,SCHIEDAM VOLKNER'S AROMATIC SCHNAPP....... 25.00 TO   35.00
BITTERS,SCHROEDERS,EMBOSSED VERTICALLY............125.00 TO  150.00
BITTERS,SEIBERTS CORONA,LABEL.............................   20.00
```

```
BITTERS,SHILOH'S CURE,SAMPLE.................................    4.00
BITTERS,SIMMON'S CENTENNIAL BITTERS,GEORGE WASHINGTON.......    2.75
BITTERS,SOL FRANCK'S,LIGHTHOUSE SHAPE,EMBOSSED,AMBER........  350.00
BITTERS,SOLOMON'S STRENGTHENING & INVIGORATING,COBALT.......   86.00
BITTERS,SOLOMON'S STRENGTHENING & INVIGORATING,COBALT.......  150.00
BITTERS,ST.DOMINGO,AMBER...................................   56.00
BITTERS,STEWART'S TONIC....................................   31.00
BITTERS,SUFFOLK,AMERICA'S LIFE PRESERVER,PIG...............    3.50
BITTERS,SUFFOLK,PIG SHAPE........................... 2.75 TO    7.50
BITTERS,SUFFOLK'S,PIG,AMBER................................  135.00
BITTERS,TIPPECANOE,LOG WITH CANOE..........................   75.00
BITTERS,TIPPECANOE,LOG,CANOE,OLIVE AMBER............ILLUS..   75.00
BITTERS,TO-NI-TA MUCOUS MEMBRANE,EMBOSSED..................   15.00
BITTERS,TONECO STOMACH.......................... 21.00 TO   23.00
BITTERS,TONIC,LABEL,CONTENTS,EMBOSSED......................   25.00
BITTERS,TRINER'S BITTER WINE,AMBER.........................    2.00
BITTERS,TURNER BROTHERS,BARREL,PUCE........................  175.00
BITTERS,UDOLPHO WOLFE'S AROMATIC SCHNAPPS..................   15.00
BITTERS,UDOLPHO WOLFE'S AROMATIC SCHNAPPS,AMBER............   28.00
BITTERS,UDOLPHO WOLFE'S SCHIEDAM AROMATIC SCHNAPPS,GREEN....   10.00
BITTERS,UNDERBERG ALBRECHT,LABEL...........................   25.00
BITTERS,UNDERBERG,HUA BASE,AMBER...........................   35.00
BITTERS,UNDERBERG,HUA ON BASE,12 IN.,RED AMBER.............   45.00
BITTERS,UNICUM,LABELS,BUDAPEST,GREEN.......................    6.50
BITTERS,VEGETABLE..........................................   85.00
BITTERS,VERMO STOMACH,SQUARE,CLEAR.........................   22.50
BITTERS,VERNE..............................................   50.00
BITTERS,W.F.SEVERA,TWO LABELS,EMBOSSED.....................   40.00
BITTERS,WA-HOO,C.1930,CLEAR,8 1/2 IN.,LABEL.........ILLUS..    3.50
BITTERS,WAHOO & CALISAYA BITTERS,J.PINKERTON'S,AMBER.......   35.00
BITTERS,WAHOO BITTERS,FLYING EAGLE FACES RIGHT,1 ARROW,AMBER   81.00
BITTERS,WAHOO,LABEL & CONTENTS.............................   23.00
BITTERS,WALKER'S V.B.,AQUA......................... 4.00 TO    9.00
BITTERS,WALKER'S VINEGAR BITTERS,AQUA......................    8.00
BITTERS,WALLACE'S TONIC,STOMACH............................   56.00
BITTERS,WARES FISCH........................................  150.00
BITTERS,WARNER'S KIDNEY & LIVER CURE,DOUBLE COLLAR,AMBER....   18.00
BITTERS,WARNER'S SAFE CURE..........................COLOR..   XX.XX
BITTERS,WARNER'S SAFE CURE,LONDON,TORONTO & ROCHESTER.......   35.00
BITTERS,WARNER'S SAFE CURE,9 1/2 IN.,LONDON,ENGLAND.........   21.00
BITTERS,WARNER'S SAFE TONIC BITTERS,AMBER..................  200.00
```

BITTERS,TIPPECANOE,
LOG,CANOE,OLIVE AMBER

BITTERS,WA-HOO,C.1930,
CLEAR,8 1/2 IN.,LABEL

```
BITTERS,WARNER'S SAFE,AMBER.......................................    10.00
BITTERS,WARNER'S TIPPECANOE,AMBER.................................    70.00
BITTERS,WARNER'S,OVAL,AMBER.......................................    40.00
BITTERS,WARNERS SAFE KIDNEY & LIVER CURE,LEFT HINGE..........       60.00
BITTERS,WATSON'S FISH.............................................   175.00
BITTERS,WEBB'S,LABEL..............................................    76.00
BITTERS,WEST INDIA................................................   120.00
BITTERS,WEST INDIA,AMBER......................... 60.00 TO          65.00
BITTERS,WILLARD'S GOLDEN SEAL,AQUA................................    60.00
BITTERS,WILLIAM ALLEN'S CONGRESS,IMPRESSED PANELS,AQUA,
   10 1/4 IN......................................................   120.00
BITTERS,WORMSER BROS.,SAN FRANCISCO,BARREL,AMBER.............       500.00
BITTERS,YERBA BUENA,AMBER........................ 60.00 TO          70.00
BITTERS,ZINGARI...................................................    65.00
BITTERS,ZOELLER'S STOMACH,ROUNDED CORNER,AMBER..............        50.00
BLACK & WHITE SCOTCH,SCOTTY,BLACK.....................COLOR..        30.00
BLACK & WHITE SCOTCH,SCOTTY,WHITE.....................COLOR..        30.00
BLACK BAR WHISKEY,INVERTED HOBNAILS,PONTIL,BLUE.............        45.00
BLACK GLASS,APPLIED SEAL,EMBOSSED A.S.C.R.,CIRCA 1790,QUART.        59.00
BLOB,GREEN........................................................     2.50
BLOUNT SPRINGS,NATURAL SULFUR,S OVER B TRADEMARK,BLUE.......        24.00
BLOWN IN MOLD,AQUA................................................     1.50
BLOWN IN MOLD,GREEN...............................................    15.00
BLOWN IN MOLD,WHITTLE,AQUA........................................     2.00
BLOWN MOLD,PONTIL,TWELVE PANEL....................................     5.00
BLOWN,CARPENTER & WOOD,INC.,EST.1883,CLEAR.................         1.00
BLOWN,ENGRAVED,ENGLISH,C.1820,APPLIED DECORATION.....ILLUS..        20.00
BLOWN,PONTIL,LIP FOLD OVER,AQUA,C.1860...............ILLUS..        15.00
BLUE BOTTLE EXTRACTS,RECTANGULAR,COBALT....................         6.00
```

```
       BORGHINI CERAMIC CONTAINERS ARE FILLED IN PISA, ITALY.
       THE MORE RECENT IMPORTS ARE STAMPED WITH THE WORDS
       'BORGHINI COLLECTION MADE IN ITALY, 1969.'
BORGHINI,ALPINE HOUSE.............................................     4.00
BORGHINI,CAT,BLACK................................................     7.00
BORGHINI,CLOWN WITH MANDOLIN......................................    26.00
BORGHINI,DOG......................................................    26.00
BORGHINI,FORD.................................... 3.00 TO           9.00
BORGHINI,HORSE'S HEAD.............................................    26.00
```

BLOWN,ENGRAVED,ENGLISH,
C.1820,APPLIED DECORATION

BLOWN,PONTIL,LIP FOLD
OVER,AQUA,C.1860

BORGHINI,MERCEDES-BENZ............................. 3.00 TO   4.00
BORGHINI,NUBIAN GIRL............................... 4.00 TO   7.00
BORGHINI,SANTA MARIA.......................................   4.00
BRANDY,ALCOHOL ON LABEL,SQUARE,CLEAR.......................   4.00
BRANDY,AMETHYST,9 1/4 IN...................................   6.00
BRANDY,AMIDON'S UNION,GINGE BRANDY REG.,AMETHYST...........   8.00
BRANDY,AMIDON'S UNION,GINGE BRANDY REG.,CLEAR.............   8.00
BRANDY,APPLE,GAL...   3.60
BRANDY,APPLE,QUART...   .90
BRANDY,BINNINGER,HANDLED PEACH JUG......................... 196.00
BRANDY,BLACKBERRY,GAL......................................   2.00
BRANDY,BLOWN IN MOLD,BALL NECK,AMBER.......................   3.00
BRANDY,BLOWN IN MOLD,11 1/4 IN. TALL,AMBER.................   2.50
BRANDY,CALIFORNIA ORANGE,GAL...............................   4.00
BRANDY,CHERRY BOUNCE,10 YEARS OLD,GAL......................   4.00
BRANDY,CHICAGO FANCY BOTTLER,11 3/4 IN. TALL,AMETHYST......   8.00
BRANDY,CHICAGO FANCY BOTTLER,11 3/4 IN. TALL,CLEAR.........   8.00
BRANDY,CHICAGO FANCY BOTTLER,11 3/4 IN. TALL,RUBY RED......   10.00
BRANDY,CLEAR...................................... 5.00 TO   6.00
BRANDY,COGNAC BRANDY,XX,IMPORTED,GAL.......................   4.00
BRANDY,COGNAC BRANDY,XXX,IMPORTED,GAL......................   5.00
BRANDY,COGNAC,CALIFORNIA,GAL...............................   3.60
BRANDY,COGNAC,CALIFORNIA,QUART.............................   .90
BRANDY,CRESCENT ON SHOULDER,AMBER..........................   6.00
BRANDY,DALLEMAND & CO. INC.,CHICAGO,BLOB NECK,AMBER........   6.00
BRANDY,FROSTED CHERUBS HOLDING CLEAR GLOBE,PONTIL,DESPOSE,
   SIGNED...   35.00
BRANDY,GRAPE,CALIFORNIA,GAL................................   3.60
BRANDY,GRAPE,CALIFORNIA,QUART..............................   .90
BRANDY,GREEN...................................... 3.00 TO   4.00
BRANDY,HOMER'S CALIFORNIA GINGER,AMBER............. 8.00 TO   10.00
BRANDY,IMPORTED COGNAC,GAL.................................   5.00
BRANDY,IMPORTED COGNAC,QUART...............................   1.25
BRANDY,JUICE OF BLACKBERRIES & BRANDY,GAL..................   3.00
BRANDY,JUICE OF BLACKBERRIES & BRANDY,QUART................   .75
BRANDY,KENTUCKY APPLE JACK,GAL.............................   3.50
BRANDY,OLD TIMES BLACKBERRY JUICE,10 YEARS OLD,GAL.........   3.00
BRANDY,PEACH BRANDY,GAL....................................   3.60
BRANDY,PEACH,QUART...   .90
BRANDY,PLAIN,AMBER,8 1/2 IN................................   4.00
BRANDY,PLAIN,AMBER,9 1/4 IN................................   4.00
BRANDY,PLAIN,BEER TYPE,AMBER,8 1/2 IN......................   4.00
BRANDY,PLAIN,BEER TYPE,BLOB NECK,OLIVE GREEN,9 3/4 IN......   4.00
BRANDY,PLAIN,BLOB NECK,RED AMBER,10 1/2 IN.................   5.00
BRANDY,PLAIN,CRESCENT,GREEN,11 1/2 IN......................   3.00
BRANDY,PLAIN,CRESCENT,ROUND,AMETHYST,11 5/8 IN.............   3.00
BRANDY,PLAIN,CRESCENT,ROUND,AMETHYST,12 IN.................   3.00
BRANDY,PLAIN,CRESCENT,ROUND,CLEAR,11 5/8 IN................   3.00
BRANDY,PLAIN,CRESCENT,ROUND,CLEAR,12 IN....................   3.00
BRANDY,PLAIN,OLIVE,11 1/2 IN...............................   4.00
BRANDY,PLAIN,OLIVE,12 IN...................................   4.00
BRANDY,PLAIN,ROUND,LADY LEG,OLIVE GREEN,11 1/2 IN..........   4.00
BRANDY,PLAIN,ROUND,LADY LEG,OLIVE GREEN,12 IN..............   4.00
BRANDY,PLAIN,ROUND,SHORT NECK,AMBER,11 1/2 IN..............   4.00
BRANDY,PLAIN,SQUARE,AMBER..................................   4.00
BRANDY,PLAIN,SQUARE,AMETHYST,9 1/4 IN......................   6.00
BRANDY,PLAIN,SQUARE,CLEAR,9 1/4 IN.........................   6.00
BRANDY,SQUARE,CRESCENT,AMBER,10 IN.........................   6.00
BRANDY,TENNESSEE PEACH,GAL.................................   3.00
BRANDY,TURN MOLD,OLIVE AMBER,12 IN.........................   3.00
BRANTS INDIAN PULMONARY BALSAM,PONTIL......................   3.00
BRISTOL'S EXTRACT OF SARSAPARILLA,OPEN PONTIL..............   34.00
BRISTOL'S SARSAPARILLA.....................................   14.00
BRIZARD,KIOSK..   4.95
   BROOKS,SEE EZRA BROOKS

BRUNI,TURTLE..   17.95
BRUNI,TWO HEADED DUCK.......................................   17.95
BUDWINE..   2.00
BUFFALO LITHIA WATER.......................................   5.00
BUREAU,PRESSED,DIAMOND,4 MEDALLIONS,HAND PAINTED,PAIR.......   30.00
C.H.MAYER & CO.,HAMMOND,IND.,WHITE PORCELAIN TOP,AMBER,8 IN.   10.00
C.W.BRINKERHOFF'S,OLIVE GREEN...............................   110.00
C.HEIMSTREET & CO.,COBALT...................................   12.00
CABIN SHAPE,AMBER..   3.50
    CABIN STILL, SEE OLD FITZGERALD
CALABASH,HUNTER & FISHERMAN.................................   45.00
CALABASH,MC KEARIN G I-35,AQUA..............................   25.00
CALABASH,MC KEARIN G I-112,US STEAM FRIGATE MISSISSIPPI,
    GREEN..   330.00
CALABASH,SHEAF OF RYE REVERSE TREE,AQUA.....................   65.00
CALFIG SYRUP OF FIGS.......................................   3.00
CAMEL SADDLE,HAND-BLOWN....................................   30.00
CAMERON SCOTCH,BARREL......................................   14.95
CAMPHOR,COLOGNE,PANSIES,BRASS CHAIN FOR HOLDER..............   16.00
CANADA DRY,CARNIVAL GLASS,MARIGOLD..........................   12.00
CANADIAN MIST,MOUNTY.............................. 12.95 TO   14.95

        CANDY CONTAINERS OF GLASS WERE VERY POPULAR AFTER
        WORLD WAR I. SMALL GLASS FIGURAL BOTTLES HELD
        DIME-STORE CANDY. TODAY MANY OF THE SAME SHAPES HOLD
        MODERN CANDY IN PLASTIC BOTTLES.
CANDY CONTAINER,AIRPLANE....................................   5.00
CANDY CONTAINER,AIRPLANE,TIN WINGS,ORIGINAL CANDY...........   18.50
CANDY CONTAINER,ARMY HAT,EAGLE ON FRONT,AMBER...............   15.00
CANDY CONTAINER,ARMY TANK,CANDY............................   4.50
CANDY CONTAINER,AUTO,ELECTRIC COUPE,PAT.FEB,18,1913,EMBOSSED   35.00
CANDY CONTAINER,BATTLESHIP,CONTENTS,CARDBOARD BOTTOM........   12.50
CANDY CONTAINER,BOOT,SANTA CLAUS,MERRY CHRISTMAS............   15.00
CANDY CONTAINER,BUCKET,HANDLE..............................   7.50
CANDY CONTAINER,BULLDOG,ON ROUND BASE,PAINTED,4 1/4 IN......   16.00
CANDY CONTAINER,BULLDOG,STANDING ON ROUND BASE,PAINT,
    4 1/2 IN...   18.00
CANDY CONTAINER,BUS..   8.50
CANDY CONTAINER,CAP,MILITARY STYLE,1942....................   10.00
CANDY CONTAINER,CHICKEN....................................   12.50
CANDY CONTAINER,CHICKEN ON SAGGING BASKET..................   15.00
CANDY CONTAINER,CLUCK,ALARM,PEWTER CLOSURE.................   25.00
CANDY CONTAINER,CLOCK,TIN BOTTOM,GILT,MILK GLASS,SOUVENIR...   12.00
CANDY CONTAINER,DOG,CROSSETT...............................   2.50
CANDY CONTAINER,DOG,ORIGINAL CANDY.........................   7.50
CANDY CONTAINER,DONKEY & CART..............................   10.00
CANDY CONTAINER,DONKEY PULLING BARREL......................   24.00
CANDY CONTAINER,ELECTRIC IRON WITH CORD....................   7.50
CANDY CONTAINER,ENGINE.............................ILLUS..   2.50
CANDY CONTAINER,FIRE ENGINE...................... 5.50 TO   12.00
CANDY CONTAINER,FIRE ENGINE,CLEAR..........................   6.00
CANDY CONTAINER,FIRE ENGINE,METAL BASE.....................   8.50
CANDY CONTAINER,FIRE ENGINE,TIN WHEELS,CLOSURE.............   14.50
CANDY CONTAINER,FISH,EMBOSSED FEATURES,CLEAR,8 1/2 X
    2 1/2 IN...   18.00
CANDY CONTAINER,FLASK,U.S.ON SIDE..........................   8.00
CANDY CONTAINER,GUN.................................ILLUS..   3.50
CANDY CONTAINER,GUN,4 IN...................................   5.50
CANDY CONTAINER,HEARSE,NO.2................................   35.00
CANDY CONTAINER,HEN ON NEST...................... 5.00 TO   7.50
CANDY CONTAINER,HEN ON NEST,NO CLOSURE.....................   7.00
CANDY CONTAINER,HORSE & CART..................... 8.00 TO   12.00
CANDY CONTAINER,HOUND PUPPY,STIPPLED HAT...................   6.00

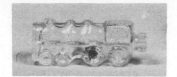

CANDY CONTAINER, ENGINE

CANDY CONTAINER, GUN

CANDY CONTAINER, JEEP.................................. 5.00 TO	9.50
CANDY CONTAINER, LADY'S LEG, FROSTED STOCKING, RED GARTER......	13.00
CANDY CONTAINER, LAMP, GLASS, RED CHIMNEY......................	4.00
CANDY CONTAINER, LANTERN.............................. 5.00 TO	5.50
CANDY CONTAINER, LANTERN, BARN TYPE...........................	25.00
CANDY CONTAINER, LANTERN, ELECTRIC, BOND......................	15.00
CANDY CONTAINER, LANTERN, GREEN GLASS, METAL..................	7.50
CANDY CONTAINER, LIBERTY BELL, BLUE, TIN CLOSURE..............	20.00
CANDY CONTAINER, LIBERTY BELL, 3 1/4 IN. HIGH.................	8.75
CANDY CONTAINER, LIGHTHOUSE...................................	10.00
CANDY CONTAINER, LOCOMOTIVE.......................... 6.50 TO	30.00
CANDY CONTAINER, LOCOMOTIVE, CORK, NUMBER ON SIDE, PATENTED.....	9.00
CANDY CONTAINER, LOCOMOTIVE, LITHOGRAPHED CLOSURE.............	8.50
CANDY CONTAINER, LOCOMOTIVE, PAINTED WHEELS, 4 7/8 X 2 1/8 IN..	6.00
CANDY CONTAINER, MONKEY, 7 3/4 IN.............................	45.00
CANDY CONTAINER, MULE PULLING TWO-WHEELED BARREL WITH DRIVER.	38.00
CANDY CONTAINER, NURSING BOTTLE, RUBBER NIPPLE................	2.50
CANDY CONTAINER, OLD OAKEN BUCKET, GLASS BOTTOM, TIN TOP.......	15.00
CANDY CONTAINER, PIG, PAPIER-MACHE, GOLD, GERMAN, 6 IN. LONG.....	4.00
CANDY CONTAINER, PISTOL, CLEAR, TIN CLOSURE...................	12.00
CANDY CONTAINER, PISTOL, MERCURY-LINED.......................	35.00
CANDY CONTAINER, POWDER HORN, EMBOSSED PAT. APPLIED FOR, TIN LID	8.00
CANDY CONTAINER, PT BOAT......................................	9.00
CANDY CONTAINER, PUPPY, SITTING...............................	2.75
CANDY CONTAINER, RABBIT EATING CARROT................. 9.50 TO	12.50
CANDY CONTAINER, RABBIT IN EGGSHELL, PAINT....................	35.00
CANDY CONTAINER, RABBIT, PAPIER-MACHE, 8 IN. HIGH, 3 1/4 IN. BASE.	7.50
CANDY CONTAINER, RABBIT, SITTING..................... 6.50 TO	8.00
CANDY CONTAINER, REVOLVER.....................................	8.00
CANDY CONTAINER, REVOLVER, AQUA, SCREW TOP, 4 1/2 IN..........	8.75
CANDY CONTAINER, REVOLVER, TIN SCREW CAP......................	8.50
CANDY CONTAINER, SANTA BOOT...................................	4.00
CANDY CONTAINER, SANTA CLAUS......................... 18.00 TO	25.00
CANDY CONTAINER, SANTA CLAUS BOOT, CLEAR, ORIGINAL CANDY.......	7.50
CANDY CONTAINER, SANTA CLAUS, STANDING, PAINTED...............	10.00
CANDY CONTAINER, SATCHEL, WIRE HANDLE, TIN SLIDING BASE.......	10.00
CANDY CONTAINER, SCOTTIE DOG, SAYS NIAGARA FALLS..............	40.00
CANDY CONTAINER, SCOTTIE, OPEN TOP............................	6.00
CANDY CONTAINER, SCOTTY DOG...................................	3.00
CANDY CONTAINER, SEDAN..	7.00
CANDY CONTAINER, SITTING RABBIT...............................	5.00
CANDY CONTAINER, SPARK PLUG, 1923.............................	35.00
CANDY CONTAINER, STATUE OF LIBERTY............................	5.00
CANDY CONTAINER, SUITCASE, CLEAR, HANDLE, TIN CLOSURE..........	16.50
CANDY CONTAINER, SUITCASE, FEB. 1, 1906.......................	18.00
CANDY CONTAINER, TANK, CONTENTS, COVER........................	7.00
CANDY CONTAINER, TELEPHONE....................................	4.00

```
CANDY CONTAINER,TELEPHONE,FRENCH,METAL ARM..................    9.50
CANDY CONTAINER,TELEPHONE,WITH CANDY.......................   12.00
CANDY CONTAINER,TELEPHONE,WOODEN HANDLE....................   15.00
CANDY CONTAINER,TRAIN ENGINE,NO.1028,5 IN.LONG.............   11.00
CANDY CONTAINER,TRAIN,ENGINE,COAL CAR,TWO PASSENGER CARS,SET   50.00
CANDY CONTAINER,TRAIN,TIN CLOSURE..........................   16.00
CANDY CONTAINER,TURKEY,PAPIER-MACHE........................    9.00
CANDY CONTAINER,WINDMILL...................................   25.00
  CANNING JAR, SEE FRUIT JAR
CAPTAIN,ONION,SQUAT,OPEN PONTIL,BLACK GLASS,CIRCA 1700......   65.00
CAPTAIN,SQUATTY,ONION,FREE BLOWN,PONTIL,CIRCA 1700..........  135.00
CARAFE,MARKED LIBBEY,HOBSTARS,DIAMOND,CUT GLASS............   43.00
CARBONA,AQUA...................................... 4.00 TO    6.00
CARRIE NATION..............................................    9.00


    CASE BOTTLES ARE THOSE OF THE TRADITIONAL SHAPE KNOWN
    BY THIS NAME.  THE BOTTLES HAVE FLAT SIDES AND ARE
    ALMOST SQUARE.  SOME TAPER AND ARE NARROWER AT THE
    BOTTOM.  CASE BOTTLES CAN BE OF ANY AGE FROM THE
    MID-1600'S TO THE PRESENT DAY.
CASE GIN,A.B.M.,TAPERED,OLIVE GREEN,8 IN...................    4.00
CASE GIN,DARK OLIVE.......................................    7.50
CASE GIN,EMBOSSED,OLIVE GREEN.............................   14.00
CASE GIN,FLARED MOUTH,FREE BLOWN,BLACK GLASS,CIRCA 1790.....   16.00
CASE GIN,FREE BLOWN,COLLAR TOP,BLACK GLASS,CIRCA 1810.......   10.00
CASE GIN,PANELED CORNERS,BLOB MOUTH AQUA...................   14.00
CASTOR,HONEYCOMB CUT,ETCHED FLOWERS,ROUND.................    7.00
CASTOR,INVERTED THUMBPRINT,NEW SILVER TOPS,SET OF 5........   35.00
CASTOR,MUSTARD,CUT GLASS..................................    2.50
CASTOR,VINEGAR,CUT GLASS..................................    2.50
CATHEDRAL PICKLE,GREEN,14 IN..............................   65.00
CATHEDRAL,BLUE............................................    7.00
CATHEDRAL,PICTURES BEEHIVE & BEES,MARKED 1 POUND PURE HONEY,
    AQUA..................................................    8.50
CATSUP,BLOWN IN MOLD,7 1/2 IN. TALL,CLEAR..................    1.50
CATSUP,BLOWN IN MOLD,7 3/4 IN. TALL,AMETHYST..............    2.50
CATSUP,BLOWN IN MOLD,9 3/8 IN. TALL,AMETHYST..............    1.50
CATSUP,H.J.HEINZ CO.,130 PAT'D,BLOWN IN MOLD,AMETHYST.......    1.50
CATSUP,PANELED,SCREW TYPE,EMBOSSED........................    1.00
CATSUP,8-SIDED............................................    5.00
CATSUP,10-SIDED...........................................    5.00
CELLO,SCALES ON BACK,PALE AMBER,8 1/2 IN..................   22.00
CETTI,CANARY.............................................    9.95
CHAMPAGNE,G.H.MURNUM,CORK,LABELS,GREEN,21 IN.HIGH..........   16.50
CHAMPAGNE,LABEL,CORK,1928,BLACK GLASS.....................    5.00
CHARLES H.FLETCHER,EMBOSSED,AQUA.........................    2.00
CHEMUNG SPRING WATER,THIS BOTTLE IS LOANED AND NEVER TO BE
    SOLD..................................................   35.00
CHERO COLA...............................................    3.00
CHERRY HEERING,BLUE & WHITE,LABELS,STAMP,TAX,BING & GRONDAHL   30.00
CHESTNUT,CLEAR OLIVE AMBER,5 IN...........................   80.00
CHESTNUT,WEST JERSEY,SWIRL,TAPERED LIP,BULBOUS,11 IN........  150.00
CHICKEN ON NEST,10 X 4 1/2 IN.............................   25.00
CHLOROX,AMBER............................................    3.00
CHLOROX,32 OZ.,CORK TOP,BROWN.............................   14.50
CIAO LIQUORE,ITALIAN,MINIATURE............................    2.50
CLARK & WHITE NEW YORK,SEEDS,WHITTLE MARKED,GREEN,PINT......   25.00
CLARK & WHITE,LARGE C,WHITTLED,PINT.......................   22.00
CLARKE & SON,NEW YORK,SARATOGA TYPE,BLACK GLASS...........   95.00
CLEANER,LESTOIL,AMBER....................................    2.00
CLEANER,LESTOIL,AMETHYST.................................    2.00
CLEANER,LESTOIL,GREEN....................................    2.00
CN BALLINGER,MONMOUTH,CODD,AQUA,7 1/2 IN..............ILLUS..    8.00
COACHMAN,GENEVER VAN DUNCK,AMBER.........................   70.00
```

COCA MARIANI,WHITTLED,IRIDESCENT,GREEN....................... 7.50

COCA-COLA WAS FIRST MADE IN 1886. SINCE THAT TIME THE
DRINK HAS BEEN SOLD IN ALL PARTS OF THE WORLD IN A
VARIETY OF BOTTLES. THE 'WAISTED' BOTTLE WAS FIRST
USED IN 1916.

COCA-COLA,AMBER....................................... 10.00 TO 12.50
COCA-COLA,AMBER,CIRCA 1905................................. 9.00
COCA-COLA,AQUA,8 1/2 IN.................................... 6.00
COCA-COLA,ARABIC,1960'S.............................ILLUS.. 2.00
COCA-COLA,ARROW BOTH SIDES,AMBER................... 15.00 TO 17.00
COCA-COLA,BERLIN,N.H.,MACHINE MADE,7 FLUID OZ.,GREEN........ 4.00
COCA-COLA,BLOWN IN MOLD,APPLIED TOP........................ 12.50
COCA-COLA,BLOWN IN MOLD,APPLIED TOP,EMBOSSED,LABEL......... 12.50
COCA-COLA,BOTTLING CO.,CHARLESTON,S.C.,TRADE MARK REG.,AQUA. 4.00
COCA-COLA,BOTTLING CO.,CHARLESTON,S.C.,TRADE MARK REG.,CLEAR 4.00
COCA-COLA,BOTTLING CO.,LAKELAND,FLA.,TEN PIN TYPE,1908,AQUA. 6.00
COCA-COLA,BOTTLING WORK,6 1/4 FLUID OZ.,AQUA............... 4.00
COCA-COLA,BOTTLING WORK,6 1/4 FLUID OZ.,CLEAR.............. 4.00
COCA-COLA,BOWLING GREEN,KY.,AMBER.......................... 15.00
COCA-COLA,BUBBLY,CITRON,6 1/2 OZ........................... 6.00
COCA-COLA,CLEAR,8 1/2 IN................................... 6.00
COCA-COLA,CROWN.. 6.00
COCA-COLA,CROWN TOP,BIMAL,AMBER............................ 10.00
COCA-COLA,DATED DEC.25,1923................................ 5.00
COCA-COLA,DEC.25,1923................................ILLUS.. 5.00
COCA-COLA,EMBOSSED,BLOWN IN MOLD,APPLIED TOP............... 12.50
COCA-COLA,EMBOSSED,DARK AMBER.............................. 16.00
COCA-COLA,FLINT GLASS,WASHBOARD DESIGN,1900'S....... 5.50 TO 6.00
COCA-COLA,FLINT GLASS,7 1/2 OZ.,1900....................... 5.50
COCA-COLA,GEORGIA,PRE-1919,STRAIGHT SIDES.................. 4.00
COCA-COLA,GREEN,1910-1920................................. 10.00
COCA-COLA,LABEL......................................ILLUS.. 12.50
COCA-COLA,LEXINGTON,KY.,AMBER.............................. 13.00
COCA-COLA,ME CASCO,INDIAN HEAD EMBOSSED.................... 5.00

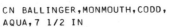

CN BALLINGER,MONMOUTH,CODD,
AQUA,7 1/2 IN

COCA-COLA,
LABEL

COCA-COLA,ARABIC,
1960'S

COCA-COLA,DEC.25,
1923

```
COCA-COLA,MINIATURE,CROWN CAP,2 1/4 IN..............ILLUS..    2.00
COCA-COLA,MINIATURE,2 1/4 IN........................ILLUS..    1.50
COCA-COLA,MOLD BLOWN,APPLIED TOP,PAPER LABEL................   13.00
COCA-COLA,NAME ON SHOULDER,CENTER & TRUNK,AQUA..............    4.00
COCA-COLA,NAME ON SHOULDER,CENTER & TRUNK,CLEAR............     4.00
COCA-COLA,POTTERY,1900 LABEL...............................   15.00
COCA-COLA,PRESENTATION,GOLD..................... 10.00 TO     27.50
COCA-COLA,PROPERTY OF WACO,DRINK DELICIOUS BLUDWINE,AQUA....    4.00
COCA-COLA,ROUND WHITE......................................    2.00
```

COCA-COLA,MINIATURE,CROWN CAP,2 1/4 IN

COCA-COLA,MINIATURE,2 1/4 IN

```
COCA-COLA,SELTZER,SIPHON,10 SIDED,GREEN,PEWTER..............   17.50
COCA-COLA,SODA WATER,EMBOSSED..............................    5.00
COCA-COLA,SODA WATER,ROUND.................................    2.00
COCA-COLA,SODA WATER,SQUARE,GREEN..........................    2.25
COCA-COLA,SODA WATER,SQUARE,WHITE..........................    2.25
COCA-COLA,SODA,CLEAR,2 1/2 IN..............................    2.00
COCA-COLA,SODA,COCA-COLA BOTTLING CO.,STARS.........ILLUS..    5.50
COCA-COLA,SODA,PROPERTY OF COCA COLA BOTTLING CO.,AQUA......    4.00
COCA-COLA,SODA,PROPERTY OF COCA COLA,TYLER,TEXAS,AQUA.......    4.00
COCA-COLA,SQUARE,GREEN.....................................    2.00
COCA-COLA,SQUARE,WHITE.....................................    2.25
COCA-COLA,TEN SIDED,GREEN..................................   17.50
COCA-COLA,TRADE MARK REG.,PORTLAND,OREGON,AMBER............     6.00
COCA-COLA,TRADE MARK REGISTERED,WAYCROSS,GA.,AQUA..........     4.00
COCA-COLA,TRADE MARK REGISTERED,WAYCROSS,GA.,CLEAR.........     4.00
COCA-COLA,WAN-ETA COCOA,QUART,AMBER........................    4.00
COCA-COLA,WILMINGTON N.C.,AQUA.............................    4.00
COCA-COLA,WILMINGTON N.C.,CLEAR............................    4.00
COCA-COLA,WOODEN SIX PACK,FROM TWENTIES....................    8.50
COCA-COLA,1894-1899................................ILLUS..    15.00
COCA-COLA,1899.....................................ILLUS..    15.00
COCA-COLA,1900,LABEL...............................ILLUS..    25.00
COCA-COLA,1900-1916,LABEL..........................ILLUS..    25.00
COCA-COLA,1915.....................................ILLUS..     4.00
COCA-COLA,1916,LABEL,AMBER.........................ILLUS..    25.00
COCA-COLA,1937.....................................ILLUS..     4.00
COCO MARIANI PARIS,9 IN.,SQUAT,WHITTLED,GREEN..............    8.00
COLOGNE,ACID CUT,FILLIGREE,GOLD ENAMEL,PAIR,CRANBERRY......    85.00
COLOGNE,BACCARAT,AMBER SCROLLS ON CLEAR....................   12.50
COLOGNE,BLUE BIRD,COLLECTOR'S ART COLOGNE..................   10.95
COLOGNE,BLUE,BLOWN,AMBER STOPPER,MARKED 54 IN GOLD.........   20.00
COLOGNE,CATHEDRAL TYPE,RING TOP,COBALT.....................   25.00
COLOGNE,COSMOS DESIGN,SIGNED C.G.CO.,CUT GLASS.............    28.00
COLOGNE,CUT GLASS,SIGNED HAWKES,FACET CUT,FLAME STOPPER.....   47.00
COLOGNE,CUTOUT DECOR,BIRDS,FLOWERS,PANELS,SILVER BASE &
```

COCA-COLA, SODA,
COCA-COLA BOTTLING
CO., STARS

COCA-COLA,
1894-1899

COCA-COLA, 1899

COCA-COLA,
1900, LABEL

COCA-COLA, 1900-1916, LABEL

COCA-COLA, 1915

COCA-COLA, 1916,
LABEL, AMBER

COCA-COLA, 1937

```
COLLAR.....................................................    35.00
COLOGNE,DECORATED TRUNK & SHOULDER,APPLIED LIP,AMETHYST.....     5.00
COLOGNE,DECORATED TRUNK & SHOULDER,APPLIED LIP,CLEAR........     5.00
COLOGNE,ENAMELED SCENE,GROUND PONTIL,STOPPER,3 3/4 IN.HIGH..    25.00
COLOGNE,HOLT'S NICKEL,ROUND,AMETHYST.......................     4.00
COLOGNE,HOLT'S NICKEL,ROUND,CLEAR..........................     4.00
COLOGNE,HOYT'S GERMAN,BLOWN IN MOLD,CLEAR..................      3.00
COLOGNE,LACY SCROLL,HOUR GLASS SHAPE,AQUA,5 5/8 IN. TALL....    32.50
COLOGNE,OVAL,BLOWN IN MOLD,CLEAR...........................      1.00
COLOGNE,PAPERWEIGHT,CLEAR FACETED STOPPER,BUBBLE INSIDE.....    18.50
COLOGNE,PINECONES,HAND-PAINTED,GROUND STOPPER,6 1/2 IN.,PAIR    13.00
COLOGNE,PLAIN,ROUND,CLEAR..................................      2.00
COLOGNE,PLAIN,ROUND,OPALESCENT.............................      2.00
COLOGNE,SANDWICH GLASS,6 IN. TALL,BLUE TO RED AT BASE......     80.00
COLOGNE,SCENE,GIRL IN WOODS,WINTER,POLISHED PONTIL,CUT
  STOPPER..................................................     25.00
COLOGNE,SHAPE OF LADY'S SHOE,3 IN..........................      4.00
COLOGNE,SILVER OVERLAY,FLOWERS,LEAVES,CIRCA 1850,PAIR.......    65.00
COLOGNE,ST.CLAIR,MULTICOLORED FLOWERS......................     15.00
COLOGNE,TOWER, FROM HEMISFAIR..............................      3.00
COLOGNE,TWO CRYING DOGS,HAND-COLORED FACES,PINT............     15.00
COLOGNE,VASELINE GLASS.....................................     18.50
COLOGNE,VENETIAN,ENAMELED DESIGN,STEEPLE STOPPER,BLUE,PAIR.,    67.50
COLOGNE,WHITE OPALESCENT GLASS,SKIRT SHAPE,BALL STOPPER,
  BRISTOL.................................................      22.50
COLOGNE,1000 EYE,FACETED KNOB STOPPER,2 5/8 X 7 1/2 IN.HIGH.     9.00
CONGRESS & EMPIRE,PINT.....................................     16.50
CONGRESS & EMPIRE,QUART....................................     16.50
CONGRESS WATER.....................................20.00 TO     25.00
CONGRESS WATER,LARGE C & SARATOGA,N.Y.,APPLIED LIP,7 3/4 IN.    28.00
CORDIAL,CLEAR,GREEN STOPPER,GILT,SIX PEDESTAL-TYPE GLASSES..     8.00
CORDIAL,PINE TREE TAR,DARK GREEN...........................     35.00
CORDIAL,TREE TAR,L.Q.C.,WISHARTS,GREEN,PINT................     20.00
COSMETIC,A.S.HINDS,BLOWN IN MOLD,CLEAR.....................      1.50
COSMETIC,BLOWN IN MOLD,2 7/8 IN. TALL,WHITE................      1.00
COSMETIC,C.DAMSRHINSKY LIQUID HAIR DYE,AQUA................      6.00
COSMETIC,CLARKE & CO.,WOODARD,SQUARE,COBALT................      2.00
COSMETIC,CROWN PERFUMERY COMPANY,GREEN,C.1888........ILLUS..    12.00
COSMETIC,DAGGETT & RAMSDELL PERFECT COLD CREAM,ROUND,CLEAR..     2.00
COSMETIC,DEWITTS TOILET CREAM,BLOWN IN MOLD,CLEAR..........      1.25
COSMETIC,FRENCH TOILET WATER,BLOWN IN MOLD,BLUE............      3.00
COSMETIC,FROSTILLA,FRAGRANT LOTION,ELMIRA,N.Y.,CLEAR.......      6.00
COSMETIC,HAGON'S MAGNOLIA BALM,RECTANGULAR,CLEAR...........      8.00
COSMETIC,HAGON'S MAGNOLIA BALM,RING TOP,MILK GLASS.........     12.00
COSMETIC,HALL'S HAIR RENEWER,RECTANGULAR,PEACOCK BLUE......     20.00
COSMETIC,HARMONY OF BOSTON,COLD CREAM,SCREW TOP,AMETHYST....     3.00
COSMETIC,HEFFRON CO.,BLOWN IN MOLD,CLEAR...................      3.00
COSMETIC,HOOD'S TOOTH POWDER,BLOWN IN MOLD,CLEAR...........      2.80
COSMETIC,HUBBARD,HARRIET,SQUARE,SCREW TOP,MILK GLASS.......      2.00
COSMETIC,INGRAM'S MILKWEED CREAM,SCREW TOP,MILK GLASS,WHITE.     2.00
COSMETIC,INGRAM'S SHAVING CREAM,ROUND,SCREW TOP,COBALT......     3.00
COSMETIC,JAR,COLD CREAM,ROUND,TALL.........................      4.00
COSMETIC,JATAMANSI TOILET WATER,BLOWN IN MOLD,AMBER........      3.00
COSMETIC,KRANK'S COLD CREAM,ROUND,SCREW TOP,MILK GLASS......     2.00
COSMETIC,LARKIN CO.,BLOWN IN MOLD,AMETHYST.................      2.50
COSMETIC,LARKIN CO.,BLOWN IN MOLD,CLEAR....................      1.50
COSMETIC,LARKIN CO.,BLOWN IN MOLD,GLASS STOPPER,CLEAR......      1.25
COSMETIC,LARKIN CO.,BLOWN IN MOLD,2 3/4 IN. TALL,WHITE......     1.50
COSMETIC,LARKIN CO.,MACHINE MADE,2 IN.TALL,WHITE...........      1.00
COSMETIC,LARKIN CO.,TOILET WATER,BLOWN IN MOLD,CLEAR.......      2.00
COSMETIC,MACHINE MADE,1 1/2 IN. TALL,WHITE.................      1.00
COSMETIC,MACHINE MADE,2 IN. TALL,WHITE.....................       .75
COSMETIC,MACHINE MADE,3 IN. TALL,WHITE.....................      1.00
COSMETIC,MARY GARDEN TOILET POWDER,C.1930............ILLUS..     4.00
COSMETIC,MILK GLASS,COLD CREAM,RIGAUD,EMBOSSED.......ILLUS..     3.00
```

COSMETIC, CROWN
PERFUMERY COMPANY,
GREEN, C.1888

COSMETIC, MARY GARDEN
TOILET POWDER, C.1930

COSMETIC, MILK GLASS,
COLD CREAM, RIGAUD,
EMBOSSED

```
COSMETIC,NEW SKIN,MACHINE MADE,COBALT BLUE..................    1.00
COSMETIC,ODO-RO-NO.MACHINE MADE,CLEAR.......................     .75
COSMETIC,PEARLADENT TOOTH POWDER,BLOWN IN MOLD,CLEAR........    2.00
COSMETIC,PLAIN,SQUARE,METAL SCREW TOP,COBALT................    2.00
COSMETIC,RUBIFOAM FOR THE TEETH,BLOWN IN MOLD,CLEAR.........    2.50
COSMETIC,SIGN OF HARRIET HUBBARD AYER,BLOWN IN MOLD,CLEAR...    1.50
COSMETIC,TOILET CREAM,BLOWN IN MOLD,CLEAR...................    1.00
COSMETIE,WOOD'S TOOTH POWDER,BLOWN IN MOLD,CLEAR...........     2.00
COSMETIC,X ZALIA TRADEMARK,BLOWN IN MOLD,BALL NECK,CLEAR....    2.50
CREATIVE WORLD,CUCKOO CLOCK,10 1/2 IN.HIGH.................    22.50
CREME DE MINT,HORSESHOE,CLOVER,GOOD LUCK,GREEN,11 1/2 IN....    5.75
CROCK,MARKED COWDEN & WILCOX,GALLON........................    7.00
CRYSTAL BACK,PEACH BRANDY IN LARGE ENAMEL SCRIPT...........    16.00
CUT GLASS,COGNAC,STRAWBERRY & DIAMOND,SQUARE,STOPPER.......    31.00
CUT GLASS,COLOGNE,DORFLINGER,STOPPER,PAIR..................   161.00
CUT GLASS,COLOGNE,PARISIAN,DORFLINGER......................    76.00
CUT GLASS,DECANTER,CROSSCUT DIAMOND & FAN,GREEN TO CLEAR....   111.00
CUT GLASS,DECANTER,CROSSCUT DIAMOND,FAN & STRAWBERRY,PAIR...   276.00
CUT GLASS,DECANTER,FLAT HOBNAIL,32 POINT STAR BOTTOM........   110.00
CUT GLASS,DECANTER,HARVARD & FLORAL,BOWLING PIN SHAPE.......   226.00
CUT GLASS,DECANTER,HAWKES SIGNED,DIAMOND,12 RING NECK.......   171.00
CUT GLASS,DECANTER,HAWKES SIGNED,3 RING NECK,HANDLELESS.....   111.00
CUT GLASS,DECANTER,HOBSTAR,FAN,CROSSCUT & STRAWBERRY DIAMOND    76.00
CUT GLASS,DECANTER,HOBSTAR,HONEYCOMB & NOTCHED PRISM,SIGNED.    56.00
CUT GLASS,DECANTER,RUSSIAN,BALL SHAPED.....................    96.00
CUT GLASS,DECANTER,ST.LOUIS,STOPPER........................   136.00
CUT GLASS,DECANTER,STRAWBERRY,DIAMOND,STARS,FANS,PYRAMID
  SHAPE....................................................    61.00
CUT GLASS,DECANTER,SUNBURST,12 1/4 IN. HIGH................   176.00
CUT GLASS,GOLD TOP.........................................    14.00
CUT GLASS,GOLD TOP,6 IN....................................    14.00
CUT GLASS,HAWKE'S SIGNED,VINEGAR,STOPPER...................    61.00
CUT GLASS,HONEYCOMB NECK,INTAGLIO DAISIES,HARVARD BOTTOM....    86.00
CUT GLASS,PERFUME,BULBOUS,HOBSTARS,STARRED VESICAS.........    75.00
CUT GLASS,PERFUME,BULBOUS,STOPPER..........................    45.00
CUT GLASS,PERFUME,CORINTHIAN,16 POINT HOBSTARS,PAIR........   185.00
CUT GLASS,PERFUME,CROWN SHAPE,HOBSTARS,STRAWBERRY,FAN.......    85.00
CUT GLASS,PERFUME,HEART SHAPE,STERLING CAP.................    36.00
CUT GLASS,PERFUME,PURSE SIZE,CUT TO CLEAR..................     9.50
```

```
CUT GLASS,RUSSIAN,SILVER EMBOSSED STOPPER,PAIR..............   301.00
CUT GLASS,WATER,BEDSIDE,6 1/2 IN. HIGH......................    25.00
D.EVANS CAMOMILE PILLS,OPEN PONTIL,AQUA.....................    10.00
DAISY,F.E.WARD & CO.,AQUA.PINT.......................        6.50
DALTON,OLD CROW.............................................    70.00
DALTON,SANDEMAN.............................................    25.00
DAMIANA,FERTILITY.................................... 8.50 TO     9.50
DANDY,CLEAR,QUART...........................................    27.00
```

```
        DANT FIGURAL BOTTLES FIRST WERE RELEASED IN 1968 TO
        HOLD J.W.DANT ALCOHOLIC PRODUCTS.  THE COMPANY HAS MADE
        THE AMERICANA SERIES, FIELD BIRDS, SPECIAL BOTTLINGS,
        AND CERAMIC BOTTLES.
DANT,ALAMO...................................................COLOR..    6.95
DANT,AMERICAN LEGION.........................................ILLUS..    9.00
DANT,BOBWHITE................................................COLOR..    5.95
DANT,BOEING 747..............................................ILLUS..    9.00
```

DANT,AMERICAN LEGION

DANT,BOEING 747

```
DANT,BOSTON TEA PARTY.................................COLOR..    4.00
DANT,BOURBON,1881,PENDENNIS CLUB......................COLOR..   XX.XX
DANT,CALIFORNIA QUAIL.................................COLOR..    5.95
DANT,CHUKAR PARTRIDGE.................................COLOR..    5.95
DANT,CONSTITUTION & GUERRIERE.........................COLOR..    6.00
DANT,DUEL BETWEEN BURR & HAMILTON.....................COLOR..    6.00
DANT,EAGLE...........................................           2.50
DANT,FORT SILL CENTENNIAL,1969........................ILLUS..   10.00
DANT,INDIANAPOLIS 500.................................          9.00
DANT,MOUNTAIN QUAIL..................................COLOR..    5.95
DANT,MT.RUSHMORE.....................................COLOR..   19.00
DANT,PATRICK HENRY...................................COLOR..    6.00
DANT,PAUL BUNYAN.....................................ILLUS..    6.00
```

DANT, FORT SILL CENTENNIAL, 1969   DANT, PAUL BUNYAN

```
DANT,PRAIRIE CHICKEN.....................................COLOR..    5.95
DANT,REVERSE EAGLE...........................................     12.00
DANT,RING-NECKED PHEASANT................................COLOR..    5.95
DANT,RUFFED GROUSE.......................................COLOR..    5.95
DANT,SAN DIEGO...........................................ILLUS..    3.00
DANT,SPEEDWAY 500 .......................................ILLUS..    9.00
DANT,TEA PARTY,WHITE.........................................      3.00
DANT,WASHINGTON CROSSING DELAWARE........................COLOR..    7.00
DANT,WOODCOCK............................................COLOR..    5.95
DANT,WRONG WAY CHARLIE........................... 15.00 TO         34.95
```

     DECANTERS WERE FIRST USED TO HOLD THE ALCOHOLIC
     BEVERAGES THAT HAD BEEN STORED IN KEGS. AT FIRST A
     NECESSITY, THE DECANTER LATER WAS MERELY AN ATTRACTIVE
     SERVING VESSEL.
     DECANTER, SEE ALSO BEAM, BISCHOFF, KORD, ETC.

```
DECANTER,AMERICAN EAGLE,BLUE,1970,CHRISTMAS..................      6.00
DECANTER,B-BAR,OHIO RIVER,PONTIL............................      17.50
DECANTER,BACCARAT,GREEN CUT,GOLD APPOINTMENTS...............     110.00
DECANTER,BACCARAT,SQUARE,MUSHROOM LID.......................      25.00
DECANTER,BOHEMIAN,DEER & CARTOUCHE,AMBER....................      40.00
DECANTER,BOHEMIAN,ETCHED FLORAL,RED & CLEAR.................      61.00
DECANTER,CALVERT SOFT WHISKEY,1/2 GAL.......................       2.00
DECANTER,CAPTAIN'S,CROWN & LETTERS C.E.,GREEN...............      18.00
DECANTER,CORK GLASS,HANDBLOWN,ROUGH PONTIL,C.1790...........      65.00
DECANTER,CORONATION OF KING GEORGE V,1911............COLOR..      XX.XX
DECANTER,CRANBERRY,ENCASED IN LACY PEWTER...................     111.00
DECANTER,CRANBERRY,PANELED,WHITE ENAMEL SCROLL & FLORAL.....      66.00
DECANTER,CRYSTAL,EGG SHAPE,STOPPER,SIGNED ORREFORS,6 IN.,
   PAIR.....................................................      85.00
DECANTER,CUT GLASS,HONEYCOMB,STOPPER........................      48.00
DECANTER,CUT GLASS,PANEL FLUTES,3 NECK RINGS................      23.00
DECANTER,CUT GLASS,STAR-CUT FLAT-TOPPED STOPPER,CIRCA 1810,
   PAIR.....................................................      85.00
DECANTER,CUT GLASS,TEARDROP STOPPER,ST.LOUIS NECK,LEAF,
   FLORAL...................................................      43.00
```

DANT, SAN DIEGO   DANT, SPEEDWAY 500

```
DECANTER,CUT RAYED BASE,OVAL SHAPE,CRANBERRY.................    75.00
DECANTER,DIAMOND QUILTED,FLANGE BASE,CRANBERRY..............    65.00
DECANTER,DIE SCHWESTER,CERAMIC,OLD STYLE COLONY WINERY,INC..    14.95
DECANTER,DOUGLAS CLUB...............................COLOR..    XX.XX
DECANTER,ENAMELED FLORAL,ROSES,OVERLAY,STOPPER,
  CZECHOSLOVAKIA...........................................    45.00
DECANTER,FEATHERED RINGS AROUND NECK,MARK CORK GLASS CO.,
  PAIR....................................................   125.00
DECANTER,FIGURAL,ROOSTER,CRYSTAL BODY,SILVER HEAD,STOPPER,
  BASE....................................................   135.00
DECANTER,FOUR-PART,SPIRITS,PRESSED GLASS....................    50.00
DECANTER,FRY,DECAL,DOG,CLEAR...............................    27.50
DECANTER,GEORGE WASHINGTON,FROSTED CAMPHOR GLASS...........    10.00
DECANTER,GLASS STOPPER,CLEAR TO CRANBERRY..................    35.00
DECANTER,GREEN,QUILTED PATTERN,CLEAR HANDLE,BLOWN STOPPER,
  10 IN...................................................    35.00
DECANTER,GREEN,SILVER OVERLAY,FLORAL,LEAVES,STOPPER,
  9 1/4 IN................................................    18.50
DECANTER,HEISEY,WATER,BLOWN,COLONIAL,10 1/4 IN. TALL.......    22.50
DECANTER,HORN OF PLENTY,STOPPER............................    55.00
DECANTER,INTAGLIO CUT GOLD GRAPES & LEAVES,CLEAR...........    60.00
DECANTER,INTAGLIO DAISY,MITER CUT LEAVES & FERN,CUT GLASS,.
  11 IN...................................................    60.00
DECANTER,INVERTED THUMBPRINT,PEDESTAL FOOT,STOPPER,AMBER....    25.00
DECANTER,JAMES PEPPER,1960...........................ILLUS..     5.00
DECANTER,JENNY LIND,CALABASH,BUST OF JENNY LIND,NEW........     2.75
DECANTER,LAKEWOOD RYE,SILVER & GLASS................COLOR..    XX.XX
DECANTER,LIGHT GREEN,ENAMEL FLORAL,CLEAR STOPPER,
  9 1/4 IN.HIGH...........................................    19.00
DECANTER,LILIES OF THE VALLEY,OLIVE GREEN,HAND-BLOWN,STOPPER    35.00
DECANTER,LOCOMOTIVE,7 1/2 IN. HIGH.........................     2.75
DECANTER,MC KEARIN G II-33,BLOWN MOLD,PINT.................    70.00
DECANTER,MC KEARIN G III-5,BLOWN THREE MOLD.........COLOR..    XX.XX
DECANTER,MC KEARIN G V-8,PINT,STOPPER,CLEAR................    95.00
```

```
DECANTER,MC KEARIN G V-8,QUART,STOPPER,3 MOLD,CLEAR,PAIR....     195.00
DECANTER,MC KEARIN G V-14,QUART,STOPPER,CLEAR,PAIR..........     250.00
DECANTER,METAL TRIM,METAL STOPPER,BLACK AMETHYST............      20.00
DECANTER,MINIATURE,SANDWICH,3 IN. TALL,STOPPER,GEOMETRIC....     200.00
DECANTER,MISS LIBERTY,AMBER,1970,CHRISTMAS.................        6.00
DECANTER,OHIO RIVERBOAT,BLOWN IN MOLD,BLOWN STOPPER........       25.00
DECANTER,OLD IRONSTONES,GREEN,1970 XMAS....................        6.00
DECANTER,OLD KENTUCKY TAVERN,1960....................ILLUS..       5.00
DECANTER,PASHA PIPE,TURKISH................................        7.50
DECANTER,PAUL JONES................................COLOR..       XX.XX
DECANTER,PITTSBURGH,APPLIED NECK RINGS,RED FLORAL,RIBS,FLINT      95.00
DECANTER,POTTERY,ROUND,BLUE HANDPAINTED,WHITE..............       23.00
DECANTER,PRESSED GLASS,HANDLE......................ILLUS..         2.00
DECANTER,PRESSED GLASS,MELROSE.....................ILLUS..         7.50
DECANTER,RIB,DRAPE,SNAPPED PONTIL,MOLD-BLOWN,14 IN.,PAIR...       40.00
DECANTER,RIVER BOAT TYPE,STOPPER MARKED NO.10,SIGNED LIBBEY.      87.50
DECANTER,RUM & MOLLANDS GIN,BLACK LACQUER STAND,BLUE,PAIR...     125.00
DECANTER,RYE,WM.H.LEE & CO.,ST.LOUIS................COLOR..       XX.XX
DECANTER,SANDWICH GLASS,BLOWN,OVERSHOT.....................       36.00
DECANTER,SANDWICH GLASS,PANELED,9 IN.TALL..................       80.00
DECANTER,SANDWICH,BAROQUE ARCH & LEAF,3 MOLD,BLOWN.........      111.00
DECANTER,SILVER DEPOSIT,GORHAM,PAIR................ILLUS..         4.00
DECANTER,SPODE,CRYSTAL,MAYFLOWER ON PEWTER SEAL............       45.00
DECANTER,STERLING SILVER OVERLAY,12 IN.HIGH,TUMBLER........       72.50
DECANTER,SWIRL RIBS,VINTAGE COPPER WHEEL ENGRAVING,BLOWN,
  STOPPER..................................................       12.00
DECANTER,THREE-MOLD,THREE DOUBLE RIGAREE NECK RINGS,BLOWN...      70.00
DECANTER,VASELINE GLASS, 12 IN. HIGH,FLARE LIP,CIRCA 1840....    100.00
DECANTER,VENETIAN,ENAMEL FLORAL & GOLD MEDALLIONS,PAIR,RUBY.     215.00
DECANTER,VIENNESE SCENE,AMETHYST,SILVER OVERLAY,8 1/2 IN....      27.75
DECANTER,WATERFORD,TEARDROP STOPPER,PAIR...................      101.00
DECANTER,WEBB SIGNED,CUT GLASS.............................       26.50
DECANTER,WINE,BLUE ENAMEL FLORAL,WHEAT,CRYSTAL,TWO WINES....      20.00
DECANTER,WINE,HAND-PAINTED FLORAL,VERSE IN GERMAN SCRIPT,
  12 IN...................................................       18.50
DECANTER,WINE,PETTICOAT FORM,BLOWN,9 1/2 IN.HIGH...........       25.00
DECANTER,WINE,SILVER ON CRYSTAL,SILVER STOPPER.............       25.00
DELFT CHINA,SCENIC,WINDMILL SCENE.........................       12.50
DEMIJOHN,OLIVE AMBER,15 IN.HIGH...........................       40.00
DEMIJOHN,SAYS HOE LARGER LIENER,ORANGE BLOESEEM,STOPPER,PAIR      75.00
DIAMOND PATTERN,FLIP GLASS,SANDWICH,QUART..................      150.00
DIAMOND THUMBPRINT,DECANTER,PINT..........................      116.00
DIAMOND THUMBPRINT,DECANTER,QUART.........................      136.00
DICKEL,GOLF CLUB..........................................        7.50
DICKEL,POWDER HORN.................................COLOR..        6.00
DILL'S BALM OF LIFE,THE DILL CO.,NORRISTOWN,PA.,AQUA.......        4.00
DOUBLE SPRING,BULL........................................       15.00
DOUBLE SPRING,CADILLAC....................................       25.00
DOUBLE SPRING,MATADOR.....................................       15.00
DOUBLE SPRING,STUTZ BEARCAT...............................       25.00
DOUBLE SPRING,TIN LIZZIE..................................       27.50
DOUBLE SPRINGS,BULL,BROWN,1968............................       12.00
DOUBLE SPRINGS,BULL,RED,1968..............................       12.00
DOUBLE SPRINGS,MAN........................................        5.95
DOUBLE SPRINGS,MATADOR,1969...............................       15.00
DOUBLE SPRINGS,OWL,BROWN..........................  6.95 TO       9.95
DOUBLE SPRINGS,WATER TOWER........................ 39.95 TO      65.00
DOUBLE SPRINGS,WILD CATTER................................       12.00
DOUBLE SPRINGS,WOMAN......................................        5.95
DOWSER,BULBOUS,3 LION FACED,MILK GLASS....................       11.50
DR.J.F.CHURCHILL,HYPOPHOSPHITE,PECTORAL....................        3.00
DR.MC LANES,AMERICAN WORM SPECIFIC,PONTIL,AQUA,3 1/2 IN.LONG      14.00
DR.PEPPER,INDENTED LETTERS................................        2.50
DRESSER,ACTRESS HEAD,STOPPER..............................       35.00
DRESSER,BULBOUS,BLUE,IVORY,FLORAL,STOPPER,PORCELAIN,FRANCE..      15.00
```

DECANTER, JAMES PEPPER, 1960

DECANTER, OLD KENTUCKY TAVERN, 1960

DECANTER, PRESSED
GLASS, HANDLE

DECANTER, PRESSED
GLASS, MELROSE

DECANTER, SILVER DEPOSIT, GORHAM, PAIR

```
DRESSER,CHINA,HANDPAINTED,RED POPPIES & LILIES OF VALLEY,
   PAIR.................................................    15.00
DRESSER,GARGOYLE,STOPPER.................................    30.00
DRESSER,GILT EDGE,AQUA...................................    12.00
DRESSER,MILK GLASS,FRENCH,RECTANGULAR,FLORAL,PAIR........    43.00
DRESSER,MILK GLASS,GREEN & GOLD PAINT,PAIR...............    14.00
DRESSER,PAINTED PINK ROSE,SATIN FINISH,STOPPER,9 IN.....     15.00
DRESSER,RAISED LADY CAMEO,STOPPER,MILK GLASS,PAIR.......     19.00
DU QUOIN BOTTLING,DU QUOIN,ILL.,GREEN....................     2.50
DUFFY MALT WHISKEY,BROWN,25 OZ...........................     6.00
DURAND,PERFUME,SIGNED DE VILBISS,ORANGE IRIDESCENT.......    71.00
DURAND,SIGNED,COVERED,DECORATED & THREADED,GOLD.........    650.00
DYOTTVILLE GLASS WORKS,AQUA,6 1/2 IN.HIGH................    15.00
E.KIDERLEN,7 1/2 IN......................................    30.00
EASTMAN KODAK,1/2 GAL,,BIMAL.............................     5.50
EL DORADO BREWING,STOCKTON,CALIFORNIA,11 1/2 IN.........     5.00
EMANUEL COLLEGE SEAL,PONTIL,CIRCA 1810...................    70.00
ENAMELED FLORAL ON TOP & STOPPER,BLOWN,BROWN,SQUARE,
   9 1/2 IN.TALL.........................................    12.50
ERROR,CENTRAL CITY BOTTLING CO.,SELMA,ALA.,SELAM IN ERROR...    18.50
```

```
ERROR,DR.LOVEGOOD'S FAMILY BITTRS,AMBER....................    260.00
ERROR,OLD DUFFY'S 1842 APPLE JUICE VINEGAR,BACKWARD Z.......     15.00
ERROR,PALLISER,MOBILE,ALA.,AQUA............................     12.00
ERROR,TIPPECANOE,ROCHETER ON BOTTOM,AMBER..................     65.00
ERROR,W.N.WALTON'S,S BACKWARDS,8 INSTEAD OF S IN SEPT.,AMBER    45.00
ERROR,WINERAL WATER,HONESDALE GLASSWORKS,AP................     10.00
EXCELSIOR SPRING,OLIVE GREEN,PINT..........................     25.00
EYEWASH,EYECUP ON GROUND STOPPER,WYETH,COBALT....... 8.00 TO    12.50
```

```
         EZRA BROOKS FANCY BOTTLES WERE FIRST MADE IN 1964.  THE
         EZRA BROOKS DISTILLING COMPANY IS FROM FRANKFORT,
         KENTUCKY.
EZRA BROOKS,ANNAPOLIS TECUMSEH,BUST,1969....................     14.00
EZRA BROOKS,ANTIQUE CANNON,1969..................... 6.25 TO     14.75
EZRA BROOKS,ANTIQUE PHONOGRAPH,1970...................ILLUS..    15.00
EZRA BROOKS,ARCH,RENO,1968......................... 14.95 TO     26.50
EZRA BROOKS,ARIZONA,1969............................ 6.99 TO     19.95
EZRA BROOKS,ASTRONAUT,1970......................... 13.45 TO     16.50
EZRA BROOKS,BEAR,GOLDEN,1968........................ 5.95 TO     11.99
EZRA BROOKS,BERTHA ELEPHANT,1969......................ILLUS..    30.00
EZRA BROOKS,BIG DADDY,FLORIDA,1969................. 14.50 TO     19.00
EZRA BROOKS,BIG RED,1970........................... 15.50 TO     18.50
EZRA BROOKS,BIRD DOG,1971..................................     20.00
EZRA BROOKS,BORDERTOWN,1970........................ 21.50 TO     24.00
EZRA BROOKS,BUCKET OF BLOOD,1970................... 21.00 TO     32.00
EZRA BROOKS,THE BUFFALO HUNT,1971..........................     19.95
EZRA BROOKS,CABLE CAR,BROWN,1968......................ILLUS..     8.00
EZRA BROOKS,CABLE CAR,GRAY,1968..................... 4.95 TO     10.00
EZRA BROOKS,CABLE CAR,GREEN,1968.................... 4.95         10.00
EZRA BROOKS,CALIFORNIA QUAIL,1970.....................ILLUS..    12.00
EZRA BROOKS,CANNON,ANTIQUE,GOLD,1969............... 6.25 TO     14.75
EZRA BROOKS,CEREMONIAL INDIAN,N.M.,1970............ 24.50 TO     34.50
EZRA BROOKS,CHEYENNE FRONTIER DAYS,1970....................     19.95
EZRA BROOKS,CHICAGO WATER TOWER,1969.............. 12.00 TO     24.50
EZRA BROOKS,CHRISTMAS DECANTER,1964................ 6.00 TO      8.00
EZRA BROOKS,CHRISTMAS DECANTER,1968................ 7.00 TO      8.00
EZRA BROOKS,CHURCHILL,1969............................ILLUS..    12.50
```

EZRA BROOKS,
ANTIQUE PHONOGRAPH,1970

EZRA BROOKS,
BERTHA ELEPHANT,1969

EZRA BROOKS,
CABLE CAR,BROWN,1968

```
EZRA BROOKS,CIGAR STORE INDIAN,1968................. 4.95 TO    11.00
EZRA BROOKS,CLASSIC GUN,SET OF 4,GLASS,1969........ 18.00 TO    18.50
EZRA BROOKS,CLUB BOTTLE,1970.......................150.00 TO   250.00
EZRA BROOKS,DEAD WAGON,1970..........................ILLUS..    22.00
EZRA BROOKS,DELTA BELLE,1969....................... 5.95 TO    12.00
EZRA BROOKS,DICE,RED,HAROLD'S,1968................. 5.95 TO    14.50
```

EZRA BROOKS,
CALIFORNIA QUAIL,1970

EZRA BROOKS,
CHURCHILL,1969

EZRA BROOKS,
DEAD WAGON,1970

```
EZRA BROOKS,DISTILLERY,1970...........................COLOR..    20.00
EZRA BROOKS,DUELING PISTOL,FLINTLOCK................. 9.00 TO    16.50
EZRA BROOKS,FIRE ENGINE,1971.........................          12.00
EZRA BROOKS,FLINTLOCK DUELING PISTOL,1968............ 9.00 TO    16.50
EZRA BROOKS,FLINTLOCK PISTOL,JAPANESE................ 50.00 TO    65.00
EZRA BROOKS,FLORIDA,BIG DADDY,1969.................. 15.95 TO    16.95
EZRA BROOKS,FOREMOST ASTRONAUT,1970................. 13.45 TO    16.50
EZRA BROOKS,FOREMOST ASTRONAUT,2 FEET TALL,CERAMIC..........    75.00
EZRA BROOKS,FOREMOST BOY,MR.FOREMOST,1969...........           23.50
EZRA BROOKS,FRESNO GRAPE,1970........................ILLUS..    20.00
EZRA BROOKS,GAMECOCK,SOUTH CAROLINA,1970............           12.00
EZRA BROOKS,GO BIG RED,1970........................ 15.50 TO    18.50
EZRA BROOKS,GOLD CANNON,ANTIQUE,1969............... 6.25 TO    14.75
EZRA BROOKS,GOLD EAGLE,1971..........................COLOR..    19.95
EZRA BROOKS,GOLD HORSESHOE,1970.....................           79.95
EZRA BROOKS,GOLD PROSPECTOR,1970................... 8.95 TO    13.50
EZRA BROOKS,GOLDEN GRIZZLY BEAR,1968............... 6.99 TO    10.50
EZRA BROOKS,GOLDEN ROOSTER,1969......................COLOR..   140.00
EZRA BROOKS,GRANDFATHER'S CLOCK,1970.................COLOR..    13.50
EZRA BROOKS,GRIZZLY BEAR,GOLDEN..................... 6.99 TO    10.50
EZRA BROOKS,HAMBLETONIAN,1971.......................           19.95
EZRA BROOKS,HAROLD'S CLUB DICE,1968................ 5.95 TO    14.50
EZRA BROOKS,HISTORIC FLASKS,SET OF 4,GLASS,1970.............   115.00
EZRA BROOKS,HORSESHOE,GOLD,1970.................... 39.95 TO   125.00
EZRA BROOKS,INDIAN CEREMONIAL,GALLUP,N.M........... 24.50 TO    34.50
EZRA BROOKS,INDIAN,CIGAR STORE,1968................ 4.95 TO    11.00
EZRA BROOKS,INDIANAPOLIS RACE CAR,1970...............COLOR..    24.00
EZRA BROOKS,JUMPING MAN,1970....................... 15.00 TO    16.95
EZRA BROOKS,KANSAS JAYHAWK,1969......................ILLUS..    11.50
EZRA BROOKS,KATZ CAT,PHILHARMONIC,BROWN,1970....... 12.95 TO    17.95
EZRA BROOKS,KING-O-CLUBS,1969...................... 5.95 TO    12.50
EZRA BROOKS,LIBERTY BELL,1970...................... 9.50 TO    14.50
EZRA BROOKS,LION ON ROCK,1971........................COLOR..    19.95
```

```
EZRA BROOKS,LOBSTER.................................. 21.50 TO   26.50
EZRA BROOKS,MAINE LOBSTER,1970...................... 21.50 TO   26.50
EZRA BROOKS,MAN-O-WAR,1969.......................... 9.95 TO   20.00
EZRA BROOKS,MINER,GOLD PROSPECTOR,1970.............. 8.95 TO   13.50
EZRA BROOKS,MISTER FOREMOST,1969................... 14.00 TO   24.90
EZRA BROOKS,MR.MERCHANT,JUMPING MAN,1970............ILLUS..   16.00
```

EZRA BROOKS,
FRESNO GRAPE,
1970

EZRA BROOKS,DISTILLERY,1970

EZRA BROOKS,
INDIANAPOLIS RACE CAR,1970

EZRA BROOKS,
KANSAS JAYHAWK,1969

EZRA BROOKS,MR.MERCHANT,
JUMPING MAN,1970

```
EZRA BROOKS,NEW HAMPSHIRE STATE HOUSE,1970........ 18.95 TO    28.50
EZRA BROOKS,NUGGET CLASSIC,1970.................... 29.95 TO    39.95
EZRA BROOKS,OIL GUSHER,1969....................... 10.00 TO    19.90
EZRA BROOKS,ONTARIO RACE CAR,1970................. 13.00 TO    17.50
EZRA BROOKS,PBR'S ELMER THE CAMEL,GOLD............ 11.50 TO    17.95
EZRA BROOKS,PHONOGRAPH,ANTIQUE,1970............... 11.50 TO    13.50
EZRA BROOKS,PISTOL,1968...........................  9.00 TO    16.50
EZRA BROOKS,POTBELLIED STOVE,1968.....................ILLUS..   8.00
EZRA BROOKS,QUEEN-O-HEARTS,1969...................  5.95 TO    13.50
EZRA BROOKS,RAINBOW TROUT,1970....................  9.95 TO    16.50
EZRA BROOKS,RAZORBACK HOG,1970........................ILLUS..  13.00
```

EZRA BROOKS,POTBELLIED STOVE,1968

EZRA BROOKS,RAZORBACK HOG,1970

```
EZRA BROOKS,RED DICE,HAROLD'S,1968...................  5.95 TO   14.50
EZRA BROOKS,RENO ARCH,1968........................... 14.95 TO   26.50
EZRA BROOKS,ROOSTER,GOLDEN,1969...................... 95.00 TO  179.50
EZRA BROOKS,SAILFISH,1971............................             12.00
EZRA BROOKS,SAN FRANCISCO CABLE CAR,1968.............  4.95 TO   10.00
EZRA BROOKS,SILVER DOLLAR,1970........................ILLUS..    13.50
EZRA BROOKS,SPRINT RACER,1971........................            19.95
EZRA BROOKS,STAGE COACH,1969......................... 11.00 TO   12.50
EZRA BROOKS,STATE HOUSE,1970......................... 16.50 TO   28.50
EZRA BROOKS,TECUMSEH,ANNAPOLIS,1969..................  8.00 TO   12.50
EZRA BROOKS,TELEPHONE,1971...........................            19.95
EZRA BROOKS,THE LAST BUFFALO..........................           19.95
EZRA BROOKS,TICKER TAPE,1970..........................COLOR..    15.00
EZRA BROOKS,TRAIN,1969...............................  5.95 TO   14.00
EZRA BROOKS,TROUT & FLY,1970.........................  9.95 TO   16.50
EZRA BROOKS,WATER TOWER,CHICAGO,1969................. 12.00 TO   24.50
EZRA BROOKS,WEST VIRGINIA MOUNTAINEER,1971...........COLOR..    130.00
EZRA BROOKS,WHITE TURKEY,1971.........................COLOR..    19.95
EZRA BROOKS,WICHITA CENTENNIAL,1970.................. 15.95 TO   24.95
EZRA BROOKS,WINSTON CHURCHILL,1969...................  6.00 TO   14.50
EZRA BROOKS,ZIMMERMAN'S HAT,1968..................... 14.95 TO   21.50
FAMOUS FIRSTS,ALPINE BELL............................            11.45
FAMOUS FIRSTS,CENTURION..............................            17.50
FAMOUS FIRSTS,DON SYMPATICO..........................            11.45
FAMOUS FIRSTS,FRENCH TELEPHONE.......................            19.50
FAMOUS FIRSTS,HEN....................................            13.50
FAMOUS FIRSTS,LOCOMOTIVE,DEWITT CLINTON,1969........ 21.50 TO    30.00
```

EZRA BROOKS,
GOLDEN ROOSTER, 1969

EZRA BROOKS,
SILVER DOLLAR, 1970

```
FAMOUS FIRSTS,MARMON WASP,1968...................... 19.50 TO   27.00
FAMOUS FIRSTS,PHONOGRAPH.............................................   19.50
FAMOUS FIRSTS,RENAULT RACER,1969.................... 19.50 TO   28.00
FAMOUS FIRSTS,ROBERT E.LEE RIVERBOAT.........................   24.50
FAMOUS FIRSTS,ROOSTER.......................................   13.50
FAMOUS FIRSTS,SCALES,LOMBARD................................   19.50
FAMOUS FIRSTS,SEWING MACHINE................................   19.50
FAMOUS FIRSTS,SPIRIT OF ST.LOUIS,1969.............. 30.00 TO   35.00
FAMOUS FIRSTS,YACHT,AMERICA,1970................... 21.50 TO   24.00
```

```
        FIGURAL BOTTLES ARE SPECIALLY NAMED BY THE COLLECTORS
    OF BOTTLES.  ANY BOTTLE THAT IS OF A RECOGNIZABLE SHAPE,
    SUCH AS A HUMAN HEAD, OR A PRETZEL, OR A CLOCK, IS
    CONSIDERED TO BE A FIGURAL.  THERE IS NO RESTRICTION TO
    DATE OR MATERIAL.
FIGURAL,A CHAMPAGNE GIRL,PURPLE GRAPES,FRUIT,STOPPER........   14.50
FIGURAL,A.M.BINNINGER BARREL,OPEN PONTIL....................  125.00
FIGURAL,AFRICAN MASK........................................   12.50
FIGURAL,ALARM CLOCK FACE ON SIDE............................    5.00
FIGURAL,ALARM CLOCK SHAPE...................................    4.00
FIGURAL,ALARM CLOCK,METAL LID,CLEAR.........................   10.00
FIGURAL,APACHE DANCERS,PORCELAIN............................   32.50
FIGURAL,BABY BLACKAMOOR,CLEAR & FROSTED.....................   26.00
FIGURAL,BABY HOLDING CLOCK,CLEAR............................   25.00
FIGURAL,BABY,CRYING,CLEAR,6 1/2 IN.HIGH.....................   35.00
FIGURAL,BANJO,MEDLEY DIST,CLEAR.............................    6.00
FIGURAL,BARREL,BANDS & BUNG,PINT,CLEAR......................    2.50
FIGURAL,BARREL,SOUR MASH 1867,CHAPIN & GORE..........ILLUS..   70.00
FIGURAL,BASE VIOLA,AMBER....................................    8.00
FIGURAL,BEAR,BLACK,ENAMELED OVER CLEAR,SMIRNOFF.............   10.00
FIGURAL,BEAR,SEATED,DARK AMETHYST....................ILLUS..   30.00
FIGURAL,BEAR,9 IN.,CLEAR.............................ILLUS..    3.00
FIGURAL,BELL'S BELL,ROYAL DOULTON...........................   32.50
FIGURAL,BINOCULAR,FULL SIZE,BLACK...........................    5.00
FIGURAL,BIRD,HEAD FORMS STOPPER,MILK GLASS,8 IN.TALL........   10.00
FIGURAL,BIRD,HEAD FORMS STOPPER,MILK GLASS,10 IN.TALL.......   12.00
FIGURAL,BULLDOG CANDY CONTAINER.............................    3.00
```

FIGURAL, BARREL, SOUR MASH 1867,
CHAPIN & GORE

FIGURAL, BEAR, SEATED,
DARK AMETHYST

```
FIGURAL,BULLDOG SHAMPOO.......................................    3.00
FIGURAL,BUST OF GALLIANO......................................   25.00
FIGURAL,BUST OF GEORGE WASHINGTON,MINIATURE...................    6.50
FIGURAL,BUST OF LADY..........................................   10.00
FIGURAL,BUST OF REGINA ELENA,CLEAR,BLOWN......................   30.00
FIGURAL,BUST OF WASHINGTON,JACQUIN............................    9.00
FIGURAL,CALABASH,1936,AQUA....................................   35.00
FIGURAL,CANNON,BININGER.......................................  350.00
FIGURAL,CAPTAIN MERIWETHER LEWIS..............................   25.00
FIGURAL,CARRIE NATION.........................................    8.00
FIGURAL,CAT,13 IN.,AMBER......................................    5.00
FIGURAL,CAT,13 IN.,BLUE.......................................    5.00
FIGURAL,CAT,13 IN.,GREEN......................................    5.00
FIGURAL,CHERUB HOLDING CLOCK,PAINTED CLOCK FACE,FRANCE,
  14 IN.HIGH..................................................   25.00
FIGURAL,CHERUB HOLDING MEDALLION,CLEAR,13 3/4 IN. HIGH........   16.00
FIGURAL,CHICKEN,VIRIGONI,WINE SAMPLE..........................    3.00
FIGURAL,CHILDREN CLIMBING TREE,BIRD'S NEST STOPPER............   75.00
FIGURAL,CHRISTMAS TREE........................................   35.00
FIGURAL,CLAM SHELL,CLEAR........................... 11.00 TO    20.00
FIGURAL,CLAM SHELL,LAY-DOWN...................................   18.75
FIGURAL,CLEVELAND,FROSTED..........................ILLUS..      45.00
FIGURAL,CLOCK,KIDDIE...............................ILLUS..       3.50
FIGURAL,CLOCK,5 IN.,CLEAR..........................ILLUS..       6.50
FIGURAL,CLOCK,7 IN.,CLEAR..........................ILLUS..       7.50
FIGURAL,CLOWN.................................................    1.00
FIGURAL,CLOWN,BANK............................................    3.00
FIGURAL,CLOWN,HEAD IS STOPPER,HAND BLOWN IN MULTICOLORS,
  PAYASO.....................................................    6.50
FIGURAL,CLOWN,12 IN.,CLEAR....................................   22.00
FIGURAL,COACHMAN,VAN DUNCK'S GENEVER,BLACK AMBER..............  125.00
FIGURAL,COACHMAN,11 IN.,HEAD STOPPER,TAN......................   22.00
FIGURAL,COCKATOO,DECANTER,CREME DE MENTHE,GARNIER.............   25.00
FIGURAL,COMIC SAILOR,PORCELAIN................................   30.00
FIGURAL,CROSSBONES,SKULL......................................    5.50
FIGURAL,CROWN SHAPE,PURPLE....................................    3.50
FIGURAL,CUCUMBER,7 3/4 IN.,CLEAR..............................   18.00
FIGURAL,CUT LOG,SUN-COLORED...................................   45.00
```

```
FIGURAL,CZAR BUST,MILK GLASS.....................................   300.0
FIGURAL,CZAR NICHOLAS,STANDING,16 1/2 IN.....................   150.0
FIGURAL,CZARINA,MILK GLASS......................................   275.0
FIGURAL,DAGGER,SCREW CAP........................................    25.0
FIGURAL,DAUGHTER,JAPANESE.......................................    12.9
FIGURAL,DOG,R.C.A.VICTOR........................................   145.0
FIGURAL,EAR OF CORN,FITZPATRICK & CO.,AMBER..........ILLUS..    95.0
```

FIGURAL,CLEVELAND,
FROSTED

FIGURAL,CLOCK,KIDDIE

FIGURAL,CLOCK,
5 IN.,CLEAR

FIGURAL,CLOCK,
7 IN.,CLEAR

FIGURAL,EAR OF CORN,
FITZPATRICK & CO.,AMBER

```
FIGURAL,EAR OF CORN,HUSK HANDLE,5 IN.,CLEAR...................    45.00
FIGURAL,EAR OF CORN,6 1/2 IN.,METAL CAP,CLEAR................    18.00
FIGURAL,EGYPTIAN PITCHER........................................    17.50
FIGURAL,EIFFEL TOWER........................................ILLUS..    12.00
FIGURAL,EISENHOWER,JAPANESE....................................    12.95
FIGURAL,ELEPHANT,BANK...........................................     4.00
FIGURAL,ELEPHANT,OLD SOL,9 IN.,AMBER..........................    35.00
```

```
FIGURAL,ELEPHANT,SITTING,UPRAISED TRUNK HAS CORK,
   8 1/2 IN.TALL..........................................   12.50
FIGURAL,EMANUEL COLLEGE,APPLIED SEAL NEAR BASE..............   28.00
FIGURAL,ENAMELED KUMMEL ON SIDE,BALL & CLAW,AMBER..........   35.00
FIGURAL,FAITHFUL RETAINER,JAPANESE.........................   21.95
FIGURAL,FERTILITY GOD......................................   12.50
FIGURAL,FISH.........................................COLOR..   XX.XX
FIGURAL,FISH,AMBER,10 IN...................................    8.00
FIGURAL,FISH,BROWN.........................................    5.00
FIGURAL,FISH,COD LIVER OIL,AMBER,1/4 PINT..................    7.50
FIGURAL,FISH,COD LIVER OIL,AMBER,1 PINT....................    6.50
FIGURAL,FISH,CORK TOP,AMBER,8 1/4 IN.......................   18.00
FIGURAL,FISH,CORK TOP,AMBER,9 3/4 IN.......................   18.00
FIGURAL,FISH,LAYS,PAINT,SCREW TOP..........................   25.00
FIGURAL,FISH,LILLY,AMBER.............................ILLUS..   12.00
FIGURAL,FISH,6 1/4 IN.,AMBER...............................   12.00
FIGURAL,FISH,9 3/4 IN.,AMBER...............................   10.00
FIGURAL,FISH,13 IN.,CLEAR..................................    5.00
FIGURAL,FLAPPER HOLDS WHISKEY BOTTLE,PORCELAIN.............   30.00
FIGURAL,GENERAL,JAPANESE...................................   19.95
FIGURAL,GEORGE WASHINGTON............................COLOR..   XX.XX
```

FIGURAL,EIFFEL TOWER

FIGURAL,FISH,LILLY,AMBER

```
FIGURAL,GEORGE WASHINGTON,BUST.............................    4.00
FIGURAL,GEORGE WASHINGTON,BY OLEAN CO.,PAT.1936............   30.00
FIGURAL,GEORGE WASHINGTON,CLEAR,9 1/2 IN...................   12.50
FIGURAL,GEORGE WASHINGTON,STANDING.........................    8.00
FIGURAL,GIRL WITH PARASOL..................................   10.00
FIGURAL,GONDOLA,VIARENGO...................................   18.00
FIGURAL,GRAPE..............................................    3.00
FIGURAL,GROVER CLEVELAND,FROSTED,9 IN......................   70.00
FIGURAL,GUITAR SHAPE,HARMONY WINE,LABEL,SPAIN,AMBER........    7.50
FIGURAL,GUITAR,AMBER.......................................    9.00
FIGURAL,GUITAR,BROWN,16 IN.................................    5.00
FIGURAL,HAND HOLDING MIRROR,OPEN PONTIL....................   48.00
FIGURAL,HAND,PROBABLY FRENCH.........................COLOR..   XX.XX
FIGURAL,HAPPY MOON FACE,PORCELAIN..........................   25.00
FIGURAL,HARD ROLL,CERAMIC..................................   18.00
FIGURAL,HAWAIIAN GOD OF WER,KU.............................   26.95
FIGURAL,HEAD OF FRENCHMAN,RED BERET,CLEAR..................   30.00
FIGURAL,HEART SHAPE PERFUME................................   20.00
FIGURAL,HEN & EGG ON NEST,VIARENGO.........................   15.00
FIGURAL,HIPPIE.............................................    8.00
```

```
FIGURAL,HIPPIE,FLOWER GIRL,PAIR...............................   9.90
FIGURAL,HORSEHEAD COLOGNE,CLEAR...............................   1.50
FIGURAL,HOT TAMALE,CERAMIC....................................  10.00
FIGURAL,HOUND,SAD.............................................  25.00
FIGURAL,HUNTER,LADY,PAIR......................................  25.00
FIGURAL, IMPERIAL CROWN,VICTYLITE,OSHKOSH,WIS.,MADE IN ITALY,
  AMBER.......................................................   8.00
FIGURAL,IN BASKET,APPLIED HANDLE,PONTIL,CLEAR.................  25.00
  FIGURAL, INDIAN QUEEN, SEE BITTERS, BROWN'S INDIAN QUEEN
FIGURAL,IRISHMAN ON BARREL,ENAMEL.............................  25.00
FIGURAL,JACQUIN,BUST OF WASHINGTON,BLUE.......................   9.00
FIGURAL,JENNY LIND CALABASH,AQUA..............................  50.00
FIGURAL,JENNY LIND,EMPIRE GLASS WORKS.........................   7.50
FIGURAL,JENNY LIND,EMPIRE GLASS WORKS,NEW.....................   2.75
FIGURAL,JENNY LIND,GREEN......................................   8.00
FIGURAL,JENNY LIND,REVERSE GLASS FACTORY......................  25.00
FIGURAL,JESTER,7 IN.,CLEAR....................................  30.00
FIGURAL,JOAN OF ARC,MILK GLASS,FULL ARMOR..................... 250.00
FIGURAL,JOSEPH & CHILD,PAINTED,16 1/2 IN.,CLEAR.............. 150.00
FIGURAL,KAHLUA GODDESS,FERTILITY GODDESS,PAIR.................  35.00
FIGURAL,KAIMYO,JAPANESE.......................................  15.75
FIGURAL,KENNEDY,JAPANESE......................................  12.95
FIGURAL,KENTUCKY GENTLEMAN....................................  18.50
FIGURAL,KITTY,BANK,ORIGINALLY HELD SOFT DRINK,4 X 7 IN.HIGH.   3.50
FIGURAL,KNIGHT ON HORSE,CLEAR.................................  12.00
FIGURAL,KUMMEL BEAR,OLIVE GREEN...............................  35.00
FIGURAL,KUMMEL,BALL & CLAW,ENAMELED,AMBER.....................  35.00
FIGURAL,LADY LEG,PLAIN,KICKUP,GREEN...........................  25.00
FIGURAL,LADY,RED,YELLOW COLONIAL STYLE DRESS,HOLDS FAN,
  PORCELAIN...................................................  12.50
FIGURAL,LADY'S LEG,AMBER......................................  30.00
FIGURAL,LADY'S LEG,APPLIED RING TOP,1860,AMBER................  50.00
FIGURAL,LADY'S LEG,BITTERS TYPE,GREEN.........................  25.00
FIGURAL,LADY'S LEG,GREEN......................................  40.00
FIGURAL,LADY'S LEG,NECK,3 PIECE MOLD,AMBER....................  10.00
FIGURAL,LADY'S LEG,NECK,3 PIECE MOLD,GREEN....................  10.00
FIGURAL,LADY'S LEG,PONTILED,QUART,OLIVE AMBER.................  36.00
FIGURAL,LADY'S LEG,TURN MOLD,12 1/2 IN. HIGH,AMBER...........  21.00
FIGURAL,LADY'S LEG,12 IN.,GREEN...............................  50.00
FIGURAL,LADY'S LEG,13 IN.,GREEN...............................  75.00
FIGURAL,LANTERN,GREEN.........................................  20.00
FIGURAL,LANTERN,RED,FULL & BOXED..............................  20.00
FIGURAL,LEARNED FOX...........................................  19.00
FIGURAL,LEG,LADY'S,AMBER...................................... 100.00
FIGURAL,LEG,LADY'S,GREEN...................................... 100.00
FIGURAL,LIGHTHOUSE,C.T.MORRIS,QUART,AMBER..................... 501.00
FIGURAL,LIGHTHOUSE,CANDLESTICK STOPPERS,17 IN.,PAIR,CLEAR...  45.00
FIGURAL,LINCOLN,BANK,CLEAR,8 3/4 IN...........................   5.50
FIGURAL,LINCOLN,JAPANESE......................................  12.95
FIGURAL,LIPPIZANER VETERINARY,EMBOSSED MAN,SADDLE,WHIP,GREEN  20.00
FIGURAL,MADONNA,COBALT BLUE,10 IN. TALL.......................   3.00
FIGURAL,MADONNA,HAND BLOWN,DATED 1932,AMBER...................   4.00
FIGURAL,MADONNA,HAND BLOWN,DATED 1932,COBALT BLUE............   4.00
FIGURAL,MADONNA,HAND BLOWN,PONTIL,COBALT,10 IN. TALL.........   3.00
FIGURAL,MADONNA,HAND BLOWN,PONTIL,1932,AMBER,13 IN. TALL....   3.00
FIGURAL,MADONNA,HAND BLOWN,PONTIL,1932,COBALT,13 IN. TALL...   3.00
FIGURAL,MADONNA,PONTIL,AMBER,1932,13 IN. TALL................   4.00
FIGURAL,MADONNA,PONTIL,COBALT BLUE,1932,13 IN. TALL..........   4.00
FIGURAL,MAIDEN,JAPANESE.......................................  12.95
FIGURAL,MAN IN BLACK CAPE,DOULTON,YELLOW CUP..................  20.00
FIGURAL,MAN IN BLACK CAPE,ROYAL DOULTON.......................  35.00
FIGURAL,MAN IN BLACK CAPE,WADE,ENGLAND,8 IN..................  40.00
FIGURAL,MAN ON BARREL,EMBROS,SCREW TOP........................  20.00
FIGURAL,MAN WITH HANDS IN BACK AGAINST STUMP OF TREE,12 IN..  12.00
FIGURAL,MAN,BLACK DERBY,HUGH POCKETS,CERAMIC,GERMANY.........   6.50
```

```
FIGURAL,MAN,CHRISTMAS TREE,TOYS,BROWN,HANDLE,STOPPER,
   PORCELAIN...................................................   37.50
FIGURAL,MAN,FAT,AMBER.................................ILLUS..   50.00
FIGURAL,MAN,SEATED,VAN DUNCKS,GENEVER,AMBER..........ILLUS..   45.00
FIGURAL,MARIE BRIZARD,KIOSK.................................    6.50
FIGURAL,MARSHALL,CIGAR SHAPE,4 3/8 IN. LONG,AMBER...........    7.50
FIGURAL,MASSEY & JENKINS,APPLIED HANDLE.....................   20.00
FIGURAL,MERMAID,ROCKINGHAM TYPE.............................   17.95
FIGURAL,MONK,BENNINGTON TYPE,10 1/2 IN.HIGH................. 150.00
FIGURAL,MONKEY CLIMBING,GREEN...............................    7.50
FIGURAL,MONKEY TRIO,JAPANESE................................    6.95
FIGURAL,MOSES,AQUA..........................................   59.95
FIGURAL,MOSES,RICKER & SONS,CLEAR...........................   60.00
FIGURAL,MOSES,WOODEN CARRYING HANDLE,QUART,CLEAR............   45.00
FIGURAL,MOSES,1ST FACSIMILE OF MOSES POLAND WATER,CLEAR.....    2.00
FIGURAL,MR.PICKWICK.........................................    8.00
FIGURAL,MRS.FRANKLIN,HANDLE,7 IN.,PAIR......................   32.00
FIGURAL,NAPOLEON,CERAMIC,11 IN.,HEAD STOPPER................   18.00
FIGURAL,NAPOLEON,SATIN GLASS,12 IN.......................... 130.00
FIGURAL,NATIONAL 210,COCK-EYED,FREE BLOWN,AMBER.............   35.00
FIGURAL,NEGRO BABY,PARTLY FROSTED,FRANCE....................   26.00
FIGURAL,NUDE WITH BOTTLE,DEPOSE,13 IN.......................   45.00
FIGURAL,OLD HICKORY,JACKSON.................................   22.50
FIGURAL,OLD MAN SITTING ON BARREL,GREEN.....................   40.00
FIGURAL,OLD SOL,ELEPHANT,AMBER..............................   35.00
FIGURAL,ONION,BLACK......................................... 125.00
FIGURAL,ONION,CIRCA 1700,BLACK..............................   65.00
FIGURAL,OWL,BROWN...........................................   10.50
FIGURAL,OWL,ENAMEL,GLASS EYES,6 3/4 IN.TALL.................   22.50
FIGURAL,OWL,MILK GLASS,SCREW CAP.....................ILLUS..   40.00
FIGURAL,OWL,RED.................................... 8.50 TO   10.50
FIGURAL,OYSTER SHELL................................COLOR..  XX.XX
FIGURAL,PAGODA,JAPANESE.....................................   10.95
FIGURAL,PEACOCK,5 IN.,CLEAR.................................   18.00
FIGURAL,PEASANT WOMAN.......................................   10.00
FIGURAL,PELICAN,14 IN.,GREEN................................    6.00
```

FIGURAL,MAN,FAT,AMBER

FIGURAL,MAN,SEATED,
VAN DUNCKS,GENEVER,AMBER

FIGURAL,OWL,
MILK GLASS,SCREW TOP

```
FIGURAL,PERSIAN SADDLE,BLUE-GREEN.............................      13.00
FIGURAL,PIG,DUFFY CRESCENT SALOON,AMBER...............ILLUS..     250.00
FIGURAL,PIG,NINETEENTH CENTURY........................COLOR..      XX.XX
FIGURAL,PINEAPPLE PATTERN,AMBER.......................ILLUS..     160.00
FIGURAL,PINEAPPLE,AMBER......................................     100.00
FIGURAL,PIRATE,DECANTER,11 1/2 IN. TALL,BLACKBEARD,SCOTCH...       17.50
FIGURAL,PISTOL,PERCUSSION CAP,TIN SCREW TOP,AMBER...........       30.00
FIGURAL,PLAYBOY,JAPANESE.....................................      12.95
FIGURAL,POODLE,13 IN.,GREEN..................................       7.50
FIGURAL,POTATO,PAINT.........................................      22.00
FIGURAL,POTATO,PAINTED,CLEAR.................................      15.00
FIGURAL,POTATO,SCREW CAP,AQUA................................      20.00
FIGURAL,POWDER HORN,GROUND MOUTH,PEWTER TOP,CLEAR............      16.00
FIGURAL,POWDER HORN,HALF PATTERN,SCREW CAP...................      15.00
FIGURAL,POWDER HORN,PRESSED GLASS,HANG UP....................       8.00
FIGURAL,PRETZEL,CERAMIC......................................      22.50
FIGURAL,PRINCESS,JAPANESE....................................      12.95
FIGURAL,PRIZEFIGHTER STATUE,OLD-FASHIONED BOXING OUTFIT.....        3.50
FIGURAL,QUEEN ALEXANDRIA,BOURNES POTTERIES,GLAZE,TAN & BROWN       50.00
FIGURAL,QUEEN ELIZABETH......................................      10.00
FIGURAL,RAVEN,BLACK..........................................      29.95
FIGURAL,RAVEN,GERMAN.........................................      17.50
FIGURAL,REVOLVER,SCREW TOP,AMBER,9 3/4 IN....................      12.00
FIGURAL,REVOLVER,TIN SCREW CAP,9 1/2 IN.,AMBER...............      22.00
FIGURAL,RIVER QUEEN BOAT........................... 10.50 TO      11.75
FIGURAL,ROCKINGHAM BOOT,SQUARE TOES,6 IN.....................      90.00
FIGURAL,ROCKINGHAM BOOT,SQUARE TOES,7 IN.....................     100.00
FIGURAL,ROLLING PIN..........................................       7.00
FIGURAL,ROLLING PIN,CORK.....................................       9.00
FIGURAL,ROLLING PIN,SCREW CAP................................       5.50
FIGURAL,ROOSEVELT,JAPANESE...................................      12.95
FIGURAL,ROOSTER,ASHTRAY......................................      17.50
FIGURAL,ROUND THE WORLD,STRATOSPHERE BALLOON,P.LUS,D.SHERMAN      16.50
FIGURAL,SAD HOUND............................................      25.00
FIGURAL,SAILOR........................................COLOR..      XX.XX
FIGURAL,SAMURAI,JAPANESE.....................................      21.95
FIGURAL,SCROLL,PINT,AQUA.....................................      35.00
FIGURAL,SEDAN CHAIR,JAPANESE.................................       9.95
FIGURAL,SENORITA.............................................       8.50
FIGURAL,SENORITA,HEAD FORMS STOPPER,MILK GLASS,10 IN.TALL...       12.00
FIGURAL,SHAMPOODLE,COBALT....................................      14.00
FIGURAL,SHOE SHAPED,CURLED TOE,EMBOSSED,PHALON & SON,N.Y.,
  CLEAR......................................................      10.00
FIGURAL,SHOE,SCREW TOP,AMETHYST.......................ILLUS..      65.00
FIGURAL,SITTING BEAR.........................................       3.00
FIGURAL,SITTING BEAR,MILK GLASS,WHITE........................     110.00
FIGURAL,SMILING INDIAN,BUBBLY GREEN,LIMA,PERU,FEDERAL LAW...       22.00
FIGURAL,SMOKISAN,JAPANESE....................................       6.95
FIGURAL,SOLDIER.......................................COLOR..      XX.XX
FIGURAL,SPARK PLUG...........................................       8.00
FIGURAL,STATUE OF LIBERTY,MILK GLASS.........................     125.00
FIGURAL,TARBABY,2 IN.,HAND DECORATED,CIRCA 1915..............       1.50
FIGURAL,TEDDY BEAR,GREEN.....................................      10.00
FIGURAL,TOILET WATER,SATIN FINISH,MILK GLASS,WHITE,PAIR.....       46.00
FIGURAL,TOREADOR.............................................       8.50
FIGURAL,TSUNODARU,JAPANESE...................................      14.95
FIGURAL,TURKEY TROT,CHINA,COUPLE DANCING.....................      12.00
FIGURAL,TURKEY,ROAST,4 1/2 IN.,AMBER.........................      27.00
FIGURAL,TURNIP,8 IN.,CORKER..................................      15.00
FIGURAL,TURTLE,HEAD IS STOPPER,AMBER.........................      40.00
FIGURAL,TURTLE,MERRY CHRISTMAS ON STOMACH,TIN SCREW CAP.....       10.00
FIGURAL,TURTLE,TIN CAP,5 1/2 IN.,CLEAR.......................      35.00
FIGURAL,TURTLE,5 1/2 X 4 IN.,CLEAR...........................      20.00
FIGURAL,TWIN BIRD BY STRIKOW.................................      30.00
FIGURAL,TWO LOVERS,JAPANESE..................................      26.95
```

FIGURAL, PIG,
DUFFY CRESCENT SALOON, AMBER

FIGURAL, PINEAPPLE
PATTERN, AMBER

FIGURAL, SHOE, SCREW TOP,
AMETHYST

```
FIGURAL,UNION CLASPED HANDS,WHITTLED,1/2 PINT,AMBER.........     95.00
FIGURAL,VAN DUNCK COACHMAN,AMBER...........................    110.00
FIGURAL,VIOLIN,AMBER.......................................      1.50
FIGURAL,VIOLIN,BLUE,HANGER,PAIR............................     45.00
FIGURAL,VIOLIN,BRACKET,MUSIC SCALE ON BACK,10 IN.,PALE BLUE.    20.00
FIGURAL,VIOLIN,COBALT BLUE.................................      2.00
FIGURAL,VIOLIN,EARS,CLEAR..................................      5.00
FIGURAL,VIOLIN,6 IN.,CLEAR.................................      8.00
FIGURAL,VIOLIN,8 IN.,PAIR,COBALT...........................      7.00
FIGURAL,VIOLIN,10 IN.,COBALT...............................     15.00
FIGURAL,WAITER,BLACK HEAD..................................    200.00
FIGURAL,WASHINGTON BUST,JACQUIN,COBALT.....................     25.00
FIGURAL,WASHINGTON,JAPANESE.................................     12.95
FIGURAL,WEEPING HOUND,PURPLE...............................     11.50
FIGURAL,WHISKBROOM,BISQUE..................................     35.00
FIGURAL,WHISKBROOM,CLEAR...................................     14.00
FIGURAL,WHISKBROOM,PINT,CLEAR..............................     14.00
FIGURAL,WHISKBROOM,1/2 PINT,CLEAR..........................     14.00
FIGURAL,WORLD'S FAIR 1969 EMBOSSED MAP,MILK GLASS..........      8.00
FIGURAL,WORLD'S FAIR,NEW YORK 1939,MILK GLASS..............     11.50
FIGURAL,6 IN.,AMBER.......................................      10.00
FIRE EXTINGUISHER,ACID LINE,AMETHYST.......................      2.00
FIRE EXTINGUISHER,ACID LINE,AQUA...........................      2.00
FIRE EXTINGUISHER,CONN.FACTORY.............................      3.50
FIRE EXTINGUISHER,CORSET SHAPE,ICE BLUE,PAIR...............     32.50
FIRE EXTINGUISHER,HARDEN'S STAR,7 IN.,BLUE.................     20.00
FIRE EXTINGUISHER,HARDEN'S STAR,7 IN.,QUILTED,DATED,FOOTED,
  BLUE....................................................      20.00
FIRE EXTINGUISHER,HARDEN'S,BLUE............................     22.00
FIRE EXTINGUISHER,12 SIDED,1880,AMBER......................      3.50
FIRE GRENADE,HARDEN'S,RIBBED,BLUE..........................     20.00
FIRE GRENADE,3 SECTION,QUILTED,COBALT,AMBER & CLEAR........     60.00
  FITZGERALD, SEE OLD FITZGERALD
```

FLASKS HAVE BEEN MADE SINCE THE 18TH CENTURY IN
AMERICA. THE FREE BLOWN, MOLD BLOWN, AND DECORATED
FLASKS ARE ALL POPULAR WITH COLLECTORS. THE NUMBERS
THAT APPEAR WITH SOME OF THE ENTRIES ARE THOSE USED IN
THE MC KEARIN BOOK, AMERICAN GLASS.

```
FLASK,A LITTLE MORE GRAPE CAPTAIN BRAGG,1847.........COLOR..   XX.XX
FLASK,A.M.BININGER & CO.,BOURBON,& BARREL,AMBER..............  110.00
FLASK,A.M.BININGER & CO.,HANDLE,AMBER........................  150.00
FLASK,ALBANY GLASS WORKS,CLEVENGER,AMETHYST..................   25.00
FLASK,ALE,MILK GLASS,WHITE...................................    5.00
FLASK,AMBER.............................................. 4.00 TO
                                                                7.00
FLASK,AMERICAN EAGLE,AQUA....................................   67.50
FLASK,AMERICAN EAGLE,PONTIL,G-11 73..........................  100.00
FLASK,ANCHOR SADDLE,ANCHOR & ROPE IN CENTER,PINT,AMBER......    10.00
FLASK,ANCHOR SADDLE,ANCHOR IN CENTER,1/2 PINT,AMBER.........    10.00
FLASK,ANCHOR-EAGLE,NEW LONDON GLASS WORKS,1/2 PINT,AQUA.....   121.00
FLASK,BACK BAR,PRESSED GLASS,PAIR,CLEAR.....................     5.00
FLASK,BALD EAGLE,PETT'S,1/2 PINT,CLEAR......................     5.00
FLASK,BALTIMORE GLASS WORKS,ANCHOR,SHEATH,QUART,AQUA........    85.00
FLASK,BELLOWS SHAPED,BLOWN...................................    9.00
FLASK,BEN HUR,J.CROSSMAN'S SONS,PINT,AMBER...................   10.00
FLASK,BIMAL.................................................     1.00
FLASK,BINSWANGER & BRO.,SIMON IN HORSESHOE,CLEAR............     4.00
FLASK,BLAN KENHEYM & NOLET,APPLIED COLLAR,OLIVE.............     5.00
FLASK,BLOWN IN MOLD,GROUND TOP,CLEAR........................     6.00
FLASK,BLOWN IN MOLD,STRAP SIDE,CLEAR........................     2.50
FLASK,BLOWN IN MOLD,STRAP SIDE,PINT,AMBER...................     4.00
FLASK,BLOWN IN MOLD,STRAP SIDE,YELLOW GREEN.................     4.00
FLASK,BLOWN,PINCHED DOUBLE NECK,CLEAR.......................     2.50
FLASK,BOTTOM HALF ENCASED IN PEWTER,TOP HALF IN LEATHER,
     1865...................................................     3.95
FLASK,BRYON-SCOTT,AMBER.....................................   165.00
FLASK,BUBBLE NECK,AMBER.....................................     3.00
FLASK,BUNKER HILL,PIREY OPALESCENT MILK WHITE...............    90.00
FLASK,BUST OF COLUMBIA WEARING LIBERTY CAP..........COLOR..   XX.XX
FLASK,BYRON-SCOTT,AMBER.....................................   176.00
FLASK,CAHN BELT & CO........................................     4.00
FLASK,CALABASH,APPLIED ROUND DOUBLE COLLAR,GREEN............    35.00
FLASK,CALABASH,HUNTER & FISHERMAN,APPLIED COLLAR,AQUA.......    25.00
FLASK,CALABASH,HUNTER & FISHERMAN,QUART,AMBER...............    55.00
FLASK,CALABASH,HUNTER & FISHERMAN,QUART,AQUA................    32.50
FLASK,CALABASH,HUNTER & FISHERMAN,QUART,BURGUNDY............    90.00
FLASK,CALABASH,HUNTER & FISHERMAN,QUART,GOLDEN AMBER........    65.00
FLASK,CALABASH,HUNTER & FISHERMAN,QUART,GREEN...............    85.00
FLASK,CALABASH,MASONIC,UNION & EAGLE,AQUA.......... 35.00 TO    45.00
FLASK,CALABASH,TREE,WHEAT SHEAF,PEACOCK GREEN...............   126.00
FLASK,CALABASH,UNION & CLASPED HANDS,AQUA...................    38.50
FLASK,CANNON & FLAG,UNION & CLASPED HAND,1/2 PINT.....;.....    50.00
FLASK,CAPTAIN BRAGG,TAYLOR-WASHINGTON,QUART,AQUA............    90.00
FLASK,CHAPIN & GORE SOUR MASH 1867,AMBER....................    40.00
FLASK,CHESTNUT,AMBER HANDLE.................................    27.00
FLASK,CHESTNUT,FLANGED LIP,RIBS,COBALT BLUE.................    65.00
FLASK,CHESTNUT,FLAT HANDLED,AMBER...........................    45.00
FLASK,CHESTNUT,FLATTENED,APPLIED HANDLE,AMBER...............    38.00
FLASK,CHESTNUT,FREE BLOWN,7 1/2 IN.,CLEAR OLIVE OPALINE.....    50.00
FLASK,CHESTNUT,GREEN........................................     1.00
FLASK,CHESTNUT,GROVE,POCKET.................................   110.00
FLASK,CHESTNUT,HANDLED,FREE BLOWN,PONTIL,AMBER..............    25.00
FLASK,CHESTNUT,LUDLOW,9 IN.,GREENISH AQUA...................    45.00
FLASK,CHESTNUT,MIDWESTERN,1/2 PINT,AMBER....................    50.00
FLASK,CHESTNUT,MIDWESTERN,6 1/4 IN. HIGH,16 SWIRLED RIBS,
     AQUA...................................................    75.00
FLASK,CHESTNUT,MIDWESTERN,14 RIB,AQUA.......................   110.00
FLASK,CHESTNUT,MIDWESTERN,24 RIB,SWIRL,AMBER................   190.00
FLASK,CHESTNUT,ZANESVILLE,24 RIB,AMBER......................    55.00
FLASK,CHESTNUT,ZANESVILLE,24 RIB,AQUA.......................    85.00
FLASK,CHESTNUT,2 MOLD,HANDLED,WHITTLED,RED AMBER............    25.00
FLASK,CHESTNUT,7 IN.,GREEN & CLEAR..........................    19.00
FLASK,CHESTNUT,36 VERTICAL RIBS,QUART,AMBER.................    45.00
FLASK,CLARK & WHITE SARATOGA TYPE,WHITTLED,OLIVE............    18.00
```

```
FLASK,CLASPED HAND,PINT,AQUA...................................    32.50
FLASK,CLASPED HANDS & DOVE UNION,PINT..........................    45.00
FLASK,CLASPED HANDS & DOVE UNION,1/2 PINT......................    50.00
FLASK,CLASPED HANDS UNION,QUART................................    55.00
FLASK,CLASPED HANDS,SHIELD,STARS,UNION,MEDALLION,REVERSE,
   AQUA,QUART.................................................    47.50
FLASK,CLEVENGER,PINT,AMETHYST..................................     2.50
FLASK,CLEVENGER,PINT,DARK AMBER................................     2.00
FLASK,CLEVENGER,PINT,GREEN.....................................     3.00
FLASK,CLEVENGER,PINT,ROYAL BLUE................................     2.00
FLASK,CLUB BOTTLE,24 RIBS SWIRLED TO LEFT,AQUA.................    40.00
FLASK,CLUB,MIDWESTERN,16 RIBS SWIRLED TO LEFT,AQUA.............    35.00
FLASK,CLUB,MIDWESTERN,16 RIBS,AQUA.............................    22.50
FLASK,CLUB,MIDWESTERN,24 RIBS SWIRLED TO LEFT,AQUA.............    40.00
FLASK,CLUB,24 RIBS SWIRLED TO RIGHT,30 VERTICAL RIBS,AQUA...    50.00
FLASK,CLYDE GLASS WORKS,N.Y.,EMBOSSED ON FACE,AQUA,PINT.....    35.00
FLASK,COFFIN...................................................     3.00
FLASK,COFFIN,EMBOSSED,EMERALD,8 OZ.............................    12.00
FLASK,COFFIN,METAL & CORK CAP,1/2 PINT,AMETHYST...............    10.00
FLASK,COFFIN,METAL & CORK CAP,1/2 PINT,CLEAR..................    10.00
FLASK,COLOGNE,SCROLL,BRASS SCREW CAP,MACHINE MADE,CLEAR.....     1.00
FLASK,COLONIAL,EAGLE,GREEN,NEW.................................     2.00
FLASK,COLONIAL,EAGLE,PURPLE,NEW................................     2.00
FLASK,CONGRESS & EMPIRE SARATOGA,WHITTLED,EMERALD.............    15.00
FLASK,CORN FOR THE WORLD,OPEN PONTIL,AQUA.........115.00 TO   125.00
FLASK,CORNUCOPIA,BASKET OF FLOWERS,OLIVE GREEN,1/2 PINT.....    55.00
FLASK,CORNUCOPIA,BASKET OF FRUIT,1/2 PINT,OLIVE..............    75.00
FLASK,CORNUCOPIA,BASKET,OLIVE GREEN,PINT.......................    50.00
FLASK,CORNUCOPIA,EAGLE,KEENE...................................    90.00
FLASK,CORNUCOPIA,EAGLE,OLIVE GREEN,PINT........................    75.00
FLASK,CORNUCOPIA,EAGLE,X TO LEFT,PINT,AQUA.....................    90.00
FLASK,CORNUCOPIA,PINT,OLIVE GREEN................ 75.00 TO     80.00
FLASK,CORNUCOPIA,URN,PINT,AMBER.................. 95.00 TO    110.00
FLASK,CORNUCOPIA,URN,PINT,GREEN................................    95.00
FLASK,CORNUCOPIA,URN,1/2 PINT..................................    76.00
FLASK,CORNUCOPIA,URN,1/2 PINT,AMBER............................    50.00
FLASK,CORNUCOPIA,URN,1/2 PINT,AQUA.............................    95.00
FLASK,CORNUCOPIA,1/2 PINT,AQUA.................................   150.00
FLASK,CORNUCOPIA,1/2 PINT,GREEN................................    85.00
FLASK,CORNUCOPIA,1/2 PINT,OLIVE GREEN............. 75.00 TO    85.00
FLASK,CRYSTAL,STERLING HINGED LID & JACKET,STEEPLECHASE
   SCENE.....................................................    15.00
FLASK,CUT GLASS,ORNATE GOLD TOP................................    14.00
FLASK,DOUBLE APPLIED LIP,1/2 POST,3 PART MOLD,BRISTOL BLACK.    25.00
FLASK,DOUBLE EAGLE,APPLIED RING MOUTH,PINT,AQUA..............    30.00
FLASK,DOUBLE EAGLE,AQUA,1/2 PINT...............................    37.50
FLASK,DOUBLE EAGLE,BLUE,PINT...................................    34.00
FLASK,DOUBLE EAGLE,CUNNINGHAM & CO.,PITTSBURGH,AQUA,QUART...    47.50
FLASK,DOUBLE EAGLE,OLIVE AMBER.................................   200.00
FLASK,DOUBLE EAGLE,PINT,AQUA...................................    35.00
FLASK,DOUBLE EAGLE,PITTSBURGH IN OVAL,PINT,AQUA..............    40.00
FLASK,DOUBLE EAGLE,PITTSBURGH,PENNA.,AQUA,1/2 PINT...........    43.00
FLASK,DOUBLE EAGLE,PLAIN OVAL PANEL,PINT.......................    35.00
FLASK,DOUBLE EAGLE,RINGED TOP,PINT,AQUA........................    40.00
FLASK,DOUBLE EAGLE,SHEARED MOUTH,1/2 PINT,AMBER..............    45.00
FLASK,DOUBLE EAGLE,STODDARD,1/2 PINT...........................    76.00
FLASK,DOUBLE EAGLE,1/2 PINT,AQUA...............................    28.00
FLASK,DOUBLE EAGLE,1/2 PINT,PITTSBURG PA.IN OVAL,AQUA........    25.00
FLASK,DOUBLE EAGLES,3 STARS,3 BARS,APPLIED COLLAR,AQUA......    30.00
FLASK,DOUBLE SHEAF OF RYE,PINT,AQUA............................    70.00
FLASK,E.PLURIBUS UNUM,EAGLE DESIGN,NEW.........................     2.75
FLASK,EAGLE & GRAPES,EAGLE & STARS ON FRONT,GRAPES,NEW......     2.75
FLASK,EAGLE & GRAPES,EMPIRE GLASS WORKS,NEW...................     2.75
FLASK,EAGLE & 18 STARS,REVERSE CORNUCOPIA,1/2 PINT,GREEN....   100.00
FLASK,EAGLE OVER SHIELD,UNION,1/2 PINT,AMBER.................    90.00
```

```
FLASK,EAGLE,AQUA,QUART.......................................    45.00
FLASK,EAGLE,BASKET OF FRUIT,OLIVE COLOR,MARKED KEENE,PINT...    95.00
FLASK,EAGLE,C & I IN CIRCLE,1/2 PINT,AQUA...................    95.00
FLASK,EAGLE,C.1860.......................................COLOR..  XX.XX
FLASK,EAGLE,CORNUCOPIA,PINT,AMBER..........................   150.00
FLASK,EAGLE,DOUBLE,1/2 PINT,GREEN..........................    70.00
FLASK,EAGLE,EAGLE TO LEFT,CUNNINGHAM-PITTS.IN OVAL,PINT,AQUA   85.00
FLASK,EAGLE,EMPIRE GLASS WORKS.............................     2.75
FLASK,EAGLE,HEAD TO LEFT,1/2 PINT,AMBER....................    80.00
FLASK,EAGLE,LARGE HEAD,PINT,AQUA...........................    70.00
FLASK,EAGLE,LOUISVILLE,QUART,AQUA..........................   135.00
FLASK,EAGLE,LOUISVILLE,1/2 PINT,AQUA.......................   110.00
FLASK,EAGLE,PINT,AQUA......................................    95.00
FLASK,EAGLE,PINT,GREEN.....................................   160.00
FLASK,EAGLE,TREE,PINT,AQUA.................................    95.00
FLASK,EAGLE,WELLINGTON,QUART,OLIVE AMBER...................   115.00
FLASK,EAGLE,WREATH,1/2 PINT,AQUA...........................    75.00
FLASK,EAGLE,12 STARS,CLEAR,GEORGE WASHINGTON,1732-1932,
  8 IN.TALL................................................    10.00
FLASK,EARLY FORM,16 VERTICAL MELON RIB,AQUA................    35.00
FLASK,EARLY 19TH CENTURY.................................COLOR..  XX.XX
FLASK,EMBOSSED ANCHOR AND CHAIN,1/2 PT.....................     9.00
FLASK,EMBOSSED E.R.BETTERTON & CO.,DISTILLERS,CHATTANOOGA,
  TENN.....................................................     7.00
FLASK,EMBOSSED IN CIRCLE,PRESCRIBED BY R.V.PIERCE,M.D.,BLUE.    8.00
FLASK,ENCASED PEWTER & LEATHER COVER,PEWTER TOP,1/2 PINT....    8.50
FLASK,ETCHED SHIP,PEWTER CAP,GERMAN HALF POST METHOD.......    75.00
FLASK,FLAG,FOR OUR COUNTRY,EAGLE REVERSE,PINT,AQUA.........    96.00
FLASK,FLANGED LIP,CIRCA 1600,HOLLAND,DEEP RED..............    27.50
FLASK,FOR PIKE'S PEAK,APPLIED RING TOP,PINT,AQUA...........    70.00
FLASK,FOR PIKE'S PEAK,C.1872.............................COLOR..  XX.XX
FLASK,FOR PIKE'S PEAK,HUNTER & DEER,PINT,BLUE..............    25.00
FLASK,FOR PIKE'S PEAK,MAN WITH CAP WALKING TO LEFT,PINT,AQUA   40.00
FLASK,FOR PIKE'S PEAK,MAN WITH CAP WALKING TO LEFT,1/2 PINT,
  AQUA.....................................................    32.50
FLASK,FOR PIKE'S PEAK,MAN WITH HAT WALKING TO LEFT,EAGLE,
  PINT.....................................................    40.00
FLASK,FOR PIKE'S PEAK,MAN,KNAPSACK,CANE,FOR PIKE'S PEAK,
  1/2 PINT.................................................    42.00
FLASK,FOR PIKE'S PEAK,PROSPECTOR,EAGLE,CREDO ON REVERSE....    86.00
FLASK,FOR PIKE'S PEAK,TRAVELER & OLD RYE IN OVAL,AQUA......    45.00
FLASK,FREE BLOWN,APPLIED RING COLLAR,AMBER.................    50.00
FLASK,FREE BLOWN,LONG NECK APPLIED COLLAR LIP,GREEN........    15.00
FLASK,FREE BLOWN,MIDWEST,APPLIED COLLAR LIP,GREEN..........    22.50
FLASK,FREE BLOWN,PINT,BLACK................................    20.00
FLASK,FRIEBERG & KAHN,TAPERED & RIBBED,1/2 PINT............     5.00
FLASK,FULL MEASURE 1/2 PINT,CLEAR..........................     1.50
FLASK,G I-28,GREENISH AQUA.................................   175.00
FLASK,GENERAL TAYLOR NEVER SURRENDERS,NEW..................     2.75
FLASK,GENERAL WASHINGTON,BEADED EDGE,PINT,AQUA.............   215.00
FLASK,GEORGE WASHINGTON CENTENNIAL,NEW.....................     2.50
FLASK,GIN,CRUDE,ROUGH PONTIL,APPLIED LIP,OLIVE.............    25.00
FLASK,GIRL ON BIKE,PINT,AQUA...............................   140.00
FLASK,GLOBULAR,FREE BLOWN,APPLIED COLLAR MOUTH,AQUA........    40.00
FLASK,GLOBULAR,MIDWEST,REDDISH AMBER.......................   200.00
FLASK,GLOBULAR,MIDWEST,24 RIBS SWIRL TO RIGHT,GREEN........   350.00
FLASK,GLOBULAR,MIDWESTERN,AQUA.............................    80.00
FLASK,GLOBULAR,ZANESVILLE,AMBER............................   140.00
FLASK,GLOBULAR,ZANESVILLE,24 RIB,SWIRL,AMBER...............   200.00
FLASK,GLOBULAR,ZANESVILLE,24 RIBS SWIRLED TO LEFT,AMBER....   225.00
FLASK,GLOBULAR,ZANESVILLE,24 RIBS SWIRLED TO RIGHT,AQUA....    70.00
FLASK,GLOBULAR,24 RIBS SWIRLED TO RIGHT,AMBER..............   190.00
FLASK,GLOBULAR,24 RIBS,SWIRL,APPLE GREEN...................   350.00
FLASK,GRANITE GLASS CO.,AMBER..............................    70.00
FLASK,GREEN,LEATHER COVERED,ORANTE KEY OPENS STOPPER.......   125.00
```

```
FLASK,GUARANTEED FULL 1/2 PINT,BLOWN IN MOLD,CLEAR..........      2.25
FLASK,HANDBLOWN,GROUND PONTIL,ENGLISH C.1800,AMETHYST.......     95.00
FLASK,HISTORICAL,CLASPED HANDS,UNION & STARS,QUART,AQUA.....     58.00
FLASK,HISTORICAL,EAGLE,1/2 PINT,1825.......................    300.00
FLASK,HISTORICAL,LIBERTY WITH EAGLE,WILLINGTON GLASS CO.,
   GREEN..................................................    135.00
FLASK,HISTORICAL,SAPPHIRE BLUE,QUART.......................    475.00
FLASK,HISTORICAL,SUMMER-WINTER,BIRD,BUBBLY,QUART,AQUA.......     49.50
FLASK,HISTORICAL,WASHINGTON-TAYLOR,BUBBLY,PINT,AQUA.........     45.00
FLASK,HOLLAND,FLANGED LIP,DEEP RED,CIRCA 1600..............     27.50
FLASK,HUNTER & FISHERMAN,CALABASH,QUART,AQUA...............     75.00
FLASK,HUNTER & FISHERMAN,NINETEENTH CENTURY..........COLOR..     XX.XX
FLASK,INDIAN QUEEN,1867,AMBER..............................     96.00
FLASK,INDIAN,REVERSE EAGLE.................................    150.00
FLASK,J & E MAHONEY........................................      5.00
FLASK,J.K.B.MASONIC,PINT,GREEN.............................    850.00
FLASK,J.P.,JUSTUS PERRY,AQUA...............................     51.00
FLASK,J.P.,JUSTUS PERRY,PINT,BLUE-GREEN....................    275.00
   FLASK, JENNY LIND, SEE ALSO FIGURAL, JENNY LIND
FLASK,JENNY LIND...................................ILLUS..     50.00
```

FLASK,JENNY LIND

```
FLASK,JENNY LIND,C.1850............................COLOR..     XX.XX
FLASK,JOS.A.MANGUS & CO.,EMBOSSED DRAGON,1/2 PINT,CLEAR.....      3.50
FLASK,K.C.C.N.C. MASONIC,PINT,OLIVE........................    250.00
FLASK,KNIGHTS OF PYTHIAS BIENNIAL,BOSTON,1908,EMBLEM,AMBER..      8.50
FLASK,KOSSUTH,TREE IN FOLIAGE,AQUA.........................     60.00
FLASK,KOSSUTH,U.S.STEAM FRIGATE MISSISSIPPI,AQUA...........    110.00
FLASK,LEATHER COVER,SHERMAN HOUSE BOURBON,FT.DEARBORN HOTEL.      9.00
FLASK,LEWIS 66.............................................      5.00
FLASK,LIBERTY & EAGLE,WILLINGTON GLASS CO.,1/2 PINT,AMBER..     70.00
FLASK,LIQUOR,TRADE MARK D & R SPECIAL,BLOWN IN MOLD,AMBER...      3.00
FLASK,LITTLEMORE...........................................      4.00
FLASK,LOG CABIN,ANCHOR,SPRING GARDEN,PINT,AQUA.............     80.00
FLASK,LOTION BOTTLE,STAMPED SEARS,AMBER,1/2 PINT...........     10.00
FLASK,LOUISVILLE DOUBLE EAGLE,QUART,AQUA...................    106.00
FLASK,LOUISVILLE,DOUBLE EAGLE,PINT,AQUA....................    106.00
FLASK,LOUISVILLE,RIBBED,PINT...............................    135.00
FLASK,MAIL ORDER HOUSE.....................................      4.00
FLASK,MAJOR RINGOLD,TAYLOR,PINT,AQUA ......................    110.00
FLASK,MANTUA,16 RIB,SWIRLED CHESTNUT.......................    150.00
FLASK,MASONIC INSIGNIA.............................2.75 TO      7.50
FLASK,MASONIC-EAGLE,ZANESVILLE,PINT,BLUE AQUA..............    150.00
FLASK,MASONIC,C.1815...............................COLOR..     XX.XX
```

```
FLASK,MASONIC,C.1815-1860............................COLOR..      XX.XX
FLASK,MASONIC,EAGLE,PINT,AMBER...........................         210.00
FLASK,MASONIC,MC KEARIN G IV-1.......................COLOR..      XX.XX
FLASK,MASONIC,UNION & EAGLE,QUART,AQUA......................      25.00
FLASK,MASONIC,7 1/2 IN. HIGH...............................       2.75
FLASK,MC KEARIN G I-1,GENERAL WASHINGTON,BLUISH GREEN.......      40.00
FLASK,MC KEARIN G I-2,PINT,GREEN...........................       120.00
FLASK,MC KEARIN G I-3,PINT,GENERAL WASHINGTON,BLUISH GREEN..      35.00
FLASK,MC KEARIN G I-3,TOILET BOTTLE,3 MOLD,BLOWN,CLEAR......      12.50
FLASK,MC KEARIN G I-6,PINT,GENERAL WASHINGTON,AQUA..........      35.00
FLASK,MC KEARIN G I-10,GREENISH AQUA.......................       245.00
FLASK,MC KEARIN G I-24,AQUA................................       115.00
FLASK,MC KEARIN G I-26,CLEAR,AMETHYST TINT.................       375.00
FLASK,MC KEARIN G I-29,BLOWN 3 MOLD,PRESSED STOPPER,CLEAR...      30.00
FLASK,MC KEARIN G I-31,AMBER...............................       165.00
FLASK,MC KEARIN G I-34,AQUA................................       65.00
FLASK,MC KEARIN G I-34,OLIVE AMBER.........................       160.00
FLASK,MC KEARIN G I-35,AQUA................................       70.00
FLASK,MC KEARIN G I-38,QUART,AQUA..........................       30.00
FLASK,MC KEARIN G I-39,EMERALD GREEN.......................       110.00
FLASK,MC KEARIN G I-50,AQUA................................       50.00
FLASK,MC KEARIN G I-55,DARK AMBER..........................       160.00
FLASK,MC KEARIN G I-60,LOCKPORT GLASS WORKS,QUART,AQUA......      200.00
FLASK,MC KEARIN G I-65,PINT,AQUA...........................       265.00
FLASK,MC KEARIN G I-71,PINT,MAJOR RINGGOLD,CLEAR............      20.00
FLASK,MC KEARIN G I-79,AQUA................................       185.00
FLASK,MC KEARIN G I-80,DE WITT CLINTON,1825..........COLOR..      XX.XX
FLASK,MC KEARIN G I-80,LAFAYETTE COVENTRY,PINT,OLIVE AMBER..      440.00
FLASK,MC KEARIN G I-85,LAFAYETTE COVENTRY,PINT,AMBER........      350.00
FLASK,MC KEARIN G I-86,LAFAYETTE COVENTRY C-T,1/2 PINT,AMBER      130.00
FLASK,MC KEARIN G I-89,OLIVE...............................       285.00
FLASK,MC KEARIN G I-96,BENJAMIN FRANKLIN..............COLOR..     XX.XX
FLASK,MC KEARIN G I-97,QUART,YELLOW GREEN...................      99.00
FLASK,MC KEARIN G I-103,AQUA...............................       85.00
FLASK,MC KEARIN G I-112,FRIGATE,MISSISSIPPI..........COLOR..      XX.XX
FLASK,MC KEARIN G I-121,AQUA...............................       150.00
FLASK,MC KEARIN G II-11,AQUA.....................175.00 TO       195.00
FLASK,MC KEARIN G II-22,BLOWN 3 MOLD,STOPPER,CLEAR..........      30.00
FLASK,MC KEARIN G II-24,AQUA...............................       165.00
FLASK,MC KEARIN G II-24,PINT,DOUBLE EAGLE,AQUA.............       80.00
FLASK,MC KEARIN G II-26,QUART,DOUBLE EAGLE,BLUE.............      135.00
FLASK,MC KEARIN G II-31,DARK OLIVE.........................       175.00
FLASK,MC KEARIN G II-35,AQUA...............................       120.00
FLASK,MC KEARIN G II-48,AQUA...............................       95.00
FLASK,MC KEARIN G II-55,AQUA...............................       85.00
FLASK,MC KEARIN G II-60,AQUA...............................       275.00
FLASK,MC KEARIN G II-60,1/2 PINT,CHARTER OAK & EAGLE,AMBER..      325.00
FLASK,MC KEARIN G II-65,OLIVE AMBER........................       135.00
FLASK,MC KEARIN G II-70,PINT,DOUBLE EAGLE,AMBER.............      100.00
FLASK,MC KEARIN G II-72,PONTIL,OLIVE GREEN.................       85.00
FLASK,MC KEARIN G II-73,PINT,EAGLE & CORNUCOPIA,OLIVE AMBER.      55.00
FLASK,MC KEARIN G II-76,EAGLE.......................COLOR..       XX.XX
FLASK,MC KEARIN G II-112,LOUIS KOSSUTH,C.1850........COLOR..      XX.XX
FLASK,MC KEARIN G III-4,CORNUCOPIA & RUN,GREEN.............       19.00
FLASK,MC KEARIN G III-4,PINT,CORNUCOPIA & PRODUCE,OLIVE
   GREEN...................................................       37.50
FLASK,MC KEARIN G III-5,OLIVE AMBER........................       95.00
FLASK,MC KEARIN G III-7,CORNUCOPIA & URN,AMBER.............       20.00
FLASK,MC KEARIN G III-7,OLIVE AMBER........................       55.00
FLASK,MC KEARIN G III-7,1/2 PINT,CORNUCOPIA & BASKET,GREEN..      45.00
FLASK,MC KEARIN G III-7,1/2 PINT,LIP FOLDED INWARD,OLIVE
   AMBER...................................................       35.00
FLASK,MC KEARIN G III-15,SUNBURST,BLOWN 3 MOLD,PRESSED
   STOPPER.................................................       40.00
FLASK,MC KEARIN G III-19,QUART,SUNBURST,AMBER..............       470.00
```

```
FLASK,MC KEARIN G IV-1,CLEAR GREEN...........................    245.00
FLASK,MC KEARIN G IV-18,AMBER...............................    240.00
FLASK,MC KEARIN G IV-18,AMBER...............................    195.00
FLASK,MC KEARIN G IV-32,BLUISH AQUA.........................     65.00
FLASK,MC KEARIN G IV-32,PINT,MASONIC COLLAR LIP,AMBER.......    170.00
FLASK,MC KEARIN G IV-32,YELLOW AMBER........................    265.00
FLASK,MC KEARIN G IV-34,MASONIC,AQUA........................    225.00
FLASK,MC KEARIN G IV-38,AQUA................................     37.50
FLASK,MC KEARIN G IV-40,REDDISH AMBER.......................     85.00
FLASK,MC KEARIN G IV-42,EMERALD GREEN,YELLOWISH TINT........    115.00
FLASK,MC KEARIN G V,SUCCESS TO THE RAILROAD..........COLOR..     XX.XX
FLASK,MC KEARIN G V-3,OLIVE AMBER...........................    195.00
FLASK,MC KEARIN G V-5,OLIVE AMBER...........................    195.00
FLASK,MC KEARIN G V-8,YELLOW AMBER..........................    165.00
FLASK,MC KEARIN G V-10,RAILROAD,SHEARED LIP,1/2 PINT........    300.00
FLASK,MC KEARIN G VI-67,PINEAPPLE,QUART,AMBER...............    150.00
FLASK,MC KEARIN G VII-3,OLIVE AMBER.........................    425.20
FLASK,MC KEARIN G VII-4,E.G.BOOZ'S OLD CABIN WHISKEY,AMBER..     80.00
FLASK,MC KEARIN G VII-9,KEENE SUNBURST,OLIVE GREEN..........    425.00
FLASK,MC KEARIN G VII-17,1/2 PINT,CLEAR.....................    525.00
FLASK,MC KEARIN G VII-28,1/2 PINT,SUNBURST,PONTIL,AQUA......    310.00
FLASK,MC KEARIN G VIII-2,PINT,SUNBURST,GREEN................    150.00
FLASK,MC KEARIN G VIII-9,AMBER..............................    215.00
FLASK,MC KEARIN G VIII 9,OLIVE GREEN........................    215.00
FLASK,MC KEARIN G VIII-16,1/2 PINT,YELLOW OLIVE.............     20.00
FLASK,MC KEARIN G IX,QUART,AQUA.............................    300.00
FLASK,MC KEARIN G IX-1/2 PINT,AQUA..........................     70.00
FLASK,MC KEARIN G IX-1,AQUA.................................     55.00
FLASK,MC KEARIN G IX-1,QUART,CORNFLOWER BLUE.........ILLUS..    140.00
FLASK,MC KEARIN G IX-1,QUART,DEEP BLUISH AQUA...............     25.00
FLASK,MC KEARIN G IX-1,QUART,GOLDEN AMBER...................     60.00
FLASK,MC KEARIN G IX-1,QUART,LIGHT EMERALD GREEN............     50.00
FLASK,MC KEARIN G IX-1,QUART,RINGED NECK,DEEP AQUA..........     30.00
FLASK,MC KEARIN G IX-1,QUART,SAPPHIRE BLUE..................    180.00
FLASK,MC KEARIN G IX-1,QUART,STRONG CORNFLOWER BLUE.........    140.00
FLASK,MC KEARIN G IX-2,AQUA.................................     60.00
FLASK,MC KEARIN G IX-2,QUART,AQUA...........................     25.00
FLASK,MC KEARIN G IX-2,QUART,BENT NECK,MOONSTONE............     60.00
FLASK,MC KEARIN G IX-2,QUART,BRILLIANT CITRON..............    180.00
FLASK,MC KEARIN G IX-2,QUART,DEEP SAPPHIRE BLUE.............    200.00
FLASK,MC KEARIN G IX-2,QUART,DOUBLE RINGED COLLAR,YELLOW....    180.00
FLASK,MC KEARIN G IX-2,QUART,LONG NECK,MEDIUM TO DARK AMBER.     80.00
FLASK,MC KEARIN G IX 2,QUART,MEDIUM EMERALD GREEN,..........     60.00
FLASK,MC KEARIN G IX-2,QUART,PINK MOONSTONE........ 45.00 TO     50.00
FLASK,MC KEARIN G IX-2,QUART,ROUGH LIP,AQUA.................     20.00
FLASK,MC KEARIN G IX-2,QUART,SAPPHIRE BLUE...........ILLUS..    200.00
FLASK,MC KEARIN G IX-2,QUART,SPARKLING AQUA.................     25.00
FLASK,MC KEARIN G IX-2,QUART,YELLOWISH OLIVE................    120.00
FLASK,MC KEARIN G IX-2A,GOLDEN AMBER........................    125.00
FLASK,MC KEARIN G IX-3,QUART,AMBER...................ILLUS..    110.00
FLASK,MC KEARIN G IX-3,QUART,APPLIED RINGED NECK,AQUA.......     20.00
FLASK,MC KEARIN G IX-3,QUART,GOLDEN AMBER...................    120.00
FLASK,MC KEARIN G IX-3,QUART,LEANS BACK 10 DEGREES,AMBER....    110.00
FLASK,MC KEARIN G IX-3,QUART,OVAL WHIRLPOOL ON SIDE,SAPPHIRE    160.00
FLASK,MC KEARIN G IX-3,QUART,RINGED NECK,MOSS GREEN.........    200.00
FLASK,MC KEARIN G IX-3,QUART,TURQUOISE......................     50.00
FLASK,MC KEARIN G IX-3,QUART,YELLOWISH CITRON........ILLUS..    140.00
FLASK,MC KEARIN G IX-4,QUART,GREENISH AQUA..................     25.00
FLASK,MC KEARIN G IX-4,QUART,RINGED NECK,AQUA...............     30.00
FLASK,MC KEARIN G IX-5,QUART,BLUISH GREEN...................     35.00
FLASK,MC KEARIN G IX-5,QUART,EMERALD GREEN..................     85.00
FLASK,MC KEARIN G IX-6,AQUA.................................    110.00
FLASK,MC KEARIN G IX-6,QUART,GREENISH AQUA..................     55.00
FLASK,MC KEARIN G IX-6,QUART,LOUISVILLE KY & GLASSWORKS,
  CITRON....................................................    130.00
```

```
FLASK,MC KEARIN G IX-6,QUART,LOUISVILLE KY & GLASSWORKS,
  GREEN...................................................     55.00
FLASK,MC KEARIN G IX-8,PINT,GREEN...........................     40.00
FLASK,MC KEARIN G IX-8,PINT,LOUISVILLE KY.& GLASSWORKS,AQUA.     60.00
FLASK,MC KEARIN G IX-8,PINT,ROUGH FIRE POLISHED LIP,GREEN...     40.00
FLASK,MC KEARIN G IX-9,PINT,GOLDEN AMBER....................    120.00
FLASK,MC KEARIN G IX-9,PINT,LOUISVILLE KY.& GLASSWORKS,AQUA.     80.00
FLASK,MC KEARIN G IX-9,PINT,ROUGH FIRE POLISHED LIP,GREEN...     85.00
FLASK,MC KEARIN G IX-10,APPLIED BAND BELOW LIP,TURQUOISE....     25.00
FLASK,MC KEARIN G IX-10,CLEAR,PINKISH EFFECT................    185.00
FLASK,MC KEARIN G IX-10,EMERALD GREEN.......................    185.00
FLASK,MC KEARIN G IX-10,MOONSTONE...........................    185.00
FLASK,MC KEARIN G IX-10,PINT,AMBER..........................     90.00
FLASK,MC KEARIN G IX-10,PINT,AMBER SWIRLS,AQUA..............    160.00
FLASK,MC KEARIN G IX-10,PINT,AMETHYSTINE....................     60.00
FLASK,MC KEARIN G IX-10,PINT,AQUA...........................     30.00
FLASK,MC KEARIN G IX-10,PINT,BUBBLY,YELLOWISH GREEN.........     80.00
FLASK,MC KEARIN G IX-10,PINT,DEEP AMETHYST..................     35.00
FLASK,MC KEARIN G IX-10,PINT,EMERALD GREEN..................     90.00
FLASK,MC KEARIN G IX-10,PINT,FLARED MOUTH,CLEAR & PINK......     50.00
FLASK,MC KEARIN G IX-10,PINT,FLARED MOUTH,KEYED BASE,AQUA...     25.00
FLASK,MC KEARIN G IX-10,PINT,GRAYISH MOONSTONE..............     50.00
FLASK,MC KEARIN G IX-10,PINT,KELLY GREEN....................    200.00
FLASK,MC KEARIN G IX-10,PINT,MOONSTONE......................     35.00
FLASK,MC KEARIN G IX-10,PINT,RIDGED NECK,SAPPHIRE BLUE......    185.00
FLASK,MC KEARIN G IX-10,PINT,ROLLED COLLAR,AMBER............    110.00
FLASK,MC KEARIN G IX-10,PINT,ROUGH FIRED LIP,AQUA...........     20.00
FLASK,MC KEARIN G IX-10,PINT,SAPPHIRE BLUE..................    190.00
FLASK,MC KEARIN G IX-10,PINT,VERTICAL GLASS BRIDGE INSIDE,-
  AMBER.................................................     80.00
FLASK,MC KEARIN G IX-10,PINT,YELLOWISH OLIVE................    140.00
FLASK,MC KEARIN G IX-10A,PINT,AQUA..........................     35.00
FLASK,MC KEARIN G IX-10A,PINT,BLUE.............. 60.00 TO      90.00
FLASK,MC KEARIN G IX-11,EMERALD GREEN.......................    195.00
FLASK,MC KEARIN G IX-11,PINT,AMBER.............. 85.00 TO      95.00
FLASK,MC KEARIN G IX-11,PINT,AQUA...........................     20.00
FLASK,MC KEARIN G IX-11,RED AMBER...........................    195.00
FLASK,MC KEARIN G IX-11,TURQUOISE...........................    135.00
FLASK,MC KEARIN G IX-11A,PINT,APPLIED COLLAR,GOLDEN AMBER...     90.00
FLASK,MC KEARIN G IX-11A,PINT,AQUA..........................     20.00
FLASK,MC KEARIN G IX-11A,PINT,BLUE..........................    170.00
FLASK,MC KEARIN G IX-11A,PINT,GHOST SCROLL,EMERALD GREEN....     75.00
FLASK,MC KEARIN G IX-11A,PINT,GOLDEN AMBER..................    130.00
FLASK,MC KEARIN G IX-11A,PINT,OLIVE.........................    195.00
FLASK,MC KEARIN G IX-11B,PINT,AQUA..........................     30.00
FLASK,MC KEARIN G IX-11B,PINT,BLUE..................110.00 TO   260.00
FLASK,MC KEARIN G IX-11B,PINT,DOUBLE BAND LIP,AQUA..........     35.00
FLASK,MC KEARIN G IX-11B,PINT,GREEN.........................     40.00
FLASK,MC KEARIN G IX-11B,PINT,SAPPHIRE BLUE..........ILLUS..    260.00
FLASK,MC KEARIN G IX-12,PINT,ROUGH FIRE POLISHED LIP,GREEN..    160.00
FLASK,MC KEARIN G IX-12B,PINT,BLUE..........................     45.00
FLASK,MC KEARIN G IX-13,PINT,AQUA...........................     40.00
FLASK,MC KEARIN G IX-13,PINT,DOUBLE COLLAR,TURQUOISE........     70.00
FLASK,MC KEARIN G IX-13,PINT,YELLOWISH GREEN.........ILLUS..     60.00
FLASK,MC KEARIN G IX-14,AMBER...............................     30.00
FLASK,MC KEARIN G IX-14,FLARED NECK,OLIVE...................    135.00
FLASK,MC KEARIN G IX-14,GREEN...............................     45.00
FLASK,MC KEARIN G IX-14,PINT,AMBER..........................     40.00
FLASK,MC KEARIN G IX-14,PINT,CITRON & YELLOW................    130.00
FLASK,MC KEARIN G IX-14,PINT,CLEAR & GREEN..................     30.00
FLASK,MC KEARIN G IX-14,PINT,TURQUOISE BLUE.................     60.00
FLASK,MC KEARIN G IX-14,PINT,VERTICAL BRIDGE ON SHOULDER,
  AQUA..................................................     40.00
FLASK,MC KEARIN G IX-15,AQUA................................     35.00
FLASK,MC KEARIN G IX-15,CRYSTAL CLEAR.......................     45.00
```

```
FLASK,MC KEARIN G IX-15,FIRE POLISHED LIP,CITRON............     105.00
FLASK,MC KEARIN G IX-16,PINT,DOT IMPRESSION,BLUE............     150.00
FLASK,MC KEARIN G IX-16,PINT,ROUGH FIRE POLISHED LIP,GRAY...      70.00
FLASK,MC KEARIN G IX-16,YELLOW BAND ACROSS MIDDLE,BLUE......      30.00
FLASK,MC KEARIN G IX-16A,PINT,STARS,LONG NECK,AMBER.........     170.00
FLASK,MC KEARIN G IX-16A,PINT,TURQUOISE....................      55.00
FLASK,MC KEARIN G IX-17,PINT,EMERALD GREEN.................      35.00
FLASK,MC KEARIN G IX-17,PINT,GREEN.........................      70.00
FLASK,MC KEARIN G IX-17,PINT,GREEN,CHIP..............ILLUS..      35.00
FLASK,MC KEARIN G IX-17,PINT,OLIVE..................ILLUS..     200.00
FLASK,MC KEARIN G IX-17,PINT,ROUGH FIRE POLISHED LIP,AQUA...      35.00
FLASK,MC KEARIN G IX-17,PINT,YELLOWISH GREEN...............      80.00
FLASK,MC KEARIN G IX-17A,PINT,BLUE.........................      55.00
FLASK,MC KEARIN G IX-18,PINT,AQUA..........................      45.00
FLASK,MC KEARIN G IX-20,PINT,AQUA..........................      25.00
FLASK,MC KEARIN G IX-20,PINT,FLARED MOUTH YELLOWISH GREEN...      65.00
FLASK,MC KEARIN G IX-20,PINT,FLARED MOUTH,AQUA..............      50.00
FLASK,MC KEARIN G IX-20,PINT,GOLDEN AMBER..................      90.00
FLASK,MC KEARIN G IX-20,PINT,YELLOWISH CITRON..............     100.00
FLASK,MC KEARIN G IX-23,PINT,EMERALD GREEN.................     300.00
FLASK,MC KEARIN G IX-23,PINT,GREEN.........................     300.00
FLASK,MC KEARIN G IX-24,PINT,AQUA..........................      85.00
FLASK,MC KEARIN G IX-25,PINT,AMBER IN NECK,TURQUOISE........      30.00
FLASK,MC KEARIN G IX-25,PINT,APPLIED COLLAR,TURQUOISE.......      50.00
FLASK,MC KEARIN G IX-25,PINT,AQUA..........................      50.00
FLASK,MC KEARIN G IX-25,PINT,BANDED NECK,TEAL BLUE..........      55.00
FLASK,MC KEARIN G IX-25,PINT,ROLLED COLLAR,AMBER IN NECK,
   GREEN...................................................      70.00
FLASK,MC KEARIN G IX-25,PINT,ROUGH FIRE POLISHED LIP,AQUA...      55.00
FLASK,MC KEARIN G IX-26,PINT,GREEN.........................     275.00
FLASK,MC KEARIN G IX-28A,PINT,GREEN........................      55.00
FLASK,MC KEARIN G IX-29,2 1/2 QUART,AQUA.............ILLUS..     140.00
FLASK,MC KEARIN G IX-31,1/2 PINT,AQUA......................      30.00
FLASK,MC KEARIN G IX-31,1/2 PINT,YELLOW GREEN..............      60.00
FLASK,MC KEARIN G IX-33,1/2 PINT,BLUE......................      50.00
FLASK,MC KEARIN G IX-33,1/2 PINT,YELLOW GREEN..............      85.00
FLASK,MC KEARIN G IX-33A,1/2 PINT,AQUA.....................      25.00
FLASK,MC KEARIN G IX-33A,1/2 PINT,LONG NECK,BLUE...........      25.00
FLASK,MC KEARIN G IX-34,CLEAR,LAVENDER TINT................     175.00
FLASK,MC KEARIN G IX-34,1/2 PINT,AQUA............. 25.00 TO      40.00
FLASK,MC KEARIN G IX-34,1/2 PINT,CLEAR............ 35.00 TO      40.00
FLASK,MC KEARIN G IX-34,1/2 PINT,OLIVE.....................     110.00
FLASK,MC KEARIN G IX-34,1/2 PINT,YELLOW OLIVE........ILLUS..      80.00
FLASK,MC KEARIN G IX-34A,1/2 PINT,AQUA.....................      35.00
FLASK,MC KEARIN G IX-35,1/2 PINT...........................       3.00
FLASK,MC KEARIN G IX-35,1/2 PINT,AQUA......................      40.00
FLASK,MC KEARIN G IX-35,1/2 PINT,AQUA............. 30.00 TO      50.00
FLASK,MC KEARIN G IX-35,1/2 PINT,BLUE......................     180.00
FLASK,MC KEARIN G IX-35,1/2 PINT,CLEAR.....................      35.00
FLASK,MC KEARIN G IX-35,1/2 PINT,EMERALD GREEN.............      50.00
FLASK,MC KEARIN G IX-35,1/2 PINT,MOONSTONE.................     100.00
FLASK,MC KEARIN G IX-35,1/2 PINT,TURQUOISE.................      60.00
FLASK,MC KEARIN G IX-35,1/2 PINT,YELLOW GREEN..............      75.00
FLASK,MC KEARIN G IX-36,1/2 PINT,AMBER.....................      75.00
FLASK,MC KEARIN G IX-36,1/2 PINT,AQUA......................      35.00
FLASK,MC KEARIN G IX-37,1/2 PINT,AQUA......................      40.00
FLASK,MC KEARIN G IX-37,1/2 PINT,GREEN.....................     175.00
FLASK,MC KEARIN G IX-38,1/2 PINT,AQUA......................      45.00
FLASK,MC KEARIN G IX-39,1/2 PINT,AQUA...............ILLUS..      70.00
FLASK,MC KEARIN G IX-39,1/2 PINT,GREEN.....................     400.00
FLASK,MC KEARIN G IX-41,1/2 PINT,GREEN.....................      50.00
FLASK,MC KEARIN G IX-42,1/2 PINT,LAVENDER..................     600.00
FLASK,MC KEARIN G IX-43,PINT,AQUA..........................     230.00
FLASK,MC KEARIN G IX-44,PINT,AQUA..........................     125.00
FLASK,MC KEARIN G IX-45,PINT,AQUA.................150.00 TO     160.00
```

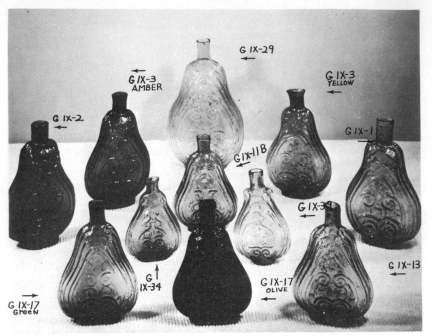

FLASKS, MC KEARIN

G IX-29, 2 1/2 QUART, AQUA

G IX-3, QUART, AMBER

G IX-2, QUART, SAPPHIRE BLUE

G IX-17, PINT, OLIVE

G IX-17, PINT, GREEN, CHIP

G IX-13, PINT, YELLOWISH GREEN

G IX-11B, PINT, SAPPHIRE BLUE

G IX-1, QUART, CORNFLOWER BLUE

G IX-3, QUART, YELLOWISH CITRON

G IX-34, 1/2 PINT, YELLOW OLIVE

G IX-39, 1/2 PINT, AQUA

```
FLASK, MC KEARIN G IX-46, QUART, EMERALD GREEN.................  275.00
FLASK, MC KEARIN G IX-51, QUART, GREEN..........................   75.00
FLASK, MC KEARIN G IX-53, PINT, BLUE............................  250.00
FLASK, MC KEARIN G IX-54, PINT, GREEN...........................  190.00
FLASK, MC KEARIN G IX-56, PINT, AQUA.................. 35.00 TO   40.00
FLASK, MC KEARIN G X-15, BROKEN PONTIL, AQUA....................   57.50
FLASK, MC KEARIN G X-15, SUMMER, WINTER, PONTIL, PINT, AQUA......   70.00
FLASK, MC KEARIN G X-16, IMPROVED PONTIL, AQUA..................   75.00
FLASK, MC KEARIN G X-17, IMPROVED PONTIL, AQUA..................   90.00
FLASK, MC KEARIN G X-18, BROKEN PONTIL, AQUA....................   65.00
FLASK, MC KEARIN G X-18, BROKEN PONTIL, LIME GREEN..............  180.00
FLASK, MC KEARIN G X-18, SUMMER & WINTER, QUART, AMBER..........  340.00
FLASK, MC KEARIN G X-19, IMPROVED PONTIL, AQUA.................    6.00
FLASK, MC KINLEY CAMPAIGN, 1/2 PINT, AQUA.......................   90.00
FLASK, MEDICINE, BLOWN IN 2 PART MOLD, CYLINDRICAL, GREEN.......   22.51
FLASK, MERRY CHRISTMAS AND HAPPY NEW YEAR, AMBER................   10.00
FLASK, METAL BEE SMOKER BELLOWS.................................    8.50
FLASK, MIDWESTERN, 10 1/4 IN. DIA., AQUA........................   35.00
FLASK, MILK GLASS KLONDIKE......................................   60.00
FLASK, MINIATURE, APPLIED RING BELOW LIP, GREEN.................   22.50
FLASK, NAILSEA, APPLIED COBALT MOUTH, RED, WHITE & BLUE.........   37.50
FLASK, NAILSEA, WHITE & ORANGE, STOPPER.........................   27.50
```

```
FLASK,NAILSEA,1/2 PINT,WHITE LOOKINGS,OLIVE..................    85.00
FLASK,OAK LEAVES & ACORNS DECOR,COPPER,SIGNED JAMES DIXON...    25.00
FLASK,ONION,SQUAT,APPLIED RIGHT BELOW LIP,AMBER.............    40.00
FLASK,OVAL-SHAPED SADDLE,BLOWN,OLIVE GREEN,IN WICKER & TIN
   HOLDER..................................................    35.00
FLASK,PATENT,PINT,AMBER....................................    27.50
FLASK,PATENT,PINT,AQUA.....................................    22.50
FLASK,PAUL JONES,EMBOSSED,AMBER............................    10.00
FLASK,PERSIAN SADDLE............................. 14.95 TO    20.00
FLASK,PEWTER...............................................     5.00
FLASK,PICNIC,CLOCK & WEB DESIGN,PINT,CLEAR.................    16.00
FLASK,PICNIC,CLOCK & WEB DESIGN,1/2 PINT,CLEAR.............    16.00
FLASK,PICNIC,LIQUOR SAMPLER,BLOWN IN MOLD,CLEAR............     7.00
FLASK,PICNIC,PUMPKIN SEED,EMBOSSED.........................    10.00
FLASK,PICNIC,SMALL BIMAL...................................     3.00
FLASK,PICNIC,WEB DESIGN,CLEAR..............................     7.00
FLASK,PICNIC,WEB DESIGN,PINT,CLEAR.........................     7.00
FLASK,PICNIC,WEB DESIGN,1/4 PINT,CLEAR.....................     7.00
FLASK,PIG,C.F.KNAPP,PHILA.,CLEAR,2 OUNCES..................    35.00
FLASK,PIKE'S PEAK,PINT,AQUA................................    65.00
FLASK,PIKE'S PEAK,REVERSE EAGLE,STARS,LETTERED MY COUNTRY,
   AQUA....................................................    75.00
FLASK,PINK,STAFFORDSHIRE,CIRCA 1830........................    55.00
FLASK,PINT,AMETHYST........................................    90.00
FLASK,PINT,BIGELOW-KENNARD STERLING,CRYSTAL................    35.00
FLASK,PINT,BUNKER HILL PICTURE,AMBER.......................    25.00
FLASK,PINT,EMBOSSED VINOL,PATENT APRIL 19,1893,AMBER.......    75.00
FLASK,PINT,GREEN...........................................    55.00
FLASK,PINT,HIGH BASE,SMALL STARS,YELLOW GREEN..............    80.00
FLASK,PINT,OLIVE AMBER.....................................    55.00
FLASK,PINT,SMALL 8 POINT STARS,TURQUOISE...................    40.00
FLASK,PITKIN TYPE,19TH CENTURY.....................COLOR..    XX.XX
FLASK,PITKIN,MIDWESTERN,12 RIB,CLEAR.......................    30.00
FLASK,PITKIN,MIDWESTERN,32 RIB,SWIRL,GREEN.................    55.00
FLASK,PITKIN,NEW ENGLAND,36 RIB,BROKEN SWIRL,OLIVE YELLOW...    35.00
FLASK,PITKIN,SWIRL,SHEARED LIP,GREEN.......................   300.00
FLASK,PITKIN,32 RIBS,BROKEN SWIRL,OLIVE GREEN..............   130.00
FLASK,PITTSBURGH DOUBLE EAGLE,PINT,AQUA....................    47.00
FLASK,PITTSBURGH,PA.,1 PINT,APPLIED RING AT TOP,AQUA.......    35.00
FLASK,PLAIN,1/2 PINT,AMBER.................................     8.00
FLASK,PLAIN,1/2 PINT,BULBOUS NECK..........................     5.00
FLASK,POCKET,DIAMOND PATTERN,SHEARED LIP,GREEN.............    40.00
FLASK,POCKET,EAGLE,SCREW CAP,SHIELD SHAPE,CLEAR............     9.00
FLASK,POCKET,16 VERTICAL RIBS,CLEAR........................    11.00
FLASK,PRIMITIVE FORM,MIDWESTERN,RIM FOLDED OUTWARDS,AQUA....    20.00
FLASK,PUMPKINSEED................................... 3.00 TO     5.25
FLASK,PUMPKINSEED,CLOCK ON FACE,REGULATOR,CLEAR............    26.00
FLASK,PUMPKINSEED,EMBOSSED MERRY CHRISTMAS & HAPPY NEW YEAR.    25.00
FLASK,PUMPKINSEED,SUNBURST PATTERN,AMETHYST................    18.00
FLASK,PUMPKINSEED,SUNBURST PATTERN,CLEAR...................    18.00
FLASK,PUMPKINSEED,1/2 PINT,AMBER...........................    27.00
FLASK,QUART,BANDED NECK,AQUA...............................    40.00
FLASK,QUART,BANDED NECK,CROWSFOOT OFF POTSTONE,AMBER.......    56.00
FLASK,QUART,UPPER STAR ON OBVERSE,GREEN....................   150.00
FLASK,R.B.CUTTER'S PURE BOURBON,2 PIECE MOLD,AMBER.........   100.00
FLASK,R.DENNER WINE & SPIRIT MERCHANT,COFFIN,CROCK,TAN &
   CREAM...................................................    10.00
FLASK,RAVENNA GLASS WORKS,IRON PONTIL,BUBBLE BURST,PINT,AQUA    51.00
FLASK,RAVENNA GLASS WORKS,APPLIED ROLLED COLLAR,PINT,AQUA...    37.50
FLASK,RED TOP,R.D.WESTHEIMER & SONS,1/2 PINT,AMBER.........     6.00
FLASK,RESURGAM,BALTIMORE GLASS WORKS,ANCHOR IN REVERSE,AQUA,
   PINT....................................................    68.50
FLASK,RICHMOND,AMERICAN GLASS PLATE NO.259.................   500.00
FLASK,RING DANDY,BLOWN IN MOLD,CLEAR.......................     2.00
FLASK,S.CLAY MILLER,UNION OVAL,LIGHT GOLD AMBER............    18.00
```

```
FLASK,SADDLE,FREE-BLOWN,EMERALD GREEN,CIRCA 1700,9˜ IN.......    23.50
FLASK,SADDLE,HONEST MEASURE,PINT,CLEAR......................     6.00
FLASK,SADDLE,HONEST MEASURE,1/2 PINT,CLEAR.................      4.00
FLASK,SADDLE,STAR WITH CIRCLE,1/2 PINT,AMBER................    12.00
FLASK,SAILING SHIP,MAN O WAR,YANKEE..................COLOR..    XX.XX
FLASK,SALT,FOOTED,16 RIBS SWIRLED TO RIGHT,CLEAR............    25.00
FLASK,SCROLL & STARS,ROUGH PONTIL,AQUA,QUART...............     35.00
FLASK,SCROLL,IRON PONTIL,PINT,AQUA.................. 40.00 TO    60.00
FLASK,SCROLL,RINGED LIP,IRON PONTIL,AQUA,QUART..............   115.00
FLASK,SCROLL,VIOLIN,AQUA...................................     46.00
FLASK,SEEING EYE,PINT,OLIVE AMBER..........................    145.00
FLASK,SHEAF OF RYE,STAR,PINT,AQUA..........................     65.00
FLASK,SHEAF OF WHEAT,MARKED WESTFORD,CONNECTICUT,AMBER,HALF
  PINT.....................................................     70.00
FLASK,SHIP ON REVERSE,ALBANY GLASS WORKS,AMBER.............    125.00
FLASK,SHOO-FLY,BLOWN IN MOLD,CLEAR.........................      8.00
FLASK,SIX PETALS TO FLOWERS,QUART,AQUA.....................     40.00
FLASK,SMALL BOY FIREMAN HOSING DOWN FIREWATER BOTTLE,
  PORCELAIN................................................     32.50
FLASK,SOLDIER,DANCING GIRL,PINT,AQUA.......................    125.00
FLASK,SOUTH CAROLINA DISPENSARY,PALM TREE,1/2 PINT,UNION,
  AQUA.....................................................     25.00
FLASK,SOUTH CAROLINA DISPENSARY,1/2 PINT,AMBER.............     13.50
FLASK,SPIRIT,W.H.JONES & CO.,BOSTON,TRADEMARK 1851,SILVER
  CAP......................................................      7.50
FLASK,SPRING GARDEN GLASS WORKS,ANCHOR,REVERSE LOG CABIN,
  AQUA.....................................................     76.00
FLASK,SPRING GARDEN GLASS WORKS,REVERSE LOG CABIN,1/2 PINT,
  AQUA.....................................................     76.00
FLASK,SPRING GARDEN GLASS WORKS,1/2 PINT...................     65.00
FLASK,STARS & SLOOP,1/2 PINT,AQUA..........................    130.00
FLASK,STARS & UPPER SCROLLS,QUART,CLEAR....................     50.00
FLASK,STEIGEL TYPE,BLOWN FLIP,32 RIB,CLEAR.................     12.50
FLASK,STIEGEL TYPE,INSERTED NECK,DATE 1748 IN REVERSE.......    45.00
FLASK,STIEGEL TYPE,INSERTED NECK,TULIP & LILY OF VALLEY,
  CLEAR....................................................     30.00
FLASK,STIEGEL TYPE,POCKET,GERMAN INSCRIPTION,TULIP DECORATED    40.00
FLASK,STODDARD DOUBLE EAGLE,1/2 PINT,AMBER..................    90.00
FLASK,STODDARD TYPE,WHITTLED,SNAP CASE,AMBER...............     21.50
FLASK,STODDARD TYPE,1 GAL.,GREEN...........................    125.00
FLASK,STODDARD TYPE,1 QUART,GREEN..........................     75.00
FLASK,STONEWARE,PINT.......................................     25.00
FLASK,STRAP SIDE,PINT,AMBER................................      3.50
FLASK,STRAP,NEIL DOHERTY,WINE & LIQUORS,AMBER..............      8.00
FLASK,STRAP,PINT,AMBER.....................................      5.00
FLASK,STRAP,1/2 PINT,AMBER.................................      5.00
FLASK,STRAPSIDED,1/2 PINT,CIRCA 1880,AMBER.................      6.00
FLASK,SUCCESS TO RAILROAD,PINT,AMBER.......................    325.00
FLASK,SUCCESS TO RAILROAD,PINT,CLEAR TO GREEN..............    225.00
FLASK,SUCCESS TO THE RAILROAD..............................     40.00
FLASK,SUCCESS TO THE RAILROAD,EAGLE,STARS,REVERSE,PINT,GREEN   210.00
FLASK,SUMMER,WINTER,BAD WINTER,PINT,AQUA...................     10.00
FLASK,SUMMER,WINTER,PINT,AQUA..............................     58.00
FLASK,SUNBURST,PINT,AMBER..................................    185.00
FLASK,SUNBURST,PINT,GREEN..................................     35.00
FLASK,SUNBURST,1/2 PINT,GREEN..............................    256.00
FLASK,TAYLOR & WASHINGTON,AQUA,PINT........................     45.00
FLASK,TAYLOR & WASHINGTON,AQUA,QUART.......................     55.00
FLASK,TAYLOR & WASHINGTON,BUST OF WASHINGTON,8 IN. HIGH.....     2.75
FLASK,TAYLOR & WASHINGTON,GEN.TAYLOR NEVER SURRENDERS.......     7.50
FLASK,TAYLOR & WASHINGTON,8 IN. LONG.......................      2.75
FLASK,THE WALDORF CAFES,SAN FRANCISCO,1915,NEW YEARS,PINT,
  CLEAR....................................................      9.75
FLASK,THOMAS L.SMITH & SONS................................      4.00
FLASK,TURTLE,CLEAR,GROUND MOUTH,PEWTER TOP.................     20.00
```

```
FLASK,UNGLAZED POTTERY,PINT...................................    25.00
FLASK,UNION & CLASPED HANDS IN SHIELD,CANNON & BALLS,PINT,
  AQUA........................................................    30.00
FLASK,UNION CLASPED HANDS,FLYING EAGLE REVERSE,1/2 PINT,
  AMBER.......................................................    66.00
FLASK,UNION EAGLE,PINT,AQUA...................................    56.00
FLASK,UNION EAGLE,1/2 PINT,AQUA...............................    35.00
FLASK,UNION FLAG & CO.,CANNON & FLAG,1/2 PINT,CLEAR..........    40.00
FLASK,UNION OVAL,BLOWN IN MOLD,AQUA...........................     1.50
FLASK,UNION OVAL,BLOWN IN MOLD,STRAP SIDE,AMBER,NEW..........     9.00
FLASK,UNION OVAL,BLOWN IN MOLD,STRAP SIDE,BLUE,NEW...........     9.00
FLASK,UNION OVAL,BLOWN IN MOLD,STRAP SIDE,CLEAR..............     2.25
FLASK,UNION OVAL,BLOWN IN MOLD,STRAP SIDE,GOLD,NEW...........    10.00
FLASK,UNION,A F MADE,CLEAR,NEW................................     5.00
FLASK,UNION,CALABASH,AQUA.....................................    45.00
FLASK,UNION,CLASPED HANDS,PINT,AQUA...........................    32.50
FLASK,UNION,CLASPED HANDS,13 STARS,REVERSE EAGLE,BLUE,
  1/2 PT.....................................................   110.00
FLASK,UNION,HANDS & EAGLE,BLUE................................    45.00
FLASK,UNION,QUART,AQUA........................................    50.00
FLASK,UNION,STAR IN CIRCLE ON SHOULDER,AMBER,NEW.............     6.00
FLASK,UNION,WHITTLED,AMBER....................................    10.00
FLASK,VINOL 1898 CHESTNUT TIMBER..............................     6.00
FLASK,WARRANTED,BLOWN IN MOLD,STRAP SIDE,CLEAR..............     4.50
FLASK,WASHINGTON & TAYLOR.....................................    60.00
FLASK,WASHINGTON & TAYLOR,AQUA,PINT...........................    65.00
FLASK,WASHINGTON CENTENNIAL,CALABASH,1932,CLEAR.............     6.50
FLASK,WASHINGTON COMMEMORATIVE,CLEAR,NEW.....................     3.00
FLASK,WASHINGTON SPRING CO.,GREEN.............................   100.00
FLASK,WASHINGTON,FELLS POINT,PINT,AQUA.......................   145.00
FLASK,WASHINGTON,JACKSON,PINT,AMBER...........................   155.00
FLASK,WASHINGTON,JACKSON,PINT,OLIVE AMBER.....................   165.00
FLASK,WASHINGTON,PLAIN,PINT,AQUA..............................    50.00
FLASK,WASHINGTON,PLAIN,QUART,AQUA.............................    50.00
FLASK,WASHINGTON,SHEATH,1/2 PINT,AQUA.........................    75.00
FLASK,WASHINGTON,TAYLOR.......................................    65.00
FLASK,WASHINGTON,TAYLOR,DYOTT,PINT,TOOLED LIP,AQUA..........    50.00
FLASK,WASHINGTON,TAYLOR,PINT,AQUA.............................    55.00
FLASK,WASHINGTON,TAYLOR,PINT,GREEN............................    95.00
FLASK,WASHINGTON,TAYLOR,QUART,AMBER...........................   150.00
FLASK,WASHINGTON,TAYLOR,QUART,BLUISH GREEN...................   110.00
FLASK,WASHINGTON,TAYLOR,QUART,GREEN...........................   175.00
FLASK,WASHINGTON,TAYLOR,ROUGH PONTIL,QUART,AQUA.............    95.00
FLASK,WASHINGTON,TAYLOR,TOOLED LIP,GREEN.....................    95.00
FLASK,WASHINGTON,TAYLOR,1/2 PINT,AQUA...............  55.00 TO    75.00
FLASK,WESTFORD GLASS CO.,AMBER................................    70.00
FLASK,WESTFORD GLASS CO.,OLIVE AMBER..........................    85.00
FLASK,WESTFORD GLASS CO.,SHEAF OF WHEAT & TOOLS,1/2 PINT,
  AMBER.......................................................    70.00
FLASK,WESTFORD GLASS CO.,SHEAF WHEAT REVERSE,PINT,AMBER.....    75.00
FLASK,WESTFORD,PINT,AMBER.....................................   115.00
FLASK,WESTFORD,8 1/4 IN.,APPLIED LIP,BLACK AMBER............    22.00
FLASK,WHALE,PAPERWEIGHT,CLEAR.................................     4.00
FLASK,WHITNEY GLASS WORKS EMBOSSED ON BOTTOM,AQUA,AMBER,PAIR    30.00
FLASK,WILL YOU TAKE A DRINK,WILL A DUCK SWIM.........COLOR..    XX.XX
FLASK,WILLINGTON HISTORICAL,EAGLE,QUART,GREEN...............    25.00
FLASK,WILLINGTON,OLIVE GREEN..................................   160.00
FLASK,WOMEN'S SUFFRAGE COMMEMORATIVE,1920-1970..............     7.95
FLASK,ZANESVILLE CHESTNUT,24 VERTICAL RIBS,GOLD & RED AMBER.    80.00
FLASK,ZANESVILLE CITY GLASS WORKS............................    55.00
FLASK,ZANESVILLE CITY GLASS WORKS,PINT,RINGED MOUTH,GREEN...    35.00
FLASK,ZANESVILLE MASONIC,PINT,AMBER..........................   250.00
FLASK,ZANESVILLE,QUART,24 RIBS TO LEFT,BLUE.................   115.00
FLASK,ZANESVILLE,SWIRL,CHESTNUT,1820-1830,AMBER.............1,000.00
FLASK,ZANESVILLE,24 RIBS SWIRLED TO RIGHT,AQUA.............   126.00
```

```
FLASK,1/2 PINT,ANCHOR,AQUA.....................................    11.50
FLASK,1/2 PINT,AQUA-BLUE.......................................    95.00
FLASK,3 PART MOLD,TARGET BALLS,AMBER...........................    11.00
FLASK,7 1/4 IN. HIGH,GREEN.....................................    10.00
FLASK,8 IN. STRAP WITH SLUG PLATE,GREEN........................     5.00
FLASK,24 RIBS SWIRLED TO RIGHT,RIBBED BOTTOM,AQUA...........       40.00
FLASK,1872 GERMAN HOP BITTERS,AMBER............................    25.00
FLYCATCHER,DATED 19TH C.,BLOB SEAL,CLEAR.......................     7.00
```

FOOD BOTTLES INCLUDE ALL OF THE MANY GROCERY STORE
CONTAINERS, SUCH AS CATSUP, HORSERADISH, JELLY, AND
OTHER FOODSTUFFS. A FEW SPECIAL ITEMS, SUCH AS
VINEGAR,ARE LISTED UNDER THEIR OWN HEADINGS.

```
FOOD,A & P EXTRACTS,EMBOSSED,CLEAR,5 1/2 IN..........ILLUS..        6.00
FOOD,A.E.B.B.,PURE OLIVE,DEPOSE FRANCE,AQUA................         3.00
FOOD,ANN PAGE PRESERVES,1 LB.,C.1930..................ILLUS..       4.50
FOOD,ARMOUR & CO.,PACKERS,BLOWN IN MOLD,WHITE..............         1.00
FOOD,ARNICA & OIL,AQUA.....................................         6.00
FOOD,B & MC K HONOR BRAND FOOD PRODUCTS,BLOWN IN MOLD,AQUA..        2.00
FOOD,BAKER'S FLAVORING EXTRACTS,BLOWN IN MOLD,AQUA.........         1.50
FOOD,BAKER'S FLAVORING EXTRACTS,MACHINE MADE,CLEAR.........         2.00
FOOD,BARREL MUSTARD,PLAIN,3 RINGS TOP & BOTTOM,AMETHYST....         3.00
FOOD,BARREL MUSTARD,PLAIN,3 RINGS TOP & BOTTOM,CLEAR.......         3.00
FOOD,BEECH NUT,MACHINE MADE,CANA JOMORIE,N.Y.,AQUA.........         3.00
FOOD,BEST FOODS,INC.......................................          3.50
FOOD,BILTMORE,QUART.......................................          2.25
FOOD,BLANKE'S AERIAL GLOBE BAKING POWDER..................         90.00
FOOD,BLUE RIBBON VACUUM PACKED COFFEE,QUART................         2.50
FOOD,BOYE NEEDLE CO.,CHICAGO,MACHINE MADE,CLEAR............         3.00
FOOD,BREWSTER'S FLAVORING EXTRACTS,BLOWN IN MOLD,AMBER.....         2.50
FOOD,BREWSTERS FLAVORING EXTRACTS,BLOWN IN MOLD,CLEAR......         1.50
FOOD,BRYANT'S ROOT BEER,DETROIT,MICH.,AMBER.........ILLUS..         6.00
FOOD,BURNETT,BLOWN IN MOLD,AQUA...........................          1.25
FOOD,BURNETT'S STANDARD FLAVORING EXTRACTS,AQUA..... 2.50 TO        3.00
FOOD,BURNETTS STANDARD FLAVORING EXTRACTS,AMETHYST.........         2.00
FOOD,BURNETTS STANDARD FLAVORING EXTRACTS,CLEAR...........          2.00
FOOD,BURNHAM'S CLAM BOUILLON,N.Y.,MACHINE MADE.............         3.00
FOOD,C.A.KING PURE MALT DEPT.,BLOWN IN MOLD,BROWN..........         3.50
```

FOOD,A & P EXTRACTS,
EMBOSSED,CLEAR,
5 1/2 IN

FOOD,ANN PAGE PRESERVES,
1 LB.,C.1930

FOOD,BRYANT'S ROOT BEER,
DETROIT,MICH.,AMBER

```
FOOD,CALIFORNIA FIG SYRUP CO.,RECTANGULAR,AMETHYST..........      4.00
FOOD,CALIFORNIA FIG SYRUP CO.,RECTANGULAR,CLEAR............       2.00
FOOD,CALIFORNIA FIG SYRUP CO.,RECTANGULAR,MACHINE MADE......      2.00
   FOOD, CALIFORNIA PERFUME CO., SEE AVON, CALIFORNIA
   PERFUME CO.
FOOD,CAPERS,GREEN.................................                7.00
FOOD,CAPERS,MACHINE MADE,PLAIN,GREEN.....................         3.00
FOOD,CAPERS,SQUARE,INDENTED PANELS,GREEN..................        9.00
   FOOD, CATSUP, SEE ALSO FOOD, KETCHUP
FOOD,CATSUP,CHAMPAGNE,APPLIED TOP,AMETHYST................        5.00
FOOD,CATSUP,CHAMPAGNE,ROUND,SCREW TOP,CLEAR..............         5.00
FOOD,CATSUP,EDDY'S HOMEMADE,PEWTER CAP,AMETHYST............       5.00
FOOD,CATSUP,PLAIN,AMETHYST................................        2.00
FOOD,CATSUP,PLAIN,CLEAR...................................        2.00
FOOD,CATSUP,PLAIN,TAPERED BODY,AMETHYST...................        6.00
FOOD,CATSUP,PLAIN,TAPERED BODY,CLEAR......................        6.00
FOOD,CATSUP,2 MID-SECTIONS,10 PANELED,AMETHYST............        5.00
FOOD,CATSUP,2 MID-SECTIONS,10 PANELED,CLEAR...............        5.00
FOOD,CATSUP,10 PANELED,10 IN. TALL,AMETHYST..............         4.00
FOOD,CATSUP,10 PANELED,10 IN.TALL,CLEAR...................        4.00
FOOD,CEREAL MILK,EMBOSSED,MACHINE MADE,BROWN.............         1.00
FOOD,CERTIFIED ALDERNEY BUTTER COLOR,AMBER..........ILLUS..       2.50
FOOD,CHERRIES,MACHINE MADE,CLEAR..........................         .75
FOOD,CHILI SAUCE,MACHINE MADE,CLEAR.......................        1.00
FOOD,CLOROX,QUART,EMBOSSED,AMBER..........................        1.75
FOOD,CONDIMENT,BLOWN IN MOLD,19TH CENTURY.................      150.00
FOOD,CONDIMENT,CAPERS,J.P.S.& CO.,AQUA....................        8.50
FOOD,CONDIMENT,J.A.SHARWOOD & CO.,CALCUTTA & LONDON,GREEN...      8.50
FOOD,CONDIMENT,JOSEPH CAMPBELL PRESERVE CO.,AMETHYST........      4.50
FOOD,CONDIMENT,MACHINE MADE,AQUA..........................         .75
FOOD,CONDIMENT,PLAIN MILK BOTTLE TYPE,AMETHYST............        3.00
FOOD,CONDIMENT,PLAIN,MILK BOTTLE TYPE,CLEAR...............        3.00
FOOD,CONDIMENT,VASE TYPE BOTTLE,AMETHYST..................        3.00
FOOD,CONDIMENT,VASE TYPE BOTTLE,CLEAR.....................        3.00
FOOD,CROWN CORDIAL EXTRACT,AQUA...........................        4.50
FOOD,CUDAHY PACKING CO.,PINT..............................        8.00
FOOD,CURTIS,GEO.M.,PURE OLIVE OIL,ROUND..................         2.00
FOOD,D.& CO.,MUSTARD,AMETHYST.............................        3.00
FOOD,D.& CO.,MUSTARD,CLEAR................................        3.00
FOOD,DR.FENNER'S CONCENTRATED EXTRACTS,CLEAR.........ILLUS..      4.00
FOOD,DURKEE & CO.,E.R.,SALAD DRESSING,PAT.APR.17,1877,CLEAR.      2.00
FOOD,DURKEE & CO.,E.R.,SALAD DRESSING,PAT.APR.18,1877,
   AMETHYST...............................................        3.00
FOOD,DURKEE CHALLENGE SAUCE,AQUA..........................       22.00
FOOD,EDDY & EDDY MFG.CO.,RELISH,ROUND,AMETHYST............        3.00
FOOD,EDDY'S RELIABLE BAKING POWDER,C.1905.............ILLUS..     6.50
FOOD,ER DURKEE & CO.,NEW YORK,CLEAR..................ILLUS..      3.50
FOOD,EXTRACT,BLOWN IN MOLD,AQUA...........................         .75
FOOD,EXTRACT,BLOWN IN MOLD,5 IN. TALL,AQUA...............         1.00
FOOD,EXTRACT,BLOWN IN MOLD,12 PANELS,AMETHYST............         2.00
FOOD,EXTRACT,BRYANT'S ROOT BEER,BLOWN IN MOLD,AMBER.........      3.00
FOOD,EXTRACT,HIRES HOUSEHOLD EXTRACT,BLOWN IN MOLD,AQUA.....      2.50
FOOD,EXTRACT,HIRES IMPROVED ROOT BEER.BLOWN IN MOLD,AQUA....      2.50
FOOD,EXTRACT,INDIAN ROOT BEER,BLOWN IN MOLD,AMBER...........      3.00
FOOD,F.N.BROWN'S ESSENCE OF JAMAICA GINGER,AQUA.............      5.00
FOOD,5 DROPS,SWANSON CO.,EMBOSSED,6 IN...............ILLUS..      7.00
FOOD,FOLGER,J.A.& CO.,FLAVORING EX.,RECTANGULAR,AMETHYST....      3.00
FOOD,FOLGER'S GOLDEN GATE FLAVORING,RECTANGULAR,AMETHYST....      2.00
FOOD,FORBES DELICIOUS FLAVORING EXTRACTS,RECTANGULAR,CLEAR..      2.00
FOOD,FOREST CITY BAKING POWDER,QUART,AQUA..................      12.50
FOOD,FORMAMIHT TABLETS,RECTANGULAR,SCREW TOP,AMBER.........       2.00
FOOD,FOSS,3 OZ. LIQUID FRUIT FLAVORS,BLOWN IN MOLD,CLEAR....      1.00
FOOD,FRANCO AMERICAN HYGENIC CO.,RECTANGULAR,AMETHYST.......      4.00
FOOD,FRANK TEA & SPICE CO.,JUMBO PEANUT BUTTER,ROUND,CLEAR..      2.00
FOOD,FRANK,THE TEA & SPICE CO.,TURPINTINE,FLASK,AQUA.........     8.00
FOOD,FRENCH MEDFORD BRAND MUSTARD.........................       10.00
```

FOOD,FRENCH MUSTARD,CHAS.GULDEN,N.Y.,CLEAR..........ILLUS..   7.50
FOOD,FROST'S LEMON FRUIT EXTRACT,ROCHESTER,NY.......ILLUS..   3.50
FOOD,FROSTILLA,HOLMES FRAGRANT.....................ILLUS..   3.00
FOOD,FRUIT FLAVOR,EMBOSSED MC GONAGLE & ROGERS..............   2.50
FOOD,FULL MEASURE,J.A.FOLGER & CO.,FLAVORING EXTRACT........   4.00
FOOD,GARRETT'S FOOD PRODUCTS,ROUND GREEN...................   8.00
FOOD,GEBHARDT EAGLE,CHILE POWDER,RECTANGULAR,CLEAR..........   4.00
FOOD,GEM BUTTER JAR,QUART,AQUA.............................   24.50
FOOD,GLEN ROSE PURE FOOD PROD.,MADE IN L.A.,QUART,CLEAR.....   1.25
FOOD,GOLDEN WEST PEANUT BUTTER ON BASE,EMBOSSED,QUART.......   4.50
FOOD,GOLDEN WEST PEANUT BUTTER,PINT,CLEAR..................   2.50
FOOD,HALFORD LEICESTERSHIRE,SAUCE,AQUA,8 IN..........ILLUS..   3.50

FOOD,CERTIFIED ALDERNEY
BUTTER COLOR,AMBER

FOOD,DR.FENNER'S
CONCENTRATED EXTRACTS,CLEAR

FOOD,EDDY'S RELIABLE
BAKING POWDER,C.1905

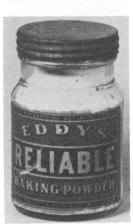

FOOD,ER DURKEE & CO.,
NEW YORK,CLEAR

FOOD, 5 DROPS,
SWANSON CO.,
EMBOSSED,6 IN

FOOD,
FRENCH MUSTARD,
CHAS.GULDEN,
N.Y.,CLEAR

FOOD,FROST'S LEMON FRUIT
EXTRACT,ROCHESTER,NY

FOOD,FROSTILLA,
HOLMES FRAGRANT

FOOD,HALFORD
LEICESTERSHIRE,
SAUCE,AQUA,8 IN

FOOD,HARPER EXTRACT & PERFUME CO.,1/2 GAL.,CLEAR.............	8.50
FOOD,HEINZ & NOBLE,HORSERADISH,1873.................ILLUS..	10.00
FOOD,HEINZ,CATSUP,1889-1894......................ILLUS..	12.00
FOOD,HEINZ,CATSUP,1889-1894......................ILLUS..	18.00
FOOD,HEINZ,CELERY SAUCE..........................ILLUS..	10.00
FOOD,HEINZ,CHOW CHOW.............................ILLUS..	10.00
FOOD,HEINZ,CHUTNEY,1895-1900.....................COLOR..	10.00
FOOD,HEINZ,GHERKINS..............................COLOR..	10.00
FOOD,HEINZ,H.J.CO.,APPLE BUTTER,BASKET,1885.........COLOR..	18.00
FOOD,HEINZ,H.J.CO.,APPLE BUTTER,CROCK..............ILLUS..	16.00
FOOD,HEINZ,H.J.CO.,HORSE RADISH,NO.37 GOTHIC,AQUA...........	4.00
FOOD,HEINZ,H.J.CO.,HORSE RADISH,1880'S..............ILLUS..	3.00
FOOD,HEINZ,H.J.CO.,PAT.ON BOTTOM,8 PANELED,AMETHYST........	4.00
FOOD,HEINZ,H.J.CO.,PAT.1890 ON BASE,8 SIDES,KEY IN SHIELD...	8.00
FOOD,HEINZ,H.J.CO.,ROUND,18 PANELED,CLEAR..................	5.00
FOOD,HEINZ,H.J.CO.,VINEGAR,BARREL,SAMPLING..........ILLUS..	60.00
FOOD,HEINZ,HORSE RADISH,1896-1904...................ILLUS..	7.00
FOOD,HEINZ,HORSE RADISH,1904-1918...................ILLUS..	6.00
FOOD,HEINZ,HORSE RADISH,1918-1931...................ILLUS..	2.00
FOOD,HEINZ,HORSERADISH,COVERED DISH.................ILLUS..	65.00
FOOD,HEINZ,HORSERADISH,1869.........................ILLUS..	12.00
FOOD,HEINZ,KETCHUP,1880-1905........................ILLUS..	5.00
FOOD,HEINZ,KETCHUP,1887-1895........................ILLUS..	6.00
FOOD,HEINZ,KETCHUP,1889-1910........................COLOR..	8.00
FOOD,HEINZ,KETCHUP,1906-1910........................ILLUS..	3.00
FOOD,HEINZ,KETCHUP,1916-1920........................ILLUS..	2.00
FOOD,HEINZ,KEYSTONE KETCHUP,JUG.....................COLOR..	25.00
FOOD,HEINZ,PAT.MAR.14,1882,CLEAR,8 IN...............ILLUS..	4.00
FOOD,HEINZ,PRESERVED SWEET PICKLES..................COLOR..	18.00
FOOD,HEINZ,SARATOGA RELISH,C.1873...................ILLUS..	25.00
FOOD,HERB JUICE,RECTANGULAR,CLEAR..........................	5.00
FOOD,HIRE'S ROOT BEER,MAKES 5 GALLONS,SQUARE,AQUA..........	3.00
FOOD,HIRES EXTRACT,EMBOSSED FOR BREWING ROOT BEER AT HOME...	5.50
FOOD,HIRES ROOT BEER,PHILADELPHIA...................ILLUS..	5.00
FOOD,HIRES,AMBER..	25.00
FOOD,HORLICK'S MALTED MILK EMBOSSED,CLEAR LID,3 1/4 IN. TALL	2.00
FOOD,HORLICK'S MALTED MILK JAR,EMBOSSED HMM,10 3/4 IN. TALL.	6.00
FOOD,HORLICK'S MALTED MILK,BLOWN IN MOLD,CLEAR...... 1.50 TO	2.00
FOOD,HORLICK'S MALTED MILK,EMBOSSED HMM....................	6.00
FOOD,HORLICK'S MALTED MILK,GAL.,AQUA......................	4.00
FOOD,HORLICK'S MALTED MILK,MACHINE MADE,AQUA..............	1.50

FOOD, HEINZ,
CATSUP,
1889-1894

FOOD, HEINZ,
CHOW CHOW

FOOD, HEINZ,
CELERY SAUCE

FOOD, HEINZ,
GHERKINS

FOOD, HEINZ, CHUTNEY,
1895-1900

FOOD, HEINZ, H.J.CO.,
APPLE BUTTER, CROCK

FOOD, HEINZ, H.J.CO.,
APPLE BUTTER, BASKET, 1885

FOOD,HEINZ,H.J.CO.,
HORSE RADISH,1880'S

FOOD,HEINZ,H.J.CO.,
VINEGAR,BARREL,SAMPLING

FOOD,HEINZ,
HORSERADISH,1869

FOOD,HEINZ,
HORSERADISH,COVERED DISH

FOOD,HEINZ &
NOBLE,
HORSERADISH,1873

FOOD,HEINZ,
HORSE RADISH,
1896-1904

FOOD,HEINZ,
HORSE RADISH,
1904-1918

FOOD,HEINZ,
HORSE RADISH,
1918-1931

FOOD, HEINZ, KETCHUP, 1880-1905

FOOD, HEINZ, KETCHUP, 1887-1895

FOOD, HEINZ,
CATSUP,
1889-1894

FOOD, HEINZ,
KETCHUP,
1889-1910

FOOD, HEINZ,
KETCHUP, 1906-1910

FOOD, HEINZ,
KEYSTONE KETCHUP JUG

FOOD, HEINZ, PAT. MAR. 14, 1882, CLEAR, 8 IN

FOOD, HEINZ, SARATOGA RELISH, C.1873

FOOD, HIRES ROOT BEER, PHILADELPHIA

FOOD, HEINZ, KETCHUP, 1916-1920

```
FOOD,HORLICK'S MALTED MILK,RACINE WIS.,GAL.,AQUA.............      8.95
FOOD,HORLICK'S MALTED MILK,TIN LID,5 IN....................      3.50
FOOD,HORLICK'S MALTED MILK,1 GAL.,ROUND,CLEAR..............      3.00
FOOD,HORSE-RADISH,MACHINE MADE,CLEAR.......................      1.25
FOOD,HORSFORD'S BAKING POWDER,BLOWN IN MOLD,AQUA...........      2.50
FOOD,JOHNSTON'S FLUID BEEF,RED.................... 10.00 TO     15.00
FOOD,JUMBO BRAND PEANUT BUTTER,ELEPHANT....................      4.50
FOOD,JUMBO PEANUT BUTTER...................................      5.00
FOOD,JUMBO PEANUT BUTTER & EMBOSSED ELEPHANT HEAD,PINT......      2.00
FOOD,JUMBO PEANUT BUTTER & EMBOSSED ELEPHANT HEAD,1/2 PINT..      3.50
FOOD,JUMBO PEANUT BUTTER,PINT,CLEAR........................      2.75
FOOD,JUMBO PEANUT BUTTER,PINT,PRESTO LID...................      1.50
FOOD,KATSUP,REIF'S SPECIAL,AMBER...........................      4.00
FOOD,KB ON BOTTOM,8 PANEL..................................      4.00
FOOD,KELLOGG'S EMBOSSED ON BOTTOM,BLOB TOP.................      2.00
   FOOD, KETCHUP, SEE ALSO CATSUP
FOOD,KETCHUP,G & R,AQUA,10 IN.,LABEL.................ILLUS..     15.00
FOOD,KISS ME GUM,1/2 GAL..................................     18.00
FOOD,KITTEN SYRUP,BANK LID.................................      2.50
FOOD,LADY BETTY PRUNE JUICE,1/2 GAL.,RED INK & HANDLE......      2.25
FOOD,LARKIN WINTERGREEN FLAVORING EXTRACT............ILLUS..      5.50
FOOD,LEA & PERRINS WORCESTERSHIRE,AQUA............. 2.00 TO      2.50
FOOD,LEMON ACID,PONTIL,EMBOSSED,LABEL,CONTENTS.............     13.00
FOOD,LESTOIL,AMBER,FLASK..................................      2.00
FOOD,LESTOIL,AMETHYST,FLASK................................      2.00
FOOD,LESTOIL,GREEN,FLASK...................................      2.00
FOOD,LIBERTY BELL MUSTARD,CLEAR............................      5.00
FOOD,LITTLE RIVER PICKLE JAR,GLASS COVER...................     18.50
FOOD,LORILLARD............................................      8.00
FOOD,MACLAREN'S IMPERIAL CHEESE,BLOWN IN MOLD,WHITE........      1.00
FOOD,MAURICE BAKER & CO.,FLAVORING EXTRACTS,CLEAR..........      3.00
FOOD,MCMONAGLE & ROGERS PREMIUM FRUIT FLAVORS........ILLUS..      4.00
FOOD,MCMONAGLE & ROGERS PREMIUM FRUIT FLAVORS........ILLUS..      5.00
FOOD,MELLIN'S FOOD CO.,BLOWN IN MOLD,AQUA..................      1.50
FOOD,MELLIN'S FOOD CO.,BOSTON,QUART,CLEAR..................      6.50
FOOD,MILLER'S FINE FLAVORS,3 FLIES EMBOSSED,2 QUART........     15.00
FOOD,MONARCH IN SHIELD,QUART,CLEAR.........................      8.00
FOOD,MONARCH,LION'S HEAD EMBLEM,QUART,CLEAR................      3.70
FOOD,MR.PEANUT,EMBOSSED FIGURE,5 CENT SIGN,COVER...........     23.50
FOOD,MRS.B.SMITH'S BUTTER COLOR.....................ILLUS..      3.50
```

FOOD,KETCHUP,G & R,AQUA,
10 IN.,LABEL

FOOD,LARKIN WINTERGREEN
FLAVORING EXTRACT

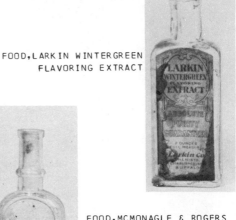

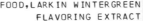

FOOD,MCMONAGLE & ROGERS
PREMIUM FRUIT FLAVORS

FOOD,MCMONAGLE & ROGERS
PREMIUM FRUIT FLAVORS

FOOD,MRS.B.SMITH'S
BUTTER COLOR

```
FOOD,MRS.BUTTERSWORTH SYRUP,AMBER............................    3.00
FOOD,MRS.BUTTERWORTH'S,12 OZ.,AMBER...........................     .75
FOOD,MRS.BUTTERWORTH'S,24 OZ.,AMBER...........................    1.25
FOOD,MRS.CHAPINS MAYONNAISE,BOSTON,MASS.,PINT,CLEAR..........    3.75
FOOD,MRS.CHAPINS,PINT.........................................    2.50
    FOOD, MUSTARD, SEE ALSO FOOD, BARREL, MUSTARD
FOOD,MUSTARD PICKLE,8 IN.,AQUA................................    1.75
FOOD,MUSTARD,BLOWN IN MOLD,AMETHYST...........................    1.00
FOOD,MUSTARD,LIBERTY BELL,CLEAR...............................    5.00
FOOD,NEW ENGLAND MAPLE SYRUP CO...............................    6.00
FOOD,NEW ENGLAND MAPLE SYRUP,1 1/2 PINT.......................    5.00
FOOD,NEWMAN'S PURE GOLD BAKING POWDER,FAIRPORT,N.Y.,TIN LID,
```

```
AQUA.......................................................  8.50
FOOD,NORTH OF ENGLAND SAUCE,WOODEN PEG,AQUA................. 32.00
FOOD,NU GRAPE,HOUR GLASS SHAPE,GREEN........................  2.00
FOOD,OLD JUDGE COFFEE.......................................  1.50
FOOD,OLD JUDGE COFFEE,EMBOSSED OWL,1 GAL.................... 10.00
FOOD,OLD JUDGE COFFEE,OWL SITTING ON BRANCH................. 10.00
FOOD,OLD JUDGE COFFEE,OWL,LID,GALLON........................  6.50
FOOD,OLD JUDGE COFFEE,QUART,CLEAR...........................  2.00
FOOD,OLD JUDGE COFFEE,QUART,CLEAR...........................  3.75
FOOD,OLIVE OIL,BLOWN IN MOLD,AMETHYST.......................  5.00
FOOD,OLIVE OIL,BLOWN IN MOLD,CLEAR..........................  4.50
FOOD,OLIVE OIL,FREE BLOWN,PUSH UP,AQUA...................... 10.00
FOOD,OLIVE OIL,GREEN........................................  2.00
FOOD,OLIVE OIL,PLAIN,ROUND,TAPERED NECK,AQUA................  8.00
FOOD,OLIVE OIL,PLAIN,TAPERED BODY,COBALT.................... 12.00
FOOD,OLIVE OIL,POMPEIAN BRAND VIRGIN LUCCA,AQUA.............  4.00
FOOD,OLIVE OIL,PURE,S.S.P.,CLEAR............................  4.00
FOOD,OLIVE OIL,ROUND,AMBER..................................  4.00
FOOD,OLIVE OIL,SLIM,BULBOUS NECK,AQUA....................... 10.00
FOOD,OLIVE OIL,SLIM,BULBOUS NECK,CLEAR...................... 10.00
FOOD,OLIVE OIL,SYLMAR BRAND,BLOWN IN MOLD,AMETHYST..........  2.50
FOOD,OLIVE OIL,TURN MOLD,CLEAR..............................  4.00
FOOD,OLIVE OIL,8 IN.,COBALT BLUE........................... 12.00
FOOD,OLIVE,CLEAR................................... 5.00 TO  6.00
FOOD,OLIVES,BLOWN IN MOLD,AMETHYST..........................  2.00
FOOD,OLIVES,BLOWN IN MOLD,CLEAR.............................  2.00
FOOD,OLIVES,TONNEAU NO.14,PATENT APPLIED FOR,BLOWN IN MOLD,
   CLEAR...................................................  3.50
FOOD,P.LORILLARD........................................... 10.00
FOOD,P.LORILLARD & CO.,PINT,AMBER.......................... 14.25
FOOD,P.LORILLARD & CO.,QUART,AMBER......................... 14.25
FOOD,P.LORILLARD & CO.,1/2 GAL.,AMBER...................... 14.25
FOOD,P.LORILLARD,AMBER..................................... 10.00
FOOD,P.LORILLARD,GLASS TOP,1872,QUART......................  9.75
FOOD,PARKER BROS.,CLUB SAUCE,ROUND,LONDON,AQUA.............  6.00
   FOOD, PEPPERSAUCE, SEE PEPPERSAUCE
FOOD,PERRIN & CO.,D S,QUART,CLEAR.......................... 12.50
   FOOD, PICKLE, SEE ALSO PICKLE
FOOD,PICKLE,ARMOUR,PANELED.................................  6.00
FOOD,PICKLE,GRAPES,12 1/2 IN. TALL......................... 15.00
FOOD,PICKLE,PARROTS,9 1/2 IN. TALL......................... 12.00
FOOD,PLANTERS PEANUT,HEXAGON,EMBOSSED COVER,PEANUT FINIAL... 12.50
FOOD,PLANTERS PEANUT,PAPER LABEL........................... 16.00
FOOD,PLANTERS PEANUT,PEANUT ON LID,10 IN........... 12.00 TO 17.50
FOOD,PLANTERS PEANUT,SQUARE,EMBOSSED PLANTERS,COVER........ 14.50
FOOD,PRESERVE JAR,BLOWN,NEW ENGLAND,YELLOW OLIVE........... 60.00
FOOD,PRUNE WATER & JUICE,40 OZ.,GREEN......................  2.25
FOOD,PURES,EMBOSSED,QUART,AMBER............................  1.75
FOOD,QUONG HOP & CO.,CALIF.,CHINESE WRITING,PINT,CLEAR.....  3.50
FOOD,QUONG HOP & CO.,CHINESE WRITING,PINT,CLEAR............  3.50
FOOD,QUONG YUEN SING & CO.,CHINESE WRITING,PINT,CLEAR......  3.50
FOOD,RAINBOW,EMBOSSED,QUART,AMBER..........................  1.75
FOOD,RAISED PEANUTS ON FRONT & SIDES,MARKED A.H.,1 1/2 PINT.  2.50
FOOD,RAWLEIGH'S TRADE MARK,BLOWN IN MOLD,BALL NECK,CLEAR...  2.00
FOOD,RAWLEIGH'S,MACHINE MADE,AQUA..........................  1.00
FOOD,RELISH,BLOWN IN MOLD,AMETHYST.........................  2.50
FOOD,ROSEBUD CHERRIES,1915,CLEAR,6 IN...............ILLUS..  4.00
FOOD,ROSES LIME JUICE,14 IN................................ 10.50
FOOD,ROYAL CUP COFFEE JAR,1 LB.,ZINC LID,EMBOSSED..........  4.00
FOOD,ROYAL CUP COFFEE,1 LB.,ZINC LID.......................  4.00
FOOD,SALT SAUCE,ROUGH PONTIL,INITIALS H.C.K.,AQUA.......... 35.00
FOOD,SANG YUEN CO.,CALIF.,CHINESE WRITING,QUART,CLEAR......  6.50
FOOD,SAUCE,PLAIN,8 ROUND PANELS,AQUA.......................  8.00
FOOD,SHARP 3 DOHME,AMBER...................................  4.00
FOOD,SHREWSBURY,BEETS,AQUA,9 IN.,LABEL..............ILLUS.. 22.00
```

```
FOOD,SLADE'S SALAD CREAM,BLOWN IN MOLD,CLEAR.................    1.50
FOOD,SOY SAUCE JUG,POTTERY,GREEN..............................   12.00
FOOD,SOY SAUCE,POTTERY JUG,RING TOP,BROWN.....................    8.00
FOOD,SPARK'S HORSE RADISH,DENVER,AQUA,7 IN...........ILLUS..      5.50
FOOD,SPE TRADEMARK,5 IN.,CLEAR......................ILLUS..       3.50
FOOD,SPECIAL BRAND EXTRACT JAMAICA GINGERS,AQUA..............     2.00
FOOD,ST.LOUIS SYRUP & PRESERVING CO.,QUART,BLUE.............     18.00
FOOD,ST.LOUIS SYRUP & PRESERVING,QUART,AQUA..................    10.25
FOOD,ST.LOUIS SYRUP & PRESERVING,QUART,CLEAR.................    10.25
FOOD,STORE,PEANUT,SQUIRREL,TIN COVER,BAIL,WOODEN KNOB.......      8.50
FOOD,SUNNY BROOK COFFEE JAR,WEATHERSBY-BRUNNER CO...........     10.00
FOOD,TAYLOR & CO.,QUART,AQUA..................................    6.25
FOOD,TOMATO CATSUP,CLEAR,8 IN.,EXTRA FINE............ILLUS..     18.00
FOOD,TRIAL MARK WATKINS,MACHINE MADE,BROWN...................     1.50
FOOD,TRIAL MARK,WATKINS,MACHINE MADE,CLEAR...................     1.00
FOOD,TROPICAL CANNERS,PINT,CLEAR.............................     2.75
FOOD,TROPICAL CANNERS,QUART,CLEAR............................     2.75
FOOD,VALENTINE'S MEAT JUICE,BLOWN IN MOLD,AMBER.............      2.50
FOOD,VALENTINES MEAT SAUCE,AMBER.............................     3.00
FOOD,VIRGINIA FRUIT JUICE CO.,PARTIAL TORPEDO...............      2.00
FOOD,VIRGINIA FRUIT JUICE CO.CROWN,PARTIAL TORPEDO..........      2.00
FOOD,WAN-ETA COCOA,BOSTON,AMBER..............................     5.00
FOOD,WAN-ETA COCOA,BOSTON,QUART,AMBER........................     5.00
FOOD,WAN-ETA COCOA,MIDGET,1/2 PINT,AMBER.....................     6.00
FOOD,WAN-ETA COCOA,QUART,AMBER...............................     4.50
FOOD,WAN-ETA COCOA,QUART,AQUA................................     6.00
FOOD,WAN-ETA COCOA,QUART,LID,AMBER...........................     3.50
FOOD,WAN-ETA COCOA,1/2 PINT,AMBER............................     8.00
FOOD,WATKINS EXTRACT,BLOWN IN MOLD,CLEAR...................-..    2.00
FOOD,WING WAH SING,PINT,CLEAR................................     6.25
FOOD,WING WAH SING,QUART,CLEAR...............................     6.25
FOOD,WO HOP CO.,CALIF.,BEAN CAKE,CHINESE WRITING,PINT,CLEAR.     20.25
FOOD,WO HOP CO.,CALIF.,BEAN CAKE,CHINESE WRITING,QUART......     20.25
FOOD,YACHT CLUB SALAD DRESSING,AMETHYST......................     3.00
FOOD,YACHT CLUB SALAD DRESSING,CLEAR.........................     3.00
FOOD,YORK PEANUT BUTTER,COW/PEANUT EMBLEM,PINT,CLEAR........      1.25
FOOD,33,EMBOSSED,QUART,AMBER..................................    1.75
FREE BLOWN CYLINDER,BLACK GLASS,CIRCA 1790..................     15.00
FREE BLOWN,DIP MOLD,BLACK GLASS,QUART........................     8.00
```

FOOD,ROSEBUD CHERRIES,
1915,CLEAR,6 IN

FOOD,SPARK'S
HORSE RADISH,
DENVER,
AQUA,7 IN

FOOD,
SHREWSBURY,
BEETS,AQUA,
9 IN.,LABEL

FOOD,SPE TRADEMARK,
5 IN.,CLEAR

FOOD,TOMATO CATSUP,CLEAR,
8 IN., EXTRA FINE

```
FREE BLOWN,ROLLED LIP,CIRCA 1820,GREEN......................    32.00
FRENCH DRESSING,FLORAL,OIL,VINEGAR,CUT GLASS,HAWKES,JUNE
   1916...................................................      17.00
FROSTILE HOLMES FRAGRANT,ELMIRA,N.Y.,U.S.A.,CLEAR...........     6.00
```

FRUIT JARS MADE OF GLASS HAVE BEEN USED IN THE UNITED
STATES SINCE THE 1850'S. OVER ONE THOUSAND DIFFERENT
JARS HAVE BEEN FOUND WITH VARIETIES OF CLOSURES,
EMBOSSING, AND COLORS. THE DATE 1858 ON MANY JARS
REFERS TO A PATENT, NOT THE AGE OF THE BOTTLE. BE SURE
TO LOOK IN THIS LISTING UNDER ANY NAME OR INITIAL THAT
APPEARS ON YOUR JAR.

```
FRUIT JAR,A & C,QUART,AQUA.................................    35.00
FRUIT JAR,A & C,QUART,GREEN................................    45.00
FRUIT JAR,A & D.H.CHAMBERS UNION,WAX SEALER,QUART,AQUA.....    12.00
FRUIT JAR,A & DH CHAMBERS,PITTSBURGH,UNION ON BASE,1/2 GAL.,
   AQUA...................................................      8.00
FRUIT JAR,A & DH CHAMBERS,UNION,PITTSBURGH ON SIDE,QUART,
   AQUA...................................................     18.00
FRUIT JAR,A IN H ON BASE,PINT,CLEAR.......................      4.00
FRUIT JAR,A.B.G.A.MASON IMPROVED,QUART,AQUA...............     12.00
FRUIT JAR,A.B.G.A.MASON PERFECT,QUART,AQUA................      8.00
FRUIT JAR,A.G.W.L.PITTS PA. ON BASE,QUART,AQUA............     18.00
FRUIT JAR,A.G.W.L.PITTS PA. ON BASE,QUART,CLEAR...........      9.00
FRUIT JAR,A.K.KLINE,WHITTLED,1/2 GAL......................     25.00
FRUIT JAR,ABC ON BASE,QUART,AQUA..........................      8.00
FRUIT JAR,ABC ON SIDE,QUART,AQUA..........................     25.00
FRUIT JAR,ACHERSON OIL DAG CO.,QUART......................     12.00
FRUIT JAR,ACME IN SHIELD,PINT,CLEAR.......................      4.00
FRUIT JAR,ACME IN SHIELD,PINT,GREEN.......................      5.00
FRUIT JAR,ACME IN SHIELD,QUART,CLEAR......................      3.00
FRUIT JAR,ACME IN SHIELD,QUART,GREEN......................      5.00
FRUIT JAR,ACME IN SHIELD,1/2 GAL.,CLEAR...................      5.00
FRUIT JAR,ACME SEAL,QUART,CLEAR...........................      8.00
FRUIT JAR,ACME,PINT.............................. 3.00 TO      5.00
FRUIT JAR,ACME,QUART............................. 2.00 TO      3.00
```

```
FRUIT JAR,ADLER,PINT,CLEAR.....................................      3.00
FRUIT JAR,ADLER,QUART,CLEAR....................................      3.00
FRUIT JAR,ADLER,1/2 GAL.,CLEAR.................................      3.00
FRUIT JAR,ADLER,1/2 GAL.,GREEN.................................      4.00
FRUIT JAR,ADLER,1/2 PINT,CLEAR.................................      5.00
FRUIT JAR,ADLER,1/2 PINT,GREEN.................................      6.00
FRUIT JAR,ADVANCE,QUART,AQUA...................................     75.00
FRUIT JAR,ADVANCE,TRADE MARK,PAT.APLD.FOR,WJ EMBLEM,QUART,
   AQUA.......................................................     35.00
FRUIT JAR,ADVANCE,TRADE MARK,PAT.APLD.FOR,WJ EMBLEM,QUART,
   GREEN......................................................     45.00
FRUIT JAR,AGEE QUEEN,QUART,CLEAR...............................     10.00
FRUIT JAR,AGEE VICTORY,QUART,CLEAR.............................     10.00
FRUIT JAR,AGNEW,QUART,AQUA.....................................     14.00
FRUIT JAR,AGNEW,QUART,GREEN....................................     17.00
FRUIT JAR,AIR TIGHT,QUART,AQUA.................................     60.00
FRUIT JAR,AIR TIGHT,QUART,GREEN................................     75.00
FRUIT JAR,ALL RIGHT,PAT.JAN.25,1868,QT.,AQUA.......  38.00 TO     40.00
FRUIT JAR,ALL RIGHT,PAT.JAN.25,1868,QT.,GREEN......  42.00 TO     44.00
FRUIT JAR,ALL RIGHT,PRESERVE,AQUA,QUART........................     22.00
FRUIT JAR,ALLEN'S PAT.1871,LID.................................     35.00
FRUIT JAR,ALMY,QUART,AQUA......................................     28.00
FRUIT JAR,ALSTON PAT'D,PINT,CLEAR..............................     40.00
FRUIT JAR,ALSTON PAT'D,QUART,CLEAR.............................     30.00
FRUIT JAR,AMAZON SWIFT SEAL IN CIRCLE,PINT,AQUA...............      5.00
FRUIT JAR,AMAZON SWIFT SEAL IN CIRCLE,QUART,AQUA..............      4.00
FRUIT JAR,AMAZON SWIFT SEAL,AQUA...............................      5.00
FRUIT JAR,AMAZON SWIFT SEAL,PINT...............................      5.00
FRUIT JAR,AMAZON SWIFT SEAL,PINT,AQUA..........................      4.50
FRUIT JAR,AMAZON SWIFT SEAL,QUART..............................      4.00
FRUIT JAR,AMAZON SWIFT SEAL,QUART,AQUA.........................      4.50
FRUIT JAR,AMAZON SWIFT SEAL,1/2 GAL............................      6.00
FRUIT JAR,AMERICAN FRUIT JAR,EAGLE EMBLEM,AQUA................     25.00
FRUIT JAR,AMERICAN FRUIT JAR,EAGLE EMBLEM,OLIVE GREEN.........     40.00
FRUIT JAR,AMERICAN PORCELAIN LINED,NAGCO MONO,QUART,GREEN...     25.00
FRUIT JAR,AMERICAN SODA FOUNTAIN CO.,1/2 GAL.,CLEAR.........      6.00
FRUIT JAR,AMERICAN,NAGCO MONO,QT.,AQUA..............  20.00 TO     22.00
FRUIT JAR,AMERICAN,PORCELAIN LINED,1/2 GAL..................     23.00
FRUIT JAR,AMERICAN,THE PORCELAIN LINED,NAGCO MONO,1/2 GAL.,
   AQUA.......................................................     22.00
FRUIT JAR,ANCHOR H LIGHTNING,PINT..............................      4.00
FRUIT JAR,ANCHOR H MONO,LIGHTNING,PINT,CLEAR..................      4.00
FRUIT JAR,ANCHOR H MONO,LIGHTNING,QUART,CLEAR.................      3.00
FRUIT JAR,ANCHOR H,MASON,REVERSE,PINT..........................      2.00
FRUIT JAR,ANCHOR HOCKING MASON,ANCHOR H MONO,PINT,CLEAR.....      2.00
FRUIT JAR,ANCHOR HOCKING MASON,ANCHOR H MONO,QUART,CLEAR....      1.00
FRUIT JAR,ANCHOR HOCKING MASON,ANCHOR H MONO,1/2 GAL.,CLEAR.      2.00
FRUIT JAR,ANCHOR HOCKING MASON,PINT,CLEAR......................      5.00
FRUIT JAR,ANCHOR HOCKING,ATLAS MASON'S PATENT,QUART.........      2.00
FRUIT JAR,ANCHOR HOCKING,BALL MASON,QUART,GREEN..............      2.00
FRUIT JAR,ANCHOR HOCKING,BALL PERFECT MASON'S,QUART.........      2.00
FRUIT JAR,ANCHOR HOCKING,METRO EASY PAK MASON,QUART.........      2.00
FRUIT JAR,ANCHOR HOCKING,PINT..................................      2.00
FRUIT JAR,ANCHOR HOCKING,QUART......................  1.00 TO      2.00
FRUIT JAR,ANCHOR MASON,QUART,CLEAR..................  2.00 TO      6.00
FRUIT JAR,ANCHOR MASON'S PATENT,QUART,CLEAR....................      4.00
FRUIT JAR,ANCHOR,ANCHOR-CHAIN MONO,QUART,CLEAR................     14.00
FRUIT JAR,ANCHOR,ANCHOR-CHAIN MONO,1/2 GAL.,AMETHYST........     18.00
FRUIT JAR,ANDERSON PRESERVING CO.,QUART,AMETHYST.............     10.00
FRUIT JAR,AQUA,GLOBE,1 PINT,DATED 1886.........................     15.00
FRUIT JAR,AQUA,1/8 PINT..............................ILLUS..      1.00
FRUIT JAR,AQUA,1/2 PINT..............................ILLUS..      1.00
FRUIT JAR,ARS,QUART,AQUA.......................................     45.00
FRUIT JAR,ATHERHOLT FISHER & CO.,PHILAD.,QUART,AQUA.........     35.00
FRUIT JAR,ATHERHOLT FISHER & CO.,PHILAD.,QUART,CLEAR........     30.00
FRUIT JAR,ATLAS................................................      1.50
```

Whiskey, Old Quarter
Century, Weller

Figural, Violin

Whiskey, Chestnut Grove, C. W.

I. W. Harper, Decanter, 1885

Dant,
Bourbon, 1881,
Pendennis Club

Decanter,
Coronation
of King George V, 1911

Left to Right: Flasks: Masonic, Mc Kearin G IV-1;
Masonic, c. 1815-1860; Masonic, c. 1815

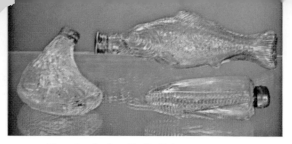

Figurals, Oyster Shell, Fish, Ear of Corn

Flask, Mc Kearin G II-76, Eagle

Figurals, Soldier
Sailor

Flask, Mc Kearin G II-112
Louis Kossuth, c. 1850

Dant, Mt. Rushmore

Flask, Hunter & Fisherman, Nineteenth Century

Bitters,
Atwood's Jaundice,
Moses Atwood

Figural, Hand,
Probably French

I. W. Harper, Ceramic, 1913, Nautical

Flask, Will You Take A Drink,
Will A Duck Swim

Gemel, Nailsea, 1st Half
Nineteenth Century

Decanter, Mc Kearin
G III-5, Blown Three Mold

Bennington, Coachman,
c. 1846-1848
Bennington, Book, c. 1850

Flask, Jenny Lind, c. 185

Figural, Pig, Nineteenth Century

I. W. Harper, G.A.R., 1895

Flask,
Eagle,
c. 186

Flask, Bust of Columbia
Wearing Liberty Cap

Whiskey, A Merry Christmas
and a Happy New Year

Whiskey, Corn Shape, Old Elk,
front and side views

Flask, A Little More Grape
Captain Bragg, 1847

DANT

Left to Right: Top row:
Washington Crossing Delaware, Patrick Henry, Constitution & Guerriere, Duel Between Burr and Hamilton

Bottom row: Boston Tea Party, Back of Bottle, no label, Alamo

WHEATON NULINE PRESIDENTIAL SERIES
Left to Right: Top row: John F. Kennedy, Franklin D. Roosevelt;
Middle row: Dwight D. Eisenhower, Abraham Lincoln, General
Eisenhower; Bottom row: Woodrow Wilson, George Washington,
Theodore Roosevelt

WHEATON NULINE GREAT AMERICAN SERIES
Left to Right: Top row: Martin Luther King, Robert Kennedy, Douglas MacArthur; Middle row: Charles Lindbergh, Thomas Alva Edison, Robert E. Lee, Betsy Ross; Bottom row: Will Rogers, Benjamin Franklin, Billy Graham

Lionstone, Cowboy

Lionstone, Proud Indian

Apollo XII

Apollo XI   Apollo XIII

WHEATON NULINE ASTRONAUT SERIES

FRUIT JAR, AQUA,
1/8 PINT

FRUIT JAR, AQUA,
1/2 PINT

FRUIT JAR, ATLAS CLOVERLEAF GOODLUCK, PINT........................	3.00
FRUIT JAR, ATLAS CLOVERLEAF GOODLUCK, QUART........... 3.00 TO	4.00
FRUIT JAR, ATLAS CORNFLOWER, QUART, AQUA.......................	7.00
FRUIT JAR, ATLAS CORNFLOWER, 1/2 GAL., AQUA...................	9.00
FRUIT JAR, ATLAS E-Z SEAL, AMBER.............................	28.00
FRUIT JAR, ATLAS E-Z SEAL, AQUA....................... 3.00 TO	7.00
FRUIT JAR, ATLAS E-Z SEAL, AQUA LID........................	10.00
FRUIT JAR, ATLAS E-Z SEAL, CLEAR...........................	6.00
FRUIT JAR, ATLAS E-Z SEAL, IN CIRCLE, QUART.................	12.75
FRUIT JAR, ATLAS E-Z SEAL, PINT, AMBER.....................	30.00
FRUIT JAR, ATLAS E-Z SEAL, PINT, AQUA......................	3.00
FRUIT JAR, ATLAS E-Z SEAL, PINT, OLIVE GREEN...............	12.00
FRUIT JAR, ATLAS E-Z SEAL, QUART, AMBER.............. 22.00 TO	30.00
FRUIT JAR, ATLAS E-Z SEAL, QUART, APPLE GREEN.......... 6.50 TO	7.50
FRUIT JAR, ATLAS E-Z SEAL, QUART, AQUA................ 3.00 TO	7.00
FRUIT JAR, ATLAS E-Z SEAL, QUART, BLUE................ 10.00 TO	12.00
FRUIT JAR, ATLAS E-Z SEAL, QUART, CLEAR............... 1.00 TO	2.50
FRUIT JAR, ATLAS E-Z SEAL, QUART, GREEN....................	8.00
FRUIT JAR, ATLAS E-Z SEAL, QUART, OLIVE GREEN......... 10.00 TO	12.00
FRUIT JAR, ATLAS E-Z SEAL, SQUATTY PINT, AQUA..............	3.00
FRUIT JAR, ATLAS E-Z SEAL, 1/2 GAL., AMBER................	30.00
FRUIT JAR, ATLAS E-Z SEAL, 1/2 GAL., AQUA............. 3.00 TO	4.00
FRUIT JAR, ATLAS E-Z SEAL, 1/2 GAL., OLIVE GREEN...........	12.00
FRUIT JAR, ATLAS E-Z SEAL, 1/2 PINT, AMBER................	45.00
FRUIT JAR, ATLAS E-Z SEAL, 1/2 PINT, AQUA.................	6.00
FRUIT JAR, ATLAS E-Z SEAL, 1/2 PINT, OLIVE GREEN..........	16.00
FRUIT JAR, ATLAS E-Z SEAL, 2 PINT.........................	30.00
FRUIT JAR, ATLAS E-Z SEAL, 2 QUART........................	25.00
FRUIT JAR, ATLAS GOOD LUCK, CLOVER MONO, PINT, CLEAR.......	3.00
FRUIT JAR, ATLAS GOOD LUCK, CLOVER MONO, QUART, CLEAR......	2.00
FRUIT JAR, ATLAS GOOD LUCK, CLOVER MONO, 1/3 PINT, CLEAR...	12.00
FRUIT JAR, ATLAS GOOD LUCK, CLOVER MONO, 1/2 GAL., CLEAR...	5.00
FRUIT JAR, ATLAS GOOD LUCK, PINT, CLEAR....................	3.00
FRUIT JAR, ATLAS GOOD LUCK, QUART, CLEAR...................	3.00
FRUIT JAR, ATLAS GOOD LUCK, 1/3 PINT, CLEAR................	5.00
FRUIT JAR, ATLAS GOOD LUCK, 1/2 GAL.................. 3.00 TO	10.00
FRUIT JAR, ATLAS GOOD LUCK, 1/2 GAL., GLASS LID, WIRE CLAMP.....	4.00
FRUIT JAR, ATLAS GOOD LUCK, 1/2 PINT................. 6.00 TO	6.50
FRUIT JAR, ATLAS IMPROVED MASON, PINT, AQUA................	4.50
FRUIT JAR, ATLAS IMPROVED MASON, QUART, AQUA.......... 4.00 TO	4.50
FRUIT JAR, ATLAS IMPROVED MASON, QUART, GREEN..............	5.00
FRUIT JAR, ATLAS JUNIOR MASON, PINT, CLEAR.................	3.00
FRUIT JAR, ATLAS MASON IMPROVED PAT., PINT, AQUA....... 4.50 TO	9.00
FRUIT JAR, ATLAS MASON IMPROVED PAT'D, PINT, CLEAR.........	7.00

```
FRUIT JAR,ATLAS MASON IMPROVED PAT'D,QUART,AQUA.............      9.00
FRUIT JAR,ATLAS MASON IMPROVED PAT'D,QUART,CLEAR............      7.00
FRUIT JAR,ATLAS MASON IMPROVED PATENT............... 5.00 TO     9.00
FRUIT JAR,ATLAS MASON IMPROVED PATENT,PINT,AQUA............      2.50
FRUIT JAR,ATLAS MASON IMPROVED PATENT,QUART,AQUA...........      4.50
FRUIT JAR,ATLAS MASON IMPROVED PATENT,1/2 GAL.,AQUA........      5.00
FRUIT JAR,ATLAS MASON IMPROVED,PATENT,QUART,CORNFLOWER BLUE.     6.00
FRUIT JAR,ATLAS MASON,HA MONO IN CIRCLE,QUART,CLEAR........      2.00
FRUIT JAR,ATLAS MASON,HA MONO,PINT,CLEAR...................      1.00
FRUIT JAR,ATLAS MASON,HA MONO,1/2 GAL.,CLEAR...............      1.00
FRUIT JAR,ATLAS MASON,HA MONO,1/2 PINT,CLEAR...............      2.00
FRUIT JAR,ATLAS MASON'S IMPROVED PATENT,PINT,AQUA..........      3.00
FRUIT JAR,ATLAS MASON'S PAT................................      3.00
FRUIT JAR,ATLAS MASON'S PAT.NOV.30,1858,SCREW TOP,GREEN....      4.00
FRUIT JAR,ATLAS MASON'S PATENT NOV 30TH 1858,1/2 GAL.,AQUA..     4.00
FRUIT JAR,ATLAS MASON'S PATENT NOV 30TH 1858,1/2 GAL.,GREEN.     6.00
FRUIT JAR,ATLAS MASON'S PATENT,QUART,AQUA........... 3.00 TO     4.00
FRUIT JAR,ATLAS MASON'S PATENT,QUART,CLEAR.................      3.00
FRUIT JAR,ATLAS MASON'S PATENT,QUART,OLIVE GREEN...........     10.00
FRUIT JAR,ATLAS SPECIAL MASON,PINT,CLEAR...................      1.00
FRUIT JAR,ATLAS SPECIAL MASON,QUART,AQUA...................      3.00
FRUIT JAR,ATLAS SPECIAL MASON,QUART,CLEAR..................      1.00
FRUIT JAR,ATLAS SPECIAL,QUART,AQUA.........................      4.00
FRUIT JAR,ATLAS SPECIAL,QUART,CLEAR........................      1.00
FRUIT JAR,ATLAS STRONG SHOULDER MASON EMBOSSED,VASELINE.....     8.00
FRUIT JAR,ATLAS STRONG SHOULDER MASON,PINT,AQUA..... 1.00 TO     2.00
FRUIT JAR,ATLAS STRONG SHOULDER MASON,PINT,CLEAR.... 1.00 TO     3.00
FRUIT JAR,ATLAS STRONG SHOULDER MASON,PINT,CORNFLOWER BLUE..     5.00
FRUIT JAR,ATLAS STRONG SHOULDER MASON,PINT,OLIVE GREEN......    12.00
FRUIT JAR,ATLAS STRONG SHOULDER MASON,PINT,YELLOW GREEN.....    20.00
FRUIT JAR,ATLAS STRONG SHOULDER MASON,QUART,AQUA.... 1.00 TO     2.00
FRUIT JAR,ATLAS STRONG SHOULDER MASON,QUART,CLEAR... 1.00 TO     3.00
FRUIT JAR,ATLAS STRONG SHOULDER MASON,QUART,OLIVE GREEN.....    12.00
FRUIT JAR,ATLAS STRONG SHOULDER MASON,1/2 GAL.,AMBER........     2.50
FRUIT JAR,ATLAS STRONG SHOULDER MASON,1/2 GAL.,AQUA.........     2.00
FRUIT JAR,ATLAS STRONG SHOULDER MASON,1/2 GAL.,CLEAR........     1.00
FRUIT JAR,ATLAS STRONG SHOULDER MASON,1/2 GAL.,OLIVE GREEN..    12.00
FRUIT JAR,ATLAS STRONG SHOULDER,LID,QUART..................      5.00
FRUIT JAR,ATLAS WHOLEFRUIT JAR,PINT,CLEAR..................      4.00
FRUIT JAR,ATLAS WHOLEFRUIT JAR,QUART,CLEAR.................      3.00
FRUIT JAR,ATLAS WHOLEFRUIT JAR,1/2 GAL.,CLEAR..............      4.00
FRUIT JAR,ATLAS-MASON'S PATENT NOV.30TH 1858,1/2 GAL.,AQUA..     6.00
FRUIT JAR,ATLAS-MASON'S PATENT NOV.30TH 1858,1/2 GAL.,GREEN.     9.00
FRUIT JAR,ATLAS-MASON'S PATENT,QUART,CLEAR.................      5.00
FRUIT JAR,ATLAS,CLOVERLEAF,GOOD LUCK,PINT..................      4.00
FRUIT JAR,ATLAS,E-Z SEAL,AQUA,PINT....................ILLUS..   20.00
FRUIT JAR,ATLAS,E-Z SEAL,AQUA,QUART...................ILLUS..    6.00
FRUIT JAR,ATLAS,GOOD LUCK,FOUR-LEAF CLOVER,QUART...........      3.50
FRUIT JAR,ATLAS,SQUATTY,BLUE..............................      1.50
FRUIT JAR,ATLAS,STRONG SHOULDER,MASON,PINT...........ILLUS..     3.00
FRUIT JAR,ATLAS,1/2 PINT..................................      4.50
FRUIT JAR,ATMORE & SON,QUART,AQUA.........................     15.00
FRUIT JAR,AUTOMATIC SEALER,THE,BASE CLAYTON N.J.,QUART,AQUA.    20.00
FRUIT JAR,AUTOMATIC SEALER,THE,BASE CLAYTON N.J.,QUART,GREEN    23.00
FRUIT JAR,AYNER,THE,GLASS TOP,QUART,CLEAR..................      6.25
FRUIT JAR,AZEL,ATLAS E-Z SEAL,QUART,CLEAR..................      6.25
FRUIT JAR,B.B.WILCOX,1867,2 QUART.........................     30.00
FRUIT JAR,B.P.&CO.,IN CIRCLE ON BASE,QUART,AQUA............      8.00
FRUIT JAR,B,MASONS PATENT,NOV 30TH,1858,QUART,AQUA.........      6.00
FRUIT JAR,BAGLEY & CO.,LONDON,MIDGET,GREEN.................     25.25
FRUIT JAR,BAGLEY & COMPANY LTD LONDON,ON CLOSURE,PINT,GREEN.     7.00
FRUIT JAR,BAGLEY,1/2 GAL..................................     12.00
FRUIT JAR,BAIL HANDLE,1/2 PINT,CLEAR.................ILLUS..     1.50
FRUIT JAR,BAKER BROS & CO.,BALTIMORE,ON BASE,PINT,AQUA......     9.00
FRUIT JAR,BAKER,J.C.,QUART,AQUA...........................     25.00
```

```
FRUIT JAR,BALDT MASON,SCREW CAP,QUART,AQUA................... 37.50
FRUIT JAR,BALL DE LUXE,PINE PREENED OFF...................  8.00
FRUIT JAR,BALL DELUXE JAR,QUART,CLEAR.....................  3.00
FRUIT JAR,BALL ECLIPSE WIDE MOUTH,PINT,CLEAR...............  3.00
FRUIT JAR,BALL ECLIPSE WIDE MOUTH,QUART,CLEAR..............  2.00
FRUIT JAR,BALL ECLIPSE WIDE MOUTH,1/2 GAL.,CLEAR...........  3.00
FRUIT JAR,BALL ECLIPSE,PINT,CLEAR.........................  3.00
FRUIT JAR,BALL ECLIPSE,QUART,CLEAR........................  1.00
FRUIT JAR,BALL ECLIPSE,1/2 GAL...........................  4.50
FRUIT JAR,BALL ECLIPSE,1/2 GAL.,CLEAR.....................  3.00
FRUIT JAR,BALL ECLIPSE,QUART,CLEAR........................  2.00
FRUIT JAR,BALL FREEZER JAR,PINT,CLEAR.....................  1.00
FRUIT JAR,BALL IDEAL,AQUA................................  7.50
FRUIT JAR,BALL IDEAL,BAIL HANDLE,PINT.............ILLUS..  2.00
FRUIT JAR,BALL IDEAL,BLUE................................  1.50
FRUIT JAR,BALL IDEAL,DATED,PINT,AQUA......................  3.50
FRUIT JAR,BALL IDEAL,DATED,QUART,GREEN.................... 10.00
FRUIT JAR,BALL IDEAL,MADE IN USA,AQUA.....................  2.00
FRUIT JAR,BALL IDEAL,MADE IN USA,CLEAR....................  2.00
FRUIT JAR,BALL IDEAL,MADE IN USA,1/2 PINT,AQUA............  4.00
FRUIT JAR,BALL IDEAL,MADE IN USA,1/2 PINT,CLEAR...........  4.00
FRUIT JAR,BALL IDEAL,PAT'D AQUA..........................  2.00
FRUIT JAR,BALL IDEAL,PAT'D JULY 14,1908,AQUA,.............  2.00
FRUIT JAR,BALL IDEAL,PAT'D JULY 14,1908,CLEAR.............  2.00
FRUIT JAR,BALL IDEAL,PAT'D JULY 14,1908,QUART........ILLUS..  4.00
FRUIT JAR,BALL IDEAL,PAT'D,CLEAR.........................  2.00
FRUIT JAR,BALL IDEAL,PAT'D,1/2 PINT,AQUA..................  4.00
FRUIT JAR,BALL IDEAL,PAT'D,1/2 PINT,CLEAR.................  4.00
FRUIT JAR,BALL IDEAL,PATENT JULY 14,1908,PINT.............  5.00
FRUIT JAR,BALL IDEAL,PATENT JULY 14,1908,QUART,CLEAR.......  1.50
FRUIT JAR,BALL IDEAL,PINT................................  2.00
FRUIT JAR,BALL IDEAL,PINT,APPLE GREEN.....................  9.00
FRUIT JAR,BALL IDEAL,PINT,AQUA...........................  4.00
FRUIT JAR,BALL IDEAL,PINT,BLUE...........................  1.50
FRUIT JAR,BALL IDEAL,PINT,CLEAR..........................  3.00
FRUIT JAR,BALL IDEAL,PROP.OF SO.METH.,QUART,CLEAR.......... 14.00
FRUIT JAR,BALL IDEAL,PROP.OF SQ.METH.,1/2 GAL.,CLEAR....... 14.00
FRUIT JAR,BALL IDEAL,QUART...............................  1.25
```

FRUIT JAR,ATLAS,
E-Z SEAL,AQUA,
PINT

FRUIT JAR,ATLAS,
STRONG SHOULDER,
MASON,PINT

FRUIT JAR,ATLAS,
E-Z SEAL,AQUA,
QUART

FRUIT JAR,BAIL
HANDLE,1/2 PINT,
CLEAR

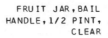

FRUIT JAR,BALL IDEAL,BAIL HANDLE,PINT

FRUIT JAR,BALL IDEAL,PAT'D JULY 14,1908,QUART

```
FRUIT JAR,BALL  IDEAL,QUART,AQUA..................... 2.00 TO   3.00
FRUIT JAR,BALL  IDEAL,QUART,CLEAR.............................   2.00
FRUIT JAR,BALL  IDEAL,WAX SEALER.............................    7.00
FRUIT JAR,BALL  IDEAL,1/4 PINT,CLEAR.........................    4.25
FRUIT JAR,BALL  IDEAL,1/2 GAL.,AMBER.........................   15.50
FRUIT JAR,BALL  IDEAL,1/2 GAL.,AQUA................... 2.00 TO   4.00
FRUIT JAR,BALL  IDEAL,1/2 GAL.,CLEAR................. 2.00 TO    3.00
FRUIT JAR,BALL  IDEAL,1/2 PINT...................... 1.25 TO     6.00
FRUIT JAR,BALL  IDEAL,1/2 PINT,AQUA..........................    5.00
FRUIT JAR,BALL  IDEAL,1/2 PINT,BLUE..........................   10.00
FRUIT JAR,BALL  IDEAL,1/2 PINT,CLEAR................. 2.50 TO    5.00
FRUIT JAR,BALL  IDEAL,1/2 PINT,GREEN.........................    7.75
FRUIT JAR,BALL  IDEAL,1/2 PINT,1908,BLUE.....................   12.00
FRUIT JAR,BALL  IDEAL,1/2 PINT,1908,CLEAR....................    3.00
FRUIT JAR,BALL  IDEAL,1908,CLAMPS,QUART,AQUA.................    2.50
FRUIT JAR,BALL  IDEAL,1908,PINT,BLUE.........................     .75
FRUIT JAR,BALL  IDEAL,1908,QUART,BLUE........................     .25
FRUIT JAR,BALL  IMPROVED MASON,AQUA..........................    4.00
FRUIT JAR,BALL  IMPROVED MASON,CLEAR.........................    4.00
FRUIT JAR,BALL  IMPROVED MASON'S PATENT,QUART,AQUA...........    2.50
FRUIT JAR,BALL  IMPROVED MASONS PATENT 1858,QUART,AQUA.......    5.00
FRUIT JAR,BALL  IMPROVED,CLEAR...............................    2.00
FRUIT JAR,BALL  IMPROVED,MADE IN USA,QUART,CLEAR.............    4.00
FRUIT JAR,BALL  IMPROVED,PINT,AQUA...........................    4.00
FRUIT JAR,BALL  IMPROVED,PINT,CLEAR..........................    3.00
FRUIT JAR,BALL  IMPROVED,QUART,AQUA.................. 2.50 TO    4.00
FRUIT JAR,BALL  IMPROVED,QUART,CLEAR.........................    3.00
FRUIT JAR,BALL  IMPROVED,1/2 GAL.,AQUA.......................    4.00
FRUIT JAR,BALL  IMPROVED,1/2 GAL.,CLEAR......................    3.00
FRUIT JAR,BALL  MASON PATENT,QUART...........................    6.00
FRUIT JAR,BALL  MASON,AQUA...................................    3.00
FRUIT JAR,BALL  MASON,GREEN..................................    2.00
FRUIT JAR,BALL  MASON,PERFECT NO.6,BLUE,QUART................    3.50
FRUIT JAR,BALL  MASON,PINT...................................    2.00
FRUIT JAR,BALL  MASON,PINT,AQUA..............................    3.00
FRUIT JAR,BALL  MASON,PINT,OLIVE GREEN.......................   17.00
FRUIT JAR,BALL  MASON,QUART,APPLE GREEN......................   12.50
FRUIT JAR,BALL  MASON,QUART,AQUA.............................    3.00
FRUIT JAR,BALL  MASON,QUART,OLIVE AMBER......................   35.00
FRUIT JAR,BALL  MASON,QUART,OLIVE GREEN......................   17.00
```

```
FRUIT JAR,BALL MASON,1/2 GAL.,AQUA.........................       3.00
FRUIT JAR,BALL MASON,1/2 GAL.,OLIVE GREEN..................      17.00
FRUIT JAR,BALL MASON'S PATENT NOV.30,1858,QUART,AQUA........       7.00
FRUIT JAR,BALL MASON'S PATENT NOV.30TH,1858,QUART,
  AQUA.............................................. 4.00 TO       5.00
FRUIT JAR,BALL MASON'S PATENT NOV.30TH,1858,1/2 GAL.,AQUA...       6.00
FRUIT JAR,BALL MASON'S PATENT 1858,PINT,AQUA...............       4.00
FRUIT JAR,BALL MASON'S PATENT 1858,QUART,AQUA....... 4.00 TO       5.00
FRUIT JAR,BALL MASON'S PATENT 1858,1/2 GAL.,AQUA...........       4.00
FRUIT JAR,BALL MASON'S PATENT,PINT,AQUA....................       3.00
FRUIT JAR,BALL MASON'S PATENT,QUART,AQUA............. 3.00 TO       5.00
FRUIT JAR,BALL MASON'S PATENT,1/2 GAL.,AQUA................       3.00
FRUIT JAR,BALL MASONS PATENT NOV 30TH 1858,QUART,AQUA......       5.00
FRUIT JAR,BALL PERFECT MASON,PERFECT OFF CENTER,QUART,AQUA..       2.00
FRUIT JAR,BALL PERFECT MASON,PINT,AMBER....................      24.00
FRUIT JAR,BALL PERFECT MASON,PINT,AQUA.....................       1.00
FRUIT JAR,BALL PERFECT MASON,PINT,CLEAR....................       1.00
FRUIT JAR,BALL PERFECT MASON,PINT,1963,GREEN...............       3.00
FRUIT JAR,BALL PERFECT MASON,QUART.........................       3.50
FRUIT JAR,BALL PERFECT MASON,QUART,AMBER...................      24.00
FRUIT JAR,BALL PERFECT MASON,QUART,AQUA............. 3.00 TO       5.00
FRUIT JAR,BALL PERFECT MASON,QUART,CLEAR...................       1.00
FRUIT JAR,BALL PERFECT MASON,1/3 PINT......................       6.00
FRUIT JAR,BALL PERFECT MASON,1/2 GAL.,AMBER................      24.00
FRUIT JAR,BALL PERFECT MASON,1/2 GAL.,AQUA.................       1.00
FRUIT JAR,BALL PERFECT MASON,1/2 GAL.,CLEAR................       1.00
FRUIT JAR,BALL PERFECT MASON,1/2 PINT,AQUA.................       3.00
FRUIT JAR,BALL PERFECT MASON,1/2 PINT,CLEAR........ 3.00 TO       5.00
FRUIT JAR,BALL PERFECT,1/2 PINT,AQUA.......................       3.50
FRUIT JAR,BALL SANITARY SURE SEAL,QUART....................       4.00
FRUIT JAR,BALL SANITARY SURE SEAL,QUART,AQUA...............       3.00
FRUIT JAR,BALL SPECIAL,AQUA................................       3.00
FRUIT JAR,BALL SPECIAL,CLEAR...............................       1.00
FRUIT JAR,BALL SPECIAL,MADE IN USA,AQUA....................       3.00
FRUIT JAR,BALL SPECIAL,MADE IN USA,CLEAR...................       1.00
FRUIT JAR,BALL SPECIAL,WIDE MOUTH,MADE IN USA,CLEAR........       1.00
FRUIT JAR,BALL SQUARE MASON,SQUARE MONO,CLEAR..............       3.00
FRUIT JAR,BALL STANDARD WAX SEALER,QUART,PEBBLY............      22.00
FRUIT JAR,BALL STANDARD,AQUA...............................       3.00
FRUIT JAR,BALL STANDARD,OLIVE GREEN........................      18.00
FRUIT JAR,BALL STANDARD,QUART,AQUA.........................       2.50
FRUIT JAR,BALL STANDARD,WAX SEALER,QUART,AQUA..............       2.00
FRUIT JAR,BALL STANDARD,WAX SEALER,1/2 GAL.,AQUA...........       2.00
FRUIT JAR,BALL SURE PAT'D JULY 14TH 1908,PINT,AQUA.........       3.00
FRUIT JAR,BALL SURE PAT'D JULY 14TH 1908,QUART,AQUA........       3.00
FRUIT JAR,BALL SURE PAT'D JULY 14TH 1908,1/2 GAL.,AQUA.....       3.00
FRUIT JAR,BALL SURE SEAL,PACKED IN,QUART,AQUA..............       7.00
FRUIT JAR,BALL SURE SEAL,PINT,AQUA.........................       2.00
FRUIT JAR,BALL SURE SEAL,PINT,BLUE.........................       2.00
FRUIT JAR,BALL SURE SEAL,QUART.............................       5.00
FRUIT JAR,BALL SURE SEAL,QUART,AQUA........................       2.00
FRUIT JAR,BALL SURE SEAL,1/2 PINT,AQUA.....................       2.00
FRUIT JAR,BALL,AQUA........................................       3.00
FRUIT JAR,BALL,PERFECT MASON,2 QUART.................ILLUS..       1.00
FRUIT JAR,BALL,PINT,AQUA...................................       3.00
FRUIT JAR,BALL,QUART.......................................       3.00
FRUIT JAR,BALL,QUART,AQUA..................................       2.00
FRUIT JAR,BALL,STANDARD,GLASS TOP,QUART..............ILLUS..       3.00
FRUIT JAR,BALL,THE MASON,QUART,AQUA........................       4.00
FRUIT JAR,BALL,1/2 GAL.,AMBER..............................      18.00
FRUIT JAR,BALL,1/2 GAL.,AQUA...............................       4.00
FRUIT JAR,BALL,3 L'S IN SCRIPT.............................       5.00
FRUIT JAR,BALTIMORE GLASS WORKS,QUART,AQUA.................      35.00
FRUIT JAR,BAMBERGER'S LUSTRE TONGUE BROS.,QUART,AQUA.......       8.00
FRUIT JAR,BAMBERGER'S MASON,QUART,AQUA............. 10.00 TO      18.75
```

FRUIT JAR,BALL,STANDARD,
GLASS TOP,QUART

FRUIT JAR,BALL,
PERFECT MASON,2 QUART

```
FRUIT JAR,BANNER.................................................  10.00
FRUIT JAR,BANNER TRADEMARK,WARRANTED,QUART,AQUA..............   7.00
FRUIT JAR,BANNER TRADEMARK,WIDE MOUTH,REG US PAT OFF.,GREEN.   9.00
FRUIT JAR,BANNER TRADEMARK,WIDE MOUTH,REG US PAT OFF.,PINT,
  AQUA..........................................................   8.00
FRUIT JAR,BANNER TRADEMARK,WIDE MOUTH,REG US PAT OFF.,QUART,
  AQUA..........................................................   6.00
FRUIT JAR,BANNER TRADEMARK,1/2 GAL..........................  12.50
FRUIT JAR,BARREL SHAPE,ZINC LID,PINT........................   4.50
FRUIT JAR,BARREL SHAPE,ZINC LID,QUART.......................   4.50
FRUIT JAR,BBGM CO.,MONO,PORCELAIN LINED,QUART,AQUA..........  14.50
FRUIT JAR,BBGM CO.,MONO,QUART,AQUA..........................  14.00
FRUIT JAR,BBGM CO.,MONO,UPRIGHTS OF M LIKE LETTER I,QUART,
  AQUA..........................................................  18.00
FRUIT JAR,BBGM CO.,QUART....................................  11.00
FRUIT JAR,BEACH & CLARRIDGE CO.,BOSTON MASS.,QUART,AQUA.....  11.00
FRUIT JAR,BEACH & CLARRIDGE CO.,BOSTON MASS.,QUART,CLEAR....   9.00
FRUIT JAR,BEACH & CLARRIDGE CO.,MASON'S IMPROVED,QUART,AQUA.  12.00
FRUIT JAR,BEACH & CLARRIDGE CO.,MASON'S IMPROVED,QUART,CLEAR  10.00
FRUIT JAR,BEAVER,AQUA,QUART.................................  12.50
FRUIT JAR,BEAVER,BEAVER MONO,FACES LEFT.....................  70.00
FRUIT JAR,BEAVER,BEAVER MONO,FACES RIGHT,PINT,AMBER.........  60.00
FRUIT JAR,BEAVER,BEAVER MONO,FACES RIGHT,PINT,AQUA..........  20.00
FRUIT JAR,BEAVER,BEAVER MONO,FACES RIGHT,PINT,CLEAR.........  14.00
FRUIT JAR,BEAVER,BEAVER MONO,FACES RIGHT,QUART,AMBER........  60.00
FRUIT JAR,BEAVER,BEAVER MONO,FACES RIGHT,QUART,AQUA.........  20.00
FRUIT JAR,BEAVER,BEAVER MONO,FACES RIGHT,QUART,CLEAR........  14.00
FRUIT JAR,BEAVER,CLEAR,QUART................................  12.00
FRUIT JAR,BEAVER,MIDGET,PINT................................  35.00
FRUIT JAR,BEAVER,QUART......................................  10.00
FRUIT JAR,BEAVER,QUART,AMETHYST.............................  12.50
FRUIT JAR,BEAVER,QUART,AQUA.................................  12.00
FRUIT JAR,BEAVER,QUART,CLEAR................................   7.00
FRUIT JAR,BEAVER,1/2 GAL.,GROUND MOUTH,CLEAR................  10.00
FRUIT JAR,BEAVER,1/2 GAL.,SHARP BEAVER,WEAK NAME............   8.00
FRUIT JAR,BEE,QUART,AQUA....................................  18.00
FRUIT JAR,BEECH TRADE MARK NUT,LEAVES & NUT MONO,PINT,AMBER.   9.00
FRUIT JAR,BEEHIVE,TRADEMARK,BEEHIVE MONO,AQUA...............  24.00
FRUIT JAR,BEEHIVE,TRADEMARK,BEEHIVE MONO,CLEAR..............  18.00
FRUIT JAR,BEEHIVE,1/2 GAL...................................  50.00
FRUIT JAR,BENNETT,QUART,AQUA................................  75.00
FRUIT JAR,BENNETT'S NO 1,QUART,AQUA.........................  25.00
FRUIT JAR,BENNETT'S NO.2,QUART,AQUA.........................  30.00
FRUIT JAR,BENNETT'S NO.2,2 IS REVERSED,QUART,AQUA...........  40.00
FRUIT JAR,BERNARDIN MASON,QUART,CLEAR.......................   4.00
FRUIT JAR,BERNARDIN MASON,RIDGES ON CORNERS,QUART,CLEAR.....   5.00
```

```
FRUIT JAR,BERNARDIN MASON,1/2 PINT,CLEAR...................      6.00
FRUIT JAR,BEST WIDE MOUTH,MADE IN CANADA,CLEAR.............      1.00
FRUIT JAR,BEST WIDE MOUTH,MADE IN CANADA,GREEN.............      2.00
FRUIT JAR,BEST,FRUIT KEEPER,QUART,GREEN....................     25.00
FRUIT JAR,BEST,QUART,AMBER.................................     25.00
FRUIT JAR,BEST,QUART,AQUA..................................     18.00
FRUIT JAR,BEST,QUART,CLEAR.................................     12.00
FRUIT JAR,BEST,QUART,GREEN.................................     18.00
FRUIT JAR,BISHOPS,QUART,AQUA...............................      9.00
FRUIT JAR,BLOESER JAR,QUART,AQUA...........................     30.00
FRUIT JAR,BLOESER,QUART,CLEAR..............................     50.00
FRUIT JAR,BLUE RIBBON VACUUM PACKED COFFEE,QUART,CLEAR.....      6.00
FRUIT JAR,BLUE,ZINC COVER,PAT.NOVEMBER 30,1858.............      4.50
FRUIT JAR,BOLDT MASON,PINT,AQUA............................     14.00
FRUIT JAR,BOLDT MASON,QUART,AQUA...........................     14.00
FRUIT JAR,BOSCO DOUBLE SEAL,QUART,CLEAR....................      4.00
FRUIT JAR,BOSTWICK PERFECT SEALER,QUART,CLEAR..............     28.00
FRUIT JAR,BOYD MASON,IN RIBBON,PINT,AQUA...................      3.00
FRUIT JAR,BOYD MASON,IN RIBBON,PINT,CLEAR..................      3.00
FRUIT JAR,BOYD MASON,IN RIBBON,PINT,OLIVE GREEN............     14.00
FRUIT JAR,BOYD MASON,IN RIBBON,QUART,AQUA..................      3.00
FRUIT JAR,BOYD MASON,IN RIBBON,QUART,CLEAR.................      3.00
FRUIT JAR,BOYD MASON,IN RIBBON,QUART,OLIVE GREEN...........     14.00
FRUIT JAR,BOYD PERFECT MASON,PINT,AQUA.....................      4.00
FRUIT JAR,BOYD PERFECT MASON,QUART,AQUA....................      3.00
FRUIT JAR,BOYD PERFECT MASON,1/2 PINT,AQUA.................      5.00
FRUIT JAR,BOYDS GENUINE MASON,QUART,GREEN..................      7.00
FRUIT JAR,BOYDS PERFECT MASON,PINT,AQUA....................      6.00
FRUIT JAR,BOYDS PERFECT MASON,QUART,AQUA............. 5.00 TO    6.00
FRUIT JAR,BOYDS PERFECT MASON,1/2 PINT,AQUA................      7.00
FRUIT JAR,BOYDS,GENUINE,MASON,QUART,CLEAR..................      3.00
FRUIT JAR,BRAUN SAFETEE MASON,QUART,CLEAR..................      4.00
FRUIT JAR,BRELLE,THE JAR,PINT,CLEAR........................     10.00
FRUIT JAR,BRELLE,THE JAR,QUART,CLEAR.......................     12.00
FRUIT JAR,BRELLE,THE JAR,1/2 PINT,CLEAR....................     10.00
FRUIT JAR,BRIGHTON,QUART,CLEAR.............................     25.00
FRUIT JAR,BROCKWAY CLEAR-VU MASON,PINT,CLEAR...............      2.00
FRUIT JAR,BROCKWAY CLEAR-VU MASON,QUART,CLEAR..............      2.00
FRUIT JAR,BROCKWAY SUR-GRIP MASON,PINT,CLEAR...............      3.00
FRUIT JAR,BROCKWAY,QUART...................................      2.50
FRUIT JAR,BROMSONS FRUIT JAR,QUART,CLEAR...................     32.00
FRUIT JAR,BROOKS,C.D.,QUART,AMBER..........................     22.00
FRUIT JAR,BROOKS,C.D.,QUART,AQUA...........................     14.00
FRUIT JAR,BROOKS,C.D.,QUART,CLEAR..........................     12.00
FRUIT JAR,BROUGH,J.H.,& CO.,SWAN EMBLEM,QUART,AQUA.........     18.00
FRUIT JAR,BROWN,GEO.D.,& CO.,QUART,CLEAR...................     24.00
FRUIT JAR,BROWN,GEO.D.,& CO.,QUART,OLIVE GREEN.............     30.00
FRUIT JAR,BSKG PAT.NOV.30,1858,EMBOSSED,CLEAR........ILLUS..     6.50
FRUIT JAR,BUCKEYE,QUART,AQUA...............................     28.00
FRUIT JAR,BULACH, IN DIAMOND,ON LID ONLY,QUART,GREEN.......      4.00
FRUIT JAR,BULACH,ON LID ONLY,QUART,GREEN...................      4.00
FRUIT JAR,BUNNEL'S,F.A.,QUART,CLEAR........................     24.00
FRUIT JAR,BURLINGTON,THE B.G.CO.,R'D 1875,QUART,CLEAR......     27.00
FRUIT JAR,BURLINGTON,THE B.G.CO.,R'D 1875,QUART,GREEN......     33.00
FRUIT JAR,BURLINGTON,THE B.G.CO.,R'D 1876,QUART,CLEAR......     22.00
FRUIT JAR,BURLINGTON,THE B.G.CO.,R'D 1876,QUART,GREEN......     28.00
FRUIT JAR,BURNHAM,ARTHUR,& CO.,QUART,AQUA..................     65.00
FRUIT JAR,BURNHAM,C.& CO.,QUART,GREEN......................     65.00
FRUIT JAR,BURNLEY,QUART,CLEAR..............................      7.00
FRUIT JAR,C.C.CO.,QUART,AQUA...............................     25.00
FRUIT JAR,C.C.CO.,QUART,GREEN..............................     35.00
FRUIT JAR,C.F.J.CO.,MONO ONLY,QUART,AQUA..................      10.00
FRUIT JAR,C.F.SPENCER'S PATENT,MISSPELLED,ROCHESTER,N.Y.,
   QUART...................................................     55.00
FRUIT JAR,C.G.CO.,MONO,QUART,AQUA..........................     14.00
```

FRUIT JAR,BSKG PAT.NOV.30,1858,EMBOSSED,CLEAR

```
FRUIT JAR,C.J.CO.,MONO,QUART,CLEAR..........................    15.75
FRUIT JAR,C.S.& CO.,ON BASE,QUART,AQUA......................    12.00
FRUIT JAR,C.U.THOMSEN & SONS,PITTS.,PA.,WAX SEALER,TIN LID,
  QUART.....................................................    12.00
FRUIT JAR,CALCUTT'S PAT.,ON LID ONLY,QUART,CLEAR............    18.00
FRUIT JAR,CALCUTT'S PAT.,ON LID ONLY,QUART,GREEN............    23.00
FRUIT JAR,CALCUTT'S PAT'D 1893,QUART........................    28.00
FRUIT JAR,CALCUTT'S,ON SIDE,QUART,AQUA......................    27.00
FRUIT JAR,CANADA TRADE MARK,COMPASS MONO,AQUA...............     5.00
FRUIT JAR,CANADIAN JEWEL,MADE IN CANADA,CLEAR...............     2.00
FRUIT JAR,CANADIAN JEWEL,MADE IN CANADA,QUART...............     2.50
FRUIT JAR,CANADIAN KING,WIDE MOUTH ADJUSTABLE,PINT,CLEAR....     4.00
FRUIT JAR,CANADIAN KING,WIDE MOUTH ADJUSTABLE,QUART,CLEAR...     4.00
FRUIT JAR,CANADIAN KING,WIDE MOUTH ADJUSTABLE,1/2 PINT,CLEAR     4.00
FRUIT JAR,CANADIAN MASON JAR,MADE IN CANADA,PINT,CLEAR......     2.00
FRUIT JAR,CANADIAN MASON JAR,MADE IN CANADA,QUART,CLEAR.....     2.00
FRUIT JAR,CANADIAN MASON JAR,MADE IN CANADA,1/2 GAL.,CLEAR..     2.00
FRUIT JAR,CANADIAN SURE JELL,QUART,CLEAR....................     5.00
FRUIT JAR,CANADIAN SURE SEAL,MADE IN CANADA,PINT,CLEAR......     2.00
FRUIT JAR,CANADIAN SURE SEAL,MADE IN CANADA,QUART,CLEAR.....     2.00
FRUIT JAR,CANADIAN SURE SEAL,MADE IN CANADA,1/2 GAL.,CLEAR..     2.00
FRUIT JAR,CANTON DOMESTIC,PINT..................... 60.00 TO    65.00
FRUIT JAR,CANTON ELECTRIC,QUART,COBALT BLUE.................   450.00
FRUIT JAR,CANTON MAGIC JAR,QUART,CLEAR......................    45.00
FRUIT JAR,CANTON,THE DOMESTIC FRUIT JAR,QUART,AMBER.........    75.00
FRUIT JAR,CANTON,THE DOMESTIC FRUIT JAR,QUART,CLEAR.........    45.00
FRUIT JAR,CANTON,THE,DOMESTIC FRUIT JAR,QUART,AQUA..........    55.00
FRUIT JAR,CANTON,THE,DOMESTIC FRUIT JAR,QUART,COBALT BLUE...   100.00
FRUIT JAR,CARROLLS TRUE SEAL,QUART,CLEAR....................     5.00
FRUIT JAR,CASEY MASON.......................................     1.50
FRUIT JAR,CASSIDY,QUART,CLEAR...............................    45.00
FRUIT JAR,CFJ REVERSED......................................     4.00
FRUIT JAR,CFJ 1858,1/2 GAL.,CORNFLOWER......................    25.00
FRUIT JAR,CHALMERS,QUART,AQUA...............................    30.00
FRUIT JAR,CHAMPION SYRUP REFINING CO.,INDIANAPOLIS,QUART,
  AQUA......................................................    13.00
FRUIT JAR,CHAMPION,QUART....................................    75.00
FRUIT JAR,CHAMPION,THE,PAT AUG 31,1869,QUART,AQUA...........    35.00
FRUIT JAR,CHAMPION,2 QUART,AQUA.............................    37.00
FRUIT JAR,CHATTANOOGA MASON,C IN CIRCLE OF MANY DOTS,PINT,
  CLEAR.....................................................     7.00
FRUIT JAR,CHATTANOOGA MASON,C IN CIRCLE,QUART,CLEAR.........     7.00
FRUIT JAR,CHATTANOOGA MASON,C IN CIRCLE,1/2 GAL.,CLEAR......     7.00
FRUIT JAR,CHATTANOOGA MASON,C MONO IN CIRCLE,PINT,CLEAR.....     5.00
FRUIT JAR,CHATTANOOGA MASON,C MONO IN CIRCLE,QUART,CLEAR....     5.00
FRUIT JAR,CHATTANOOGA MASON,C MONO IN CIRCLE,1/2 GAL.,CLEAR.     5.00
```

```
FRUIT JAR,CHATTANOOGA MASON,QUART,SQUARE,CLEAR...............    5.00
FRUIT JAR,CHEF TRADE MARK,CHEF MONO,PINT,CLEAR..............    7.00
FRUIT JAR,CHEF TRADE MARK,CHEF MONO,QUART,CLEAR.............    5.00
FRUIT JAR,CHEF TRADE MARK,PAT'D JULY 14,1908,MONO,PINT,CLEAR    9.00
FRUIT JAR,CHEF TRADE MARK,PAT'D JULY 14,1908,MONO,QUART,
  CLEAR......................................................    7.00
FRUIT JAR,CHEF,THE BURDEN CO.,PINT..........................    6.00
FRUIT JAR,CHEF,THE BURDEN CO.,QUART.........................    6.00
FRUIT JAR,CHEF,WIRE BAIL,GLASS LID,QUART....................    6.50
FRUIT JAR,CHIEF,QUART AQUA..................................   10.00
FRUIT JAR,CHIEF,THE,QUART,AQUA..............................   30.00
FRUIT JAR,CINCINNATI,BLUE...................................   35.00
FRUIT JAR,CJF CO.,PAT.NOV.30TH,1858,AQUA.............ILLUS..    5.00
FRUIT JAR,CLARK'S PEERLESS,AQUA,PINT........................   12.00
FRUIT JAR,CLARK'S PEERLESS,IN CIRCLE,PINT...................    2.50
FRUIT JAR,CLARK'S PEERLESS,IN CIRCLE,QUART,AQUA.............    7.00
FRUIT JAR,CLARK'S PEERLESS,IN CIRCLE,QUART,CLEAR............    5.00
FRUIT JAR,CLARK'S PEERLESS,PINT.............................    8.75
FRUIT JAR,CLARK'S PEERLESS,PINT,GREEN.......................   12.00
```

FRUIT JAR,CJF CO.,PAT.NOV.30TH,1858,AQUA

```
FRUIT JAR,CLARK'S PEERLESS,QUART,AQUA.......................    6.00
FRUIT JAR,CLARK'S PEERLESS,QUART,CLEAR..............  4.00 TO    8.75
FRUIT JAR,CLARK'S PEERLESS,QUART,GREEN......................    8.00
FRUIT JAR,CLARK'S PEERLESS,1/2 GALLON.......................    7.00
FRUIT JAR,CLARK'S PEERLESS,1/2 GALLON,AQUA..................    9.50
FRUIT JAR,CLARKE FRUIT JAR CO.,CLEVE.,O.,QUART,AQUA.........   30.00
FRUIT JAR,CLARKE,QUART......................................   42.50
FRUIT JAR,CLEAR,GLASS LID WITH CLAMP,CHINESE INSCRIPTION,
  PINT......................................................    4.75
FRUIT JAR,CLEVELAND FRUIT JUICE CO.,1/2 GAL.........  3.00 TO    6.00
FRUIT JAR,CLIMAX ON SHOULDER,SQUARE,MACHINE MADE,CLEAR......    6.00
FRUIT JAR,CLIMAX,TRADE MARK,REG. BACK PAT'D,PINT,AQUA.......    6.00
FRUIT JAR,CLIMAX,TRADE MARK,REG. BACK PAT'D,QUART,CLEAR.....    4.00
FRUIT JAR,CLOVE & MOLLINS,QUART,CLEAR.......................    5.00
FRUIT JAR,CLYDE GLASS WORKS,ON LID,QUART,CLEAR..............   10.00
FRUIT JAR,CLYDE GLASS WORKS,ON LID,QUART,GREEN..............   12.00
FRUIT JAR,CLYDE IMPROVED....................................    5.00
FRUIT JAR,CLYDE IMPROVED MASON,QUART,AQUA...................   14.00
FRUIT JAR,CLYDE IMPROVED MASON,QUART,CLEAR..................   10.00
FRUIT JAR,CLYDE LIGHTNING,QUART,AQUA........................   15.00
FRUIT JAR,CLYDE MASON,QUART,GREEN...........................   17.00
FRUIT JAR,CLYDE MASON'S IMPROVED EMBOSSED ON FRONT,CLEAR....   11.00
FRUIT JAR,CLYDE,HEAVY SCRIPT,PINT...........................    7.00
FRUIT JAR,CLYDE,HEAVY SCRIPT,QUART..........................    7.00
FRUIT JAR,CLYDE,IN CIRCLE,PINT..............................    8.00
FRUIT JAR,CLYDE,N.Y.,REVERSED...............................    6.00
```

```
FRUIT JAR,CLYDE,PINT,CLEAR...........................  4.00 TO   10.00
FRUIT JAR,CLYDE,PURPLE...................................           5.00
FRUIT JAR,CLYDE,QUART....................................           4.00
FRUIT JAR,CLYDE,THE,QUART,CLEAR.........................           15.00
FRUIT JAR,COFFEEVILLE...................................           10.00
FRUIT JAR,COHANSEY GLASS MFG.CO.,PAT.MAR.20,77,QUART,AQUA...       35.00
FRUIT JAR,COHANSEY GLASS MFG.CO.,QUART,AQUA................        14.00
FRUIT JAR,COHANSEY,PINT.................................           25.00
FRUIT JAR,COHANSEY,PINT,AMBER...........................           40.00
FRUIT JAR,COHANSEY,PINT,AQUA............................           28.00
FRUIT JAR,COHANSEY,QUART.........................  8.00 TO       14.00
FRUIT JAR,COHANSEY,QUART,AQUA....................  10.00 TO      18.00
FRUIT JAR,COHANSEY,WIRE RING CLAMP......................           12.00
FRUIT JAR,COHANSEY,1/2 GAL.,AQUA........................           22.00
FRUIT JAR,COLBURN'S FOUNTAIN STOPPLE JAR,QUART,AQUA.........       38.00
FRUIT JAR,COLUMBIA,QUART,AMBER..........................           40.00
FRUIT JAR,COLUMBIA,QUART,CLEAR..........................           17.00
FRUIT JAR,COLUMBIA,QUART,GREEN..........................           22.00
FRUIT JAR,COLUMBIA,1/2 PINT,AMBER.......................           38.00
FRUIT JAR,COMMON SENSE JAR,QUART,AQUA...................           40.00
FRUIT JAR,COMMON SENSE JAR,QUART,CLEAR..................           35.00
FRUIT JAR,COMMONWEALTH,QUART,GREEN......................           30.00
FRUIT JAR,CONSERVE JAR,PINT,AMBER.......................            6.00
FRUIT JAR,CONSERVE JAR,PINT,CLEAR.......................            4.00
FRUIT JAR,CONSERVE JAR,QUART,AMBER......................            6.00
FRUIT JAR,CONSERVE JAR,QUART,CLEAR......................            4.00
FRUIT JAR,CORKSEALER,BBC ON BASE........................            6.00
FRUIT JAR,CORKSEALER,BBC ON BASE,QUART,AQUA.............            6.00
FRUIT JAR,CORNFLOWER,1/2 PINT...........................            6.00
FRUIT JAR,CORONA JAR,MADE IN CANADA,QUART,CLEAR.............         2.00
FRUIT JAR,CORONA,IMPROVED,JAR MADE IN CANADA,PINT,CLEAR.....        2.00
FRUIT JAR,CORONA,IMPROVED,JAR MADE IN CANADA,QUART,CLEAR....        2.00
FRUIT JAR,CORONA,IMPROVED,JAR MADE IN CANADA,1/2 GAL.,CLEAR.        2.00
FRUIT JAR,CRANDALL,THE,& GODLEY PERFECTO FRUIT JUICES,AQUA..        5.00
FRUIT JAR,CROSS,MASON'S PATENT NOV.30,1858,QUART............        3.50
FRUIT JAR,CROSS,MASON'S PATENT NOV.30,1858,1/2 GAL.........         3.50
FRUIT JAR,CROWN CORDIAL & EXTRACT CO.,N.Y.,ROUND,AMETHYST...        6.00
FRUIT JAR,CROWN CORDIAL & EXTRACT CO.,N.Y.,1/2 GAL.,AMBER...        6.00
FRUIT JAR,CROWN CORK & SEAL CO.,VICTORY JAR,1/2 GAL.,AQUA...        7.00
FRUIT JAR,CROWN EMBLEM,QUART,AQUA.......................            3.75
FRUIT JAR,CROWN IMPERIAL PINT,CLEAR.....................            4.00
FRUIT JAR,CROWN IMPERIAL PINT,CROWN EMBLEM,AQUA.........            4.00
FRUIT JAR,CROWN IMPERIAL PINT,CROWN EMBLEM,MIDGET,AQUA......       12.00
FRUIT JAR,CROWN IMPERIAL PINT,CROWN EMBLEM,MIDGET,CLEAR.....       12.00
FRUIT JAR,CROWN IMPERIAL QUART,CROWN EMBLEM,AQUA............        4.00
FRUIT JAR,CROWN IMPERIAL QUART,CROWN EMBLEM,CLEAR...........        4.00
FRUIT JAR,CROWN IMPERIAL QUART,CROWN EMBLEM,MIDGET,AQUA.....       12.00
FRUIT JAR,CROWN IMPERIAL QUART,CROWN EMBLEM,MIDGET,CLEAR....       12.00
FRUIT JAR,CROWN IMPERIAL,CROWN EMBLEM,MADE IN CANADA,QUART..        3.00
FRUIT JAR,CROWN IMPERIAL,TWO-PIECE LID,PINT.................        6.00
FRUIT JAR,CROWN IMPROVED,QUART,AQUA.....................            3.00
FRUIT JAR,CROWN MASON,PINT,CLEAR........................            2.00
FRUIT JAR,CROWN MASON,QUART.............................            2.00
FRUIT JAR,CROWN MASON,QUART,CLEAR.......................            2.00
FRUIT JAR,CROWN MASON,1/2 GAL.,CLEAR....................            2.00
FRUIT JAR,CROWN MIDGET,AQUA.............................            8.50
FRUIT JAR,CROWN MIDGET,CLEAR............................            3.00
FRUIT JAR,CROWN MIDGET,PURPLE...........................            8.50
FRUIT JAR,CROWN,CANADA,GLASS SCREW LID,PINT,CLEAR...........        3.00
FRUIT JAR,CROWN,CROWN EMBLEM,BACK,TEATON CO.,LTD.,MIDGET,
   AQUA.................................................           15.00
FRUIT JAR,CROWN,CROWN EMBLEM,BACK,TEATON CO.,LTD.,QUART,AQUA        7.00
FRUIT JAR,CROWN,CROWN EMBLEM,MIDGET,CLEAR...................       18.00
FRUIT JAR,CROWN,CROWN EMBLEM,TEATON CO.,LTD.,PINT,AQUA......        7.00
FRUIT JAR,CROWN,CROWN EMBLEM,TEATON CO.,LTD.,1/2 GAL.,AQUA..        7.00
```

```
FRUIT JAR,CROWN,GREEN-AMBER,1/2 GAL...........................     8.00
FRUIT JAR,CROWN,IMPROVED,CROWN EMBLEM,QUART,CLEAR............     4.00
FRUIT JAR,CROWN,MADE IN CANADA,CROWN MONO,PINT,CLEAR........     2.00
FRUIT JAR,CROWN,MADE IN CANADA,CROWN MONO,QUART,CLEAR.......     2.00
FRUIT JAR,CROWN,MADE IN CANADA,CROWN MONO,1/2 GAL.,CLEAR....     2.00
FRUIT JAR,CROWN,MADE IN CANADA,PINT,CLEAR...................     2.50
FRUIT JAR,CROWN,MADE IN CANADA,QUART,CLEAR..................     2.50
FRUIT JAR,CROWN,QUART,CLEAR.................................     3.50
FRUIT JAR,CROWN,QUART,CLEAR ZINC & GLASS LID................     3.50
FRUIT JAR,CRYSTAL JAR CG.,QUART,CLEAR.......................    24.00
FRUIT JAR,CRYSTAL JAR,PINT,AQUA.............................    30.00
FRUIT JAR,CRYSTAL JAR,PINT,CLEAR............................    22.00
FRUIT JAR,CRYSTAL JAR,QUART,AQUA............................    30.00
FRUIT JAR,CRYSTAL JAR,QUART,CLEAR...........................    18.00
FRUIT JAR,CRYSTAL JAR,1/2 GAL.,AQUA.........................    30.00
FRUIT JAR,CRYSTAL JAR,1/2 GAL.,CLEAR........................    22.00
FRUIT JAR,CRYSTAL,DATED,SCREW TOP LID.......................    25.00
FRUIT JAR,CRYSTAL,MASON'S JAR,QUART,CLEAR...................    28.00
FRUIT JAR,CRYSTAL,QUART.....................................    28.00
FRUIT JAR,CRYSTAL,QUART,AQUA..................... 20.00 TO     28.00
FRUIT JAR,CRYSTAL,QUART,CLEAR.................... 33.00 TO     40.00
FRUIT JAR,CRYSTALVAC,QUART,AMBER............................    14.00
FRUIT JAR,CUNNINGHAM'S & CO.,PITTSBURGH,UN BASE,QUART,AQUA..    14.00
FRUIT JAR,CUNNINGHAM'S & IHMSEN PITTSBURGH,ON BASE,QUART,
   AQUA....................................................    12.00
FRUIT JAR,CUNNINGHAM'S & IHMSEN PITTSBURGH,ON BASE,1/2 GAL.,
   AQUA....................................................    10.00
FRUIT JAR,CURTICE BROS.,ROCHESTER,N.Y.,QUART,AQUA...........    20.00
FRUIT JAR,CURTIS & MOORE,BOSTON,MASS.,QUART,AQUA............    22.00
FRUIT JAR,CURTIS & MOORE,BOSTON,MASS.,QUART,CLEAR...........    18.00
FRIIT JAR,DG CO.,MONO,QUART,AQUA............................    30.00
FRUIT JAR,D.O.C.,ON BASE,QUART,AQUA.........................    12.25
FRUIT JAR,D.O.C.,ON BASE,QUART,CLEAR........................     8.00
FRUIT JAR,D.O.C.WAX SEALER,1/2 GAL.,AQUA....................    14.00
FRUIT JAR,DAISY JAR,QUART,CLEAR.............................    25.50
FRUIT JAR,DAISY,F.E.WARD & CO.,PINT.........................     5.00
FRUIT JAR,DAISY,F.E.WARD & CO.,QUART........................     8.00
FRUIT JAR,DAISY,PINT,AQUA...................................     6.00
FRUIT JAR,DAISY,QUART,AQUA..................................     8.00
FRUIT JAR,DAISY,THE,F.E.WARD & CO.,IN CIRCLE,QUART,AQUA.....     8.75
FRUIT JAR,DAISY,THE,F.E.WARD & CO.,PINT,AQUA................    12.75
FRUIT JAR,DAISY,THE,F.E.WARD & CO.,QUART,AQUA...............    14.50
FRUIT JAR,DALBEY'S,R.M.,FRUIT JAR PAT.NOV.16,1858,QUART,AQUA    45.00
FRUIT JAR,DALBEY'S,R.M.,PATENT BY,DATE,QUART,GREEN..........    38.80
FRUIT JAR,DANDY,QUART,AMBER.................................    50.00
FRUIT JAR,DANDY,THE,TRADE MARK,QUART,AMBER..................    30.75
FRUIT JAR,DANDY,THE,TRADE MARK,QUART,AQUA...................    22.50
FRUIT JAR,DANDY,THE,TRADE MARK,QUART,CLEAR..................    35.50
FRUIT JAR,DARLING IMPERIAL,QUART,AQUA.......................    26.00
FRUIT JAR,DARLING,THE IMPERIAL,ADM MONO,QUART,AQUA..........    18.75
FRUIT JAR,DARLING,THE,ADM MONO,QUART,AQUA...................    18.75
FRUIT JAR,DARLING,THE,ADM MONO,QUART,CLEAR..................    22.50
FRUIT JAR,DAVENPORT,IA.,QUART...............................    10.00
FRUIT JAR,DECKER DEPENDABLE FOOD,QUART,CLEAR................     2.50
FRUIT JAR,DECKER'S IOWANA,PAT'D,PINT,CLEAR..................     2.00
FRUIT JAR,DECKER'S IOWANA,PAT'D,QUART,CLEAR.................     2.25
FRUIT JAR,DECKER'S IOWANA,PAT'D,1/2 GAL.,CLEAR..............     2.75
FRUIT JAR,DECKER'S VICTOR,QUART.............................     6.50
FRUIT JAR,DETROIT SALT CO.,MASON'S PATENT,SALT SHAKER.......    10.00
FRUIT JAR,DEXTER,FRUIT WREATH AROUND NAME,QUART,AQUA........    22.50
FRUIT JAR,DEXTER,QUART,AQUA.................................    15.75
FRUIT JAR,DIAMOND FRUIT JAR,IMPROVED TRADE MARK,PINT,CLEAR..     4.25
FRUIT JAR,DIAMOND FRUIT JAR,IMPROVED TRADE MARK,1/2 GAL.,
   CLEAR...................................................     4.50
FRUIT JAR,DIAMOND FRUIT JAR,TRADE MARK,ON BASE,QUART,CLEAR..     6.75
```

```
FRUIT JAR,DIAMOND,IMPROVED,TRADEMARK,QT.,CLEAR...... 3.00 TO    4.50
FRUIT JAR,DICTATOR,D BACK,D.I.HOLCOMB,DEC.14,1869,QUART,AQUA    27.75
FRUIT JAR,DICTATOR,PRESERVE,AQUA,QUART......................    20.00
FRUIT JAR,DICTATOR,THE,QUART,AQUA...........................    50.25
FRUIT JAR,DILLON G.CO.,ON BASE,FAIRMOUNT IND.,QUART,AQUA....    12.00
FRUIT JAR,DILLON G CO.ON BASE,FAIRMOUNT,IND.,1/2 GAL........     6.00
FRUIT JAR,DILLON G.CO.,ON BASE,FAIRMOUNT,IND.,1/2 GAL.,AQUA.    15.50
FRUIT JAR,DODGE-SWEENEY & CO.,CALIF. BUTTER,QUART,AQUA......    22.75
FRUIT JAR,DOMINION MASON,MADE IN CANADA,PINT,CLEAR..........     2.50
FRUIT JAR,DOMINION MASON,MADE IN CANADA,QUART,CLEAR.........     2.75
FRUIT JAR,DOMINION MASON,MADE IN CANADA,1/2 GAL.,CLEAR......     2.75
FRUIT JAR,DOMINION MASON,PINT,CLEAR.........................     2.25
FRUIT JAR,DOMINION MASON,QUART,CLEAR........................     2.50
FRUIT JAR,DOMINION MASON,1/2 GAL.,CLEAR.....................     2.75
FRUIT JAR,DOMINION SPECIAL,QUART,CLEAR......................     3.25
FRUIT JAR,DOMINION WIDE MOUTH SPECIAL,MADE IN CANADA,PINT,
  CLEAR.....................................................     2.25
FRUIT JAR,DOMINION WIDE MOUTH SPECIAL,MADE IN CANADA,QUART,
  CLEAR.....................................................     2.25
FRUIT JAR,DOMINION WIDE MOUTH SPECIAL,MADE IN CANADA,
  1/2 GAL...................................................     2.25
FRUIT JAR,DOMINION WIDE MOUTH SPECIAL,PINT..................     7.50
FRUIT JAR,DOMINION WIDE MOUTH SPECIAL,QUART.................     7.50
FRUIT JAR,DOMINION WIDE MOUTH SPECIAL,1/2 GAL...............     7.50
FRUIT JAR,DOOLITTLE,QUART,CLEAR.............................    22.50
FRUIT JAR,DOOLITTLE,THE,SELF SEALER,QUART,AQUA..............    20.25
FRUIT JAR,DOUBLE SAFETY,PINT,CLEAR.................. 1.00 TO     4.00
FRUIT JAR,DOUBLE SAFETY,QUART,CLEAR................. 1.00 TO     2.50
FRUIT JAR,DOUBLE SAFETY,1/2 GAL.,CLEAR......................     4.50
FRUIT JAR,DOUBLE SAFETY,1/2 PINT............................     4.00
FRUIT JAR,DOUBLE SAFETY,1/2 PINT,CLEAR......................     8.75
FRUIT JAR,DOUBLE SEAL,PINT,CLEAR............................     3.25
FRUIT JAR,DOUBLE SEAL,QUART,CLEAR...........................     3.25
FRUIT JAR,DOUBLE SEAL,1/2 GAL.,CLEAR........................     3.25
FRUIT JAR,DREY EVER SEAL,PINT,CLEAR.........................     2.75
FRUIT JAR,DREY EVER SEAL,QUART,CLEAR........................     2.25
FRUIT JAR,DREY EVER SEAL,1/2 GAL.,CLEAR.....................     2.25
FRUIT JAR,DREY IMPROVED EVER SEAL PAT'D 1920,QUART,CLEAR....     3.50
FRUIT JAR,DREY IMPROVED EVER SEAL,PINT......................     1.25
FRUIT JAR,DREY IMPROVED EVER SEAL,QUART.....................     1.25
FRUIT JAR,DREY IMPROVED EVER SEAL,1/2 GAL...................     1.25
FRUIT JAR,DREY IMPROVED,WIRE CLAMP,PINT.....................     3.00
FRUIT JAR,DREY MASON,PINT,AQUA..............................     4.50
FRUIT JAR,DREY MASON,PINT,CLEAR.............................     2.25
FRUIT JAR,DREY MASON,QUART,AQUA.............................     4.50
FRUIT JAR,DREY MASON,QUART,CLEAR............................     2.25
FRUIT JAR,DREY MASON,1/2 GAL.,AQUA..........................     4.50
FRUIT JAR,DREY MASON,1/2 GAL.,CLEAR.........................     2.25
FRUIT JAR,DREY PERFECT MASON,PINT,AQUA......................     3.50
FRUIT JAR,DREY PERFECT MASON,PINT,CLEAR............. 1.25 TO     3.00
FRUIT JAR,DREY PERFECT MASON,QUART,AMETHYST.................     1.50
FRUIT JAR,DREY PERFECT MASON,QUART,AQUA.....................     3.50
FRUIT JAR,DREY PERFECT MASON,QUART,CLEAR....................     1.25
FRUIT JAR,DREY PERFECT MASON,QUART,ROUND,AMBER..............     4.00
FRUIT JAR,DREY PERFECT MASON,QUART,ROUND,AQUA...............     4.00
FRUIT JAR,DREY PERFECT MASON,1/2 GAL.,AQUA..................     3.50
FRUIT JAR,DREY PERFECT MASON,1/2 GAL.,CLEAR.................     1.25
FRUIT JAR,DREY SQUARE MASON,PINT............................     2.00
FRUIT JAR,DREY SQUARE MASON,QUART...........................     2.00
FRUIT JAR,DREY SQUARE MASON,SQUARE EMBLEM,PINT..............     1.00
FRUIT JAR,DREY SQUARE MASON,SQUARE EMBLEM,QUART.............     1.00
FRUIT JAR,DREY SQUARE MASON,SQUARE EMBLEM,1/2 GAL...........     1.00
FRUIT JAR,DU PONT,QUART,AQUA................................    20.00
FRUIT JAR,DUNKLEY PERSERVING CO.,PAT'D SEPT.20,1898,BASE,
  QUART.....................................................    11.25
```

```
FRUIT JAR,DUR FOR,IN CIRCLE,QUART,GREEN.....................      4.50
FRUIT JAR,DURHAM,QUART,AQUA.................................     10.00
FRUIT JAR,DYSON'S PURE FOOD PRODUCTS,CROSS MONO,QUART,CLEAR.      5.50
FRUIT JAR,E.G.CO.,IMPERIAL,2 QUARTS,AQUA....................     16.00
FRUIT JAR,E.G.CO.,THE IMPERIAL,MIDGET,AQUA..................     19.75
FRUIT JAR,E.G.CO.,THE IMPERIAL,QUART,AMBER.................      45.00
FRUIT JAR,E.G.CO.,THE IMPERIAL,QUART,AQUA..................      14.00
FRUIT JAR,E.G.CO.,THE IMPERIAL,1/2 GAL.,AQUA...............      14.00
FRUIT JAR,E-Z SEAL,PINT,CORNFLOWER BLUE....................      20.00
FRUIT JAR,E-Z SEAL,1/2 PINT................................       4.50
FRUIT JAR,EAGLE,PAT.DEC.28,1858,QUART,AQUA.................      38.50
FRUIT JAR,EAGLE,PINT.......................................       1.50
FRUIT JAR,EAGLE,QUART,GREEN........................ 30.25 TO     50.00
FRUIT JAR,EAGLE,ROUND SHOULDER,GREEN.......................      50.00
FRUIT JAR,EAGLE,1/2 GAL....................................       1.50
FRUIT JAR,EASY CO.,TRADE MARK,VACUUM JAR,JVC MONO,QUART,
   CLEAR...................................................      10.50
FRUIT JAR,EASY VACUUM JAR,QUART.................... 12.00 TO     12.50
FRUIT JAR,ECLIPSE,PINT.....................................       4.00
FRUIT JAR,ECLIPSE,QUART....................................       3.00
FRUIT JAR,ECLIPSE,THE,QUART,GREEN..........................      25.00
FRUIT JAR,ECLIPSE,THE,WAX SEALER,QUART,AQUA................      25.50
FRUIT JAR,ECONOMY SEALER,PAT'D SEPT.13,1858,QUART,AQUA.....       2.00
FRUIT JAR,ECONOMY TRADE MARK,PINT,AMBER....................       3.00
FRUIT JAR,ECONOMY TRADE MARK,QUART,AMBER...................       3.00
FRUIT JAR,ECONOMY TRADE MARK,QUART,AMETHYST................       2.00
FRUIT JAR,ECONOMY TRADE MARK,1/2 GAL.,AMBER................       3.00
FRUIT JAR,ECONOMY TRADEMARK,AMETHYST.......................       2.50
FRUIT JAR,ECONOMY TRADEMARK,CLEAR..........................       3.00
FRUIT JAR,ECONOMY TRADEMARK,PINT,CLEAR.............. 2.50 TO      3.25
FRUIT JAR,ECONOMY TRADEMARK,QUART,CLEAR............. 2.50 TO      3.25
FRUIT JAR,ECONOMY TRADEMARK,1/2 GAL.,CLEAR.......... 2.50 TO      3.25
FRUIT JAR,ECONOMY,SUN-COLORED..............................       6.00
FRUIT JAR,ELECTRIC,GLOBE EMBLEM,QUART,AQUA.................      26.75
FRUIT JAR,ELECTRIC,REPRO CLAMP,QUART............... 30.00 TO     35.00
FRUIT JAR,ELECTRIC,REPRO CLAMP,1/2 GAL.....................      35.00
FRUIT JAR,ELECTRIC,TRADE MARK,IN CIRCLE,QUART,AQUA.........       9.25
FRUIT JAR,ELECTRIC,TRADEMARK,PINT,AQUA.....................      11.00
FRUIT JAR,ELECTRIC,TRADEMARK,QUART,AQUA....................       8.00
FRUIT JAR,ELECTROGLAS,N.W.,PINT,CLEAR......................       2.00
FRUIT JAR,ELECTROGLAS,N.W.,QUART,CLEAR.....................       2.00
FRUIT JAR,ELECTROGLAS,N.W.,1/2 GAL.,CLEAR..................       2.00
FRUIT JAR,ELLWOOD,J.LEE CO.,PA.,ON LID ONLY,QUART,AMBER.....     20.25
FRUIT JAR,EMPIRE IN CROSS,PINT.............................       4.50
FRUIT JAR,EMPIRE IN CROSS,QUART,CLEAR......................       8.00
FRUIT JAR,EMPIRE IN CROSS,1/2 PINT.........................      11.00
FRUIT JAR,EMPIRE,QUART,AQUA........................ 30.25 TO     35.50
FRUIT JAR,EMPIRE,2 QUART,AQUA..............................      75.00
FRUIT JAR,ERIE LIGHTNING,PINT,CLEAR........................      10.00
FRUIT JAR,ERIE LIGHTNING,QUART,CLEAR.......................      10.00
FRUIT JAR,ERIE LIGHTNING,1/2 GAL.,CLEAR....................      10.00
FRUIT JAR,ERMEBLOK,ON LID,QUART,CLEAR......................       7.75
FRUIT JAR,EUREKA,CLEAR LID & CLAMP,18 OUNCE,PINT...........      10.00
FRUIT JAR,EUREKA,PINT,AQUA......................... 7.50 TO     15.00
FRUIT JAR,EUREKA,QUART,CLEAR....................... 9.00 TO     12.00
FRUIT JAR,EUREKA,1ST PAT'D DEC.27,1864,QUART,AQUA..........      45.50
FRUIT JAR,EVERLASTING JAR,RIBBON EMBLEM,PINT,AQUA..........      12.75
FRUIT JAR,EVERLASTING JAR,RIBBON EMBLEM,QUART,AQUA.........      10.00
FRUIT JAR,EVERLASTING JAR,RIBBON EMBLEM,1/2 GAL.,AQUA......      12.25
FRUIT JAR,EVERLASTING,IMPROVED JAR,JAR IN RIBBON,PINT,CLEAR.      7.00
FRUIT JAR,EVERLASTING,IMPROVED JAR,JAR IN RIBBON,QUART,CLEAR      7.00
FRUIT JAR,EVERLASTING,IMPROVED JAR,JAR IN RIBBON,1/2 GAL.,
   CLEAR...................................................       7.00
FRUIT JAR,EVERLASTING,IMPROVED,JAR IN CIRCLE,QUART,CLEAR....      8.50
FRUIT JAR,EVERLASTING,QUART,CLEAR..........................      25.00
```

```
FRUIT JAR,EXCELSIOR IMPROVED,QUART,AQUA......................    14.50
FRUIT JAR,EXCELSIOR,QUART,AQUA...............................    19.75
FRUIT JAR,EXWACO,ON BASE,QUART,CLEAR.........................    15.75
FRUIT JAR,F & J BODINE,QUART,AQUA............................    95.00
FRUIT JAR,F & J BODINE,2 QUART,AQUA..........................    45.00
FRUIT JAR,F & S IN CIRCLE,QUART..............................    10.00
FRUIT JAR,F ON BOTTOM........................................    10.00
FRUIT JAR,F.A.& CO.,ON BASE,QUART,AQUA.......................    30.25
FRUIT JAR,F.B.CO.,ON BASE,QUART,AQUA.........................     9.00
FRUIT JAR,F.C.G.CO.,ON BASE,QUART,AMBER......................    40.00
FRUIT JAR,F.C.G.CO.,ON BASE,QUART,AQUA.......................    10.00
FRUIT JAR,F.C.G.CO.,ON BASE,QUART,COBALT BLUE...............   100.00
FRUIT JAR,F.C.G.CO.,ON BASE,1/2 GAL.,AQUA....................    14.75
FRUIT JAR,F.H.G.W.,QUART,AQUA................................    10.50
FRUIT JAR,FAHNSTOCK ALBREE & CO.,ON BASE,QUART,AQUA.........    22.75
FRUIT JAR,FAHNSTOCK FORTUNE & CO.,ON BASE,QUART,AQUA........    22.75
FRUIT JAR,FAMOUS JAR,WIDE MOUTH,QUART,GREEN........ 17.00 TO    19.00
FRUIT JAR,FANSLER,N.O.,CLEVE.,O.QUART,AQUA...................    40.25
FRUIT JAR,FARLEY,CHICAGO,PINT,CLEAR..........................     4.50
FRUIT JAR,FARLEY,CHICAGO,QUART,CLEAR.........................     4.50
FRUIT JAR,FARLEY,QUART.......................................     9.00
FRUIT JAR,FIGHT SEAL,DATED,1/2 GAL...........................     5.00
FRUIT JAR,FINK & NASSE,QUART,AQUA............................    25.00
FRUIT JAR,FLACCUS BROS.,STEER'S HEAD,STEER MONO,QUART,AMBER.    75.00
FRUIT JAR,FLACCUS BROS.,STEER'S HEAD,STEER MONO,QUART,CLEAR.    22.50
FRUIT JAR,FLACCUS BROS.,STEER'S HEAD,STEER MONO,QUART,GREEN.    75.00
FRUIT JAR,FLACCUS BROS.,STEER'S HEAD,STEER MONO,QUART,MILK.    85.25
FRUIT JAR,FLACCUS BROS.,STEER'S HEAD,WHEELING,W.VA.,GREEN...   176.00
FRUIT JAR,FLACCUS CO.,E.C.,TRADEMARK,ELK MONO,QUART,AMBER...    85.95
FRUIT JAR,FLACCUS CO.,E.C.,TRADEMARK,ELK MONO,QUART,AMETHYST    35.50
FRUIT JAR,FLACCUS CO.,E.C.,TRADEMARK,ELK MONO,QUART,CLEAR...    28.00
FRUIT JAR,FLACCUS CO.,E.C.,TRADEMARK,ELK MONO,QUART,GREEN...    65.50
FRUIT JAR,FLACCUS CO.,E.C.,TRADEMARK,ELK MONO,QUART,MILK....    85.00
FRUIT JAR,FLACCUS,AMBER......................................    25.00
FRUIT JAR,FLACCUS,PINT,CLEAR.................................    32.50
FRUIT JAR,FLACCUS,PINT,PURPLE................................    22.50
FRUIT JAR,FLACCUS,STEER HEAD,EMBOSSED,SIMPLEX LID............    35.00
FRUIT JAR,FLETT,W.& J. LIVERPOOL,SUN EMBLEM,QUART,AQUA......    16.50
FRUIT JAR,FORSTER JAR,THE,PINT,CLEAR.........................    11.25
FRUIT JAR,FORSTER JAR,THE,QUART,CLEAR........................    11.25
FRUIT JAR,FORSTER JAR,THE,1/2 GAL.,CLEAR.....................    11.25
FRUIT JAR,FOSTER SEALFAST,CLEAR,PINT...................ILLUS..     2.00
FRUIT JAR,FOSTER SEALFAST,PINT,CLEAR.........................     2.50
FRUIT JAR,FOSTER SEALFAST,QUART,CLEAR............... 2.50 TO     4.00
FRUIT JAR,FOSTER SEALFAST,1/2 GAL.,CLEAR.....................     2.50
FRUIT JAR,FOSTER SEALFAST,1/2 PINT,CLEAR............ 4.00 TO     4.50
FRUIT JAR,FRANCIS H.LEGGETT & CO.,N.Y.,PINT,AMETHYST........     7.85
FRUIT JAR,FRANCIS H.LEGGETT & CO.,N.Y.,QUART,CLEAR..........     7.75
FRUIT JAR,FRANK,WM & SONS,ON BASE,QUART,AQUA.................    15.70
FRUIT JAR,FRANKLIN DEXTER FRUIT JAR,QUART,AQUA..............    17.95
FRUIT JAR,FRANKLIN DEXTER,QUART.................... 10.50 TO    17.00
FRUIT JAR,FRANKLIN FRUIT JAR,QUART,AQUA......................    20.75
FRUIT JAR,FRANKLIN,2 QUART,AQUA..............................    35.00
FRUIT JAR,FRUIT GROWERS TRADE-MARK,QUART,AQUA................    22.00
FRUIT JAR,FRUIT-KEEPER,CG CO. MONO,QUART,AQUA...... 17.50 TO    22.50
FRUIT JAR,FRUIT-KEEPER,GC.............................ILLUS..     3.50
FRUIT JAR,FRUIT-KEEPER,PINT..................................    21.00
FRUIT JAR,FRUIT-KEEPER,QUART,AQUA............................    18.50
FRUIT JAR,FRUIT-KEEPER,QUART,GREEN...........................    16.95
FRUIT JAR,FRUIT-KEEPER,1/2 GAL..............................    26.00
FRUIT JAR,GAYNER,THE,MASON,QUART,CLEAR.............. 4.95 TO     8.00
FRUIT JAR,GEM,BELOW HFJC CROSS,MIDGET,AQUA...................    17.00
FRUIT JAR,GEM,BELOW HFJC CROSS,QUART,AQUA....................    11.00
FRUIT JAR,GEM,BELOW HFJC CROSS,1/2 GAL.,AQUA.................    14.00
FRUIT JAR,GEM,CFJ CO. MONO,MIDGET,AQUA.......................    17.50
```

FRUIT JAR,FOSTER SEALFAST,
CLEAR,PINT

FRUIT JAR,FRUIT-KEEPER,GC

FRUIT JAR,GEM,CFJ CO. MONO,QUART,AQUA...........................	9.00
FRUIT JAR,GEM,CFJ CO.,1/2 GAL.............................	7.00
FRUIT JAR,GEM,CROSS MONO,QUART,AQUA...........................	7.50
FRUIT JAR,GEM,HGW MONO ON BACK,MIDGET,AQUA....................	16.50
FRUIT JAR,GEM,HGW MONO ON BACK,QUART,AQUA.......... 7.75 TO	9.50
FRUIT JAR,GEM,IMPROVED,MADE IN CANADA,QUART..................	2.00
FRUIT JAR,GEM,IMPROVED,MADE IN CANADA,QUART,AMBER...........	18.00
FRUIT JAR,GEM,IMPROVED,MADE IN CANADA,QUART,AQUA............	3.95
FRUIT JAR,GEM,IMPROVED,QUART,AQUA..........................	6.50
FRUIT JAR,GEM,IMPROVED,TRADE MARK,REG'D,PINT,CLEAR..........	1.50
FRUIT JAR,GEM,IMPROVED,TRADE MARK,REG'D,QUART,CLEAR.........	1.50
FRUIT JAR,GEM,IMPROVED,TRADE MARK,REG'D,1/2 GAL.,CLEAR......	1.50
FRUIT JAR,GEM,MIDGET,AQUA.................................	15.00
FRUIT JAR,GEM,MIDGET,TWO-PIECE TOP........................	10.00
FRUIT JAR,GEM,NEW,PINT,CLEAR..............................	2.00
FRUIT JAR,GEM,NEW,QUART,CLEAR.............................	2.00
FRUIT JAR,GEM,NEW,1/2 GAL.,CLEAR..........................	2.00
FRUIT JAR,GEM,ONE LINE,QUART,AQUA.........................	7.75
FRUIT JAR,GEM,OVER THE HERO,QUART.........................	15.00
FRUIT JAR,GEM,PINT,AQUA...................................	10.00
FRUIT JAR,GEM,QUART,AQUA........................... 5.00 TO	8.00
FRUIT JAR,GEM,QUART,CLEAR.................................	9.00
FRUIT JAR,GEM,RUTHERFORD & CO.,QUART,AQUA.................	13.50
FRUIT JAR,GEM,SHIELD ON BACK,QUART AQUA...................	5.00
FRUIT JAR,GEM,SHIELD ON BACK,QUART,AQUA...................	11.25
FRUIT JAR,GEM,SHIELD ON BACK,1/2 GAL.,AQUA................	11.25
FRUIT JAR,GEM,SHIELD ON REVERSE,DATED BASE,QUART..........	8.50
FRUIT JAR,GEM,SHIELD REVERSE..............................	8.00
FRUIT JAR,GEM,TWO LINES,QUART,AMBER.......................	20.50
FRUIT JAR,GEM,TWO LINES,QUART,AQUA........................	10.25
FRUIT JAR,GEM,UNDERLINED IN SCRIPT,QUART..................	5.00
FRUIT JAR,GEM,WALLACEBURG,PINT,CLEAR......................	4.95
FRUIT JAR,GEM,WALLACEBURG,QUART,CLEAR.....................	4.25
FRUIT JAR,GEM,WALLACEBURG,1/2 GAL.,CLEAR..................	4.25
FRUIT JAR,GEM,1/2 GAL.....................................	13.00
FRUIT JAR,GEM,1/2 GAL.,AQUA........................ 8.00 TO	10.00
FRUIT JAR,GEM,1908,PINT,CLEAR.............................	4.25
FRUIT JAR,GEM,1908,QUART,CLEAR............................	4.25
FRUIT JAR,GEM,1908,1/2 GAL.,CLEAR.........................	4.25
FRUIT JAR,GEM,2 QUART.....................................	4.00
FRUIT JAR,GEM,2 QUART,AQUA................................	10.00
FRUIT JAR,GENUINE BOYDS MASON,QUART,AQUA.......... 4.25 TO	5.25
FRUIT JAR,GENUINE MASON,IN RIBBON,QUART,AQUA..............	6.25
FRUIT JAR,GENUINE MASON,QUART,AQUA........................	8.25
FRUIT JAR,GENUINE MASON,QUART,CLEAR.......................	6.25
FRUIT JAR,GENUINE MASON,QUART,OLIVE GREEN.................	17.25

```
FRUIT JAR,GENUINE SAMCO,QUART,CLEAR.........................      1.00
FRUIT JAR,GEORGE D.BROWN CO.,QUART,CLEAR....................     13.00
FRUIT JAR,GILBERD'S IMPROVED JAR,STAR MONO,QUART,AQUA.......     35.00
FRUIT JAR,GILBERD'S IMPROVED,QUART..........................     75.00
FRUIT JAR,GILBERD'S IMPROVED,QUART,AQUA.....................     90.00
FRUIT JAR,GILBERD'S IMPROVED,1/2 GAL.,AQUA..................    125.00
FRUIT JAR,GILBERD'S JAR,STAR MONO,QUART,AQUA................     55.00
FRUIT JAR,GILCHIST,QUART....................................     16.00
FRUIT JAR,GILKA,EIGHT-SIDED,AMBER,QUART.....................     10.00
FRUIT JAR,GILLARD & CO.,LONDON,QUART,AQUA...................      9.85
FRUIT JAR,GILLARD & CO.,QUART,GREEN.........................     18.50
FRUIT JAR,GLASS BROS.& CO.,LONDON,ON LID ONLY,QUART,BROWN...      9.75
FRUIT JAR,GLASSBORO IMPROVED,PINT...........................     11.00
FRUIT JAR,GLASSBORO IMPROVED,QUART..........................     19.00
FRUIT JAR,GLASSBORO TRADE MARK IMPROVED,PINT,GREEN..........     18.25
FRUIT JAR,GLASSBORO TRADE MARK IMPROVED,QUART,GREEN.........     15.25
FRUIT JAR,GLASSBORO TRADE MARK IMPROVED,1/2 GAL.............     17.00
FRUIT JAR,GLASSBORO TRADE MARK,QUART,GREEN..................     12.25
FRUIT JAR,GLASSBORO TRADE MARK,QUART,OLIVE GREEN............     19.25
FRUIT JAR,GLENSHAW G MASON,G IN BOX,PINT,CLEAR..............      4.00
FRUIT JAR,GLENSHAW G MASON,G IN BOX,QUART,CLEAR.............      4.00
FRUIT JAR,GLENSHAW G MASON,G IN BOX,1/2 GAL.,CLEAR..........      4.00
FRUIT JAR,GLOBE BRANDS,GLOBE EMBLEM,QUART,CLEAR.............      2.00
FRUIT JAR,GLOBE,AMBER,QUART........................ILLUS..      20.00
FRUIT JAR,GLOBE,AMBER,1/2 GALLON............................     18.50
FRUIT JAR,GLOBE,AQUA,PINT...................................     14.00
```

FRUIT JAR,GLOBE,AMBER,QUART

```
FRUIT JAR,GLOBE,DATED 1886,GLASS LID,WIRE HANDLE,AMBER......     25.00
FRUIT JAR,GLOBE,HEAVILY WHITTLED............................     10.00
FRUIT JAR,GLOBE,PINT,AMBER..................... 20.50 TO      32.50
FRUIT JAR,GLOBE,PINT,CLEAR..................................      8.25
FRUIT JAR,GLOBE,PINT,GREEN..................................     12.50
FRUIT JAR,GLOBE,QUART.......................................      6.00
FRUIT JAR,GLOBE,QUART,AMBER.................... 15.00 TO      27.50
FRUIT JAR,GLOBE,QUART,CLEAR.................................      8.25
FRUIT JAR,GLOBE,QUART,GREEN.................................     12.50
FRUIT JAR,GLOBE,RED-AMBER...................................     22.50
FRUIT JAR,GLOBE,1/2 GAL.,AMBER................. 22.00 TO      26.00
FRUIT JAR,GLOBE,1/2 GAL.,CLEAR..............................      8.25
FRUIT JAR,GLOBE,1/2 GAL.,GREEN..............................     12.50
FRUIT JAR,GLOBE,1/2 GAL.,WHITTLED,AMBER.....................     35.00
FRUIT JAR,GLOBE,2 QUART.....................................      6.00
FRUIT JAR,GLOBE,2 QUART,AMBER...............................     25.00
FRUIT JAR,GLOCKER TRADE MARK,QUART,AQUA.....................     14.25
FRUIT JAR,GOLDEN STAR,CLEAR SHOO-FLY,STAR,PINT..............      7.00
FRUIT JAR,GOLDEN STATE IMPROVED,MASON,S IN TRIANGLE,QUART...      4.00
FRUIT JAR,GOLDEN STATE IMPROVED,MASON,S IN TRIANGLE,1/2 GAL.      4.00
```

```
FRUIT JAR,GOLDEN STATE MASON,LID..............................  9.00
FRUIT JAR,GOLDEN STATE MASON,PINT,PURPLE....................  9.00
FRUIT JAR,GOLDEN STATE MASON,QUART,PURPLE...................  9.00
FRUIT JAR,GOLDEN STATE PAT.,MASON,S IN TRIANGLE,QUART.......  5.95
FRUIT JAR,GOLDEN STATE PAT.,MASON,S IN TRIANGLE,1/2 GAL.....  5.95
FRUIT JAR,GOOD HOUSE KEEPERS MASON JAR,PINT,CLEAR...........  2.75
FRUIT JAR,GOOD HOUSE KEEPERS MASON JAR,QUART,CLEAR..........  2.75
FRUIT JAR,GOOD HOUSE KEEPERS MASON JAR,1/2 GAL.,CLEAR.......  2.75
FRUIT JAR,GOOD HOUSE KEEPERS REGULAR MASON,PINT.............  2.00
FRUIT JAR,GOOD HOUSE KEEPERS REGULAR MASON,PINT,CLEAR.......  2.25
FRUIT JAR,GOOD HOUSE KEEPERS REGULAR MASON,QUART............  2.00
FRUIT JAR,GOOD HOUSE KEEPERS REGULAR MASON,QUART,CLEAR......  2.25
FRUIT JAR,GOOD HOUSE KEEPERS REGULAR MASON,1/2 GAL.,CLEAR...  2.25
FRUIT JAR,GOOD HOUSE KEEPERS WIDE MOUTH MASON,PINT,CLEAR....  2.50
FRUIT JAR,GOOD HOUSE KEEPERS WIDE MOUTH MASON,QUART,CLEAR...  2.50
FRUIT JAR,GOOD HOUSE KEEPERS WIDE MOUTH MASON,1/2 GAL.,CLEAR 2.50
FRUIT JAR,GOOD LUCK,QUART...................................  2.00
FRUIT JAR,GOOD LUCK,1/2 GALLON..............................  3.00
FRUIT JAR,GRANDMA WHEATON'S OLD FASHIONED RECEIPTS.......... 10.00
FRUIT JAR,GRANDMA WHEATON'S OLD FASHIONED RECEIPTS CANNING,
  PINT......................................................  3.50
FRUIT JAR,GRAY POTTERY,GLASS LID,T SNAP,SHERWOOD............  7.50
FRUIT JAR,GREEK KEY SAFETY VALVE,1/2 GAL.,AQUA.............. 29.00
FRUIT JAR,GREEK KEY,SAFETY VALVE,1/2 GAL.,AQUA.............. 27.50
FRUIT JAR,GREEN MOUNTAIN C.A.CO.,PINT,AQUA.................. 10.25
FRUIT JAR,GREEN MOUNTAIN C.A.CO.,PINT,CLEAR.................  8.75
FRUIT JAR,GREEN MOUNTAIN C.A.CO.,QUART,AQUA................. 10.25
FRUIT JAR,GREEN MOUNTAIN C.A.CO.,QUART,CLEAR................  8.25
FRUIT JAR,GREEN MOUNTAIN C.A.CO.,1/2 GAL.,AQUA............. 10.25
FRUIT JAR,GREY MASON,QUART,CLEAR............................  4.50
FRUIT JAR,GRIFFIN,ON BASE,QUART,AQUA........................ 45.75
FRUIT JAR,H & R,ON BASE,QUART,AQUA..........................  9.00
FRUIT JAR,H & R,ON BASE,WAX SEALER,1/2 GAL.,AQUA............  4.00
FRUIT JAR,H & R,WAX SEALER,QUART,BLUE....................... 12.00
FRUIT JAR,H & S,QUART,AQUA.................................. 20.25
FRUIT JAR,H.PETTIT,AQUA,PINT............................... 10.00
FRUIT JAR,H,ON BASE,QUART,AQUA............................. 14.25
FRUIT JAR,HAHNE & CO.,STAR EMBLEM,QUART,AQUA............... 22.50
FRUIT JAR,HAINES COMBINATION,QUART,AQUA.................... 30.75
FRUIT JAR,HAINES'S IMPROVED,MARCH 1,1870,QUART,AQUA........ 30.00
FRUIT JAR,HAINES'S PATENT MARCH 1,1870,QUART,AQUA.......... 25.50
FRUIT JAR,HALF CLEVELAND,O.,QUART,AQUA..................... 26.75
FRUIT JAR,HALLER,WM.L.,QUART,AQUA.......................... 35.50
FRUIT JAR,HAMILTON GLASS WORKS,QUART,AQUA.................. 30.50
FRUIT JAR,HAMILTON NO.3 GLASS WORKS,QUART,AQUA............. 35.00
FRUIT JAR,HAMILTON,QUART,AQUA.............................. 20.50
FRUIT JAR,HAMILTON,1/2 GAL.,AMETHYST...................... 45.00
FRUIT JAR,HANDY JAR MFD BY SMALLEY,PAT.APRIL 27,1909,QUART,
  CLEAR.................................................... 25.50
FRUIT JAR,HANSEE'S H.P.EMBLEM PALACE HOME................. 36.00
FRUIT JAR,HANSEE'S PALACE HOME JAR,HO MONO,QUART,CLEAR..... 25.75
FRUIT JAR,HARRIS,QUART,GREEN.............................. 40.55
FRUIT JAR,HARTELL'S AIRTIGHT,QUART,GREEN.................. 65.00
FRUIT JAR,HARTELL'S GLASS AIR TIGHT COVER,QUART,AQUA...... 28.75
FRUIT JAR,HARVEST MASON,QUART,CLEAR....................... 10.00
FRUIT JAR,HASEROT CO.CLEVE.MASON PAT.,QUART,AQUA.... 7.50 TO 10.00
FRUIT JAR,HAVEL ATLAS E-Z SEAL...........................  8.00
FRUIT JAR,HAWLEY GLASS CO.,PA.,ON BASE,QUART,AQUA......... 12.25
FRUIT JAR,HAZARD & CO.,ON BASE,QUART,AQUA................. 12.50
FRUIT JAR,HAZEL ATLAS LIGHTNING SEAL..................... 10.00
FRUIT JAR,HAZEL PRESERVE JAR,H OVER A MONO,QUART,CLEAR....  4.00
FRUIT JAR,HAZEL PRESERVE JAR,H OVER A MONO,1/2 GAL.,CLEAR...  4.00
FRUIT JAR,HAZEL PRESERVE,1/2 PINT,CLEAR..................  5.00
FRUIT JAR,HAZEL,PRESERVE,H OVER A MONO,PINT..............  3.00
FRUIT JAR,HAZEL,ATLAS E-Z SEAL,PINT,AQUA.................  8.50
```

```
FRUIT JAR,HAZEL,ATLAS E-Z SEAL,PINT,CLEAR...................     6.50
FRUIT JAR,HAZEL,ATLAS E-Z SEAL,QUART,AQUA...................     8.25
FRUIT JAR,HAZEL,ATLAS E-Z SEAL,1/2 GAL.,AQUA...............     8.25
FRUIT JAR,HAZEL,ATLAS E-Z SEAL,1/2 GAL.,CLEAR..............     6.25
FRUIT JAR,HAZEL,ATLAS LIGHTNING SEAL,PINT,AQUA.............     8.75
FRUIT JAR,HAZEL,ATLAS LIGHTNING SEAL,QUART,AQUA............     8.75
FRUIT JAR,HAZEL,QUART,AQUA.................................    11.25
FRUIT JAR,HEART,EMBOSSED NECKLACE,STOPPER,MASON,AMBER......     8.00
FRUIT JAR,HELME'S RAILROAD MILLS,QUART,AMBER...............    14.00
FRUIT JAR,HELME'S RAILROAD MILLS,QUART,AQUA................    10.50
FRUIT JAR,HERO,ABOVE CROSS,OLIVE GREEN.....................    35.00
FRUIT JAR,HERO,ABOVE CROSS,QUART,CLEAR.....................    15.75
FRUIT JAR,HERO,IMPROVED,PINT,AQUA..........................    14.50
FRUIT JAR,HERO,QUART,AQUA..................................    10.00
FRUIT JAR,HERO,THE,IMPROVED,QUART,AQUA.....................    14.75
FRUIT JAR,HERO,THE,IMPROVED,QUART,GREEN....................    18.75
FRUIT JAR,HERO,THE,QUART,AQUA..............................    14.25
FRUIT JAR,HERO,THE,QUART,GREEN.............................    19.00
FRUIT JAR,HERO,THE,1/2 GAL.,AQUA...........................    14.25
FRUIT JAR,HERO,THE,1/2 GAL.,GREEN..........................    19.00
FRUIT JAR,HERO,1 1/2 QUART.................................    12.00
FRUIT JAR,HEROINE,THE,QUART,AQUA...........................    18.00
FRUIT JAR,HEROINE,2 QUART..................................    15.00
FRUIT JAR,HERON PICKLE JAR,METAL COVER.....................    23.00
FRUIT JAR,HILTONS PAT.,QUART,AQUA..........................    35.95
FRUIT JAR,HOLZ,CLARK & TAYLOR,SALEM N.J.,QUART,AMBER.......    50.75
FRUIT JAR,HOLZ,CLARK & TAYLOR,SALEM N.J.,QUART,AQUA........    28.50
FRUIT JAR,HOLZ,CLARK & TAYLOR,SALEM N.J.,QUART,GREEN.......    38.50
FRUIT JAR,HOLZ,CLARK & TAYLOR,THE SALEM JAR,QUART,AQUA.....    33.50
FRUIT JAR,HOM PAK MASON,PINT,CLEAR.........................     3.50
FRUIT JAR,HOM PAK MASON,QUART,CLEAR........................     3.50
FRUIT JAR,HOM PAK MASON,1/2 GAL.,CLEAR.....................     3.50
FRUIT JAR,HONEST MASON JAR,PATENT 1858,QUART,AQUA..........    14.75
FRUIT JAR,HONEST MASON JAR,PATENT 1858,QUART,CLEAR.........    10.75
FRUIT JAR,HOOSIER JAR,QUART,AQUA...........................    28.50
FRUIT JAR,HOOSIER JAR,1/2 GAL.,AQUA........................    28.50
FRUIT JAR,HORMEL GOOD FOOD,PINT,CLEAR......................     3.50
FRUIT JAR,HORMEL GOOD FOOD,QUART,CLEAR.....................     3.50
FRUIT JAR,HORMEL GOOD FOODS,OVAL,PINT.............. 2.50 TO     6.00
FRUIT JAR,HORMEL GOOD FOODS,PINT...........................     2.50
FRUIT JAR,HOWE,LID,QUART...................................    30.00
FRUIT JAR,HOWE,THE,JAR,SCRANTON,PA.,QUART,AQUA.............    29.00
FRUIT JAR,HOWE,THE,QUART,GREEN.............................    22.00
FRUIT JAR,HOWE,THE,SCRANTON,PA.,QUART,AQUA.................    36.00
FRUIT JAR,HUYLER'S NEW YORK,1/2 PINT,CLEAR.................     5.00
FRUIT JAR,I.G.CO.,QUART,AQUA...............................    17.50
FRUIT JAR,IDEAL WIDE MOUTH,MADE IN CANADA,IN SHIELD,QUART,
  CLEAR....................................................     2.25
FRUIT JAR,IDEAL,THE,PINT,CLEAR.............................    10.75
FRUIT JAR,IDEAL,THE,QUART,CLEAR............................    10.75
FRUIT JAR,IMPERIAL EGMOND MIDGET...........................    25.00
FRUIT JAR,IMPERIAL,PATENT,APRIL 20,1886,ON BASE,QUART,GREEN.   19.00
FRUIT JAR,IMPERIAL,THE,MONO,MIDGET,AQUA....................    18.75
FRUIT JAR,IMPERIAL,THE,MONO,QUART,AQUA.....................    13.00
FRUIT JAR,IMPROVED KEYSTONE,QUART,AQUA.....................     5.00
FRUIT JAR,IMPROVED,IMPERIAL,QUART,METAL RING GREEN.........     6.00
FRUIT JAR,IMPROVED,KEYSTONE EMBLEM,QUART,AQUA..............    12.75
FRUIT JAR,INDEPENDENT JAR,QUART,CLEAR......................    25.00
FRUIT JAR,INDEPENDENT,GLASS TOP,CLEAR,PINT...........ILLUS..    18.00
FRUIT JAR,IVANHOE,ON BASE,PINT,CLEAR.......................     2.50
FRUIT JAR,IVANHOE,ON BASE,QUART,CLEAR......................     2.50
FRUIT JAR,J.ELWOOD LEE,AMBER,QUART.........................    30.00
FRUIT JAR,J.G.CO.,MONO ONLY,GILCREST ON LID,QUART,AQUA.....    18.95
FRUIT JAR,J.H.S.,ON BASE,QUART,CLEAR.......................     4.50
FRUIT JAR,J.P.SMITH PITTSBURGH,PA.,WAX SEAL,QUART,AQUA.....    15.00
```

FRUIT JAR,INDEPENDENT,GLASS TOP,CLEAR,PINT

FRUIT JAR,J&B FRUIT JAR,PAT.JUNE 14,1898,OCTAGON MONO,PINT, AQUA	18.50
FRUIT JAR,J&B FRUIT JAR,PAT.JUNE 14,1898,OCTÁGON MONO,QUART, AQUA	14.50
FRUIT JAR,JAY B.RHODES,QUART	6.00
FRUIT JAR,JEANETTE HOME PACKER MASON,QUART,CLEAR	3.00
FRUIT JAR,JEANETTE HOME PACKER,INSERT BAND,QUART	3.50
FRUIT JAR,JEANETTE J MASON HOME PACKER,JIN BOX,QUART,AQUA	6.25
FRUIT JAR,JEANETTE J MASON HOME PACKER,JIN BOX,QUART,CLEAR	3.75
FRUIT JAR,JEANNETTE J MASON HOME PACKER,QUART	5.00
FRUIT JAR,JEWELL JAR,IN SHIELD,QUART,CLEAR	3.50
FRUIT JAR,JEWELL JAR,MADE IN CANADA,QUART,CLEAR	2.50
FRUIT JAR,JEWELL,MADE IN CANADA,PINT	4.00
FRUIT JAR,JHF,OVERLAPPING LETTERS MONO,QUART,AQUA	12.25
FRUIT JAR,JOHNSON & JOHNSON,QUART,AMBER	14.50
FRUIT JAR,JOHNSON,QUART,AMBER	8.00
FRUIT JAR,JOHNSON,S.G. & SONS,QUART,CLEAR	15.00
FRUIT JAR,K G,IN CIRCLE,PINT,CLEAR	4.75
FRUIT JAR,K G,IN CIRCLE,QUART,CLEAR	4.75
FRUIT JAR,K H & G,ON BASE,QUART,AQUA	10.50
FRUIT JAR,K.Y.G.W.CO.,ON BASE,QUART,AQUA	17.50
FRUIT JAR,K.Y.G.W.CO.,ON BASE,1/2 GAL.,AQUA	17.50
FRUIT JAR,K,ON BASE ONLY,QUART,AQUA	4.50
FRUIT JAR,KALAMAZOO,THE,PINT,CLEAR	5.25
FRUIT JAR,KALAMAZOO,THE,QUART,CLEAR	5.50
FRUIT JAR,KBC,QUART,AQUA	5.50
FRUIT JAR,KC FINEST QUALITY MASON SQUARE SPACESAVER,PINT, CLEAR	2.75
FRUIT JAR,KC FINEST QUALITY MASON SQUARE SPACESAVER,QUART, CLEAR	2.75
FRUIT JAR,KC FINEST QUALITY MASON SQUARE SPACESAVER,1/2 GAL.	2.75
FRUIT JAR,KEEFFER'S NO.1,QUART,AQUA	27.50
FRUIT JAR,KENTUCKY,QUART,AQUA	39.00
FRUIT JAR,KERR ANNIVERSARY,COBALT	10.00
FRUIT JAR,KERR ANNIVERSARY,QUART,GOLD	12.50
FRUIT JAR,KERR ECONOMY TRADE MARK,KERR GLASS MFG.CO.,AQUA	3.00
FRUIT JAR,KERR ECONOMY,QUART	2.00
FRUIT JAR,KERR ECONOMY,TRADE MARK,QUART,CLEAR	1.25
FRUIT JAR,KERR ECONOMY,TRADE MARK,1/2 GAL.,CLEAR	1.25
FRUIT JAR,KERR GLASS TOP MASON,PINT,CLEAR	1.25
FRUIT JAR,KERR GLASS TOP MASON,QUART,CLEAR	1.25
FRUIT JAR,KERR GLASS TOP MASON,1/2 GAL.,CLEAR	1.25
FRUIT JAR,KERR GLASS TOP,PINT,CLEAR	2.75
FRUIT JAR,KERR GLASS TOP,QUART,CLEAR	2.75
FRUIT JAR,KERR GLASS TOP,1/2 GAL.,CLEAR	2.75
FRUIT JAR,KERR MASON,QUART,AMBER	7.50
FRUIT JAR,KERR SEAL SEALING MASON,QUART,AMBER	13.00

```
FRUIT JAR,KERR SELF SEALING MASON,TRADE MARK REG.,CLEAR.....    2.00
FRUIT JAR,KERR SELF SEALING WIDE MOUTH MASON...............    2.00
FRUIT JAR,KERR SELF SEALING,TALL,ROUND,GL/WB...............    1.00
FRUIT JAR,KERR SELF SEALING,TRADE MARK,PINT,CLEAR..........    1.00
FRUIT JAR,KERR SELF SEALING,TRADE MARK,QUART,CLEAR.........    1.00
FRUIT JAR,KERR SELF SEALING,TRADE MARK,1/2 GAL.,CLEAR......    1.00
FRUIT JAR,KERR SELF SEALING,TRADE MARK,1/2 PINT............    2.00
FRUIT JAR,KERR SELF SEALING,65TH ANNIV.1903-1968,QUART,BLUE.   11.75
FRUIT JAR,KERR SELF SEALING,65TH ANNIV.1903-1968,QUART,GOLD.   13.75
FRUIT JAR,KERR SSTMR,WIDE MOUTH,1915,PINT..................    2.00
FRUIT JAR,KERR,ECONOMY,TRADE MARK,PINT,CLEAR...............    1.25
FRUIT JAR,KEYSTONE IMPROVED,QUART,AQUA.....................   10.00
FRUIT JAR,KEYSTONE MASON,TWO QUART.........................    8.00
FRUIT JAR,KEYSTONE,EMBOSSED IN CIRCLE,ONE-PIECE LID........    6.50
FRUIT JAR,KEYSTONE,TRADE MARK,REG.,PINT,CLEAR..............    8.50
FRUIT JAR,KEYSTONE,TRADE MARK,REG.,QUART,CLEAR.............    8.00
FRUIT JAR,KIEFFER'S NO.1,QUART,AQUA........................   22.75
FRUIT JAR,KILNER,QUART.....................................   18.00
FRUIT JAR,KILNER,THE,JAR,IMPROVED REG'D,QUART,CLEAR........    4.50
FRUIT JAR,KILNER,THE,JAR,PINT,CLEAR........................    5.25
FRUIT JAR,KILNER,THE,JAR,QUART,CLEAR.......................    5.25
FRUIT JAR,KING,CROWN & FLAGS EMBLEM,PINT,CLEAR.............   10.00
FRUIT JAR,KING,CROWN & FLAGS EMBLEM,QUART,CLEAR............   10.00
FRUIT JAR,KING,CROWN & FLAGS EMBLEM,1/2 PINT,CLEAR.........   15.25
FRUIT JAR,KING,HEAD EMBLEM,PINT,CLEAR......................   19.00
FRUIT JAR,KING,HEAD EMBLEM,QUART,CLEAR.....................   19.00
FRUIT JAR,KING,HEAD EMBLEM,1/2 PINT,CLEAR..................   25.00
FRUIT JAR,KING,PINT,OVAL WITH CROWN........................    9.00
FRUIT JAR,KING,QUART,AQUA..................................   10.00
FRUIT JAR,KING,QUART,CLEAR.................................    9.00
FRUIT JAR,KINSELLA TRUE MASON 1874,QUART,CLEAR.............    8.00
FRUIT JAR,KINSELLA 1874 TRUE MASON,PINT,CLEAR..............   10.25
FRUIT JAR,KINSELLA 1874 TRUE MASON,QUART,CLEAR...... 5.50 TO    8.50
FRUIT JAR,KLINE,A ON BASE,QUART,AQUA.......................    6.20
FRUIT JAR,KLINE,A.R.,OCT.27,1863 ON LID,QUART,AQUA.........   21.00
FRUIT JAR,KLINE,QUART......................................   25.00
FRUIT JAR,KNIGHT PACKING CO.,ON BASE,QUART,CLEAR...........    4.25
FRUIT JAR,KNOWLTON VACUUM FRUIT JAR,STAR EMBLEM,QUART,AQUA..   21.00
FRUIT JAR,KNOWLTON VACUUM FRUIT JAR,STAR EMBLEM,QUART,CLEAR.   14.00
FRUIT JAR,KNOWLTON VACUUM STAR,QUART,BLUE..................   20.00
FRUIT JAR,KNOWLTON VACUUM,PINT.............................   19.00
FRUIT JAR,KNOWLTON,QUART,AQUA..............................   20.00
FRUIT JAR,KNOX K MASON,K IN KEYSTONE,PINT,CLEAR............    2.50
FRUIT JAR,KNOX K MASON,K IN KEYSTONE,QUART,CLEAR...........    2.50
FRUIT JAR,KNOX K MASON,K IN KEYSTONE,1/2 PINT..............    4.75
FRUIT JAR,KNOX KEYSTONE K,MASON,CLEAR,PINT..........ILLUS..    2.50
FRUIT JAR,KOENIG 5+,FRONT & REAR,QUART,CLEAR...............    7.75
FRUIT JAR,KOHRS DAVENPORT,IA IN CIRCLE,PINT,CLEAR..........    2.50
FRUIT JAR,KOHRS DAVENPORT,IA IN CIRCLE,QUART,CLEAR.........    2.50
FRUIT JAR,KOHRS DAVENPORT,IA IN CIRCLE,1/2 GAL.,CLEAR......    2.50
FRUIT JAR,KOHRS DAVENPORT,IA,PAT.JULY 14,1908,PINT,CLEAR....   3.95
FRUIT JAR,KOHRS DAVENPORT,IA,PAT.JULY 14,1908,QUART,CLEAR..    3.95
FRUIT JAR,KOHRS DAVENPORT,IA,PAT.JULY 14,1908,1/2 GAL.,CLEAR   3.95
FRUIT JAR,L & W,IN FANCY SCRIPT,QUART,AQUA.................   13.25
FRUIT JAR,L & W,IN FANCY SCRIPT,1/2 GAL.,AQUA..............   18.50
FRUIT JAR,L G CO.,ON BASE,QUART,AMBER......................   37.00
FRUIT JAR,L G CO.,ON BASE,QUART,AQUA.......................   17.00
FRUIT JAR,L.& S. ON BASE,SIDE,PAT'D JULY 14,1908,QUART,CLEAR    4.75
FRUIT JAR,L&W,1/2 GAL.KLINE STOPPER........................   50.00
FRUIT JAR,L'IDEALE,PINT,CLEAR..............................    3.75
FRUIT JAR,L'IDEALE,QUART,CLEAR.............................    3.75
FRUIT JAR,L'IDEALE,1/2 GAL.,CLEAR..........................    3.75
FRUIT JAR,LAFAYETTE,PINT,AQUA..............................   40.75
FRUIT JAR,LAFAYETTE,PINT,CLEAR.............................   30.25
FRUIT JAR,LAFAYETTE,QUART,AQUA.............................   40.75
```

FRUIT JAR,KNOX KEYSTONE K,MASON,CLEAR,PINT

```
FRUIT JAR,LAFAYETTE,QUART,CLEAR.............................        30.75
FRUIT JAR,LAFAYETTE,SCRIPT,1/2 GAL.,AQUA....................        19.00
FRUIT JAR,LAFAYETTE,WITH PROFILE,PINT,AMBER.................        75.50
FRUIT JAR,LAFAYETTE,WITH PROFILE,PINT,AQUA..................        40.74
FRUIT JAR,LAFAYETTE,WITH PROFILE,PINT,GREEN.................        50.50
FRUIT JAR,LAFAYETTE,WITH PROFILE,QUART,AMBER................        75.25
FRUIT JAR,LAFAYETTE,WITH PROFILE,QUART,AQUA.................        41.00
FRUIT JAR,LAFAYETTE,WITH PROFILE,QUART,GREEN................        50.50
FRUIT JAR,LAFAYETTE,1/2 GAL.,AQUA...........................        95.00
FRUIT JAR,LAMB MASON,PINT......................... 3.00 TO          4.00
FRUIT JAR,LAMB MASON,PINT,CLEAR.............................        3.25
FRUIT JAR,LAMB MASON,PINT,PINK..............................        4.00
FRUIT JAR,LAMB MASON,QUART,AQUA.............................        1.00
FRUIT JAR,LAMB MASON,QUART,CLEAR............................        3.25
FRUIT JAR,LAMB MASON,QUART,PINK.............................        3.50
FRUIT JAR,LAMB MASON,1/2 GAL.,CLEAR.........................        3.25
FRUIT JAR,LEADER,THE,QUART,AMBER.................... 40.50 TO       45.00
FRUIT JAR,LEADER,THE,QUART,CLEAR............................        27.25
FRUIT JAR,LEOTRIC GM,PINT...................................        5.00
FRUIT JAR,LEOTRIC IN CIRCLE,PINT............................        2.50
FRUIT JAR,LEOTRIC,IN CIRCLE,PINT,AQUA.......................        8.50
FRUIT JAR,LEOTRIC,IN CIRCLE,QUART,AQUA......................        8.75
FRUIT JAR,LEOTRIC,IN CIRCLE,1/2 GAL.,AQUA...................        8.50
FRUIT JAR,LEOTRIC,PINT,AQUA........................ 5.00 TO         6.00
FRUIT JAR,LEOTRIC,PINT,GREEN................................        4.00
FRUIT JAR,LEOTRIC,QUART............................ 3.00 TO         7.00
FRUIT JAR,LEOTRIC,QUART,AQUA....................... 5.00 TO         6.50
FRUIT JAR,LEOTRIC,WIRE FASTENED GLASS TOP,QUART,AQUA........        6.00
FRUIT JAR,LIGHTNING PUTNAM TRADEMARK,PINT,AQUA..............        4.00
FRUIT JAR,LIGHTNING PUTNAM,PINT,AQUA............... 2.00 TO         3.50
FRUIT JAR,LIGHTNING PUTNAM,QUART,AQUA.......................        1.00
FRUIT JAR,LIGHTNING REG.U.S.PATENT OFFICE,1/2 PINT,AQUA.....        7.00
FRUIT JAR,LIGHTNING TRADEMARK REGISTERED US PATENT OFFICE,
  AQUA......................................................        4.00
FRUIT JAR,LIGHTNING TRADEMARK,PINT,GREEN....................        5.00
FRUIT JAR,LIGHTNING TRADEMARK,QUART,AQUA........... 3.00 TO         3.50
FRUIT JAR,LIGHTNING TRADEMARK,ROUND,AQUA....................        10.00
FRUIT JAR,LIGHTNING WBGT,QUART,AQUA.........................        2.50
FRUIT JAR,LIGHTNING,AMBER,1/2 GALLON........................        16.00
FRUIT JAR,LIGHTNING,BASE PUTNAM,PINT,AMBER..................        21.00
FRUIT JAR,LIGHTNING,BASE PUTNAM,PINT,AQUA...................        5.25
FRUIT JAR,LIGHTNING,BASE PUTNAM,PINT,CLEAR..................        4.00
FRUIT JAR,LIGHTNING,BASE PUTNAM,QUART,AMBER.................        18.75
FRUIT JAR,LIGHTNING,BASE PUTNAM,QUART,AQUA..................        4.50
FRUIT JAR,LIGHTNING,BASE PUTNAM,QUART,CLEAR.................        3.50
FRUIT JAR,LIGHTNING,BASE PUTNAM,1/2 GAL.,AMBER..............        23.00
FRUIT JAR,LIGHTNING,BASE PUTNAM,1/2 GAL.,AQUA...............        5.25
FRUIT JAR,LIGHTNING,BASE PUTNAM,1/2 GAL.,CLEAR..............        4.25
```

```
FRUIT JAR,LIGHTNING,DARK AMBER,TWO QUART....................      20.00
FRUIT JAR,LIGHTNING,HONEY AMBER.............................      22.00
FRUIT JAR,LIGHTNING,PINT,AMBER.................... 25.00 TO      27.50
FRUIT JAR,LIGHTNING,PINT,APPLE GREEN........................      10.00
FRUIT JAR,LIGHTNING,PINT,AQUA...............................       1.00
FRUIT JAR,LIGHTNING,PINT,CORNFLOWER BLUE........... 21.00 TO      30.00
FRUIT JAR,LIGHTNING,PUTNAM TRADEMARK,PINT...................       4.00
FRUIT JAR,LIGHTNING,PUTNAM 133,TRADEMARK,AQUA...............       6.00
FRUIT JAR,LIGHTNING,QUART,AMBER................... 16.00 TO      21.00
FRUIT JAR,LIGHTNING,QUART,AQUA.................... 4.00 TO      10.00
FRUIT JAR,LIGHTNING,QUART,HONEY AMBER.......................      20.00
FRUIT JAR,LIGHTNING,QUART,OLIVE GREEN.......................      11.50
FRUIT JAR,LIGHTNING,REG.U.S.PAT.OFFICE,1/2 PINT,CLEAR.......       5.00
FRUIT JAR,LIGHTNING,TRADE MARK,PINT,AMBER...................      17.75
FRUIT JAR,LIGHTNING,TRADE MARK,PINT,AQUA....................       3.75
FRUIT JAR,LIGHTNING,TRADE MARK,PUTMAN ON BASE,PINT,AQUA.....       2.75
FRUIT JAR,LIGHTNING,TRADE MARK,PUTMAN ON BASE,QUART,AQUA....       2.75
FRUIT JAR,LIGHTNING,TRADE MARK,PUTMAN ON BASE,1/2 PINT,AMBER      17.50
FRUIT JAR,LIGHTNING,TRADE MARK,PUTMAN ON BASE,1/2 PINT,AQUA.       2.75
FRUIT JAR,LIGHTNING,TRADE MARK,QUART,AMBER..................      17.75
FRUIT JAR,LIGHTNING,TRADE MARK,QUART,AQUA...................       3.75
FRUIT JAR,LIGHTNING,TRADE MARK,REG.US PAT.OFF.,PINT,AMBER...      17.75
FRUIT JAR,LIGHTNING,TRADE MARK,REG.US PAT.OFF.,PINT,AQUA....       4.75
FRUIT JAR,LIGHTNING,TRADE MARK,REG.US PAT.OFF.,QUART,AMBER..      17.75
FRUIT JAR,LIGHTNING,TRADE MARK,REG.US PAT.OFF.,1/2 PINT,
AMBER.......................................................      17.75
FRUIT JAR,LIGHTNING,TRADE MARK,REG.US PAT.OFF.,1/2 PINT,AQUA       4.75
FRUIT JAR,LIGHTNING,TRADE MARK,1/2 GAL.,AMBER...............      17.75
FRUIT JAR,LIGHTNING,TRADE MARK,1/2 GAL.,AQUA................       3.75
FRUIT JAR,LIGHTNING,TRADEMARK,AMBER,PINT.............ILLUS..      20.00
FRUIT JAR,LIGHTNING,TRADEMARK,LID DATED APRIL 25,1882,AMBER.      22.00
FRUIT JAR,LIGHTNING,TRADEMARK,PUTMAN,QUART,AMBER............      20.00
FRUIT JAR,LIGHTNING,TRADEMARK,PUTMAN,ROUND,QUART,AQUA.......      10.00
FRUIT JAR,LIGHTNING,TRADEMARK,PUTMAN,1/2 GAL.,ROUND,AQUA....      10.00
FRUIT JAR,LIGHTNING,TRADEMARK,ROUND,PUTNAM,PINT,AMBER.......      20.00
FRUIT JAR,LIGHTNING,TRADEMARK,ROUND,PUTNAM,1/2 GAL.,AMBER...      20.00
FRUIT JAR,LIGHTNING,WHITTLED,AMBER,QUART....................      16.50
FRUIT JAR,LIGHTNING,1/4 PINT................................      14.00
FRUIT JAR,LIGHTNING,1/2 GAL.................................      28.00
FRUIT JAR,LIGHTNING,1/2 GAL.,AMBER................. 20.00 TO      27.50
FRUIT JAR,LIGHTNING,1/2 PINT................................       5.50
FRUIT JAR,LIGHTNING,1882,AMBER,QUART........................      15.00
FRUIT JAR,LINCOLN,THE,JAR,QUART,AQUA........................      36.00
FRUIT JAR,LINDELL GLASS CO.,QUART,AQUA......................      12.50
FRUIT JAR,LOCKPORT MASON IMPROVED,CLEAR,SCREW TOP WITH GLASS       3.00
FRUIT JAR,LOCKPORT MASON IMPROVED,PINT,AQUA.................       5.25
FRUIT JAR,LOCKPORT MASON IMPROVED,QUART,AQUA................       6.25
FRUIT JAR,LOCKPORT MASON,PINT,AQUA..........................       5.50
FRUIT JAR,LOCKPORT MASON,QUART,AQUA.........................       5.50
```

FRUIT JAR,LIGHTNING,TRADEMARK,AMBER,PINT

```
FRUIT JAR,LOCKPORT MASON,1/2 GAL.,AQUA.......................     5.50
FRUIT JAR,LUSTRE IN SHIELD,QUART,CLEAR.......................     6.00
FRUIT JAR,LUSTRE,R.E.TONGUE & BROS.CO.,INC.,PHILA.,PINT.....     8.00
FRUIT JAR,LUSTRE,R.E.TONGUE & BROS.INC.,PHILA.,IN CIRCLE,
   QUART......................................................     5.00
FRUIT JAR,LYMAN,W.W.,PAT'D AUG.5,1862,QUART,AQUA............    25.50
FRUIT JAR,LYMAN,W.W.,PAT'D FEB.9,1864,QUART,AQUA............    23.30
FRUIT JAR,LYMAN,W.W.,REID'D JAN.22,1867,QUART,AQUA..........    25.50
FRUIT JAR,LYNCHBURG STANDARD MASON,PINT,GREEN...............     7.75
FRUIT JAR,LYNCHBURG STANDARD MASON,QUART,AQUA...............    15.00
FRUIT JAR,LYNCHBURG STANDARD MASON,QUART,GREEN..............     7.75
FRUIT JAR,LYON & BOSSARD'S JAR,QUART,AQUA...................    45.25
FRUIT JAR,M.F.A.,ON SHIELD WITH 3 STARS,QUART,CLEAR.........     2.50
FRUIT JAR,MF.FJ.CO.,ON BASE,1/2 GAL.,AQUA...................     7.00
FRUIT JAR,M.F.J.CO.,ON BASE,QUART,AQUA......................     7.00
FRUIT JAR,M.G.CO.,ON BASE,1/2 GAL.,AQUA.....................     4.25
FRUIT JAR,MG CO.,1/2 GAL.,AMBER.............................     1.50
FRUIT JAR,MACOMB POTTERY CO.,PAT.APL.FOR,ON BASE,PINT,BROWN.     5.50
FRUIT JAR,MACOMB POTTERY CO.,PAT.APL.FOR,ON BASE,QUART,BROWN     5.50
FRUIT JAR,MACOMB POTTERY CO.,PAT.JAN.24,1899,ON BASE,PINT,
   BROWN......................................................     8.25
FRUIT JAR,MACOMB POTTERY CO.,PAT.JAN.24,1899,ON BASE,QUART,
   BROWN......................................................     8.75
FRUIT JAR,MAGIC FRUIT JAR,QUART,AQUA........................    28.00
FRUIT JAR,MAGIC STAR,WHITTLED...............................     6.00
FRUIT JAR,MAGIC,THE STAR EMBLEM,QUART,AMBER.................    65.50
FRUIT JAR,MAGIC,THE STAR EMBLEM,QUART,AQUA..................    28.25
FRUIT JAR,MAGIC,WM MC CULLY & CO.,QUART,AMBER...............    75.25
FRUIT JAR,MAGIC,WM MC CULLY & CO.,QUART,AQUA................    38.50
FRUIT JAR,MALLINGER,QUART,CLEAR.............................     8.50
FRUIT JAR,MANSFIELD IMPROVED MASON,QUART....................    12.00
FRUIT JAR,MANSFIELD IMPROVED MASON,QUART,AQUA...............    14.25
FRUIT JAR,MANSFIELD MASON,SCREW TOP,QUART,PURPLE............    10.00
FRUIT JAR,MANSFIELD,QUART,AQUA..............................    31.00
FRUIT JAR,MARION JAR,MASON'S PAT.1858,1/2 GAL...............     8.50
FRUIT JAR,MARION JAR,THE MASON'S PATENT NOV.30,1858,PINT,
   AQUA.......................................................     9.75
FRUIT JAR,MARION JAR,THE MASON'S PATENT NOV.30,1858,QUART,
   AQUA..................................................7.75 TO    12.00
FRUIT JAR,MARION MASON,QUART,AQUA...........................     8.00
FRUIT JAR,MARION MASON'S PATENT,QUART.......................     7.00
FRUIT JAR,MARION MASON'S PATENT,1/2 GAL.....................     7.00
FRUIT JAR,MARION,FANCY LETTERS,NOV.30,1858,PINT,
   AQUA...........................................10.25 TO    15.00
FRUIT JAR,MARION,THE,FANCY LETTERS,PAT.NOV.30,1858,QUART,
   AQUA.......................................................    10.25
FRUIT JAR,MARION,1/2 GAL............................. 5.00 TO    10.00
FRUIT JAR,MARSTON'S RESTAURANT,BOSTON,QUART,CLEAR...........    13.50
FRUIT JAR,MASCOT,THE,TRADE MARK PAT'D IMPROVED,QUART,AMBER..    14.75
FRUIT JAR,MASON CBK 1858,QUART,AQUA.........................    12.00
FRUIT JAR,MASON CLYDE N.Y.,PINT.............................     3.00
FRUIT JAR,MASON FRUIT JAR,MASON IN CURVED LINE,PINT,AMBER...    40.25
FRUIT JAR,MASON FRUIT JAR,MASON IN CURVED LINE,PINT,AQUA....     5.25
FRUIT JAR,MASON FRUIT JAR,MASON IN CURVED LINE,PINT,GREEN...     9.25
FRUIT JAR,MASON FRUIT JAR,MASON IN CURVED LINE,QUART,AMBER..    40.25
FRUIT JAR,MASON FRUIT JAR,MASON IN CURVED LINE,QUART,AQUA...     5.25
FRUIT JAR,MASON FRUIT JAR,MASON IN CURVED LINE,QUART,GREEN..     9.25
FRUIT JAR,MASON FRUIT JAR,MASON IN CURVED LINE,1/2 GAL.,
   AMBER......................................................    40.25
FRUIT JAR,MASON FRUIT JAR,MASON IN CURVED LINE,1/2 GAL.,AQUA     5.25
FRUIT JAR,MASON FRUIT JAR,MASON IN CURVED LINE,1/2 GAL.,
   GREEN......................................................     9.25
FRUIT JAR,MASON FRUIT JAR,MASON IN STRAIGHT LINE,PINT,AMBER.    40.25
FRUIT JAR,MASON FRUIT JAR,MASON IN STRAIGHT LINE,PINT,AQUA..     6.25
FRUIT JAR,MASON FRUIT JAR,MASON IN STRAIGHT LINE,PINT,GREEN.     9.25
FRUIT JAR,MASON FRUIT JAR,MASON IN STRAIGHT LINE,QUART,AMBER    40.25
```

```
FRUIT JAR,MASON FRUIT JAR,MASON IN STRAIGHT LINE,QUART,AQUA.      6.25
FRUIT JAR,MASON FRUIT JAR,MASON IN STRAIGHT LINE,QUART,GREEN      9.25
FRUIT JAR,MASON FRUIT JAR,MASON IN STRAIGHT LINE,1/2 GAl.,
  AMBER.......................................................   40.25
FRUIT JAR,MASON FRUIT JAR,MASON IN STRAIGHT LINE,1/2 GAL.,
  AQUA........................................................    6.25
FRUIT JAR,MASON FRUIT JAR,MASON IN STRAIGHT LINE,1/2 GAL.,
  GREEN.......................................................    9.25
FRUIT JAR,MASON H 1858,QUART..................................    5.50
FRUIT JAR,MASON HERO CROSS 1858,QUART,AMBER...................   35.00
FRUIT JAR,MASON HOME PACKER,JEANETTE J IN SQUARE,QUART........    3.00
FRUIT JAR,MASON IMPROVED PATENT,QUART,AQUA....................    4.50
FRUIT JAR,MASON IMPROVED,HOUR GLASS ON REVERSE,QUART..........   10.00
FRUIT JAR,MASON IMPROVED,QUART.....................  4.50 TO     8.00
FRUIT JAR,MASON JAR,PINT,AQUA.................................    8.50
FRUIT JAR,MASON JAR,QUART,AQUA................................    8.50
FRUIT JAR,MASON JAR,STAR MONO,PINT,AQUA.......................   10.25
FRUIT JAR,MASON JAR,STAR MONO,QUART,AQUA......................   10.25
FRUIT JAR,MASON JAR,STAR MONO,1/2 GAL.,AQUA...................   10.25
FRUIT JAR,MASON MADE IN CANADA,QUART,AQUA.....................    5.75
FRUIT JAR,MASON MADE IN CANADA,QUART,CLEAR....................    3.75
FRUIT JAR,MASON MALTESE CROSS,1858,QUART......................   35.00
FRUIT JAR,MASON MIDGET,C.F.J.CO.,ONE-PIECE LID................    5.00
FRUIT JAR,MASON MIDGET,KEYSTONE-EMBOSSED,ONE-PIECE LID........    6.50
FRUIT JAR,MASON MIDGET,PAT.DATE,ONE-PIECE LID.................    5.00
FRUIT JAR,MASON PATENT,ERASED PORCELAIN LINED ON REVERSE,
  2 QUART.....................................................   15.00
FRUIT JAR,MASON SNOW-FLAKE,1858,QUART,AQUA....................   35.00
FRUIT JAR,MASON TRADEMARK CFJ,QUART...........................    3.00
FRUIT JAR,MASON V 1858,QUART..................................    5.50
FRUIT JAR,MASON VACUUM KNOWLTON PAT.JUNE 9TH 1908,AQUA........   30.00
FRUIT JAR,MASON 1858,HOUR GLASS ON BACK,QUART.................    5.50
FRUIT JAR,MASON 1858,M CROSS,QUART,AMBER......................   32.00
FRUIT JAR,MASON 1858,QUART,CROSS IN CIRCLE,LIME...............   30.00
FRUIT JAR,MASON 1870,4 LB. BUTTER JAR.........................   35.00
FRUIT JAR,MASON,ANCHOR H EMBLEM,QUART.........................    1.50
FRUIT JAR,MASON,AQUA,ONE QUART................................    2.00
FRUIT JAR,MASON,AQUA,TWO QUART................................    2.00
FRUIT JAR,MASON,BALL PERFECT,MEASURE ON SIDE,AMBER,
  1/2 GALLON..................................................   15.00
FRUIT JAR,MASON,BALL,AMBER,1/2 GALLON.........................   19.00
FRUIT JAR,MASON,CG-GG EMBLEM,1858,QUART.......................    8.00
FRUIT JAR,MASON,CHRISTMAS,AMBER...............................   25.00
FRUIT JAR,MASON,CHRISTMAS,PINT.....................  30.00 TO   37.50
FRUIT JAR,MASON,CROSS,1858,PINT...............................    3.50
FRUIT JAR,MASON,CROWN EMBLEM,PINT,CLEAR.......................    3.00
FRUIT JAR,MASON,CROWN EMBLEM,PINT,GREEN.......................    3.00
FRUIT JAR,MASON,CROWN EMBLEM,QUART,CLEAR......................    3.00
FRUIT JAR,MASON,CROWN EMBLEM,QUART,GREEN......................    3.00
FRUIT JAR,MASON,DATED 1858,QUART..............................    2.00
FRUIT JAR,MASON,DATED 1858,1/2 GAL............................    2.00
FRUIT JAR,MASON,ERASED PORCELAIN LINED ON REVERSE,2 QUARTS..   15.00
FRUIT JAR,MASON,GROUND MOUTH,PINT.............................    2.50
FRUIT JAR,MASON,HERO CROSS,1858,QUART,AMBER...................   35.00
FRUIT JAR,MASON,IN CURVED SHAPE,PINT,AQUA.....................    3.75
FRUIT JAR,MASON,IN CURVED SHAPE,QUART,AQUA....................    3.75
FRUIT JAR,MASON,IN CURVED SHAPE,1/2 GAL.,AQUA.................    3.75
FRUIT JAR,MASON,PAT.NOV.30,1853,QUART,AQUA....................    5.00
FRUIT JAR,MASON,PINT,AMBER....................................   20.00
FRUIT JAR,MASON,PINT,APPLE GREEN..............................    8.00
FRUIT JAR,MASON,PINT,CLEAR....................................    2.00
FRUIT JAR,MASON,QUART,AMBER...................................   20.00
FRUIT JAR,MASON,QUART,APPLE GREEN.............................    8.00
FRUIT JAR,MASON,QUART,CLEAR...................................    2.00
FRUIT JAR,MASON,RED KEY,1/2 GALLON............................    9.00
```

```
FRUIT JAR,MASON,RED OVER KEY,PINT,AQUA.....................    8.00
FRUIT JAR,MASON,SMALL MOUTH,PINT..........................    7.50
FRUIT JAR,MASON,THE,PINT,AQUA.............................    3.75
FRUIT JAR,MASON,THE,QUART,AQUA............................    3.75
FRUIT JAR,MASON,THE,1/2 GAL.,AQUA.........................    3.75
FRUIT JAR,MASON,THE,1858 TRADE MARK,FRAMED IN SQUARE,PINT,
  AQUA....................................................    8.00
FRUIT JAR,MASON,THE,1858 TRADE MARK,FRAMED IN SQUARE,QUART,
  AQUA....................................................    8.00
FRUIT JAR,MASON,THE,1872,QUART,AQUA.......................   14.25
FRUIT JAR,MASON,THE,1872,QUART,DARK GREEN.................   20.75
FRUIT JAR,MASON,UNDER KEYSTONE EMBLEM,PINT,AQUA...........    7.00
FRUIT JAR,MASON,UNDER KEYSTONE EMBLEM,QUART,AQUA..........    7.00
FRUIT JAR,MASON,UNDER KEYSTONE EMBLEM,1/2 GAL.,AQUA.......    7.00
FRUIT JAR,MASON,UNDERLINED WITH BANNER,PINT,AQUA..........    3.00
FRUIT JAR,MASON,UNDERLINED WITH BANNER,QUART,AQUA.........    3.00
FRUIT JAR,MASON,UNDERLINED WITH BANNER,1/2 GAL.,AQUA......    3.00
FRUIT JAR,MASON,WHITNEY,PAT.1858,AQUA,QUART...............    4.50
FRUIT JAR,MASON,ZINC TOP,MILK GLASS LINER,PATENT NOV.1858,
  QUART...................................................    6.00
FRUIT JAR,MASON,1/2 GAL.,AMBER............................   20.00
FRUIT JAR,MASON,1/2 GAL.,APPLE GREEN......................    8.00
FRUIT JAR,MASON,1/2 GAL.,AQUA.............................    4.00
FRUIT JAR,MASON,1/2 GAL.,CLEAR............................    2.00
FRUIT JAR,MASON,3 LINED DEVICE UNDERSCORES WORD,PINT,GREEN..   6.75
FRUIT JAR,MASON,3 LINED DEVICE UNDERSCORES WORD,PINT,OLIVE
  GREEN...................................................    8.75
FRUIT JAR,MASON,3 LINED DEVICE UNDERSCORES WORD,QUART,GREEN.   6.75
FRUIT JAR,MASON,3 LINED DEVICE UNDERSCORES WORD,1/2 GAL.,
  GREEN...................................................    3.75
FRUIT JAR,MASON,3 1858,QUART..............................    3.50
FRUIT JAR,MASON,1858,MIDGET,ONE-PIECE LID.................    7.00
FRUIT JAR,MASON,1858,PINT,C.E.J...........................    5.00
FRUIT JAR,MASON,1858,PINT,KEYSTONE........................    5.00
FRUIT JAR,MASON'S C,PATENT NOV.30,1858,PINT,AQUA..........    6.50
FRUIT JAR,MASON'S C,PATENT NOV.30,1858,QUART,AQUA.........    6.50
FRUIT JAR,MASON'S C,PATENT NOV.30,1858,1/2 GAL.,AQUA......    6.50
FRUIT JAR,MASON'S CFJ CO.,IMPROVED,CLYDE,N.Y.,PINT........    4.00
FRUIT JAR,MASON'S CFJ CO.,IMPROVED,CLYDE,N.Y.,PINT,AMETHYST.   4.00
FRUIT JAR,MASON'S CFJ CO.,IMPROVED,CLYDE,N.Y.,QUART.......    4.00
FRUIT JAR,MASON'S CFJ CO.,IMPROVED,CLYDE,N.Y.,QUART,AQUA....   5.00
FRUIT JAR,MASON'S CFJ CO.,IMPROVED,PINT,AQUA..............    3.50
FRUIT JAR,MASON'S CFJ CO.,IMPROVED,QUART,AQUA.............    3.50
FRUIT JAR,MASON'S CFJ CO.,IMPROVED,1/2 GAL.,AQUA..........    7.00
FRUIT JAR,MASON'S CFJ CO.MONO,IMPROVED,MIDGET.............   10.50
FRUIT JAR,MASON'S CFJ CO.MONO,PINT,AMBER..................   20.50
FRUIT JAR,MASON'S CFJ CO.MONO,QUART,AMBER.................   20.50
FRUIT JAR,MASON'S CFJ CO.MONO,1/2 GAL.,AMBER..............   20.50
FRUIT JAR,MASON'S CFJ CO.,PATENT NOV.30,1858,QUART,AQUA...    3.00
FRUIT JAR,MASON'S CFJ CO.,PATENT NOV.30,1858,QUART,CLEAR....   4.00
FRUIT JAR,MASON'S CFJ IMPROVED MIDGET............. 7.00 TO   10.00
FRUIT JAR,MASON'S CG CO.,PINT.............................    8.00
FRUIT JAR,MASON'S CROSS PATENT NOV.30,1858,QUART,AQUA.....    6.00
FRUIT JAR,MASON'S CROSS PATENT NOV.30,1858,1/2 GAL.,AQUA....   6.00
FRUIT JAR,MASON'S CROSS PATENT NOV.30,1858,PINT,AQUA......    5.00
FRUIT JAR,MASON'S CROSS PATENT NOV.30,1858,QUART,AQUA.....    3.00
FRUIT JAR,MASON'S CROSS,PAT.NOV.30,1858,AQUA.........ILLUS..   5.00
FRUIT JAR,MASON'S CROSS,PATENT NOV.30,1858,1/2 GAL.......    3.50
FRUIT JAR,MASON'S CROSS,PATENT NOV.30,1858,1/2 GAL.,AQUA....   4.00
FRUIT JAR,MASON'S HOUR GLASS MIDGET.......................   20.00
FRUIT JAR,MASON'S HOUR GLASS REV.,QUART,1858..............    8.00
FRUIT JAR,MASON'S IG CO.1858,QUART........................    8.00
FRUIT JAR,MASON'S IMPROVED,CFJ CO.,1/2 GAL.,CLEAR.........    4.00
FRUIT JAR,MASON'S IMPROVED,CLYDE,N.Y.,PINT,AMBER..........   20.50
FRUIT JAR,MASON'S IMPROVED,CLYDE,N.Y.,PINT,AQUA...........    7.50
```

FRUIT JAR,MASON'S CROSS,PAT.NOV.30,1858,AQUA

```
FRUIT JAR,MASON'S IMPROVED,CLYDE,N.Y.,QUART,AMBER............   20.50
FRUIT JAR,MASON'S IMPROVED,CLYDE,N.Y.,QUART,AQUA............    7.50
FRUIT JAR,MASON'S IMPROVED,CLYDE,N.Y.,1/2 GAL.,AMBER........   20.50
FRUIT JAR,MASON'S IMPROVED,CLYDE,N.Y.,1/2 GAL.,AQUA.........    7.50
FRUIT JAR,MASON'S IMPROVED JAR,PINT,AQUA...................    6.25
FRUIT JAR,MASON'S IMPROVED JAR,QUART,AQUA..................    6.25
FRUIT JAR,MASON'S IMPROVED JAR,1/2 GAL.,AQUA...............    6.25
FRUIT JAR,MASON'S IMPROVED LGW,QUART.......................   10.00
FRUIT JAR,MASON'S IMPROVED TRADE MARK,QUART................    9.00
FRUIT JAR,MASON'S IMPROVED,CROSS MONO,PINT,AMBER...........   34.75
FRUIT JAR,MASON'S IMPROVED,CROSS MONO,PINT,AQUA............    6.75
FRUIT JAR,MASON'S IMPROVED,CROSS MONO,PINT,GREEN...........   11.75
FRUIT JAR,MASON'S IMPROVED,CROSS MONO,QUART,AMBER..........   34.75
FRUIT JAR,MASON'S IMPROVED,CROSS MONO,QUART,AQUA...........    6.75
FRUIT JAR,MASON'S IMPROVED,CROSS MONO,QUART,GREEN..........   11.75
FRUIT JAR,MASON'S IMPROVED,CROSS MONO,1/2 GAL.,AMBER.......   34.75
FRUIT JAR,MASON'S IMPROVED,CROSS MONO,1/2 GAL.,AQUA........    6.75
FRUIT JAR,MASON'S IMPROVED,CROSS MONO,1/2 GAL.,GREEN.......   11.75
FRUIT JAR,MASON'S IMPROVED,MIDGET,AQUA.....................   12.50
FRUIT JAR,MASON'S IMPROVED,PAT.NOV.26,67,AQUA..............    7.00
FRUIT JAR,MASON'S IMPROVED,PINT,AQUA.......................    5.75
FRUIT JAR,MASON'S IMPROVED,QUART,AQUA......................    5.75
FRUIT JAR,MASON'S IMPROVED,TWO-PIECE LID,PINT..............    5.00
FRUIT JAR,MASON'S IMPROVED,1/2 GAL.,AQUA...................    6.00
FRUIT JAR,MASON'S IMPROVED,1/2 GAL.,SCREW BAND,BLUE LID,
  AMBER...................................................   45.00
FRUIT JAR,MASON'S KEYSTONE PATENT NOV.30,1858,1/2 GAL......   10.00
FRUIT JAR,MASON'S KEYSTONE,KEYSTONE MONO,PINT,AQUA.........    9.75
FRUIT JAR,MASON'S KEYSTONE,KEYSTONE MONO,QUART,AQUA........    9.75
FRUIT JAR,MASON'S KEYSTONE,PAT.NOV.30,1858,1/2 GAL.AQUA....    6.00
FRUIT JAR,MASON'S N,PATENT NOV.30,1858,1/2 GAL.,AQUA.......    5.50
FRUIT JAR,MASON'S N,PATENT NOV.30,1858,PINT,AQUA...........    5.50
FRUIT JAR,MASON'S N,PATENT NOV.30,1858,QUART,AQUA..........    5.50
FRUIT JAR,MASON'S PATENT E.T.C.,QUART,AMETHYST.............    5.00
FRUIT JAR,MASON'S PATENT NOV.30,1858,AQUA....ILLUS.. 5.00 TO   8.00
FRUIT JAR,MASON'S PATENT NOV.30,1858,AQUA,PINT.......ILLUS..   15.00
FRUIT JAR,MASON'S PATENT NOV.30,1858,BALL,MIDGET...........    9.75
FRUIT JAR,MASON'S PATENT NOV.30,1858,BALL,PINT,AMBER.......   30.25
FRUIT JAR,MASON'S PATENT NOV.30,1858,BALL,PINT,AQUA........    4.75
FRUIT JAR,MASON'S PATENT NOV.30,1858,BALL,PINT,OLIVE GREEN..    9.75
FRUIT JAR,MASON'S PATENT NOV.30,1858,BALL,QUART,AMBER.......   30.50
FRUIT JAR,MASON'S PATENT NOV.30,1858,BALL,QUART,AQUA........    4.75
FRUIT JAR,MASON'S PATENT NOV.30,1858,BALL,QUART,OLIVE GREEN.    9.75
FRUIT JAR,MASON'S PATENT NOV.30,1858,BALL,1/2 GAL.,AMBER....   30.25
FRUIT JAR,MASON'S PATENT NOV.30,1858,BALL,1/2 GAL.,AQUA.....    4.75
FRUIT JAR,MASON'S PATENT NOV.30,1858,BALL,1/2 GAL.,OLIVE
  GREEN...................................................    9.75
```

FRUIT JAR,MASON'S
PATENT NOV.30TH,1858,AQUA

FRUIT JAR,MASON'S PATENT
NOV.30TH,1858,AQUA,PINT

FRUIT JAR,MASON'S PATENT NOV.30,1858,BKG CO.MONO,PINT,AQUA..	9.00
FRUIT JAR,MASON'S PATENT NOV.30,1858,BKG CO.MONO,QUART,AQUA.	9.00
FRUIT JAR,MASON'S PATENT NOV.30,1858,BKG CO.MONO,1/2 GAL., AQUA..	9.00
FRUIT JAR,MASON'S PATENT NOV.30,1858,CFJ CO.,MIDGET.........	8.75
FRUIT JAR,MASON'S PATENT NOV.30,1858,CFJ CO.,PINT,AMBER.....	27.00
FRUIT JAR,MASON'S PATENT NOV.30,1858,CFJ CO.,PINT,AQUA......	4.75
FRUIT JAR,MASON'S PATENT NOV.30,1858,CFJ CO.,QUART,AMBER....	27.00
FRUIT JAR,MASON'S PATENT NOV.30,1858,CFJ CO.,QUART,AQUA.....	4.75
FRUIT JAR,MASON'S PATENT NOV.30,1858,CFJ CO.,1/2 GAL.,AMBER.	27.00
FRUIT JAR,MASON'S PATENT NOV.30,1858,CFJ CO.,1/2 GAL.,AQUA..	4.75
FRUIT JAR,MASON'S PATENT NOV.30,1858,CFJ CO.,1/2 GAL.,AQUA..	6.00
FRUIT JAR,MASON'S PATENT NOV.30,1858,CFJ CO.MONO,MIDGET,AQUA	8.25
FRUIT JAR,MASON'S PATENT NOV.30,1858,CFJ CO.MONO,PINT,AQUA..	2.75
FRUIT JAR,MASON'S PATENT NOV.30,1858,CFJ CO.MONO,QUART,AMBER	22.50
FRUIT JAR,MASON'S PATENT NOV.30,1858,CFJ CO.MONO,QUART,AQUA.	2.75
FRUIT JAR,MASON'S PATENT NOV.30,1858,CFJ CO.MONO,1/2 GAL., AMBER...	29.75
FRUIT JAR,MASON'S PATENT NOV.30,1858,CONCAVE CIRCLE,PINT, AQUA.................................. 7.75 TO	11.50
FRUIT JAR,MASON'S PATENT NOV.30,1858,CONCAVE CIRCLE,QUART, AQUA.................................. 7.75 TO	11.50
FRUIT JAR,MASON'S PATENT NOV.30,1858,CROSS MONO,MIDGET,AQUA.	10.25
FRUIT JAR,MASON'S PATENT NOV.30,1858,CROSS MONO,PINT,AMBER..	29.75
FRUIT JAR,MASON'S PATENT NOV.30,1858,CROSS MONO,PINT,AQUA...	4.25
FRUIT JAR,MASON'S PATENT NOV.30,1858,CROSS MONO,QUART,AMBER.	29.95
FRUIT JAR,MASON'S PATENT NOV.30,1858,CROSS MONO,QUART,AQUA..	4.00
FRUIT JAR,MASON'S PATENT NOV.30,1858,CROSS MONO,1/2 GAL., AMBER...	29.75
FRUIT JAR,MASON'S PATENT NOV.30,1858,CROSS MONO,1/2 GAL., AQUA..	4.50
FRUIT JAR,MASON'S PATENT NOV.30,1858,EHE,PINT,AQUA..........	6.75
FRUIT JAR,MASON'S PATENT NOV.30,1858,EHE,QUART,AQUA.........	6.75
FRUIT JAR,MASON'S PATENT NOV.30,1858,EHE,1/2 GAL.,AQUA......	6.75
FRUIT JAR,MASON'S PATENT NOV.30,1858,FLOWER MONO,PINT,AQUA..	7.95
FRUIT JAR,MASON'S PATENT NOV.30,1858,FLOWER MONO,QUART,AQUA.	7.95
FRUIT JAR,MASON'S PATENT NOV.30,1858,FLOWER MONO,1/2 GAL., AQUA.................................. 7.95 TO	9.50
FRUIT JAR,MASON'S PATENT NOV.30,1858,H G CO MONO,PINT,AQUA..	7.25
FRUIT JAR,MASON'S PATENT NOV.30,1858,H G CO MONO,QUART,AQUA.	7.25
FRUIT JAR,MASON'S PATENT NOV.30,1858,H G CO MONO,1/2 GAL., AQUA..	7.25
FRUIT JAR,MASON'S PATENT NOV.30,1858,HGW MONO,PINT,AQUA.....	7.95
FRUIT JAR,MASON'S PATENT NOV.30,1858,HGW MONO,QUART,AQUA....	7.75
FRUIT JAR,MASON'S PATENT NOV.30,1858,HGW MONO,1/2 GAL.,AQUA.	7.75
FRUIT JAR,MASON'S PATENT NOV.30,1858,IG CO MONO,PINT,AQUA...	6.25
FRUIT JAR,MASON'S PATENT NOV.30,1858,IG CO MONO,QUART,AQUA..	6.25

FRUIT JAR,MASON'S PATENT NOV.30,1858,IG CO MONO,1/2 GAL.,
AQUA.. 6.25
FRUIT JAR,MASON'S PATENT NOV.30,1858,KEYSTONE CIRCLE,PINT,
AQUA.. 6.25
FRUIT JAR,MASON'S PATENT NOV.30,1858,KEYSTONE CIRCLE,QUART,
AQUA.. 6.25
FRUIT JAR,MASON'S PATENT NOV.30,1858,KEYSTONE MONO,MIDGET,
AQUA.. 9.50
FRUIT JAR,MASON'S PATENT NOV.30,1858,KEYSTONE MONO,PINT,AQUA   4.00
FRUIT JAR,MASON'S PATENT NOV.30,1858,KEYSTONE MONO,QUART,
AQUA.. 4.00
FRUIT JAR,MASON'S PATENT NOV.30,1858,KEYSTONE MONO,1/2 GAL.,
AQUA.. 4.00
FRUIT JAR,MASON'S PATENT NOV.30,1858,KILNER BROS.PINT,AQUA..   20.25
FRUIT JAR,MASON'S PATENT NOV.30,1858,KILNER BROS,QUART,AQUA.   20.25
FRUIT JAR,MASON'S PATENT NOV.30,1858,KILNER BROS,1/2 GAL.,
AQUA.. 20.25
FRUIT JAR,MASON'S PATENT NOV.30,1858,N REVERSED,PINT,AQUA...   14.25
FRUIT JAR,MASON'S PATENT NOV.30,1858,N REVERSED,QUART,AQUA..   14.25
FRUIT JAR,MASON'S PATENT NOV.30,1858,N REVERSED,1/2 GAL.,
AQUA.. 14.25
FRUIT JAR,MASON'S PATENT NOV.30,1858,NCL CO MONO,PINT,AQUA..   13.25
FRUIT JAR,MASON'S PATENT NOV.30,1858,NCL CO MONO,QUART,AQUA.   13.25
FRUIT JAR,MASON'S PATENT NOV.30,1858,NCL CO MONO,1/2 GAL.,
AQUA.. 13.25
FRUIT JAR,MASON'S PATENT NOV.30,1858,OI CO MONO,PINT,AQUA...   8.75
FRUIT JAR,MASON'S PATENT NOV.30,1858,OI CO MONO,QUART,AQUA..   8.75
FRUIT JAR,MASON'S PATENT NOV.30,1858,OI MONO,1/2 GAL.,AQUA..   8.75
FRUIT JAR,MASON'S PATENT NOV.30,1858,PINT,AMBER.............   25.75
FRUIT JAR,MASON'S PATENT NOV.30,1858,PINT,AQUA..............   3.75
FRUIT JAR,MASON'S PATENT NOV.30,1858,QUART,AMBER............   25.75
FRUIT JAR,MASON'S PATENT NOV.30,1858,QUART,AMETHYST.........   3.50
FRUIT JAR,MASON'S PATENT NOV.30,1858,QUART,AQUA......3.75 TO   7.00
FRUIT JAR,MASON'S PATENT NOV.30,1858,QUART,GREEN............   4.00
FRUIT JAR,MASON'S PATENT NOV.30,1858,SG CO MONO,PINT,AQUA...   6.50
FRUIT JAR,MASON'S PATENT NOV.30,1858,SG CO MONO,QUART,AQUA..   6.52
FRUIT JAR,MASON'S PATENT NOV.30,1858,SG CO MONO,1/2 GAL.,
AQUA.. 6.50
FRUIT JAR,MASON'S PATENT NOV.30,1858,STAR/MOON EMBLEM,PINT,
AQUA.. 20.25
FRUIT JAR,MASON'S PATENT NOV.30,1858,STAR/MOON EMBLEM,QUART,
AQUA.. 20.25
FRUIT JAR,MASON'S PATENT NOV.30,1858,U G CO.,PINT,AQUA......   6.75
FRUIT JAR,MASON'S PATENT NOV.30,1858,U G CO.,QUART,AQUA.....   6.75
FRUIT JAR,MASON'S PATENT NOV.30,1858,U G CO.,1/2 GAL.,AQUA..   6.75
FRUIT JAR,MASON'S PATENT NOV.30,1858,UPRIGHT LINES IN
MASONS,QT... 30.25
FRUIT JAR,MASON'S PATENT NOV.30,1858,UPRIGHT LINES,PINT,
AMBER... 50.25
FRUIT JAR,MASON'S PATENT NOV.30,1858,1/2 GAL.,AMBER.........   25.75
FRUIT JAR,MASON'S PATENT NOV.30,1858,1/2 GAL.,AQUA..........   3.75
FRUIT JAR,MASON'S PATENT NOV.30,1858,1/2 GAL.,AQUA.........   14.50
FRUIT JAR,MASON'S PATENT NOV.30,1858,3 BALLS MONO,PINT,AQUA.   12.00
FRUIT JAR,MASON'S PATENT NOV.30,1858,3 BALLS MONO,QUART,AQUA   12.00
FRUIT JAR,MASON'S PATENT NOV.30,1858,3 BALLS MONO,1/2 GAL.,
AQUA.. 12.00
FRUIT JAR,MASON'S PATENT NOV.30,1880,PINT,AQUA..............   14.50
FRUIT JAR,MASON'S PATENT NOV.30,1880,QUART,AQUA.............   14.50
FRUIT JAR,MASON'S PATENT NOV.30TH,1858,AQUA................   7.00
FRUIT JAR,MASON'S PATENT NOV.30TH,1858,SHIELD REVERSE.......   15.00
FRUIT JAR,MASON'S PATENT NOV.30TH,1858,1/2 GAL.,MILK GLASS..   300.00
FRUIT JAR,MASON'S PATENT WITH SG MONOGRAM,QUART.............   6.00
FRUIT JAR,MASON'S PATENT 1858,BALL ON BACK,PINT,AQUA........   4.25
FRUIT JAR,MASON'S PATENT 1858,BALL ON BACK,QUART,AQUA.......   4.25
FRUIT JAR,MASON'S PATENT 1858,BALL ON BACK,1/2 GAL.,AQUA....   4.25

```
FRUIT JAR,MASON'S PATENT 1858,KEYSTONE IN CIRCLE,QUART......      3.00
FRUIT JAR,MASON'S PATENT 1858,PINT,AQUA....................      4.25
FRUIT JAR,MASON'S PATENT 1858,PORT ON BACK,PINT,AMBER.......     20.50
FRUIT JAR,MASON'S PATENT 1858,PORT ON BACK,PINT,AQUA........      4.25
FRUIT JAR,MASON'S PATENT 1858,PORT ON BACK,QUART,AMBER......     20.50
FRUIT JAR,MASON'S PATENT 1858,PORT ON BACK,QUART,AQUA.......      4.25
FRUIT JAR,MASON'S PATENT 1858,PORT ON BACK,1/2 GAL.,AMBER...     20.50
FRUIT JAR,MASON'S PATENT 1858,PORT ON BACK,1/2 GAL.,AQUA....      4.25
FRUIT JAR,MASON'S PATENT 1858,PORT ON REVERSE,QUART.........      3.00
FRUIT JAR,MASON'S PATENT 1858,QUART,AQUA...................      4.25
FRUIT JAR,MASON'S PATENT 1858,1/2 GAL.,AQUA.................      4.25
FRUIT JAR,MASON'S PATENT,PINT,AQUA.........................      3.50
FRUIT JAR,MASON'S PATENT,PINT,OLIVE GREEN..................      6.25
FRUIT JAR,MASON'S PATENT,QUART,AQUA........................      3.50
FRUIT JAR,MASON'S PATENT,QUART,OLIVE GREEN.................      6.25
FRUIT JAR,MASON'S PATENT,1/2 GAL.,AQUA.....................      3.50
FRUIT JAR,MASON'S PATENT,1/2 GAL.,OLIVE GREEN..............      6.25
FRUIT JAR,MASON'S S,PATENT 1858,CROSS MONO,PINT,AQUA.......      5.00
FRUIT JAR,MASON'S S,PATENT 1858,S BEFORE MASON'S,PINT,AQUA..     5.50
FRUIT JAR,MASON'S SG CO.,PATENT NOV.30,1858,QUART,AQUA......     3.50
FRUIT JAR,MASON'S STAR,PINT................................      3.00
FRUIT JAR,MASON'S STAR,QUART...............................      8.00
FRUIT JAR,MASON'S TRADE MARK,IMPROVED,CFJ CO MONO,MIDGET....    12.50
FRUIT JAR,MASON'S TRADE MARK,IMPROVED,CFJ CO MONO,PINT,AQUA.     5.75
FRUIT JAR,MASON'S TRADE MARK,IMPROVED,CFJ CO MONO,QUART,AQUA     5.75
FRUIT JAR,MASON'S TRADE MARK,IMPROVED,CFJ CO MONO,1/2 GAL.,
    AQUA..................................................      5.75
FRUIT JAR,MASON'S TRADE MARK,IMPROVED,PINT,AQUA.............      4.75
FRUIT JAR,MASON'S TRADE MARK,IMPROVED,QUART,AQUA............      4.75
FRUIT JAR,MASON'S TRADE MARK,IMPROVED,1/2 GAL.,AQUA.........      4.75
FRUIT JAR,MASON'S 1858 PATENT,QUART,AMBER..................     19.00
FRUIT JAR,MASON'S 1858 REVERSE BALL,PINT...................      3.00
FRUIT JAR,MASON'S 1858 REVERSE PORT,QUART..................      2.00
FRUIT JAR,MASON'S 1872 PATENT,QUART........................     18.00
FRUIT JAR,MASON'S,N,PATENT NOV.30,1858,PINT,AQUA............      5.50
FRUIT JAR,MASON'S,N,PATENT NOV.30,1858,QUART,AQUA...........      5.50
FRUIT JAR,MASON'S,S,PATENT 1858,CROSS MONO,QUART,AQUA.......      5.00
FRUIT JAR,MASON'S,S,PATENT 1858,CROSS MONO,1/2 GAL.,AQUA....      5.00
FRUIT JAR,MASON'S,S,PATENT 1858,S BEFORE MASON'S,QUART,AQUA.     5.50
FRUIT JAR,MASON'S,S,PATENT 1858,S BEFORE MASON'S,1/2 GAL.,
    AQUA..................................................      5.50
FRUIT JAR,MASON'S,SHIELD,UNION,QUART,BLUE...................     45.00
FRUIT JAR,MASON'S,THE,IMPROVED,PINT,AMBER..................     20.25
FRUIT JAR,MASON'S,THE,IMPROVED,PINT,AQUA...................      5.25
FRUIT JAR,MASON'S,THE,IMPROVED,QUART,AMBER.................     20.25
FRUIT JAR,MASON'S,THE,IMPROVED,QUART,AQUA..................      5.25
FRUIT JAR,MASON'S,THE,IMPROVED,1/2 GAL.,AMBER..............     20.25
FRUIT JAR,MASON'S,THE,IMPROVED,1/2 GAL.,AQUA...............      5.25
FRUIT JAR,MASONS UNION,WHITTLED,AQUA,EMBOSSED U.S.TREASURY
    SHIELD................................................     37.50
FRUIT JAR,MATHIAS & HENDERSON,ON BASE,QUART,CLEAR...........     18.25
FRUIT JAR,MC C & CO. WAX SEALER,QUART,AQUA.................     20.00
FRUIT JAR,MC CARTY,THE,VACUUM JAR,QUART,CLEAR...............     28.50
FRUIT JAR,MC DONALD NEW PERFECT SEAL,IN CIRCLE,QUART,AQUA...      6.50
FRUIT JAR,MC DONALD NEW PERFECT SEAL,PAT'D JULY 14,1908,
    QUART.................................................      7.25
FRUIT JAR,MC DONALD NEW PERFECT SEAL,PINT,AQUA.............      4.50
FRUIT JAR,MC DONALD NEW PERFECT SEAL,QUART,AQUA............      4.50
FRUIT JAR,MC DONALD PERFECT SEAL,IN CIRCLE,QUART,AQUA.......      6.50
FRUIT JAR,MC KEE,S,& CO.,ON BASE,QUART,CLEAR...............     15.00
FRUIT JAR,MC KEE,S,& CO.,ON SIDE,QUART,CLEAR...............     24.50
FRUIT JAR,METRO EASI-PAK MASON,PINT,CLEAR..................      1.25
FRUIT JAR,MICHIGAN MASON,QUART............................     18.00
FRUIT JAR,MICHIGAN MASON,QUART,AQUA.......................     12.25
FRUIT JAR,MICHIGAN MASON,WHITTLED,PINT,AQUA................     15.00
```

```
FRUIT JAR,MID WEST CANADIAN MADE,PINT,CLEAR..................    2.25
FRUIT JAR,MID WEST CANADIAN MADE,QUART,CLEAR................    2.25
FRUIT JAR,MID WEST CANADIAN MADE,1/2 GAL.,CLEAR............    2.25
FRUIT JAR,MID WEST,QUART,CLEAR.............................    7.00
FRUIT JAR,MIDDLEBY,JOS.,JR.,INC.,QUART,CLEAR...............   10.00
FRUIT JAR,MIDGET MASON,AMBER...................... 20.00 TO   30.25
FRUIT JAR,MIDGET MASON,CROWN EMBLEM,CLEAR..................   18.25
FRUIT JAR,MIDGET MASON,CROWN IMPERIAL PINT,CROWN EMBLEM,AQUA  12.25
FRUIT JAR,MIDGET MASON,CROWN IMPERIAL PINT,CROWN EMBLEM,
  CLEAR...................................................   12.25
FRUIT JAR,MIDGET MASON,E G COL,THE,IMPERIAL,AQUA...........   19.25
FRUIT JAR,MIDGET MASON,GEM,BACK,HGW MONO,AQUA..............   16.25
FRUIT JAR,MIDGET MASON,GEM,BELOW HF JC CROSS,AQUA..........   16.25
FRUIT JAR,MIDGET MASON,GEM,THE,CFJ CO. MONO,AQUA..........   17.25
FRUIT JAR,MIDGET MASON,IMPERIAL,THE,MONO,AQUA.............   18.25
FRUIT JAR,MIDGET MASON,MASON'S IMPROVED,CFJ MONO,AQUA.......   10.25
FRUIT JAR,MIDGET MASON,MASON'S IMPROVED,CFJ MONO,CLEAR......   10.25
FRUIT JAR,MIDGET MASON,MASON'S PAT.NOV.30,1858,CFJ MONO,AQUA   8.25
FRUIT JAR,MIDGET MASON,MASON'S PAT.NOV.30,1858,CFJ MONO,
  CLEAR...................................................    9.25
FRUIT JAR,MIDGET MASON,MASON'S PAT.NOV.30,1858,CFJ MONO,
  CLYDE...................................................   14.25
FRUIT JAR,MIDGET MASON,MASON'S PAT.NOV.30,1858,CROSS MONO,
  AQUA....................................................   10.25
FRUIT JAR,MIDGET MASON,MASON'S PAT.NOV.30,1858,E&S CO.,AQUA.   11.25
FRUIT JAR,MIDGET MASON,MASON'S PAT.NOV.30,1858,FLOWER,AQUA..   14.25
FRUIT JAR,MIDGET MASON,MASON'S PAT.NOV.30,1858,KEYSTONE,AQUA   9.25
FRUIT JAR,MIDGET MASON,MASON'S PAT.NOV.30,1858,NCL MONO,AQUA  12.25
FRUIT JAR,MIDGET MASON,MASON'S PAT.NOV.30,1858,NOV.26-67,
  AQUA....................................................   11.25
FRUIT JAR,MIDGET MASON,MASON'S PAT.NOV.30,1858,OI CO.,AQUA..   12.25
FRUIT JAR,MIDGET MASON,MASON'S PAT.NOV.30,1858,SNOWFLAKE,
  AQUA....................................................   14.25
FRUIT JAR,MIDGET MASON,MASON'S PAT.NOV.30,1858,WCD ON BASE,
  AQUA....................................................   10.25
FRUIT JAR,MIDGET MASON,MASON'S PATENT NOV.30,1858,AQUA......   10.25
FRUIT JAR,MIDGET MASON,MASON'S TRADE MARK IMPROVED,CFJ,AQUA.   12.25
FRUIT JAR,MIDGET MASON,MASON'S TRADE MARK IMPROVED,CFJ,CLEAR  12.25
FRUIT JAR,MIDGET MASON,MASON'S 1 PAT.NOV.30,1858,AQUA.......   12.25
FRUIT JAR,MIDGET MASON,1858,WHITTLE......................    8.00
FRUIT JAR,MILLVILLE ATMOSPHERIC,QUART.............. 14.00 TO   16.00
FRUIT JAR,MILLVILLE ATMOSPHERIC,QUART,AQUA.................   14.00
FRUIT JAR,MILLVILLE ATMOSPHERIC,TWO QUART.................   10.00
FRUIT JAR,MILLVILLE ATMOSPHERIC,WHITALL'S,QUART,AQUA........   22.25
FRUIT JAR,MILLVILLE ATMOSPHERIC,WHITALL'S,QUART,COBALT BLUE.  100.50
FRUIT JAR,MILLVILLE ATMOSPHERIC,WHITALL'S,1/2 GAL.,AQUA.....   22.25
FRUIT JAR,MILLVILLE ATMOSPHERIC,WHITALL'S,1/2 GAL.,COBALT
  BLUE...................................................  100.50
FRUIT JAR,MILLVILLE ATMOSPHERIC,WHITALL'S PATENT,JUNE 18,
  1861...................................................   27.50
FRUIT JAR,MILLVILLE IMPROVED,QUART,AQUA...................   22.50
FRUIT JAR,MILLVILLE IMPROVED,1/2 PINT,AQUA................   29.50
FRUIT JAR,MILLVILLE,QUART.................................   14.50
FRUIT JAR,MILLVILLE,WHITTLED,2 QUART......................   15.50
FRUIT JAR,MISSION MASON,PINT.............................    4.00
FRUIT JAR,MISSION MASON,QUART............................    4.00
FRUIT JAR,MISSION TRADE MARK MASON,CALIF.,BELL MONO,PINT,
  AQUA....................................................    6.20
FRUIT JAR,MISSION TRADE MARK MASON,CALIF.,BELL MONO,PINT,
  CLEAR...................................................    3.75
FRUIT JAR,MISSION TRADE MARK MASON,CALIF.,BELL MONO,QUART,
  AQUA....................................................    6.20
FRUIT JAR,MISSION TRADE MARK MASON,CALIF.,BELL MONO,QUART,
  CLEAR...................................................    3.75
FRUIT JAR,MISSION TRADE MARK MASON,CALIF.,BELL MONO,1/2 PINT   9.50
```

```
FRUIT JAR,MODEL MASON,QUART,AQUA...........................     10.25
FRUIT JAR,MODEL MASON,QUART,CLEAR..........................      8.50
FRUIT JAR,MOORE BROS.,QUART,AQUA...........................     25.50
FRUIT JAR,MOORE'S PATENT DEC.3,1861,QUART,AQUA..............     38.00
FRUIT JAR,MORSES CHICAGO...................................     10.00
FRUIT JAR,MOTHER'S JAR,QUART...............................     35.00
FRUIT JAR,MOTHER'S JAR,QUART,AQUA..........................     25.50
FRUIT JAR,MOTHER'S,R.E.TONGUE & BROS.,ZINC LID,PINT.........    35.00
FRUIT JAR,MOUNTAIN MASON,CLEAR.............................     20.00
FRUIT JAR,MOUNTAIN MASON,QUART,AMBER.......................     20.25
FRUIT JAR,MOUNTAIN MASON,QUART,CLEAR.......................     10.50
FRUIT JAR,MYERS TEST JAR,1/2 GAL.,AQUA.....................     40.25
FRUIT JAR,N,IN STAR/CIRCLE ON BASE,QUART,AQUA..............     14.50
FRUIT JAR,NABOB,QUART,CLEAR................................      2.75
FRUIT JAR,NATIONAL PAT.1876,EMBOSSED,QUART,AQUA............     20.00
FRUIT JAR,NATIONAL PRESERVE CAN,IN SHIELD,QUART,AQUA.......     39.75
FRUIT JAR,NATIONAL SUPER MASON,QUART,CLEAR.................     16.75
FRUIT JAR,NATIONAL SUPER MASON,1/2 GAL.....................      5.00
FRUIT JAR,NATIONAL,QUART,AQUA..............................     29.75
FRUIT JAR,NE PLUS ULTRA AIR TIGHT FRUIT JAR,QUART,AQUA......    39.75
FRUIT JAR,NEW YORK,QUART,CLEAR.............................     10.75
FRUIT JAR,NEWMARK SPECIAL SETRA MASON,QUART,AQUA...........      7.75
FRUIT JAR,NIFTY,THE,PAT.APPLIED FOR,QUART,CLEAR............     11.75
FRUIT JAR,NONPARFIL PAT'D JULY 17,1866,QUART,AQUA..........     39.75
FRUIT JAR,NORGE,PINT,AQUA..................................      5.75
FRUIT JAR,NW ELECTROGLAS WIDE MOUTH MASON,PINT,CLEAR.......      2.75
FRUIT JAR,NW ELECTROGLAS WIDE MOUTH MASON,QUART,CLEAR......      2.75
FRUIT JAR,OC,MONO,QUART,AQUA...............................      8.75
FRUIT JAR,OC,1 1/2 PINT....................................     15.00
FRUIT JAR,OG MONO,QUART,CLEAR-.............................      9.75
FRUIT JAR,OHIO QUALITY MASON EMBOSSED,CLEAR................      8.00
FRUIT JAR,OHIO QUALITY MASON,QUART,CLEAR...................      9.75
FRUIT JAR,OHIO QUALITY MASON,1/2 GAL.,CLEAR................      9.75
FRUIT JAR,OLD JUDGE COFFEE,QUART,CLEAR.....................      3.75
FRUIT JAR,OPLER BROS......................................     10.00
FRUIT JAR,OPLER BROTHERS INC.,IMPROVED,IN EMBLEM,QUART,CLEAR     7.75
FRUIT JAR,OPLER,QUART.....................................      6.50
FRUIT JAR,OSOTITE,IN DIAMOND,QUART,CLEAR...................      5.75
FRUIT JAR,OSOTITE,IN DIAMOND,1/2 GAL.,CLEAR................      5.75
FRUIT JAR,OVG CO.JAR 1881,QUART,AQUA.......................     29.75
FRUIT JAR,OWL,QUART,MILK GLASS.............................     40.50
FRUIT JAR,OWL,1/2 GAL.,MILK GLASS..........................     40.50
FRUIT JAR,OZOMULSION,AMBER.................................      6.00
FRUIT JAR,PACIFIC GLASS WORKS S F,QUART,AQUA...............     35.00
FRUIT JAR,PACIFIC MASON,QUART,CLEAR........................      5.50
FRUIT JAR,PACIFIC SAN FRANCISCO GLASS WORKS,VICTORY PAT'D,
  QUART....................................................     37.50
FRUIT JAR,PANSY,THE,QUART,AQUA.............................     50.50
FRUIT JAR,PARAGON,NEW,QUART,GREEN..........................     38.50
FRUIT JAR,PEARL,THE,QUART,AQUA.............................     25.50
FRUIT JAR,PEERLESS,QUART,AMBER.............................     55.50
FRUIT JAR,PEERLESS,QUART,AQUA..............................      4.50
FRUIT JAR,PENN,THE,QUART,AQUA..............................     30.50
FRUIT JAR,PEORIA POTTERY,ON BASE...........................     10.25
FRUIT JAR,PEORIA,12 SIDED,WAX SEALER,POTTERY,BROWN,1/2 GAL..     8.00
FRUIT JAR,PERFECT SEAL,THE WIDE MOUTH ADJUSTABLE,CANADA,PINT     2.75
FRUIT JAR,PERFECT SEAL,THE WIDE MOUTH ADJUSTABLE,CANADA,
  QUART....................................................      2.75
FRUIT JAR,PERFECT SEAL,THE WIDE MOUTH ADJUSTABLE,PINT,CLEAR.     1.75
FRUIT JAR,PERFECT SEAL,THE WIDE MOUTH ADJUSTABLE,QUART,CLEAR     1.75
FRUIT JAR,PERFECT SEAL,THE WIDE MOUTH ADJUSTABLE,1/2 GAL.,
  CLEAR....................................................      1.75
FRUIT JAR,PERFECTION,AMBER.................................     25.00
FRUIT JAR,PERFECTION,QUART,CLEAR...........................     25.25
FRUIT JAR,PET,PINT,AQUA....................................     27.50
```

```
FRUIT JAR,PET,QUART,AQUA.....................................  27.50
FRUIT JAR,PETTIT,H.W.,WESTVILLE,N.J.,ON BASE,QUART,AQUA.....   7.75
FRUIT JAR,PETTIT,PINT........................................   4.50
FRUIT JAR,PETTIT,QUART,AQUA..................................   5.00
FRUIT JAR,PETTIT,WESTVILLE,N.J..............................   9.00
FRUIT JAR,PETTIT,WESTVILLE,N.J.,QUART,AQUA..................   9.00
FRUIT JAR,PINE DELUXE JAR,1/2 GAL...........................   3.75
FRUIT JAR,PINE DELUXE,PINT,CLEAR............................   3.75
FRUIT JAR,PINE DELUXE,QUART.................................   4.25
FRUIT JAR,PINE DELUXE,QUART,CLEAR...........................   3.75
FRUIT JAR,PINE P MASON,P IN BOX,PINT........................   3.75
FRUIT JAR,PINE P MASON,P IN BOX,QUART.......................   3.75
FRUIT JAR,PINE,QUART,CLEAR..................................  11.75
FRUIT JAR,PINT P MASON,P IN BOX,1/2 GAL.....................   3.75
FRUIT JAR,POMONA PATENTED MAR.10,1868,QUART,AQUA............  45.25
FRUIT JAR,PORT,ON BASE,PAT.NOV.30,1858,QUART,AQUA...........   8.50
FRUIT JAR,PORT,ON BASE,WAX SEALER,QUART,AQUA................  12.50
FRUIT JAR,POTTER & BODINE PHIL.,QUART,AQUA..................  45.50
FRUIT JAR,PREMIUM...........................................  10.00
FRUIT JAR,PREMIUM COFFEYVILLE,LAS.,QUART,CLEAR..............  11.50
FRUIT JAR,PREMIUM COFFEYVILLE,QUART.........................  22.00
FRUIT JAR,PREMIUM IMPROVED,QUART,CLEAR......................  11.50
FRUIT JAR,PRESTO GLASS TOP,MFG ILL.GLASS CO.,PINT,CLEAR.....   1.50
FRUIT JAR,PRESTO GLASS TOP,MFG ILL.GLASS CO.,QUART,CLEAR....   1.50
FRUIT JAR,PRESTO GLASS TOP,MFG ILL.GLASS CO.,1/2 GAL.,CLEAR.   1.50
FRUIT JAR,PRESTO SUPREME MASON DURAGLAS,PINT,CLEAR..........   1.50
FRUIT JAR,PRESTO SUPREME MASON DURAGLAS,QUART,CLEAR.........   1.50
FRUIT JAR,PRESTO SUPREME MASON DURAGLAS,1/2 GAL.,CLEAR......   1.50
FRUIT JAR,PRESTO SUPREME MASON,PINT,CLEAR...........  1.50 TO   4.00
FRUIT JAR,PRESTO SUPREME MASON,QUART,CLEAR..........  1.50 TO   4.00
FRUIT JAR,PRESTO SUPREME MASON,1/2 GAL.,CLEAR.......  1.50 TO   4.00
FRUIT JAR,PRESTO WIDE MOUTH GLASS TOP,PINT,CLEAR............   1.50
FRUIT JAR,PRESTO WIDE MOUTH GLASS TOP,QUART,CLEAR...........   1.50
FRUIT JAR,PRESTO WIDE MOUTH GLASS TOP,1/2 GAL.,CLEAR........   1.50
FRUIT JAR,PRESTO,PINT,CLEAR.................................   1.50
FRUIT JAR,PRESTO,QUART,CLEAR................................   1.50
FRUIT JAR,PRESTO,1/2 GAL.,CLEAR.............................   1.50
FRUIT JAR,PRINCESS,IN SHIELD,PINT,CLEAR.....................  10.50
FRUIT JAR,PRINCESS,IN SHIELD,QUART,CLEAR....................  10.50
FRUIT JAR,PROTECTOR,EMBOSSED VERTICALLY,QUART,AQUA..........  25.50
FRUIT JAR,PROTECTOR,PINT,AQUA...............................  20.50
FRUIT JAR,PROTECTOR,QUART,AQUA..............................  20.50
FRUIT JAR,PROTECTOR,6 ARCHED PANELS.........................  25.00
FRUIT JAR,PURITAN,THE,LS CO MONO,PINT,AQUA..................  32.50
FRUIT JAR,PUTNAM GLASS WORKS,ON BASE,QUART,AMBER............  40.50
FRUIT JAR,PUTNAM GLASS WORKS,ON BASE,QUART,AQUA.............  15.50
FRUIT JAR,Q G,MONO,QUART,CLEAR..............................  12.50
FRUIT JAR,QUART,WHITTLED,AMBER..............................  25.00
FRUIT JAR,QUEEN IMPROVED WIDE MOUTH ADJUSTABLE,PINT,CLEAR...   4.50
FRUIT JAR,QUEEN IMPROVED WIDE MOUTH ADJUSTABLE,QUART,CLEAR..   4.50
FRUIT JAR,QUEEN PAT.ON FRONT OF JAR 1858 & 1868............  30.00
FRUIT JAR,QUEEN TIGHT WIDE MOUTH ADJUSTABLE,PINT,CLEAR......   3.50
FRUIT JAR,QUEEN TIGHT WIDE MOUTH ADJUSTABLE,QUART,CLEAR.....   3.50
FRUIT JAR,QUEEN,CLAMP,QUART,CLEAR...........................   3.00
FRUIT JAR,QUEEN,PINT................................  1.00 TO   2.50
FRUIT JAR,QUEEN,QUART...............................  2.50 TO   5.00
FRUIT JAR,QUEEN,REVERSE CFJ CO.,QUART,AQUA..................  16.00
FRUIT JAR,QUEEN,SIDE CLAMP,1/2 PINT.........................   7.00
FRUIT JAR,QUEEN,THE QUART,AQUA.....................  13.00 TO  16.50
FRUIT JAR,QUEEN,THE,MONO ON BACK,MIDGET,AQUA................  13.50
FRUIT JAR,QUEEN,THE,MONO ON BACK,QUART,AQUA.................  12.50
FRUIT JAR,QUEEN,THE,PINT,AQUA...............................  16.50
FRUIT JAR,QUEEN,THE,WITH PATENT DATES,QUART,AQUA............  20.50
FRUIT JAR,QUEEN,WREATH OF DATES,CLEAR LID,QUART,AQUA........  12.00
FRUIT JAR,QUEEN,2-1/2 GAL.IRON PONTIL,WHITTLED,AQUA........ 150.00
```

```
FRUIT JAR,QUICK SEAL,IN CIRCLE,PINT,AQUA.....................        2.50
FRUIT JAR,QUICK SEAL,IN CIRCLE,QUART,AQUA....................        2.50
FRUIT JAR,QUICK SEAL,PAT'D JULY 14,1908,IN CIRCLE,PINT,AQUA.         3.50
FRUIT JAR,QUICK SEAL,PAT'D JULY 14,1908,IN CIRCLE,QUART,AQUA         3.50
FRUIT JAR,QUICK SEAL,PINT,AQUA..............................        3.50
FRUIT JAR,QUICK SEAL,PINT,CLEAR.............................        2.50
FRUIT JAR,QUICK SEAL,QUART..................................        2.50
FRUIT JAR,QUICK SEAL,1908,CLEAR.............................        2.00
FRUIT JAR,RAMSEY JAR,QUART,AQUA.............................       55.50
FRUIT JAR,RATH,THE,PACKING CO.,IOWA,QUART,CLEAR.............        4.50
FRUIT JAR,RATH'S BLACKHAWK FOODS,QUART,CLEAR................        2.50
FRUIT JAR,RAU,GROOVE RING,QUART.............................       25.00
FRUIT JAR,RAU'S IMPROVED,PAT.APPL.FOR,GROOVE RING,PINT,CLEAR       35.50
FRUIT JAR,RAU'S IMPROVED,PAT.APPL.FOR,GROOVE RING,QUART,
   CLEAR...................................................       25.50
FRUIT JAR,RAVENNA GLASSWORKS OHIO,QUART,AQUA................       65.50
FRUIT JAR,RED KEY MASON,EMBLEM,PINT,AQUA....................       11.50
FRUIT JAR,RED KEY MASON,PAT.NOV.30,1858,QUART,AQUA..........       10.50
FRUIT JAR,RED KEY MASON,PAT.NOV.30,1858,QUART,GREEN.........       16.50
FRUIT JAR,RED KEY MASON,PAT.NOV.30,1858,1/2 GAL.,AQUA.......       13.50
FRUIT JAR,RED KEY MASON,PAT.NOV.30,1858,1/2 GAL.,GREEN......       16.50
FRUIT JAR,RED KEY,QUART,CLEAR...............................        8.00
FRUIT JAR,REEDS PATTIES,3 QUART,MARKED EUGENE O.REED CO.....       25.00
FRUIT JAR,REID MURDOCK & CO.,QUART,CLEAR....................        9.50
FRUIT JAR,RELIABLE HOME CANNING MASON,QUART,CLEAR...........        1.50
FRUIT JAR,RELIANCE BRAND WIDE MOUTH MASON,PINT,CLEAR........        1.50
FRUIT JAR,RELIANCE BRAND WIDE MOUTH MASON,QUART,CLEAR.......        1.50
FRUIT JAR,RELIANCE BRAND WIDE MOUTH MASON,1/2 GAL.,CLEAR....        1.50
FRUIT JAR,RESERVOIR,THE,QUART,AQUA..........................       30.50
FRUIT JAR,RETENTIVE,VERTICALLY EMBOSSED,QUART,AQUA..........       25.50
FRUIT JAR,RICE & BURNETT,QUART,AQUA.........................       30.50
FRUIT JAR,RIESSNER & CO.,ON BASE,QUART,AQUA.................       12.50
FRUIT JAR,ROCHESTER,THE,QUART,CLEAR.........................       30.50
FRUIT JAR,ROOT MASON,AQUA,QUART.............................        3.00
FRUIT JAR,ROOT MASON,PINT...................................        5.00
FRUIT JAR,ROOT MASON,PINT,AMBER.............................       35.50
FRUIT JAR,ROOT MASON,PINT,AQUA..............................        4.50
FRUIT JAR,ROOT MASON,QUART..................................        2.00
FRUIT JAR,ROOT MASON,QUART,AMBER............................       35.50
FRUIT JAR,ROOT MASON,QUART,AQUA.............................        4.50
FRUIT JAR,ROOT MASON,1/2 GAL..................... 2.00 TO           5.00
FRUIT JAR,ROOT SWAYZEES.....................................        1.50
FRUIT JAR,ROSE,THE,QUART,CLEAR..............................       15.50
FRUIT JAR,ROYAL OF 1876,LEAF BERRY INSERT...................       55.00
FRUIT JAR,ROYAL OF 1876,MASONS CFJ,QUART....................       50.00
FRUIT JAR,ROYAL OF 1876,QUART,AQUA..........................       30.50
FRUIT JAR,ROYAL TRADE MARK FULL MEASURE REG.QUART,PINT,AMBER       35.50
FRUIT JAR,ROYAL TRADE MARK FULL MEASURE REG.QUART,PINT,CLEAR        4.50
FRUIT JAR,ROYAL TRADE MARK FULL MEASURE REG.QUART,PINT,AQUA.        7.50
FRUIT JAR,ROYAL TRADE MARK FULL MEASURE REG.QUART,QUART,
   AMBER...................................................       35.50
FRUIT JAR,ROYAL TRADE MARK FULL MEASURE REG.QUART,QUART,AQUA        7.50
FRUIT JAR,ROYAL TRADE MARK FULL MEASURE REG.QUART,QUART,
   CLEAR...................................................        4.50
FRUIT JAR,ROYAL TRADE MARK FULL MEASURE REG.QUART,1/2 GAL.,
   AMBER...................................................       35.50
FRUIT JAR,ROYAL TRADE MARK FULL MEASURE REG.QUART,1/2 GAL.,
   AQUA....................................................        7.50
FRUIT JAR,ROYAL TRADE MARK FULL MEASURE REG.QUART,1/2 GAL.,
   CLEAR...................................................        4.50
FRUIT JAR,ROYAL,PINT,AMBER..................................       35.50
FRUIT JAR,ROYAL,PINT,AQUA...................................        6.50
FRUIT JAR,ROYAL,PINT,CLEAR........................... 1.50 TO       4.50
FRUIT JAR,ROYAL,PINT,COBALT BLUE............................       75.50
FRUIT JAR,ROYAL,QUART,AMBER.................................       35.50
```

```
FRUIT JAR,ROYAL,QUART,AQUA......................... 6.50 TO    7.00
FRUIT JAR,ROYAL,QUART,CLEAR................................    4.50
FRUIT JAR,ROYAL,QUART,COBALT BLUE..........................   75.50
FRUIT JAR,ROYAL,1/2 GAL.,AMBER.............................   35.50
FRUIT JAR,ROYAL,1/2 GAL.,AQUA..............................    6.50
FRUIT JAR,ROYAL,1/2 GAL.,CLEAR.............................    4.50
FRUIT JAR,ROYAL,1/2 GAL.,COBALT BLUE.......................   75.50
FRUIT JAR,S G CO.,MONO,QUART,AQUA..........................   12.50
FRUIT JAR,S G CO.,MONO,QUART,GREEN.........................   12.50
FRUIT JAR,S.B.& G.CO.,APPLIED LIP,AQUA.....................    7.00
FRUIT JAR,SAFE GLASS CO.,1893-1903.........................   40.00
FRUIT JAR,SAFE SEAL,IN CIRCLE,PINT,AQUA....................    4.50
FRUIT JAR,SAFE SEAL,IN CIRCLE,PINT,CLEAR...................    4.50
FRUIT JAR,SAFE SEAL,IN CIRCLE,QUART,AQUA...................    4.50
FRUIT JAR,SAFE SEAL,IN CIRCLE,QUART,CLEAR..................    4.50
FRUIT JAR,SAFETY SEAL MADE IN CANADA,PINT,CLEAR............    2.50
FRUIT JAR,SAFETY SEAL MADE IN CANADA,QUART,CLEAR...........    2.50
FRUIT JAR,SAFETY VALVE COMPLETE,QUART......................    4.00
FRUIT JAR,SAFETY VALVE COMPLETE,1/2 PINT...................   11.00
FRUIT JAR,SAFETY VALVE KEYSTONE,2 QUART,BLUE GREEN.........   35.00
FRUIT JAR,SAFETY VALVE PAT'D MAY 21,1895,EMBLEM BASE,QUART,
   CLEAR...................................................   10.50
FRUIT JAR,SAFETY VALVE PAT'D MAY 21,1895,EMBLEM,1/2 GAL.,
   AQUA....................................................   18.50
FRUIT JAR,SAFETY VALVE PAT'D MAY 21,1895,EMBLEM,1/2 GAL.,
   CLEAR...................................................   15.50
FRUIT JAR,SAFETY VALVE,PINT................................    5.00
FRUIT JAR,SAFETY VALVE,1895................................    9.00
FRUIT JAR,SAFETY WIDE MOUTH MASON,N.J.,1/2 GAL.,AQUA.......   10.50
FRUIT JAR,SAFETY WIDE MOUTH MASON,QUART,AQUA....... 10.50 TO   12.50
FRUIT JAR,SAFETY WIDE MOUTH MASON,QUART,CLEAR..............   12.50
FRUIT JAR,SAFETY,GAL.,AMBER................................   35.50
FRUIT JAR,SAFETY,PINT,AMBER................................   40.50
FRUIT JAR,SAFETY,PINT,CLEAR................................   35.50
FRUIT JAR,SAFETY,QUART,AMBER...............................   45.50
FRUIT JAR,SAFETY,QUART,CLEAR...............................   35.50
FRUIT JAR,SAFETY,1/2 GAL.,AMBER............................   48.50
FRUIT JAR,SAFETY,1/2 GAL.,CLEAR............................   35.50
FRUIT JAR,SALEM,THE,JAR,QUART,AQUA.........................   30.80
FRUIT JAR,SALZMAN,AMBER,1/3 GAL............................    6.00
FRUIT JAR,SALZMAN,EIGHT-SIDED,AMBER,QUART..................    8.00
FRUIT JAR,SAMCO GENUINE MASON,CIRCLE,QUART,CLEAR...........    1.50
FRUIT JAR,SAMCO GENUINE MASON,CIRCLE,1/2 GAL.,CLEAR........    1.50
FRUIT JAR,SAMCO GENUINE MASON,PINT,CLEAR........... 1.50 TO    3.50
FRUIT JAR,SAMCO SUPER MASON,PINT,CLEAR.....................    1.50
FRUIT JAR,SAMCO SUPER MASON,QUART,CLEAR....................    1.50
FRUIT JAR,SAMCO SUPER MASON,1/2 GAL.,CLEAR.................    1.50
FRUIT JAR,SAMUELS,A.R.,QUART,AQUA..........................   45.50
FRUIT JAR,SAN FRANCISCO GLASS WORKS,QUART,AQUA.............   45.50
FRUIT JAR,SANFORD MFG CO.,PAT.JULY 10,1900,QUART,CLEAR.....   11.50
FRUIT JAR,SANFORD,HA EMBLEM,QUART,CLEAR....................   12.50
FRUIT JAR,SANIJAR,PINT.....................................    1.50
FRUIT JAR,SANIJAR,QUART....................................    1.50
FRUIT JAR,SANIJAR,1/2 GAL..................................    1.50
FRUIT JAR,SANITARY FREEZER,THE,QUART,CLEAR.................    6.50
FRUIT JAR,SANITARY,QUART,AQUA..............................    9.50
FRUIT JAR,SCHAFFER,THE,N.Y.,MONO ON BACK,QUART,AQUA........   38.50
FRUIT JAR,SCHRAM AUTOMATIC SEALER B TRADE MARK REGISTERED,
   PINT....................................................    3.50
FRUIT JAR,SCHRAM AUTOMATIC SEALER B,PINT,CLEAR.............    6.50
FRUIT JAR,SCHRAM AUTOMATIC SEALER B,QUART,CLEAR............    6.50
FRUIT JAR,SCHRAM AUTOMATIC SEALER B,1/2 GAL.,CLEAR.........    6.50
FRUIT JAR,SCHRAM AUTOMATIC SEALER,PINT,CLEAR...............    7.50
FRUIT JAR,SCHRAM AUTOMATIC SEALER,QUART,CLEAR..............    7.50
FRUIT JAR,SCHRAM AUTOMATIC SEALER,1/2 GAL.,CLEAR...........    7.50
```

```
FRUIT JAR,SCHRAM FRUIT JAR,1/2 GAL............................    10.00
FRUIT JAR,SCHRAM,RIBBON UNDER SCHRAM,QUART,CLEAR.............     6.50
FRUIT JAR,SCHRAM,1/2 GAL.,AMETHYST...........................     4.50
FRUIT JAR,SCRANTON,THE,QUART,AQUA............................    40.00
FRUIT JAR,SEALFAST GOLDEN,EMBOSSED P.A.NIELSEN & SON.........    35.00
FRUIT JAR,SEALFAST SOLD BY BOLSTER & BARNES,QUART,CLEAR.....     15.50
FRUIT JAR,SEALFAST SOLD BY C B HOBBS,QUART,CLEAR.............    15.50
FRUIT JAR,SEALFAST SOLD BY L BORDEN & CO.,QUART,CLEAR.......     15.50
FRUIT JAR,SEALFAST SOLD BY MONARCH,QUART,CLEAR..............     15.50
FRUIT JAR,SEALFAST SOLD BY O P JOHNSON,QUART,CLEAR..........     15.50
FRUIT JAR,SEALFAST SOLD BY P A NIELSEN & SON,QUART,CLEAR....     15.50
FRUIT JAR,SEALFAST SOLD BY RULM HARDWARE,QUART,CLEAR........     15.50
FRUIT JAR,SEALFAST,FOSTER ON BASE,PINT,AMETHYST.............      4.00
FRUIT JAR,SEALFAST,FOSTER,PINT,CLEAR........................      3.50
FRUIT JAR,SEALFAST,FOSTER,QUART,CLEAR.......................      3.50
FRUIT JAR,SEALFAST,FOSTER,1/2 GAL.,CLEAR....................      3.50
FRUIT JAR,SEALFAST,PINT,CLEAR...............................      3.50
FRUIT JAR,SEALFAST,QUART,CLEAR..............................      3.50
FRUIT JAR,SEALFAST,1/2 GAL.,CLEAR...........................      3.50
FRUIT JAR,SEALTITE WIDE MOUTH MASON,PINT,AQUA...............      3.50
FRUIT JAR,SEALTITE WIDE MOUTH MASON,QUART,AQUA..............      3.50
FRUIT JAR,SEALTITE,QUART,CLEAR..............................      6.50
FRUIT JAR,SEASONS MASON,QUART...............................      3.50
FRUIT JAR,SECURITY SEAL,CLEAR,QUART.........................      6.50
FRUIT JAR,SECURITY SEAL,QUART,PURPLE........................      5.00
FRUIT JAR,SECURITY SEAL,TRIANGLE/FG CO.MONO,PINT,CLEAR......      3.50
FRUIT JAR,SECURITY SEAL,TRIANGLE,FG CO.MONO,QUART,CLEAR.....      3.50
FRUIT JAR,SECURITY,QUART,CLEAR..............................      8.50
FRUIT JAR,SELCO SURETY SEAL,PAT'D JULY 14,1908,PINT,AQUA....      6.25
FRUIT JAR,SELCO SURETY SEAL,PAT'D JULY 14,1908,QUART,AQUA...      6.25
FRUIT JAR,SELCO SURETY SEAL,PATENT JULY 14,1904,WIRE BALE...      5.50
FRUIT JAR,SELCO SURETY SEAL,PINT,AQUA.......................      4.25
FRUIT JAR,SELCO SURETY SEAL,QUART,AQUA......................      4.25
FRUIT JAR,SELCO SURETY SEAL,1/2 GAL.,1908,BLUE.............       7.50
FRUIT JAR,SELCO SURETY SEAL,1908,1/2 GAL.,BLUE.............       7.50
FRUIT JAR,SELLER,M.& CO.,PORTLAND,O.,QUART,AQUA.............     40.25
FRUIT JAR,SIERRA MASON,MADE IN CALIF.,PINT,CLEAR............      7.25
FRUIT JAR,SIERRA MASON,MADE IN CALIF.,QUART,CLEAR...........      7.25
FRUIT JAR,SILICON GLASS CO.,PITTS.,PINT,AQUA........ 8.00 TO    14.25
FRUIT JAR,SILICON GLASS CO.,PITTS.,QUART,AQUA....... 10.25 TO   14.25
FRUIT JAR,SILICON PITTS PA.,PINT............................      8.00
FRUIT JAR,SIMPLEX MASON,QUART,CLEAR.........................     18.25
FRUIT JAR,SIMPLEX,IN DIAMOND,PINT,CLEAR.....................      7.25
FRUIT JAR,SIMPLEX,IN DIAMOND,QUART,CLEAR....................      7.25
FRUIT JAR,SIMPLEX,PURPLE....................................      8.00
FRUIT JAR,SIMPLEX,1/2 PINT..................................      9.00
FRUIT JAR,SINCLAIR,T.M.,& CO.,PORK PACKERS,QUART,CLEAR......      6.25
FRUIT JAR,SMALLEY FULL MEASURE PINT,AGS MONO,PINT,AMBER.....     25.25
FRUIT JAR,SMALLEY FULL MEASURE PINT,AGS MONO,PINT,AQUA......      8.25
FRUIT JAR,SMALLEY FULL MEASURE PINT,AGS MONO,PINT,CLEAR.....      6.25
FRUIT JAR,SMALLEY FULL MEASURE QUART,AGS MONO,QUART,AMBER...     22.50
FRUIT JAR,SMALLEY FULL MEASURE QUART,AGS MONO,QUART,AQUA....      6.25
FRUIT JAR,SMALLEY FULL MEASURE QUART,AGS MONO,QUART,CLEAR...      4.25
FRUIT JAR,SMALLEY FULL MEASURE QUART,PAT.APR.7,1886,AMETHYST      9.00
FRUIT JAR,SMALLEY NU SEAL TRADE MARK,QUART..................      6.00
FRUIT JAR,SMALLEY SALE SEALER,WIDE MOUTH,PINT...............      4.50
FRUIT JAR,SMALLEY SELF SEALER,THE,PINT.............. 5.25 TO     6.00
FRUIT JAR,SMALLEY SELF SEALER,THE,QUART............. 3.00 TO     5.25
FRUIT JAR,SMALLEY,A.G.& CO.,PAT.DATES,BOSTON MASS.,QUART,
   AMBER....................................................     18.25
FRUIT JAR,SMALLEY,THE,JAR,QUART,CLEAR.......................     17.25
FRUIT JAR,SMALLEY,THE,TRADE MARK SELF SEALER,PINT,CLEAR.....      9.25
FRUIT JAR,SMALLEY,THE,TRADE MARK SELF SEALER,QUART,CLEAR....      9.25
FRUIT JAR,SMALLEY,THE,WIDE MOUTH SELF SEALER,PINT,CLEAR.....      5.25
FRUIT JAR,SMALLEY,THE,WIDE MOUTH SELF SEALER,QUART,CLEAR....      5.25
```

```
FRUIT JAR,SMALLEY'S NU-SEAL,TRADE MARK,IN DIAMOND,PINT,CLEAR      4.25
FRUIT JAR,SMALLEY'S NU-SEAL,TRADE MARK,IN DIAMOND,QUART,
  CLEAR...................................................       4.25
FRUIT JAR,SMALLEY'S ROYAL,CROWN EMBLEM,PINT,CLEAR...........      6.25
FRUIT JAR,SMALLEY'S ROYAL,CROWN EMBLEM,QUART,CLEAR.........       6.25
FRUIT JAR,SMALLEY'S ROYAL,CROWN EMBLEM,1/2 GAL.,CLEAR......       9.25
FRUIT JAR,SMITH,J P & SON CO.,QUART,AQUA...................      28.25
FRUIT JAR,SOCIETE,PINT,CLEAR...............................       4.25
FRUIT JAR,SOCIETE,QUART,CLEAR..............................       4.25
FRUIT JAR,SOU G.W.,ON BASE,QUART,AQUA......................      14.25
FRUIT JAR,SOUTHERN DOUBLE SEAL MASON,PINT,CLEAR............       8.25
FRUIT JAR,SOUTHERN DOUBLE SEAL MASON,QUART,CLEAR...........       8.25
FRUIT JAR,SPENCER,QUART,AQUA...............................      35.25
FRUIT JAR,SPENCER'S,C F,IMPROVED,QUART,AQUA................      30.25
FRUIT JAR,SPENCER'S,C G,PATENT,QUART,AQUA..................      28.25
FRUIT JAR,STANDARD FROM FOOTE,BAER & CO.,QUART,AQUA........      12.25
FRUIT JAR,STANDARD MASON,IN RIBBON,PINT,CLEAR..............       4.25
FRUIT JAR,STANDARD MASON,IN RIBBON,QUART,CLEAR.............       4.25
FRUIT JAR,STANDARD,EMBOSSED FRONT & BACK,1/2 GAL...........      12.00
FRUIT JAR,STANDARD,PINT,AQUA...............................       9.25
FRUIT JAR,STANDARD,QUART,AQUA..............................       9.25
FRUIT JAR,STANDARD,W.MC C & CO.,QUART,AQUA.................      11.25
FRUIT JAR,STAR & CRESCENT,STAR/MOON EMBLEM,QUART,AQUA......      35.25
FRUIT JAR,STAR & CRESCENT,STAR/MOON EMBLEM,QUART,CLEAR.....      35.25
FRUIT JAR,STAR EMBLEM,QUART,GREEN..........................      25.25
FRUIT JAR,STAR GLASS CO.,IND.,QUART,AQUA...................      17.25
FRUIT JAR,STAR GLASS CO.,IND.,1/2 GAL.,AQUA................      17.25
FRUIT JAR,STAR,STAR EMBLEM ABOVE WORD,QUART,AQUA...........      18.25
FRUIT JAR,STAR,STAR EMBLEM ABOVE WORD,QUART,CLEAR..........      18.25
FRUIT JAR,STAR,STAR EMBLEM BELOW WORD,QUART,AQUA...........      22.25
FRUIT JAR,STERLING MASON,PINT,CLEAR........................       1.25
FRUIT JAR,STERLING MASON,QUART.............................       1.50
FRUIT JAR,STEVEN'S,TIN TOP,QUART,GREEN.....................      30.25
FRUIT JAR,STONE MASON,UNION STONEWARE CO.,MINN.,PINT,POTTERY      8.25
FRUIT JAR,STONE MASON,UNION STONEWARE CO.,MINN.,QUART,
  POTTERY.................................................        8.25
FRUIT JAR,STONE,A,& CO.,PHILA.,QUART,AQUA..................      45.25
FRUIT JAR,SUEY FUNG YUEN CO.,CALIF.,PINT,CLEAR.............       6.25
FRUIT JAR,SUEY FUNG YUEN CO.,CALIF.,QUART,CLEAR............       6.25
FRUIT JAR,SUN TRADE MARK,EUN EMBLEM,QUART,AQUA.............      30.25
FRUIT JAR,SUN,PINT.........................................      27.00
FRUIT JAR,SUN,QUART........................................      27.00
FRUIT JAR,SUNSHINE JAR,PINT,CLEAR..........................      12.25
FRUIT JAR,SUNSHINE JAR,QUART,CLEAR.........................      12.25
FRUIT JAR,SUPREME MASON,PINT,CLEAR.........................       4.25
FRUIT JAR,SUPREME MASON,QUART,CLEAR........................       4.25
FRUIT JAR,SURE SEAL,BLUISH AQUA,1910.......................      12.50
FRUIT JAR,SURE SEAL,PINT,AQUA..............................       4.25
FRUIT JAR,SURE SEAL,QUART,AQUA.............................       4.25
FRUIT JAR,SURE SEAL,1/2 GAL.,AQUA..........................       4.25
FRUIT JAR,SWAYZEE'S IMPERIAL MASON,QUART,AQUA..............       6.00
FRUIT JAR,SWAYZEE'S IMPROVED MASON,EMBLEM,PINT,AQUA........       6.25
FRUIT JAR,SWAYZEE'S IMPROVED MASON,EMBLEM,QUART,AQUA.......       6.25
FRUIT JAR,SWAYZEE'S IMPROVED MASON,PINT,AQUA...............       4.25
FRUIT JAR,SWAYZEE'S IMPROVED MASON,QUART...................       4.00
FRUIT JAR,SWAYZEE'S IMPROVED MASON,QUART,AQUA..............       3.00
FRUIT JAR,SWAYZEE'S IMPROVED MASON,1/2 GAL.................       2.00
FRUIT JAR,SWAYZEES IMPROVED MASON,QUART....................       2.00
FRUIT JAR,TELEPHONE,GLASS CLOSURE,AQUA,PINT................       4.00
FRUIT JAR,TELEPHONE,PINT,AQUA.................... 4.00 TO         5.00
FRUIT JAR,TELEPHONE,QUART,AQUA.............................       4.00
FRUIT JAR,TELEPHONE,THE,TRADE MARK,REG.,WHITNEY,QUART,AMBER.     35.75
FRUIT JAR,TELEPHONE,THE,TRADE MARK,REG.,WHITNEY,QUART,AQUA..      7.25
FRUIT JAR,TELEPHONE,THE,WIDEMOUTH,TRADE MARK,REG.,QUART,AQUA      5.75
FRUIT JAR,TELEPHONE,THE,WIDEMOUTH,TRADE MARK REG.,1/2 GAL.,
```

```
AQUA.........................................................   8.75
FRUIT JAR,TEXAS MASON,MAP OF TEXAS,PINT,CLEAR...............  10.75
FRUIT JAR,TEXAS MASON,MAP OF TEXAS,QUART,CLEAR.............  10.75
FRUIT JAR,TF,COMBINED ON BASE,QUART,CLEAR..................   3.25
FRUIT JAR,THRIFT BUCK GLASS CO.,PINT,CLEAR.................   7.75
FRUIT JAR,TIGHT SEAL,CIRCLE,PINT,AQUA......................   3.75
FRUIT JAR,TIGHT SEAL,CIRCLE,PINT,CLEAR.....................   2.75
FRUIT JAR,TIGHT SEAL,CIRCLE,QUART,AQUA.....................   3.75
FRUIT JAR,TIGHT SEAL,CIRCLE,QUART,CLEAR....................   2.75
FRUIT JAR,TIGHT SEAL,CIRCLE,1/2 GAL.,AQUA..................   3.75
FRUIT JAR,TIGHT SEAL,CIRCLE,1/2 GAL.,CLEAR.................   2.75
FRUIT JAR,TIGHT SEAL,PAT.JULY 14,1908,CIRCLE,PINT,AQUA.....   4.75
FRUIT JAR,TIGHT SEAL,PAT.JULY 14,1908,CIRCLE,PINT,CLEAR....   3.75
FRUIT JAR,TIGHT SEAL,PAT.JULY 14,1908,CIRCLE,QUART,AQUA....   4.75
FRUIT JAR,TIGHT SEAL,PAT.JULY 14,1908,CIRCLE,QUART,CLEAR...   3.75
FRUIT JAR,TIGHT SEAL,PAT.JULY 14,1908,CIRCLE,1/2 GAL.,AQUA..   4.75
FRUIT JAR,TIGHT SEAL,PAT.JULY 14,1908,1/2 GAL.,CLEAR.......   3.75
FRUIT JAR,TILLYER,QUART,AQUA..................... 40.75 TO  65.00
FRUIT JAR,TRUE FRUIT TRADE MARK,CIRCLE/JHS CO MONO,QUART,
   AQUA......................................................  10.75
FRUIT JAR,TRUES IMPERIAL BRAND,FLAGS & CROWN,PINT,CLEAR.....   8.00
FRUIT JAR,TRUES IMPERIAL BRAND,FLAGS & CROWN,PINT,CLEAR.....  10.75
FRUIT JAR,TRUES IMPERIAL BRAND,FLAGS & CROWN,QUART,CLEAR....  10.75
FRUIT JAR,U G CO.,QUART,AQUA...............................  10.75
FRUIT JAR,UNION FRUIT JAR,A & D.H.CHAMBERS,PITTS.,GREEN,
   GAL.......................................................  16.50
FRUIT JAR,UNION NO.1,QUART,AQUA............................  18.75
FRUIT JAR,UNITED DRUG CO.,BOSTON,MASS.,PINT,CLEAR..........   9.75
FRUIT JAR,UNITED DRUG CO.,BOSTON,QUART,CLEAR........ 5.00 TO   9.75
FRUIT JAR,UNIVERSAL,QUART,AQUA.............................  10.75
FRUIT JAR,UNIVERSAL,1/2 GAL.,AQUA.........................  10.75
FRUIT JAR,VACU-TOP,PINT,CLEAR.............................   4.75
FRUIT JAR,VACU-TOP,QUART,CLEAR............................   4.75
FRUIT JAR,VACUUM JAR,PINT,CLEAR...........................  12.75
FRUIT JAR,VACUUM JAR,QUART,CLEAR..........................  12.75
FRUIT JAR,VACUUM TITE CO.,PINT,CLEAR......................   6.75
FRUIT JAR,VACUUM TITE CO.,QUART,CLEAR.....................   6.75
FRUIT JAR,VACUUM,THE,PAT'D NOV.1,1904,DETROIT,QUART,CLEAR..  14.75
FRUIT JAR,VALVE,THE,PHIL.,QUART,AQUA......................  45.75
FRUIT JAR,VAN VLIET,THE,JAR OF 1881,QUART,AMBER........... 100.75
FRUIT JAR,VAN VLIET,THE,JAR OF 1881,QUART,CLEAR...........  55.75
FRUIT JAR,VAN VLIET,THE,JAR OF 1881,QUART,GREEN...........  70.75
FRUIT JAR,VETERAN,PINT,CLEAR..............................   9.00
FRUIT JAR,VETERAN,QUART...................................  15.00
FRUIT JAR,VETERAN,SOLDIER EMBLEM,QUART,CLEAR..............  12.75
FRUIT JAR,VICTOR,THE,PAT.FEB.20,1900,CIRCLE MONO,QUART,AQUA.  20.75
FRUIT JAR,VICTOR,THE,PAT'D 1899,CIRCLE MONO,QUART,AQUA.....  23.75
FRUIT JAR,VICTORY HOM PAC MASON,PINT,CLEAR................   3.75
FRUIT JAR,VICTORY HOM PAC MASON,QUART,CLEAR...............   3.75
FRUIT JAR,VICTORY I,PAT.FEB.9,1864,REISS'D JUNE 22,1867,AQUA  25.75
FRUIT JAR,VICTORY NO.1 PAT.FEB.9TH,1964,QUART.............  25.00
FRUIT JAR,VICTORY NO.1 PAT.FEB.9TH,1964,2 QUART...........  25.00
FRUIT JAR,VICTORY,IN SHIELD ON LID,QUART..................   5.00
FRUIT JAR,VICTORY,IN SHIELD ON LID,1/2 GAL...............   5.00
FRUIT JAR,VICTORY,ON BASE,PINT,CLEAR......................   5.75
FRUIT JAR,VICTORY,ON BASE,QUART,CLEAR.....................   5.75
FRUIT JAR,VICTORY,PAT.FEB.9,1864,QUART,AQUA...............  25.75
FRUIT JAR,VICTORY,SHIELD BANNER ON BASE,PINT,CLEAR........   9.75
FRUIT JAR,VICTORY,SHIELD/BANNER ON BASE,QUART,CLEAR.......   9.75
FRUIT JAR,VICTORY,1/2 GAL.................................   8.00
FRUIT JAR,VICTORY,1/2 PINT................................  11.00
FRUIT JAR,VICTORY,1 QUART.................................  32.50
FRUIT JAR,W & CO.,ON BASE,QUART,AQUA......................  18.75
FRUIT JAR,W.W.LYMAN,FULL CIRCLE,PATENT DATES..............  12.00
FRUIT JAR,W.W.LYMAN,1/2 GAL...............................  12.00
```

```
FRUIT JAR,WALES,GEO.E.,ON BASE,QUART,CLEAR................    15.75
FRUIT JAR,WALLACEBURG GEM,PINT,CLEAR.......................     6.75
FRUIT JAR,WALLACEBURG GEM,QUART,CLEAR......................     6.75
FRUIT JAR,WAN-ETA COCOA,BOSTON,QUART,AMBER.................     6.75
FRUIT JAR,WAN-ETA COCOA,BOSTON,QUART,AQUA..................     7.75
FRUIT JAR,WAN-ETA COCOA,BOSTON,1/2 PINT,AMBER..............    12.75
FRUIT JAR,WAN-ETA COCOA,BOSTON,1/2 PINT,AQUA...............    12.75
FRUIT JAR,WAN-ETA COCOA,QUART..............................     5.00
FRUIT JAR,WAUWIL,PINT,CLEAR................................     3.75
FRUIT JAR,WAUWIL,QUART,CLEAR...............................     3.75
FRUIT JAR,WAUWIL,1/2 GAL.,CLEAR............................     3.75
FRUIT JAR,WEARS JAR,THE,IN CIRCLE,PINT,CLEAR...............     8.75
FRUIT JAR,WEARS JAR,THE,IN CIRCLE,QUART,CLEAR..............     8.75
FRUIT JAR,WEARS JAR,THE,IN STIPPLED SHIELD,PINT,CLEAR......     8.75
FRUIT JAR,WEARS JAR,THE,IN STIPPLED SHIELD,QUART,CLEAR.....     8.75
FRUIT JAR,WEARS,CROWN/FLAGS,PINT,CLEAR.....................     8.75
FRUIT JAR,WEARS,CROWN/FLAGS,QUART,CLEAR....................     8.75
FRUIT JAR,WECK,IN STRAWBERRY,PINT,CLEAR....................     6.75
FRUIT JAR,WECK,IN STRAWBERRY,QUART,CLEAR...................     6.75
FRUIT JAR,WECK,PINT,CLEAR..................................     7.75
FRUIT JAR,WECK,QUART,CLEAR.................................     7.75
FRUIT JAR,WEIDEMAN BOY BRAND,PINT,CLEAR............. 5.00 TO     6.75
FRUIT JAR,WEIDEMAN BOY BRAND,QUART,CLEAR............ 5.75 TO     6.75
FRUIT JAR,WEIR POTTERY,DATED,AMBER LID,1/2 GAL.............     8.00
FRUIT JAR,WEIR SEAL,QUART,BROWN & WHITE....................     8.75
FRUIT JAR,WEIR SEAL,QUART,WHITE............................     8.75
FRUIT JAR,WEIR,THE PAT'D DATE,PINT,BROWN & WHITE...........     8.75
FRUIT JAR,WEIR,THE,PAT'D DATE,QUART,BROWN & WHITE..........     8.75
FRUIT JAR,WESTERN PRICE,QUART,CLEAR........................    25.75
FRUIT JAR,WHITALL TATUM CO.,PHILA.,PAT.JUNE 11,1895,QUART,
  CLEAR...................................................    40.75
FRUIT JAR,WHITALL'S PATENT JUNE 18,1961,MILLVILLE,QUART,AQUA   22.75
FRUIT JAR,WHITE BEAR,DURAND & KASPER CO.,BEAR EMBLEM,PINT,
  CLEAR...................................................     9.00
FRUIT JAR,WHITE BEAR,DURAND & KASPER CO.,BEAR EMBLEM,QUART,
  CLEAR...................................................     9.00
FRUIT JAR,WHITE CROWN MASON,IN CIRCLE/BOX,PINT,AQUA........     6.00
FRUIT JAR,WHITE CROWN MASON,IN CIRCLE/BOX,QUART,AQUA.......     6.00
FRUIT JAR,WHITE CROWN MASON,IN CIRCLE/BOX,1/2 GAL.,AQUA....     8.50
FRUIT JAR,WHITMORE,QUART...................................   115.00
FRUIT JAR,WHITMORE'S PATENT,QUART,AQUA.....................    45.25
FRUIT JAR,WHITNEY MASON PAT'D 1858,QUART,AMBER.............    24.25
FRUIT JAR,WHITNEY MASON PAT'D 1858,QUART,AQUA..............     4.25
FRUIT JAR,WHITNEY MASON PATENT 1858,PINT,AQUA..............     4.00
FRUIT JAR,WILCOX,BB,PAT.MAR.26,1867,QUART,AQUA.............    30.25
FRUIT JAR,WILLOUGHBY,J.D.,ON LID,QUART,AQUA................    25.25
FRUIT JAR,WINSLOW JAR,QUART,AMBER..........................    50.25
FRUIT JAR,WINSLOW JAR,QUART,AQUA...........................    20.25
FRUIT JAR,WINSLOW JAR,QUART,OLIVE GREEN....................    35.25
FRUIT JAR,WOOD & SELICK,QUART,AQUA.........................    20.25
FRUIT JAR,WOOD & SELICK,1/2 GAL.,AQUA......................    20.25
FRUIT JAR,WOODBURY IMPROVED,MONOGRAM,1/2 GAL...............    24.00
FRUIT JAR,WOODBURY IMPROVED,WGW EMBLEM,TWO QUART...........    28.00
FRUIT JAR,WOODBURY IMPROVED,WGW MONO,PINT,AQUA.............    22.25
FRUIT JAR,WOODBURY IMPROVED,WGW MONO,1/2 GAL.,AQUA.........    22.25
FRUIT JAR,WOODBURY,AQUA,QUART..............................    13.50
FRUIT JAR,WOODBURY,IMPROVED,WGW MONO,QUART,AQUA............    18.25
FRUIT JAR,WOODBURY,PINT,AQUA...............................    25.25
FRUIT JAR,WOODBURY,PLAIN...................................    23.00
FRUIT JAR,WOODBURY,QUART...................................    14.00
FRUIT JAR,WOODBURY,QUART,W.G.MONOGRAM,BLUE.................    22.00
FRUIT JAR,WOODBURY,WGW EMBLEM,PINT,AQUA....................    22.25
FRUIT JAR,WOODBURY,WGW EMBLEM,QUART,AQUA...................    18.25
FRUIT JAR,WOODBURY,WGW EMBLEM,TWO QUART....................    25.00
FRUIT JAR,WOODBURY,WGW EMBLEM,1/2 GAL.,AQUA................    22.25
FRUIT JAR,WOODBURY,WHITTLED,QUART..........................    25.00
```

```
FRUIT JAR,WOODBURY,1/2 GAL.,AQUA..............................    25.25
FRUIT JAR,WORCESTER,QUART,AQUA................................    35.25
FRUIT JAR,WORCESTER,1/2 GAL.,AQUA.............................    35.25
FRUIT JAR,YEOMAN'S FRUIT BOTTLE,QUART,AQUA....................    35.25
G.W.WESTON,SARATOGA,PINT......................................    25.00
GALLE,DECANTER,ENAMELED,SILVER STOPPER,FLORAL & DRAGONFLY,
   CLEAR......................................................   601.00
GALLE,SIGNED,PART OF VINE IS SIGNATURE........................   100.00
GALLIANO,FIGURAL,SOLDIER,1 GAL.,39 IN. HIGH........ 43.00 TO     48.00
GALLIANO,GUARD 10TH...........................................     9.95
GALLIANO,LARGE................................................    10.95
GALLIANO,MAN..................................................     2.90
GALLIANO,SOLDIER.................................... 12.50 TO     15.00
GALLIANO,SOLDIER DUMMY........................................    25.00
GALLIANO,SOLDIER,1 GAL.,DUMMY.................................    43.00
GARGLING OIL,GREEN............................................     7.00
```

        GARNIER BOTTLES WERE FIRST MADE IN 1899 TO HOLD GARNIER
    LIQUEURS. THE FIRM WAS FOUNDED IN 1859 IN FRANCE.
    FIGURALS HAVE BEEN MADE THROUGH THE TWENTIETH CENTURY,
    EXCEPT FOR THE YEARS OF PROHIBITION AND WORLD WAR II.

```
GARNIER,ALADDIN'S LAMP,1963...................................    15.00
GARNIER,APOLLO..................................... 20.00 TO     29.00
GARNIER,AZTEC VASE............................................    13.00
GARNIER,BACCHUS,1967..........................................    15.00
GARNIER,BANDIT,1958...........................................    20.00
GARNIER,BELLOWS.................................... 17.50 TO     18.00
GARNIER,BIRMAN VASE...........................................    13.00
GARNIER,BOUQUET BASKET........................................    13.00
GARNIER,BULLFIGHTER...........................................    25.00
GARNIER,BURMESE CAT................................ 22.00 TO     23.00
GARNIER,CALIFORNIA VALLEY QUAIL..................... 9.50 TO     10.00
GARNIER,CANDLESTICK,1967......................................    20.00
GARNIER,CAR,ALFA ROMEO,1913 MODEL,1970........................     8.00
GARNIER,CAR,ALFA ROMEO,1929 MODEL,1970........................     8.00
GARNIER,CAR,FIAT,1913 MODEL,1970..............................     8.00
GARNIER,CAR,FIAT,1924 MODEL,1970..............................     0.00
GARNIER,CAR,RENAULT,1911 MODEL,1970...........................     8.00
GARNIER,CARAFE,FOUR COMPARTMENTS,1939.........................    25.00
GARNIER,CARDINAL................................... 10.00 TO     14.95
GARNIER,CAT,1939..............................................    35.00
GARNIER,CAT,1962 GRAY & WHITE...................... 22.00 TO     23.00
GARNIER,CAT,1962,BLACK & WHITE..................... 22.00 TO     23.00
GARNIER,CHESS SET,MINIATURES..................................   295.00
GARNIER,CHIMNEY,FIRE PLATE,1956...............................    20.00
GARNIER,CHRISTMAS TREE,1956...................................    15.00
GARNIER,CLOCK,GLASS,1958......................................    15.00
GARNIER,CLOWN,HARLEQUIN,1958..................................    50.00
GARNIER,CLOWN,LARGE...........................................    61.00
GARNIER,CLOWN,1939............................................    61.00
GARNIER,CLOWN'S HEAD,1939.....................................    35.00
GARNIER,DRUNK ON LAMPPOST,1956..................... 19.00 TO     25.00
GARNIER,DUCK WITH BASKET,1956.................................    15.00
GARNIER,DUCK,1939.................................. 15.00 TO     20.00
GARNIER,EIFFEL TOWER..........................................    15.00
GARNIER,ELEPHANT..............................................    37.00
GARNIER,FIGURAL,ROOSTER,MAROON................................    18.00
GARNIER,FISH,TROUT,1967............................ 10.00 TO     20.00
GARNIER,FOO DOG,1965..........................................    15.00
GARNIER,FOUNTAIN,1964.........................................    15.00
GARNIER,GIRAFFE.................................... 15.00 TO     25.00
GARNIER,GOOSE,1955............................................    15.00
GARNIER,GREYHOUND,1939........................................    22.00
GARNIER,GUARD NL,RED..........................................    50.00
GARNIER,HORSE,1958............................................    15.00
```

```
GARNIER,HOUSE,1956.........................................    20.00
GARNIER,INDIAN.............................................    20.00
GARNIER,JOCKEY,1961............................... 17.95 TO    20.00
GARNIER,KENTUCKY GENTLEMAN.................................    15.00
GARNIER,LAIRD HERITAGE VASE................................    15.00
GARNIER,LANCER,SOLDIER,1949................................    20.95
GARNIER,LOCOMOTIVE................................ 8.00 TO     12.75
GARNIER,LOG,1958...........................................    16.00
GARNIER,MAHARAJAH,1958.....................................    20.00
GARNIER,MARQUIS,1939.......................................    38.00
GARNIER,MARQUISE,1939......................................    38.00
GARNIER,MERRY GO ROUND.....................................    20.00
GARNIER,NAPOLEON ON HORSE..................................    22.00
GARNIER,NATIVE GIRL UNDER TREE.............................    19.75
GARNIER,NEW MEXICO ROAD RUNNER.................... 8.00 TO      9.50
GARNIER,OASIS..................................... 17.95 TO    20.00
GARNIER,PAINTING,1961......................................    18.00
GARNIER,PARROT................................... 15.00 TO     20.00
GARNIER,PARTRIDGE................................ 18.00 TO     25.00
GARNIER,PHEASANT...........................................    21.00
GARNIER,PICKETT JUG,1939...................................    17.50
GARNIER,PIGEON,GLASS,1958..................................    15.00
GARNIER,PISTOL,1964........................................    15.00
GARNIER,PONY..................................... 18.00 TO     20.00
GARNIER,POODLE.............................................    15.00
GARNIER,POODLE,BLACK.......................................    20.00
GARNIER,QUAIL.................................... 8.00 TO      15.75
GARNIER,RED GUARD..........................................    50.00
GARNIER,RED ROOSTER,LABELS.................................    30.00
GARNIER,ROCKET,1958........................................    25.00
GARNIER,ROOSTER,BLACK............................ 15.00 TO     20.00
GARNIER,ROOSTER,MAROON.....................................    18.00
GARNIER,ROOSTER,RED........................................    20.00
GARNIER,SCARECROW,1960.....................................    20.00
GARNIER,SHERIFF,1958.......................................    20.00
GARNIER,SHIP SCENE.........................................    20.00
GARNIER,SIAMESE GODDESS,1963...............................    15.00
GARNIER,SNAIL,1959.........................................    20.00
GARNIER,SOLDIER,COLONIAL,WHITE,1949........................    35.00
GARNIER,SOLDIER,GRENADIER,AQUA,1949........................    35.00
GARNIER,SOLDIER,HUSSAR,RED,1949............................    50.00
GARNIER,SOLDIER,LANCER,GREEN,1949..........................    35.00
GARNIER,SS LINER,LABELED...................................   120.00
GARNIER,ST TROPEZ..........................................    15.00
GARNIER,STREET SCENE,EMPIRE VASE................. 15.00 TO     20.00
GARNIER,SWISS CHALET,1955..................................    15.00
GARNIER,TAXI,1960................................ 25.00 TO     37.00
GARNIER,TEAPOT.............................................    20.00
GARNIER,TROUT,1967............................... 10.00 TO     20.00
GARNIER,VIOLIN,1966........................................    15.00
GARNIER,WATCH,ANTIQUE,1965.................................    18.00
GARNIER,WATERING CAN.......................................    22.50
GARNIER,WOMAN WITH JUG,1963................................    15.00
GEMEL,NAILSEA,1ST HALF NINETEENTH CENTURY............COLOR..    XX.XX
GEMEL,THREADED NECK,AQUA...................................     2.50
```

GIN WAS FIRST MADE IN THE 1600'S AND GIN BOTTLES HAVE
BEEN MADE EVER SINCE. GIN HAS ALWAYS BEEN AN
INEXPENSIVE DRINK, THAT IS WHY SO MANY OF THESE BOTTLES
WERE MADE. MANY WERE OF A TYPE CALLED CASE BOTTLES
TODAY.

```
GIN,BART E.L.,OLD ENGLISH LETTERS,GREEN....................     4.00
GIN,BEEFEATER.............................................     85.00
```

```
GIN,BERGOMASTER,GENEVA,CASE BOTTLE,OLIVE........... 10.00 TO        12.00
GIN,BINNINGER,GREAT GUN,CANNON SHAPE,AMBER.................        346.00
GIN,BINNINGER,OLD LONDON DOCK,PINT,OLIVE GREEN.............         77.00
GIN,BLOWN IN MOLD,SQUARE BASE,CLEAR........................          2.50
GIN,BOUVIER'S BUCHU,AMETHYST...............................          4.00
GIN,BOUVIER'S BUCHU,CLEAR..................................          4.00
GIN,BOUVIER'S BUCHU,QUART,11 3/4 IN.TALL...................          6.00
GIN,BOUVIER'S BUCHU,SQUARE SHOULDER & NECK,PURPLE..........         14.00
GIN,CASE,GREEN.................................... 15.00 TO         20.00
GIN,CASE,OLIVE GREEN.............................. 7.50 TO          41.00
GIN,CYLINDER,YEAR 1780,FREE BLOWN,BLACK....................         25.00
GIN,DR.RUSSELL'S KIDNEY GIN WITH JUNIPER BERRIES,AMERICAN,
   GAL......................................................          6.00
GIN,DR.RUSSELL'S KIDNEY,QUART..............................          1.50
GIN,GORDON DRY,LONDON,ENGLAND,EMBOSSED,AQUA................         12.50
GIN,GORDON'S DRY,ENGLAND,WILD BOAR,AMBER...................          8.00
GIN,GORDON'S DRY,ENGLAND,WILD BOAR,GREEN...................          6.00
GIN,GORDON'S DRY,ENGLAND,8 3/4 IN. TALL,AQUA...............          3.50
GIN,GORDON'S DRY,GREEN.....................................          3.00
GIN,GORDON'S DRY,LONDON,ENGLAND,AQUA.......................          4.00
GIN,GORDON'S,SQUARE,LIGHT GREEN............................          5.00
GIN,HAND-TWISTED NECK,OLIVE GREEN..........................          4.75
GIN,HOLLAND GIN,EXTRA,IMPORTED,GAL.........................          5.00
GIN,LONDON DOCK,IMPORTED,GAL...............................          4.00
GIN,LONDON ROYAL IMPERIAL,SQUARE,QUART,COBALT BLUE.........        201.00
GIN,OLD CASE,BUBBLES,IRON PONTIL,GREEN.....................         18.00
GIN,OLD HOLLAND,IMPORTED,GAL...............................          3.60
GIN,OLD HOLLAND,IMPORTED,QUART.............................           .90
GIN,OLD JUNIPER,FINE FOR KIDNEYS & BLADDER,IMPORTED,GAL....          4.50
GIN,OLD JUNIPER,FINE FOR KIDNEYS & BLADDER,IMPORTED,QUART...         1.13
GIN,OLD LONDON DOCK,IMPORTED,GAL...........................          3.20
GIN,OLD LONDON DOCK,IMPORTED,QUART.........................           .80
GIN,OLD TOM,DRY,AMERICAN,GAL...............................          2.50
GIN,OLD TOM,SWEET,IMPORTED,GAL.............................          3.20
GIN,OLD TOM,SWEET,IMPORTED,QUART...........................           .80
GIN,PURE MALT GIN,AMERICAN,GAL.............................          3.00
GIN,SIX DOTS,6-POINT STAR,CASE,AMBER.......................          9.00
GIN,TAPER,BLOWN IN MOLD,9 3/4 IN. TALL,OLIVE GREEN..........         7.00
GIN,TAPER,E.KIDERLEN,BLOWN IN MOLD,CLEAR...................          6.00
GIN,VAN DENBERGH,10 1/2 IN.HIGH............................         86.00
GIN,VANDENBERGH & CO.,CASE,CRUDE TOP,AVOCADO...............         35.00
GIN,VANDENBERGH & CO.,CASE,CRUDE TOP,OLIVE................         35.00
GINGER ALE,CANADA DRY......................................         10.00
GINGER ALE,CANADA,ORANGE,CARNIVAL GLASS.............. 2.00 TO        9.00
GINGER ALE,G.EBBERWEIN,AMBER...............................         22.00
GINGER BEER,BRIGGS,WATERTOWN,N.Y.,CROCKERY.................          4.00
GINGER BEER,POTTERY........................................          3.50
GINGER JAR,COVERED,ENAMELED,BLUE,RED & GOLD................         55.00
GINGER JAR,POTTERY,GREEN...................................         12.00
GLENMORE,AMARETTO DI SARONNO,SIENA GUARD,1970.........ILLUS..       12.00
GLENMORE,CAPTAIN'S QUART,1970.........................ILLUS..        5.00
GLENMORE,MASQUERS ENGLISH VODKA.......................ILLUS..        3.00
GLENMORE,MASTER'S RARE,1970...........................ILLUS..       10.00
GLUE,SPALDINGS,ROUND,CRUDE,AQUA............................          4.00
GRAPE & CABLE,COLOGNE,PURPLE...............................        151.00
GRAPE & CABLE,PERFUME,STOPPER,MARIGOLD.....................        301.00
GRAPE & CABLE,PERFUME,STOPPER,PURPLE.......................        382.00
GRATTAN & CO.,LTD.,BELFAST,IRELAND,ROUND BOTTOM,AQUA........         6.00
GRENADIER SOLDIER,BAYLORS........................... 18.95 TO       19.50
GRENADIER SOLDIER,CONTINENTAL MARINES............... 8.95 TO        21.50
GRENADIER SOLDIER,DRAGOON,17TH REGIMENT............. 17.95 TO       18.95
GRENADIER SOLDIER,EUGENE...................................         19.50
GRENADIER SOLDIER,LANNES...................................         19.50
GRENADIER SOLDIER,LASSAL........................... 18.95 TO        23.60
GRENADIER SOLDIER,MURAT....................................         19.50
```

GLENMORE,
AMARETTO DI SARONNO,
SIENA GUARD,1970

GLENMORE,CAPTAIN'S
QUART,1970

GLENMORE,
MASQUERS ENGLISH VODKA

GLENMORE,MASTER'S
RARE,1970

```
GRENADIER SOLDIER,NAPOLEON.....................................    24.50
GRENADIER SOLDIER,NEY...............................  18.95 TO   19.50
GRENADIER SOLDIER,NU RET......................................    19.50
GRENADIER SOLDIER,1ST OFFICER GUARD................  17.95 TO   18.95
GRENADIER SOLDIER,1ST PENNSLYVANIA.................  19.50 TO   31.50
GRENADIER SOLDIER,2ND MARYLAND.....................  18.95 TO   24.50
GRENADIER SOLDIER,3RD NEW YORK................................    19.50
GRENADIER SOLDIER,18TH CONTINENTAL............................    19.50
GREST BEAR SPRING CO.,5 GAL.,CLEAR............................     9.50
H.G.CO.,BEEHIVE,AQUA..........................................     3.00
HACK & SIMON,VINCENNES,IND.,GREEN.............................     2.50
   HAIR PRODUCTS, SEE MEDICINE
HAND GRENADE,HARDEN'S,STAR,BLUE...............................    15.00
HAND GRENADE,HAYWARD,AQUA.....................................    20.00
HAWAII,GOD OF WAR,KU,3 PIECE..................................    26.95
HAWAII,LAVA...................................................    26.95
```

```
HAWAII,OKOLEHAO.................................................   26.95
HAWTHORN,EMERALD,PINT...........................................   16.00
HAYNES,AMETHYST,PINT............................................   35.00
HOUSE OF KOSHU,BLUE GEISHA......................................   33.00
HOUSE OF KOSHU,DAUGHTER.........................................   12.00
HOUSE OF KOSHU,FAITHFUL RETAINER................................   23.00
HOUSE OF KOSHU,GEISHA,BLUE......................................   33.00
HOUSE OF KOSHU,GEISHA,PINK......................................   33.00
HOUSE OF KOSHU,GOLDEN PAGODA....................................   12.00
HOUSE OF KOSHU,LION MAN,RED.....................................   25.00
HOUSE OF KOSHU,MAIDEN...........................................   12.00
HOUSE OF KOSHU,NOH MASK.........................................   16.00
HOUSE OF KOSHU,OKAME MASK......................... 15.00 TO       16.00
HOUSE OF KOSHU,PAGODA,GOLDEN....................................   12.00
HOUSE OF KOSHU,PAGODA,WHITE.....................................   17.00
HOUSE OF KOSHU,PLAYBOY..........................................   12.00
HOUSE OF KOSHU,PRINCESS.........................................   12.00
HOUSE OF KOSHU,SAKE GOD,COLORFUL ROBE...........................   10.95
HOUSE OF KOSHU,SAKE GOD,WHITE...................................   10.95
HOUSE OF KOSHU,SMOKISAN.........................................    5.99
HOUSE OF KOSHU,THREE MONKEYS....................................    5.99
HOUSE OF KOSHU,TWO LOVERS.......................................    3.00
HOUSEHOLD,AMMONIA,AQUA..........................................    4.00
HOUSEHOLD,AMMONIA,PARSONS,1882,AQUA,LABEL............ILLUS..       12.00
HOUSEHOLD,CABOT'S SYLPHO-NATHOL,BLOWN IN MOLD,AMBER.........        2.50
HOUSEHOLD,CABOT'S SYLPHO-NATHOL,BLOWN IN MOLD,BROWN.........        2.50
HOUSEHOLD,CLIMAX,GRINDER..............................ILLUS..       8.00
HOUSEHOLD,COLORITE STRAW HAT COLOR,4 1/4 IN............ILLUS..      3.00
HOUSEHOLD,DEAD STUCK FOR BUGS,BLOWN IN MOLD,EMBOSSED BUG,
  AQUA.........................................................    4.00
```

HOUSEHOLD,
AMMONIA,
PARSONS,
1882,AQUA,LABEL

HOUSEHOLD,
CLIMAX,GRINDER

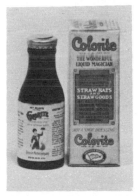

HOUSEHOLD,COLORITE STRAW
HAT COLOR,4 1/4 IN

```
HOUSEHOLD,DIOXOGEN,OAKLAND CHEMICAL COMPANY,BLOWN IN MOLD,
  BROWN.......................................................    1.50
HOUSEHOLD,DR.HUBBARD'S VEGETABLE DISINFECTANT,MACHINE MADE,
  CLEAR.......................................................    1.00
HOUSEHOLD,EVERETT & BARRONS SHOE DRESSINGS,BLOWN IN MOLD,
  AQUA........................................................    2.50
HOUSEHOLD,F L MASON MEREDITH,CLEAR,3 1/2 IN..........ILLUS..       4.00
HOUSEHOLD,FELLOWS & CO. CHEMISTS,BLOWN IN MOLD,AQUA.........       3.00
HOUSEHOLD,GRAND UNION COMPANY,BLOWN IN MOLD,CLEAR...........       1.50
HOUSEHOLD,GREER'S WASHING AMMONIA,PURPLE....................       6.00
```

HOUSEHOLD,JACQUES' CHEMICAL WORKS,AQUA...............ILLUS..   4.50
HOUSEHOLD,LA FRANCE GRAND VIN SUPERIEUR,CROOKED GREEN GLASS.   2.00
HOUSEHOLD,LARKIN CO.,BLOWN IN MOLD,STRAP SIDE,CLEAR........   1.50
HOUSEHOLD,LARKIN CO.,C.P.CLYCERINE NO.4,BLOWN IN MOLD,CLEAR.   1.50
HOUSEHOLD,LARKIN SOAP CO.,BLOWN IN MOLD,CLEAR..............   2.00
HOUSEHOLD,LARKIN SOAP CO.,STOPPER,EMERALD GREEN...........   8.00
HOUSEHOLD,LITTLE BO-PEEP AMMONIA,CLEAR...................   7.00
HOUSEHOLD,MILLIKEN'S PARLOR PRIDE STOVE ENAMEL,BLOWN,AQUA...   2.50
HOUSEHOLD,MRS.POTTER'S HYGIENIC SUPPLY CO.,BLOWN IN MOLD,
  BROWN...   2.50
HOUSEHOLD,OAKLAND CHEMICAL CO.,BLOWN IN MOLD,BROWN..........   2.50
HOUSEHOLD,OAKLAND CHEMICAL CO.,4 IN.,BROWN.................   3.00
HOUSEHOLD,PAINT,X ON BASE,BLOWN IN MOLD,8 PANELS,CLEAR......   1.00
HOUSEHOLD,PUTNAM GILDING PAINT.......................ILLUS..   4.00
HOUSEHOLD,SANITOL,MILK GLASS.........................   5.00
HOUSEHOLD,SAWYER'S CRYSTAL BLUEING,BLOWN IN MOLD,AQUA.......   2.00
HOUSEHOLD,SCOTT'S EMULSION,COD LIVER OIL WITH LIME & SODA,
  AQUA...   1.50

HOUSEHOLD,
JACQUES'
CHEMICAL
WORKS,AQUA

HOUSEHOLD,F L MASON MEREDITH,
CLEAR,3 1/2 IN

HOUSEHOLD,PUTNAM
GILDING PAINT

HOUSEHOLD, SHOE POLISH, SEE SHOE POLISH
HOUSEHOLD,SIGNET OIL,BLOWN IN MOLD,CLEAR...................   1.50
HOUSEHOLD,TABLET,BLOWN IN MOLD,CLEAR......................   1.00
HOUSEHOLD,THREE IN ONE,OIL,BLOWN IN MOLD,AQUA..............   1.00
HOUSEHOLD,TINCTURE WARBURG'S,LILLY,AMBER,5 IN........ILLUS..   4.00
HOUSEHOLD,VITRIFIED CEMENT LIQUID,BLOWN IN MOLD,CLEAR.......   1.50
HOUSEHOLD,VITRIFIED CEMENT POWDER,BLOWN IN MOLD,CLEAR.......   1.50
HOUSEHOLD,WM.F.NYE OIL,BLOWN IN MOLD,CLEAR..................   1.50
HOUSEHOLD,WOODBURY IMPROVED JAR...........................   2.00
HUTCHINSON,FRANCIS DRAKE,NEW GLASCOWNS,AQUA..........ILLUS..   5.00
HYG WILD CHERRY PHOSPHATE..............................   18.00
I.GOLDBERG,EIGHT SIDES,APPLIED LIP,AMBER,QUART.............   7.00
I.W.HARPER,AMBER............................... 10.00 TO   15.00
I.W.HARPER,CERAMIC,1913,NAUTICAL....................COLOR..   XX.XX
I.W.HARPER,CIRCA 1910..............................COLOR..   XX.XX
I.W.HARPER,DECANTER,1885...........................COLOR..   XX.XX
I.W.HARPER,ETCHED STEAMBOAT MAN,TAILS & TOP HAT.............   16.00
I.W.HARPER,G.A.R.,1895.............................COLOR..   XX.XX
I.W.HARPER,GOLD MEDALLION...........................COLOR..   XX.XX
I.W.HARPER,MAN,BLUE...................................   18.50
I.W.HARPER,MAN,GRAY...................................   18.50
I.W.HARPER,MAN,WHITE.......................... 49.95 TO   60.00

HOUSEHOLD,TINCTURE WARBURG'S, LILLY,
AMBER,5 IN

HUTCHINSON,FRANCIS DRAKE,
NEW GLASCOWNS,AQUA

I.W.HARPER,MEDAL,POTTERY,TAN.................................... 20.00
I.W.HARPER,WICKER COVER,AMBER.................................. 12.50
IMPERIAL GRAPE,DECANTER,SET,STOPPER,GREEN..................... 166.00
IMPERIAL GRAPE,DECANTER,WINE,STOPPER,GREEN.................... 86.00
IMPERIAL GRAPE,DECANTER,WINE,STOPPER,MARIGOLD................ 61.00

INK BOTTLES WERE FIRST USED IN THE UNITED STATES IN
1816. EARLY INK BOTTLES WERE OF CERAMIC AND WERE OFTEN
IMPORTED. INKS CAN BE IDENTIFIED BY THEIR SHAPE; THEY
WERE MADE TO BE HARD TO TIP OVER.
INK,ALLINGS,PAT.APRIL 23,1871,CLEAR........................... 16.00
INK,ALLINGS,PAT.APRIL 23,1871,GREEN........................... 25.00
INK,BARNACLES,POTTERY,PINT,1860............................... 10.00
INK,BIXBY,CONE.. 3.00
INK,BIXBY,QUART,SPOUT,AQUA.................................... 16.00
INK,BLOWN,1 3/4 IN.SQUARE,PEWTER TOP,CORK..................... 11.00
INK,BLOWN,1 3/4 IN.SQUARE,PEWTER TOP,FITTED CORK.............. 11.00
INK,BLOWN,3 MOLD,GEOMETRIC PATTERN,PONTIL,GREEN.............. 100.00
INK,BLUE FLOWERS,MILK GLASS................................... 12.00
INK,BOAT,PLAIN,BLUE... 6.00
INK,BOAT,PLAIN,SQUARE,BLUE.................................... 6.00
INK,BOAT,PLAIN,SQUARE,CLEAR................................... 6.00
INK,C.M.W.&A.A.S.,TURTLE,PEN SLOT..................... 15.00 TO 41.00
INK,CARTER,MR.& MRS.,DATED,PAIR..................... 30.00 TO 38.00
INK,CARTER,MRS.. 22.00
INK,CARTER'S,AMBER.. 12.00
INK,CARTER'S,BULK,QUART,AQUA......................... 6.00 TO 10.00
INK,CARTER'S,CATHEDRAL,QUART,BLUE............................. 45.00
INK,CARTER'S,CATHEDRAL,QUART,COBALT........................... 32.00
INK,CARTER'S,CONE,COBALT...................................... 15.00
INK,CARTER'S,CONE,GREEN....................................... 6.00
INK,CARTER'S,FULL 1/2 PINT,AQUA............................... 6.50
INK,CARTER'S,MINIATURE,INDELIBLE,8 SIDED,EMBOSSED,AQUA...... 6.00
INK,CARTER'S,NO.1,32 FLUID OZ.,ROUND,COBALT BLUE............. 10.00
INK,CARTER'S,PINT,3 PART MOLD,RING COLLAR,GREEN.............. 16.00
INK,CARTER'S,QUART,COBALT..................................... 36.00
INK,CARTER'S,QUART,PAT.FEB.14,99,APPLIED LIP,ROUND,AQUA..... 15.00
INK,CARTER'S,QUART,SHEARED LIP,GOLDEN AMBER.................. 18.00
INK,CARTER'S,ROUND BASE,AMETHYST.............................. 4.00
INK,CARTER'S,ROUND,AQUA....................................... 4.00
INK,CARTER'S,SCHOOLHOUSE,AQUA................................. 5.50
INK,CARTER'S,SCHOOLHOUSE,CLEAR................................ 4.50
INK,CARTER'S,1/2 PINT,APPLIED RING,ROUND,AQUA............... 12.00
INK,CARTER'S,1882.....................................ILLUS.. 8.00
INK,CARTER'S,1896.....................................ILLUS.. 6.00
INK,CARTER'S,1897.....................................ILLUS.. 6.00

INK,CARTER'S,1882   INK,CARTER'S,1896   INK,CARTER'S,1897

```
INK,CARTER'S,1897,CONE........................................    7.00
INK,CARTER'S,1897,CONE,CRUDE,AQUA.............................    4.50
INK,CARTER'S,1897,CONE,EMERALD................................   10.00
INK,CARTER'S,1897,ROUND BASE,AQUA.............................    7.00
INK,CARTER'S,1897,ROUND BASE,BROWN............................   12.00
INK,CARTER'S,1897,ROUND BASE,GREEN............................    7.00
INK,CARTER'S,1899.......................................ILLUS..   14.00
INK,CARTER'S,1906.......................................ILLUS..   15.00
INK,CARTER'S,1906.......................................ILLUS..    6.00
INK,CARTER'S,1911......................................ILLUS...    5.00
INK,CARTER'S,1911.......................................ILLUS..    7.00
INK,CARTER'S,1916.......................................ILLUS..    4.00
INK,CARTER'S,1932.......................................ILLUS..    2.00
INK,CARTER'S,2 C-101,CATHEDRAL,MACHINE MADE,COBALT BLUE.....   18.00
INK,CARTER'S,2 PART MOLD,GREEN................................   16.00
INK,CARTER'S,3 PART MOLD,QUART,GREEN..........................   16.00
INK,CARTER'S,3 PART MOLD,1/2 PINT,GREEN.......................   16.00
INK,CARTER'S,3 SIDED,CATHEDRAL,1 QUART,COBALT...... 26.00 TO   48.50
INK,CARTER'S,6 SIDED CATHEDRAL,QUART,COBALT & PINT...........   51.00
INK,CARTER'S,7 1/2 IN. ROUND,AQUA.............................    4.00
INK,CAW'S,NEW YORK,BLOWN IN MOLD,AQUA.........................    4.00
INK,CAW'S,NEW YORK,CIRCLE ON SHOULDER,AQUA....................    4.00
INK,CAW'S,NEW YORK,CIRCLE ON SHOULDER,BLUE....................    4.00
INK,CAW'S,NEW YORK,CIRCLE ON SHOULDER,CLEAR...................    4.00
INK,COBALT BLUE...................................... 4.00 TO    5.00
INK,CONE,AMBER....................................... 4.50 TO    8.00
INK,CONE,AMETHYST.................................... 3.00 TO    4.00
INK,CONE,AQUA....................................... 2.00 TO    5.00
INK,CONE,BLOWN IN MOLD,AQUA...................................    4.50
INK,CONE,BLOWN IN MOLD,BROWN..................................    6.50
INK,CONE,BLOWN IN MOLD,CLEAR..................................    4.00
```

INK,CARTER'S,1899

INK,CARTER'S,1906

INK,CARTER'S,1906

INK,	INK,	INK,	INK,
CARTER'S,1911	CARTER'S,1911	CARTER'S,1916	CARTER'S,1932

```
INK,CONE,BLOWN IN MOLD,COBALT BLUE...........................      8.00
INK,CONE,BLUE................................................      8.00
INK,CONE,BROWN...............................................      8.00
INK,CONE,CLEAR.....................................2.00 TO        3.00
INK,CONE,CRUDE,AQUA..........................................      4.50
INK,CONE,DARK AMBER..........................................      4.50
INK,CONE,EMERALD.............................................      8.00
INK,CONE,GREEN...............................................     12.00
INK,CONE,HONEY AMBER.........................................      5.00
INK,CONE,SQUARE,AQUA.........................................      1.00
INK,CONE,SQUARE,CLEAR........................................      1.00
INK,CONE,YELLOW AMBER........................................      7.00
INK,CONICAL,AMBER............................................      6.00
NK,CONICAL,BLUE..............................................      8.00
INK,CONICAL,BROWN............................................      6.00
INK,CONICAL,COBALT...........................................     10.00
INK,CONICAL,GREEN............................................      8.00
INK,CORKER,ROUND,COBALT......................................      2.00
INK,CORKER,SQUARE,COBALT.....................................      2.00
INK,COVENTRY,ROUGH PONTIL,BLOWN,3 MOLD,OLIVE AMBER...........    121.00
INK,CROCK,PLAIN,POUR LIP.....................................     10.00
INK,CROCK,ROUND POURING LIP,BROWN............................      8.00
INK,CROCK,ROUND POURING LIP,CREAM............................      8.00
INK,CROCK,SANFORD,LABEL......................................      7.00
INK,CUDE,CRYSTAL,HINGED STERLING SILVER TOP,INITIAL R.......      5.00
INK,DENBY,POTTERY............................................      7.50
INK,DENBY,POURING SPOUT......................................      3.00
INK,DESIGN PAT'D FEB.16,1886,CLEAR...........................     10.00
INK,DIAMOND INK CO.,MILWAUKEE,ROUND RING ON SHOULDER,CLEAR..     12.00
INK,DIAMOND,SQUARE,AQUA......................................      9.00
INK,DOME SHAPE,J & IEM,COBALT................................     10.00
INK,DOME SHAPE,PLAIN,AQUA....................................     10.00
INK,DOME SHAPE,PLAIN,COBALT..................................     50.00
INK,EIGHT FLAT SIDES,EMBOSSED PENN.MFG.WORKS,PHILADELPHIA,
     WHITE...................................................    145.00
INK,EMBOSSED PENN.MFG.WORKS,PHILA.,MILK GLASS................    145.00
INK,ESBIN'S INDELIBLE,SMALL VIAL.............................      7.00
INK,FARLEY'S,8 SIDED,AMBER...................................     90.00
INK,HIGGEN'S.................................................      1.00
INK,J.& I.E.M.,AMBER.........................................     76.00
INK,J.& I.E.M.,BLOWN IN MOLD,AQUA............................      8.00
INK,J.& I.E.M.,SHEARED LIP,TURTLE,AQUA.......................     12.50
INK,JACOBUS,EMBOSSED 1903,SLIDE DOOR IN METAL TOP,CLEAR.....     23.00
INK,JAPAN,HOUSE,AMBER...............................ILLUS..       1.00
INK,JAPAN,OCTAGON,PURPLE............................ILLUS..       1.00
INK,JAPAN,ROUND,GREEN...............................ILLUS..       1.00
INK,L & B,CONE SHAPE,AQUA....................................     12.00
INK,L.E.WATERMAN CO.,SQUAT BAND,MACHINE MADE,CLEAR..........      2.00
```

```
INK,MASTER,THREE MOLD,OLIVE AMBER,QUART.....................    20.00
INK,MC KEARIN G II-2,3 MOLD,GREEN...........................    80.00
INK,MILLEFIORI,PAPERWEIGHT BASE.............................    76.00
INK,MR.CARTER,MRS.CARTER,PAIR...............................    25.00
INK,NAYNARD & NOYES,BOSTON,ROUGH PONTIL,FULL LABEL..........    70.00
INK,NELSON...................................... 3.95 TO        5.00
INK,OCTAGON MUSHROOM SHAPE,PONTIL,AQUA.......................    32.00
INK,OLIVER TYPEWRITER,CLEAR.................................     6.50
INK,PALE BLUE,OCTAGON PANELS,WIDE BASE,NARROW NECK,
  2 3/4 IN.TALL............................................      6.00
INK,PATENT 1886,AMBER,QUART................................      6.00
INK,PAUL'S,1/2 PINT,COBALT BLUE............................      8.00
INK,PERRY & CO.,LONDON,PATENT,POTTERY,CREAM................     15.00
INK,POTTERY................................................      8.00
INK,POTTERY,EMBOSSING,BROWN................................      8.00
INK,POTTERY,MASTER INK,A.& S.BARNES & CO.,N.Y..............     66.00
INK,POTTERY,RING TOP,BROWN.................................      8.00
INK,POTTERY,ROUND BOTTOM,CONICAL,BROWN.....................      8.00
INK,POTTERY,ROUND BOTTOM,CONICAL,GRAY......................      8.00
INK,POTTERY,ROUND,BROWN....................................      8.00
INK,POTTERY,SHORT NECK,BLUE................................      8.00
INK,PREMIUM BLACK,OCTAGON,PAPER LABEL,AQUA..........ILLUS..     14.00
```

INK,JAPAN,HOUSE,AMBER

INK,JAPAN,
OCTAGON,
PURPLE

INK,JAPAN,
ROUND,GREEN

INK,PREMIUM BLACK,
OCTAGON,PAPER
LABEL,AQUA

```
INK,RING AROUND BASE,ROUND,CLEAR...........................      4.00
INK,RING AROUND BASE,SHOULDER & NECK,AMBER.................      6.00
INK,RING AROUND BASE,SHOULDER & NECK,AQUA..................      4.00
INK,RING AROUND BASE,SHOULDER & NECK,CLEAR.................      4.00
INK,RING TOP,MACHINE MADE,CLEAR............................      4.00
INK,ROUND BOTTOM,GREEN.....................................     10.00
INK,ROUND STANDS,BLOWN IN MOLD,BLUE........................      3.00
INK,ROUND TOP,NECK STICKING UP ON ONE SIDE,GROUND MOUTH,
  1 3/4 IN................................................       7.00
INK,ROUND,AMETHYST........................................       4.00
INK,ROUND,BLOWN IN MOLD,CLEAR.............................       3.00
INK,ROUND,CLEAR...........................................       4.00
INK,ROUND,COBALT.................................... 4.00 TO     5.25
INK,ROUND,GREEN...........................................       4.00
INK,ROUND,PEN HOLDER,CLEAR................................      30.00
INK,ROUND,4 RINGS AROUND BODY.............................      12.00
INK,S.O.DUNBAR,OPEN PONTIL,1/2 PINT,AQUA..................      50.00
INK,S.S.STAFFORD'S,QUART,AQUA.............................       8.00
INK,S.S.STAFFORD'S,QUART,BLUE.............................       8.00
INK,S.S.STAFFORD'S,QUART,2 RINGS ON BOTTOM & SHOULDER.....      16.00
INK,SANFORD,FOUNTAIN PEN,MACHINE MADE.....................       6.00
```

```
INK,SANFORD,ROUND,CLEAR.........................................    4.00
INK,SANFORD'S INKS & LIBRARY PASTE,PINT,MACHINE MADE,BROWN..    2.50
INK,SANFORD'S,BASE EMBOSSED,DOUBLE COLLAR,BIMAL,AMBER.......    6.00
INK,SANFORD'S,2 IN. SQUARE,FLATTENED DIAMONDS..............   13.00
INK,SANFORD'S,2 IN.SQUARE,SQUAT,FLATTENED DIAMONDS..........   13.00
INK,SHAPE OF LADY'S SHOE,EMBOSSED DESIGN,ROUGH PONTIL.......   35.00
INK,SHOE,CLEAR.................................................   14.00
INK,SIGNET PERMANENT FLUID,LEPAGES,COBALT............ILLUS..   12.00
INK,SLENDER,HANDLE,MARKED C NO.22,CROCK.....................    7.00
INK,SQUARE,BLOWN IN MOLD,AQUA...............................    4.00
INK,SQUARE,BLOWN IN MOLD,CLEAR..............................    3.50
INK,SQUARE,CLEAR............................... 4.00 TO   20.00
INK,SQUARE,COBALT.............................. 2.00 TO    4.00
INK,SQUARE,GREEN............................................    4.00
INK,SQUARE,MACHINE MADE,ROUNDED CORNERS,COBALT..............    4.00
INK,SQUARE,ROUNDED CORNERS,MACHINE MADE,CLEAR...............    4.00
INK,SQUAT,SQUARE,BLOWN IN MOLD,COBALT BLUE..................    4.00
INK,STAFFORD'S MASTER,DUG,GREEN.............................   15.00
INK,STAFFORD'S,MASTER POURING,AQUA,QUART....................   20.00
INK,STAFFORD'S,2 RINGS ON SHOULDER & BOTTOM,AMBER...........   12.00
INK,STICK WELL CO.,CONE SHAPE,6 PANELS,AQUA.................    8.00
INK,STIEGEL,FREE BLOWN,COBALT BLUE.......................... 126.00
INK,SUNKEN BOTTOM,AMETHYST..................................   10.00
INK,SUNKEN BOTTOM,CLEAR.....................................   10.00
```

```
INK,SIGNET PERMANENT FLUID,LEPAGES,COBALT
```

```
INK,TAN,POTTERY............................................    3.00
INK,THADUS DAVIDS MINT,OPEN PONTIL,GREEN....................   50.00
INK,TURTLE SHAPE,GROUND LIP,PEN SLOT,EMBOSSED,AQUA..........   41.00
INK,TURTLE SHAPE,SHEARED TOP,AQUA...........................    8.00
INK,U.S.TREASURY MUCILAGE,AQUA..............................    4.50
INK,UMBRELLA,AQUA...........................................    5.00
INK,UMBRELLA,AQUA...........................................    7.50
INK,UMBRELLA,GOLDEN,OLIVE-AMBER TUBULAR PONTIL,BLOWN,NEW
  ENGLAND..................................................   45.00
INK,UMBRELLA,GRAPHITE PONTIL,AQUA...........................   20.00
INK,UMBRELLA,GREEN..........................................   36.00
INK,UMBRELLA,GREEN,OPEN PONTIL..............................   40.00
INK,UMBRELLA,OCTAGON,AQUA...................................   15.00
INK,UMBRELLA,OLIVE AMBER....................................   60.00
INK,UMBRELLA,PONTIL,AMBER...................................   56.00
INK,UMBRELLA,3 1/2 IN. HIGH,CLEAR...........................    9.00
INK,UMBRELLA,6 PANELS,AQUA..................................   10.00
INK,UMBRELLA,6 PANELS,BLUE..................................   10.00
INK,UMBRELLA,6 PANELS,PONTIL,AQUA...........................   15.00
INK,UMBRELLA,8 SIDED,CRUDE,AQUA.............................    5.50
INK,UMBRELLA,8 SIDES,OPEN PONTIL,BROWN......................   12.00
INK,UMBRELLA,8 SIDES,OPEN PONTIL,CLEAR......................   10.00
INK,WARDS,4 PIECE MOLD,WHITTLE,OLIVE GREEN..................   15.00
```

```
INK,WATERMAN'S,CLEAR.........................................    4.00
INK,3 MOLD,GEOMETRIC,BLOWN,DARK AMBER........................   90.00
INK,12 SIDED,OPEN PONTIL,AQUA....................... 19.00 TO   29.00
J.A.GILKA,AMBER..............................................   20.00
J.R.WATKINS,8 1/2 IN.........................................    2.00
JACK DANIEL,HIP FLASK,SILVER TOP....................COLOR..     24.00
JACK DANIEL JUG,LYNCHBURG,TENNESSEE.................COLOR..     28.00
JACK DANIEL,JUG,OLD,NO.7............................COLOR..     XX.XX
JACK DANIEL'S,OLD LINCOLN COUNTY,LABEL...............ILLUS..    18.00
JACK DANIEL'S,GOLD MEDAL,NO.7,NEW...................COLOR..     50.00
JACK DANIEL'S,GOLD MEDAL NO.7,OLD...................COLOR..     50.00
JACK DANIEL'S,GOLD MEDAL OLD NO.7,19TH-CENTURY.......COLOR..    XX.XX
JACK DANIEL,OLD TIME DISTILLERY.....................ILLUS..     15.00
JACK DANIEL'S,TENNESSEE WHISKEY.....................ILLUS..     15.00
JACK DANIEL'S,W.T.& C.D.GUNTER......................ILLUS..     12.00
```

JACK DANIEL'S
OLD LINCOLN COUNTY,LABEL

JACK DANIEL,
OLD TIME DISTILLERY

JACK DANIEL'S,
GOLD MEDAL,OLD NO.7

JACK DANIEL'S,
TENNESSEE WHISKEY

JACK DANIEL'S,W.T.&
C.D. GUNTER

```
JAR,A 10-CENT CIGAR FOR 5 CENTS,AMBER.........................    30.00
JAR,APOTHECARY,CLEAR,GROUND STOPPER,12 IN.HIGH................     9.50
JAR,APOTHECARY,LID INVERTED IN MEASURING CUP,AMBER...........    11.50
JAR,APOTHECARY,PORCELAIN,FRANCE,10 1/2 IN.HIGH,PAIR..........   125.00
JAR,APOTHECARY,STATUE OF LIBERTY.............................    50.00
JAR,APOTHECARY,THUMBPRINT,GROUND PONTIL,BLOWN,MUSHROOM
   STOPPER...................................................     6.50
JAR,EARBASOL,EIGHT-SIDED.....................................     3.00
JAR,BLOWN,8 IN. HIGH,CLEAR...................................     2.00
JAR,BLOWN,9 1/4 IN. HIGH,CLEAR...............................     2.00
JAR,GOOFUS,CABBAGE ROSE,8 IN.,MILK GLASS.....................    12.00
JAR,HONEY,FOOTED,COVER,WATERFORD CRYSTAL,7 1/2 IN.HIGH.......    45.00
JAR,LIB,AMBER................................................      .25
JAR,POMADE,DR.L.C.DALE'S PATENT 1850,COBALT,PEWTER COVER.....    37.00
JAR,POWDER,BASE HAS STRETCH BARS,HAND-PAINTED,FOOTED,M.Z.,
   AUSTRIA...................................................    12.50
JAR,POWDER,WHITE INSIDE,PEACH OVERLAY,SWIRL PATTERN,
   5 IN.TALL.................................................    30.00
JAR,PUFF,CUT GLASS,NOTCHES,STARS,FANS........................     8.00
JAR,SNUFF,MACCOBY............................................     6.00
JAR,SNUFF,ORIGINAL LID,MARKED URJMAN.........................     5.50
JAR,SNUFF,P.LORILLARD........................................     8.00
JAR,THE PEARL,SAYS PATD.AUG.23,70 & FEB.7,71,AQUA,PINT.......    20.00
JAR,WESTERN ELECTRIC BATTERY,GROUND LIP......................     5.00
JASDO JIM,DANCER ON ROOF,....................................    25.00
JOHANN HOFF..................................................     3.00
JOHN RYAN 1866 CO.,BLUE......................................    25.00
JUG,A.M.BININGER & CO.,HANDLED,AMBER.........................    75.00
JUG,GLASS,2 GAL.,2 HANDLES,GREEN.............................   100.00
JUG,HANDLE,BOTTOM EMBOSSED MACY & JENKENS,N.Y.,AMBER.........    25.00
JUG,MEASURE MARKER,29-7 ATLAS HOCKING 5,BROWN,GALLON.........     5.00
KABUKI,DAUGHTER,HOUSE OF KOSHU SAKE..........................    11.49
KABUKI,FAITHFUL RETAINER,HOUSE OF KOSHU SAKE.................    21.99
KABUKI,GOLDEN PAGODA,HOUSE OF KOSHU SAKE.....................    11.49
KABUKI,MAIDEN,HOUSE OF KOSHU SAKE............................    11.49
KABUKI,PLAYBOY,HOUSE OF KOSHU SAKE...........................    11.79
KABUKI,PRINCESS,HOUSE OF KOSHU SAKE..........................    11.49
KABUKI,TWO LOVERS,HOUSE OF KOSHU SAKE........................    24.99
KAHLUA TIKI GOD,BLACK........................................    12.50
KAHLUA,GREEN GOD.............................................    14.95
KAHLUA,STONE MASK............................................    14.95
KALOPEAN HAIR DYE,NO.2,OPEN PONTIL...........................     8.00
```

KAMOTSURU SAKE BREWING COMPANY OF JAPAN HAS MADE SAKE
FOR CENTURIES. IN 1965 THE FIRST OF THEIR DECANTERS
WERE IMPORTED TO THE UNITED STATES.

```
KAMOTSURU,GOD OF FISHERMEN,HOLDING FAN,1965..................    12.00
KAMOTSURU,GOD OF LONGEVITY,PORCELAIN,1965....................    12.00
KAMOTSURU,GOD OF MILITARY,PORCELAIN,1965.....................    12.00
KAMOTSURU,GOD OF WEALTH,HOLDING FAN,1965.....................    12.00
KAMOTSURU,GOD OF WISDOM,HOLDING FAN,1965.....................    12.00
KAMOTSURU,GOD OF WISDOM,HOLDING SCROLL,1965..................    12.00
KAMOTSURU,GODDESS OF ART,HOLDING FAN,1965....................    12.00
KAMOTSURU,HOUSEHOLD GOD,DARBY,1967...........................    15.00
KAMOTSURU,HOUSEHOLD GODDESS,JAON,1967........................    15.00
KAMOTSURU,SEDAN CHAIR,PORCELAIN,1966.........................    15.00
KAMOTSURU,TREASURE TOWER,PORCELAIN,1966......................    15.00
KENDELL SPAVIN CURE,AMBER....................................     5.00
KIKUKAWA-UTA-HARU-HIRU.......................................    12.50
KIOSK,MARIE BRIZARD..........................................     8.95
```

KORD DISTILLERIES OF CZECHOSLOVAKIA HAVE BOTTLED
LIQUEURS IN DECANTERS FOR MANY YEARS.

```
KORD,COACH BOTTLE,GLASS,1948.................................    40.00
```

```
KORD,COUNTRY SCENE DECANTER,BOY & GIRL,1950........ 37.50 TO    40.00
KORD,DANCING,DECANTER,GLASS,BAGPIPE PLAYER,1950.............    37.50
KORD,DOLPHIN,GLASS,2 COMPARTMENTS,1949-69...................    14.00
KORD,HORSE'S HEAD DECANTER,GLASS,1947-69....................    12.00
KORD,HUNTER DECANTER,GLASS,1958.............................    18.00
KORD,HUNTER'S LADY,CRACKLE GLASS,1958.......................    18.00
KORD,RUBY ETCHED GLASS,DECANTER,CASTLE,1949.................    35.00
KORD,SLEIGH DECANTER,GLASS,1949.............................    40.00
KORD,WILD GEESE PITCHER,1952................................    26.00
KUMMEL BEAR,OLIVE GREEN.....................................    35.00
L.ROSE & CO.,VINE-COVERED,AQUA..............................    17.50
LAIRD'S JERSEY SOLDIER,BLUE.................................    16.50
LALIQUE,DECANTER,GRADUATED HOBNAIL,SIGNED & NUMBERED........    29.00
LAMP BASE,PATENT SEPT.20,1870,5 IN. HIGH....................     5.00
LAMP BASE,RIBBED,3 PIECE MOLD,APPLIED HANDLE,CLEAR..........     5.00
LAMP BASE,2 PIECE MOLD,APPLIED HANDLE,CLEAR.................     5.00
LANGLEYS,BACKWARD 9S,OPEN PONTIL............................    37.50
LAST CHANCE JOE,CAMEO.......................................    16.50
LESTOIL,FLASK,FRANKLIN,BLUE......................ILLUS..         2.00
LESTOIL,FLASK,LIBERTY,GREEN......................ILLUS..         2.00
LESTOIL,FLASK,WASHINGTON.........................ILLUS..         2.00
LIME COLA...................................................     3.00
LIME,ROSE DESIGN............................................    10.00
```

LESTOIL,FLASK,FRANKLIN,BLUE

LESTOIL,FLASK,
LIBERTY,GREEN

LESTOIL,FLASK,
WASHINGTON

LIONSTONE DISTILLERIES HAS MADE THREE SERIES OF
PORCELAIN BOTTLES TO HOLD THEIR BOURBON. THE BOTTLES
ARE ALL FIGURALS, A SINGLE MAN FOR EACH BOTTLE. EACH
FIGURE REPRESENTS A CHARACTER OF THE OLD WEST. THESE
ARE LIMITED-EDITION BOTTLES.

```
LIONSTONE,BARTENDER,VOL.I......................... 21.50 TO    25.99
LIONSTONE,BELLY ROBBER,VOL.III....................ILLUS..      21.15
LIONSTONE,CAMP COOK,VOL.I.........................COLOR..      28.50
LIONSTONE,CASUAL INDIAN,VOL.I..............................    19.95
LIONSTONE,CAVALRY SCOUT........................... 16.50 TO    19.99
LIONSTONE,CIRCUIT RIDING JUDGE,VOL.II.............ILLUS..      24.50
LIONSTONE,COUNTRY DOCTOR,VOL.II...................ILLUS..      24.50
LIONSTONE,COWBOY..................................COLOR..      20.00
LIONSTONE,FRONTIERSMAN,VOL.III....................ILLUS..      25.95
LIONSTONE,GENTLEMAN GAMBLER.................................    19.95
LIONSTONE,GOLD PANNER,VOL.I....................... 21.50 TO    25.99
LIONSTONE,HIGHWAY ROBBER.......................... 25.95 TO    28.50
LIONSTONE,JESSE JAMES,VOL.II......................ILLUS..      24.50
LIONSTONE,MISTER 500........................................    19.95
```

```
LIONSTONE,MOUNTAIN MAN,VOL.III.......................ILLUS..    25.95
LIONSTONE,PROUD INDIAN,VOL.I.........................COLOR..    20.00
LIONSTONE,RAILROAD ENGINEER,VOL.II...................ILLUS..    24.50
LIONSTONE,RENEGADE TRADER,VOL.I......................COLOR..    28.50
LIONSTONE,RIVERBOAT CAPTAIN,VOL.II...................ILLUS..    24.50
```

LIONSTONE, BELLY ROBBER, VOL.III	LIONSTONE, CIRCUIT RIDING JUDGE,VOL.II	LIONSTONE, COUNTRY DOCTOR, VOL.II	LIONSTONE, FRONTIERSMAN, VOL.III

LIONSTONE, JESSE JAMES, VOL.II	LIONSTONE, MOUNTAIN MAN, VOL.III	LIONSTONE, RAILROAD ENGINEER, VOL.II	LIONSTONE, RIVERBOAT CAPTAIN, VOL.II

```
LIONSTONE,ROADRUNNER.................................            29.95
LIONSTONE,SCOUT..............................    16.50 TO    19.99
LIONSTONE,SHEEPHERDER,VOL.I..................    21.50 TO    25.99
LIONSTONE,SHERIFF............................    16.50 TO    19.95
LIONSTONE,SODBUSTER,VOL.II...........................ILLUS..    24.50
LIONSTONE,SQUAW MAN,VOL.I....................    21.50 TO    25.95
LIONSTONE,STAGECOACH DRIVER,VOL.III..................ILLUS..    25.95
LIONSTONE,STP RACE CAR.......................    19.99 TO    21.15
LIONSTONE,TRADER.....................................            25.95
LIONSTONE,VIGILANTE..........................    19.95 TO    21.50
LIIUNSTONE,WELLS FARGO GUARD.................    19.95 TO    20.95
LIONSTONE,WOODHAWK,VOL.I.....................    25.95 TO    28.49
```

LIONSTONE,
SODBUSTER,
VOL.II

LIONSTONE,STAGECOACH DRIVER,
VOL.III

LIQUEUR,BENEDICTINE,CRESCENT EMBOSSED,GREEN......... 8.00 TO   10.00
LIQUEUR,BENEDICTINE,LIQUOR CRESCENT,GREEN........... 4.00 TO   18.00
LIQUEUR,BENEDICTINE,3 PIECE MOLD.........................   10.00
LIQUEUR,BOLS,BALLERINA............................. 7.50 TO   12.50
LIQUEUR,BOLS,CREME DE MENTHE,DELFT,SQUAT....................   10.75
LIQUEUR,BOLS,JUG,DELFT BLUE................................   10.00
LIQUEUR,COGNAC,HENNESSY & CO.,YELLOW GREEN.................   1.50
LIQUEUR,COINTREAU,BLOWN IN MOLD,GLASS STOPPER,AMBER.........   10.00
LIQUEUR,CREME DE MENTHE,BLOWN IN MOLD,7 IN. TALL,CLEAR......   2.50
LIQUEUR,TURN MOLD,11 1/2 IN. TALL,OLIVE AMBER..............   2.50
LIQUID,THE CARBONIC CO.PAT.JULY 14,1908,1/2 GAL.,CLEAR......   5.75
LIQUID,THE,CARBONIC CO.ON BASE,QUART,CLEAR.................   5.75
LIQUID,THE,CARBONIC CO.ON BASE,1/2 GAL.,CLEAR..............   5.75
LIQUID,THE,CARBONIC CO.PAT.JULY 14,1908,QUART,CLEAR.........   5.75
LIQUOZONE,BLOWN IN MOLD,PINT,BROWN........................   2.50
LORILLARD,HELMET ON LID,AMBER.............................   8.50
LOTION,HINDS HONEY & ALMOND,CLEAR.........................   1.50

LUXARDO BOTTLES WERE FIRST USED IN THE 1930'S TO BOTTLE
THE ITALIAN LIQUEURS. THE FIRM WAS FOUNDED IN 1821.
MOST OF THE LUXARDO BOTTLES FOUND TODAY DATE AFTER
1943. THE DATES GIVEN ARE THE FIRST YEAR THE BOTTLE
WAS MADE.
LUXARDO,ALABASTER FISH,1960...........................ILLUS..   30.00
LUXARDO,AMPULLA,VENETIAN GLASS,1959......................   15.00
LUXARDO,APOTHECARY JAR,MAJOLICA,1960.....................   12.00
LUXARDO,APPLE,MAJOLICA,1960..............................   8.00
LUXARDO,ASHTRAY,FIGHTING COCKS,MAJOLICA,1962.............   20.00
LUXARDO,ASHTRAY,MINIATURE,1959...........................   4.00
LUXARDO,ASHTRAY,MOSAIC,1959..............................   25.00
LUXARDO,ASSYRIAN ASHTRAY,MAJOLICA,1961...................   25.00
LUXARDO,AUTUMN LEAVES,MAJOLICA,1952......................   50.00
LUXARDO,AUTUMN WINE PITCHER,1958.........................   60.00
LUXARDO,BABY AMPHORA,1956................................   12.00
LUXARDO,BABYLON,MAJOLICA,1960............................   25.00
LUXARDO,BACCHUS..   16.00
LUXARDO,BANTU,MAJOLICA,1962..............................   25.00
LUXARDO,BAROQUE,GOLD,RUBY,AMPHORA,1951...................   55.00
LUXARDO,BAROQUE GOLD,TURQUOISE,MAJOLICA,1952-55..........   55.00
LUXARDO,BARREL,MAJOLICA,1968.............................   15.00

LUXARDO, ALABASTER FISH, 1960

LUXARDO, BLACK & GREEN AMPULLA, MAJOLICA, 1958...................	60.00
LUXARDO, BLUE & GOLD AMPHORA, MAJOLICA, 1968....................	20.00
LUXARDO, BRIZANTINA, MAJOLICA, 1959...........................	30.00
LUXARDO, BROCCA, MAJOLICA, 1958...................... 40.00 TO	50.00
LUXARDO, BUDDHA, JOGAN, BROWN, MAJOLICA, 1962...................	22.00
LUXARDO, BUDDHA, JOGAN, GRAY, MAJOLICA, 1962...................	20.00
LUXARDO, BUDDHA, MAJOLICA, 1961..............................	28.00
LUXARDO, BURMA, ASHTRAY, MAJOLICA, 1960.......................	30.00
LUXARDO, BURMA, ASHTRAY, MINIATURE, 1960......................	4.00
LUXARDO, BURMA, PITCHER, MAJOLICA, 1960.......................	25.00
LUXARDO, CALYPSO GIRL, MAJOLICA, 1962................. 10.50 TO	15.00
LUXARDO, CANDLESTICK, ALABASTER, VENETIAN GLASS, 1961...........	30.00
LUXARDO, CELLINI VASE, VENETIAN GLASS, 1958...................	20.00
LUXARDO, CELLINI, URN, MOLDED, GLASS, SILVER, 1968...............	18.95
LUXARDO, CELLINI, URN, VENETIAN GLASS........................	19.00
LUXARDO, CHERRY BASKET, MAJOLICA, 1960........................	32.00
LUXARDO, CHESS PIECES, MAJOLICA, 6, 1959......................	300.00
LUXARDO, CLASSICAL FRAGMENT, MAJOLICA, 1961...................	25.00
LUXARDO, CLOCK, VENETIAN GLASS, 1960.........................	11.00
LUXARDO, COCKTAIL SHAKER, VENETIAN GLASS, 1957................	19.00
LUXARDO, COFFEE CARAFE, MAJOLICA, 1962.......................	15.50
LUXARDO, CONGO, MAJOLICA, 1960..............................	22.50
LUXARDO, CUCCIOLO PUPPY, VENETIAN GLASS, 1961.................	24.00
LUXARDO, CURVA VASO, VENETIAN GLASS, 1961....................	25.00
LUXARDO, DECANTER, BLUE FIAMMETTA, 1957......................	20.00
LUXARDO, DECANTER, DOGAL SILVER, GREEN, GONDOLA, 1952-55........	25.00
LUXARDO, DECANTER, DOGAL SILVER, GREEN, GONDOLA, 1956..........	20.00
LUXARDO, DECANTER, DOGAL SILVER, RUBY, BUILDINGS, 1956..........	20.00
LUXARDO, DECANTER, DOGAL SILVER, RUBY, LADY, 1952-55...........	30.00
LUXARDO, DECANTER, DOGAL SILVER, SMOKE, GONDOLA, 1956..........	20.00
LUXARDO, DECANTER, DOGAL SILVER, SMOKE, GONDOLIER, 1952-55......	25.00
LUXARDO, DECANTER, DOGAL SILVER, SMOKE, NECK BANDS, GONDOLA, 1957.	20.00
LUXARDO, DECANTER, RED & GOLD, 1952..........................	500.00
LUXARDO, DECANTER, SHERATON, SILVER, BROWN, 1957...............	20.00
LUXARDO, DECANTER, SILVER AMETHYST, 1957......................	20.00
LUXARDO, DECANTER, SILVER JADE, 1957.........................	20.00
LUXARDO, DECANTER, SILVER, BLUE, 1952-55......................	20.00
LUXARDO, DECANTER, SILVER, BROWN, 1952-55.....................	20.00
LUXARDO, DECANTER, SILVER, GREEN, FLORAL, 1952-55..............	20.00
LUXARDO, DECANTER, VENETIAN GOLD WINE LEAF, 1958..............	30.00
LUXARDO, DECANTER, VENETIAN GOLD, GREEN, 1952-55..............	30.00
LUXARDO, DECANTER, VENETIAN GOLD, ROSE, 1952-55...............	30.00
LUXARDO, DECANTER, VENETIAN GOLD, VIOLET, 1952-55.............	30.00

```
LUXARDO,DECANTER,VENETIAN MERLETTO,1957......................  30.00
LUXARDO,DECANTER,VENETIAN SILVER,GREEN,FLECKED,1952-55.......  30.00
LUXARDO,DECANTER,VENETIAN SILVER,VIOLET,1952-55..............  30.00
LUXARDO,DECANTER,VERMILION FIRMMETTA,1957...................   30.00
LUXARDO,DECANTER,WHITE & GOLD,GLASS,1952....................  500.00
LUXARDO,DERUTA AMPHORA,MAJOLICA,1956........................  50.00
LUXARDO,DERUTA CAMEO AMPHORA,1959...........................  55.00
LUXARDO,DERUTA PITCHER,MAJOLICA,1953........................  60.00
LUXARDO,DIANA DECANTER,MAJOLICA,1956........................  55.00
LUXARDO,DOLPHIN,VENETIAN GLASS,1959.........................  48.00
LUXARDO,DOUGHNUT,VENETIAN GLASS,1959........................   8.00
LUXARDO,DRAGON AMPHORA,MAJOLICA,1953........................  55.00
LUXARDO,DRAGON PITCHER,MAJOLICA,1958........................  60.00
LUXARDO,DUCK,GREEN,VENETIAN GLASS,1960......................  35.00
LUXARDO,DUCK,SURREALIST,1952-55.............................  60.00
LUXARDO,EAGLE,ONYX,1970.....................................  48.00
LUXARDO,EGYPTIAN,MAJOLICA,1959..............................  15.00
LUXARDO,EGYPTIAN,MAJOLICA,1968..............................  12.50
LUXARDO,ETRUSCA,DARK BROWN,MAJOLICA,1959....................  50.00
LUXARDO,EUGANEAN BRONZE,MAJOLICA,1952-55....................  60.00
LUXARDO,EUGANEAN COPPER,MAJOLICA,1952-55....................  60.00
LUXARDO,FAENZA,1950.........................................   8.00
LUXARDO,FIORI,MAJOLICA,1956.................................  60.00
LUXARDO,FISH,ALABASTER,VENETIAN GLASS,1960......... 23.00 TO  30.00
LUXARDO,FISH,VENETIAN GLASS,GREEN & GOLD,1960...............  23.00
LUXARDO,FISH,VENETIAN GLASS,RUBY,1961.......................  24.00
LUXARDO,FLORENTINE,MAJOLICA,1956............................  50.00
LUXARDO,FORGET-ME-NOT,1959......................... 35.00 TO  38.00
LUXARDO,FRUIT MINIATURES,6,1960.............................  50.00
LUXARDO,FUSO,MAJOLICA,1959..................................  30.00
LUXARDO,GAMBIA,MAJOLICA,1961................................  10.50
LUXARDO,GAZELLE,SURREALIST,1952-54..........................  60.00
LUXARDO,GIARA,MAJOLICA,1959.................................  30.00
LUXARDO,GONDOLA,MAJOLICA,MINIATURE,1959.....................   5.00
LUXARDO,GONDOLA,MAJOLICA,MINIATURE,1960.....................   5.00
LUXARDO,GONDOLA,MAJOLICA,1959...............................  25.00
LUXARDO,GONDOLA,MAJOLICA,1960...............................  25.00
LUXARDO,GOOSE,ALABASTER,VENETIAN GLASS,1960.................  23.00
LUXARDO,GRAPES,MAJOLICA,1960................................   8.00
LUXARDO,GRAY & GOLD URN,1958................................  30.00
LUXARDO,MARABOU,SURREALIST,1957.............................  60.00
LUXARDO,MAYAN,MAJOLICA,1960.................................  21.00
LUXARDO,MAZZO AMPHORA,MAJOLICA,1954.........................  50.00
LUXARDO,MEDIEVAL PALACE,1952................................   8.00
LUXARDO,MISS LUXARDO,1970...................................  16.00
LUXARDO,NACREOUS,MAJOLICA,1957..............................  40.00
LUXARDO,NUBIAN,MAJOLICA,1959....................... 10.50 TO  14.95
LUXARDO,NUBIAN,MINIATURE,MAJOLICA,1959......................   5.00
LUXARDO,OPAL,MAJOLICA,1957..................................  40.00
LUXARDO,ORIENTAL SCREEN,MAJOLICA,1961.......................  25.00
LUXARDO,OWL,ONYX,1970.......................................  48.00
LUXARDO,PAESTUM,MAJOLICA,1959...............................   6.00
LUXARDO,PAESTUM,MINIATURE,1959..............................   5.00
LUXARDO,PAGLIACCI,VENETIAN GLASS,1959.......................  18.00
LUXARDO,PEAR,MAJOLICA,1960..................................   8.00
LUXARDO,PENGUIN,VENETIAN GLASS,1968.........................  24.00
LUXARDO,PHEASANT,BLACK,VENETIAN GLASS....................... 100.00
LUXARDO,PHEASANT,RED,CLEAR,VENETIAN GLASS,1960..............  34.50
LUXARDO,PHEASANT,RED,GOLD,VENETIAN GLASS,1960...............  23.00
LUXARDO,PIERROT,SIGNED TILE,MAJOLICA,1959...................  61.00
LUXARDO,POMPEIAN,MAJOLICA,1956..............................  50.00
LUXARDO,PRIMAVERA AMPHORA,1958..............................  50.00
LUXARDO,PUPPY,VENETIAN GLASS,1960...........................  24.00
LUXARDO,PURPLE & GOLD URN,1958..............................  30.00
LUXARDO,RUBY & GOLD AMPHORA,1958............................  55.00
LUXARDO,SAFARI,MAJOLICA,1960................................  22.50
```

```
LUXARDO,SANTA MARIA,1970........................... 9.00 TO    16.00
LUXARDO,SILHOUETTE,1961..................................      40.00
LUXARDO,SIR LANCELOT,MAJOLICA,1962.......................      22.00
LUXARDO,SLAVE GIRL,MAJOLICA,1960.........................      38.00
LUXARDO,SPRINGBOK AMPHORA,MAJOLICA,1952..................      60.00
LUXARDO,SPUGNATO,MAJOLICA,1956...........................      50.00
LUXARDO,SQUIRREL,VENETIAN GLASS,1968.....................      28.00
LUXARDO,STRUSCA,LIGHT BROWN,MAJOLICA,1959................      40.00
LUXARDO,SUDAN,AFRICA,MAJOLICA,1960.......................      20.00
LUXARDO,SWAN,SURREALIST,1952-55..........................      60.00
LUXARDO,TAMBURELLO,MAJOLICA,1959.........................      25.00
LUXARDO,TAPA PRINT.......................................       8.00
LUXARDO,TORRE AZZURA,MAJOLICA,1961.......................      20.00
LUXARDO,TORRE BIANCA,MAJOLICA,1962.......................      15.00
LUXARDO,TORRE ROSA,MAJOLICA,1962.........................      15.00
LUXARDO,TORRE TINTA,MAJOLICA,1962........................      20.00
LUXARDO,TOWER OF FLOWERS,MAJOLICA,1968...................      15.00
LUXARDO,TOWER OF FRUIT,MAJOLICA,1968.....................      15.00
LUXARDO,TRIO,MAJOLICA,1956...............................     100.00
LUXARDO,TURKEY,MINIATURE,MAJOLICA,1961...................      15.00
LUXARDO,TWO COMPARTMENT,MAJOLICA,1955....................      50.00
LUXARDO,UCTFLLO PITCHER,MAJOLICA,1958....................      50.00
LUXARDO,VASELLA ROMANA,1957...................... 50.00 TO     55.00
LUXARDO,VENETIAN CANNON,CERAMIC..........................      15.00
LUXARDO,VENUS DE MILO,MAJOLICA,1959......................      27.50
LUXARDO,VENUS DI MILO,MINIATURE,MAJOLICA,1959............       5.00
LUXARDO,VENUS DI MILO,1971...............................      14.00
LUXARDO,WARRIOR,URN,MAJOLICA,1956........................      50.00
LUXARDO,WHITE & GOLD FAUN AMPHORA,1958...................      40.00
LUXARDO,WHITE & GOLD GRIFFON AMPHORA,1958................      50.00
LUXARDO,WHITE TOPAZ,MAJOLICA,1952-55.....................      50.00
LUXARDO,WOBBLE BOTTLE,VENETIAN GLASS,1957................      35.00
LUXARDO,ZEBRA,SURREALIST,1957............................      60.00
LUXARDO,ZODIAC,ONYX,1970.................................      19.00
LYON'S KATHAIRON FOR THE HAIR,OPEN PONTIL................      11.00
MAC KAYS,SCOTT,RED.......................................      14.95
MALLET SHAPE,ENGRAVED FATHER TIME,CUT GLASS,CIRCA 1040...     120.00
MALLONY,FLOWER CHILD.....................................       6.95
MALLONY,HIPPIE...........................................       6.50
MALLONY,VILLAIN..........................................       7.50
MARY GREGORY,COLOGNE,ENAMELED GIRL CARRYING CAKE,BEIGE...      39.00
MARY GREGORY,COLOGNE,GIRL GATHERING FLOWERS,AMBER........      91.00
MARY GREGORY,DECANTER,STOPPER,CRANBERRY..................     151.00
MCCORMICK,AGING BARREL,1968..............................      10.00
MCCORMICK,AIR RACE DECANTER.......................ILLUS..      14.95
MCCORMICK,BARREL WITH STAND..............................       8.95
MCCORMICK,ENGINE.........................................      10.95
MCCORMICK,JUPITER 1960 LOCOMOTIVE........................      11.45
MCCORMICK,JUPITER 1960 MAIL CAR.................... 7.95 TO     9.45
MCCORMICK,JUPITER 1960 PASSENGER CAR.............. 10.95 TO    11.45
MCCORMICK,JUPITER 1960 WOOD TENDER................ 7.95 TO      9.45
MCCORMICK,KANSAS CITY CHIEFS,1969................. 12.00 TO    49.50
MCCORMICK,MISSOURI SESQUICENTENNIAL,1970.................      12.00
MCCORMICK,PLATTE VALLEY JUG..............................       4.95
MCCORMICK,SKIBOB,1970....................................      12.00
MCCORMICK,TRAIN,GOLDEN SPIKE CENTENNIAL,1969........ILLUS..    42.00
MCCORMICK,WOOD TENDER....................................       8.95
MCELREES WINE OF CARDUI,GREEN BIMAL......................       2.50
MCKAY,BAGPIPER...........................................       9.95
MCKENNA,JUG..............................................       3.95
```

MEDICINE BOTTLES HELD ALL OF THE MANY TYPES OF
MEDICATIONS USED IN PAST CENTURIES. MOST OF THOSE
COLLECTED TODAY DATE FROM THE 1850-1930 PERIOD.

MCCORMICK, AIR RACE DECANTER

MCCORMICK, TRAIN, GOLDEN SPIKE CENTENNIAL, 1969

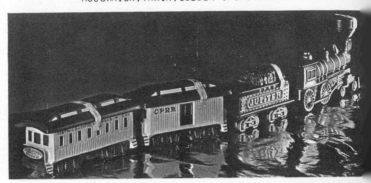

BITTERS, SARSAPARILLA, POISON, AND A FEW OTHER TYPES OF MEDICINE ARE LISTED UNDER THEIR OWN HEADINGS.

MEDICINE, A.MC ECKRON'S R.B.LINIMENT, OPEN PONTIL, AQUA.........	9.00
MEDICINE, A.TRASK, OINTMENT, SQUARE, AQUA........................	2.00
MEDICINE, A.TRASK'S MAGNETIC OINTMENT, AQUA........... 1.50 TO	2.50
MEDICINE, ABILENA, APPLIED LIP................................	3.50
MEDICINE, ACKER'S ENGLISH REMEDY, FOR THROAT & LUNGS, COBALT...	10.00
MEDICINE, ACKERS ENGLISH REMEDY, COBALT.......................	8.00
MEDICINE, AL-LAL IN WATER, AMBER..............................	11.00
MEDICINE, ALCORUB SKIN TREATMENT, GLASS STOPPER, CLEAR.........	3.00
MEDICINE, ALEXANDER'S SURE CURE FOR MALARIA, AMBER............	11.00
MEDICINE, ALEXANDERS RHEUMATIC & MALARIAL REMEDY, AMBER.......	6.00
MEDICINE, ALEXANDERS SURE CURE FOR MALARIA....................	15.00
MEDICINE, ALLEN'S LUNG BALSAM, BLUE...........................	10.00
MEDICINE, ALLENS ANTI FAT, BOTANIC MEDICINE CO.................	5.00
MEDICINE, AMBER, ROUND, 6 IN...........................ILLUS..	1.50
MEDICINE, ANDERSON'S DERMADOR.................................	4.00
MEDICINE, ANDERSON'S DERMADOR, AQUA.................. 12.50 TO	16.00
MEDICINE, ANGIER'S PETROLEUM EMULSION, AQUA........... 1.75 TO	4.00
MEDICINE, ANODYNE, APPLIED LIP................................	6.00
MEDICINE, AQUA, HAND-BLOWN, 5 IN.HIGH.........................	1.00
MEDICINE, AQUA, 6 IN...................................ILLUS..	2.00
MEDICINE, ARMOUR LABORATORIES, CHICAGO IN OVAL, AMBER..........	2.00
MEDICINE, ARNICA & OIL LINIMENT, 8 SIDED, AQUA................	1.50
MEDICINE, ARRAKS, PUNSCH, BLOB SEAL, AQUA.....................	10.00
MEDICINE, ASTYPTODYNE CHEMICAL CO., AMETHYST..................	4.00
MEDICINE, ASTYPTODYNE CHEMICAL CO., CLEAR.....................	4.00
MEDICINE, AYER'S AGUE CURE, AQUA..............................	6.00
MEDICINE, AYER'S CHERRY PECTORAL..............................	18.00
MEDICINE, AYER'S HAIR VIGOR, BLUE.............................	12.00
MEDICINE, AYER'S HAIR VIGOR, COBALT BLUE............. 10.00 TO	22.50
MEDICINE, AYER'S HAIR VIGOR, SQUARE, PEACOCK........... 8.00 TO	19.75
MEDICINE, AYER'S PILLS, SQUARE, CLEAR.........................	2.00
MEDICINE, AYER'S, SUNKEN PANEL, AQUA..........................	3.00
MEDICINE, BABY DEMIJOHN, PONTIL KICKUP........................	10.00
MEDICINE, BACHELOR'S HAIR DYE NO. 1...........................	16.00
MEDICINE, BALM X THOUSAND FLOWERS, 8 SIDED, GREEN.............	14.00
MEDICINE, BARDED FENCE LINIMENT...............................	24.00
MEDICINE, BARRY'S TRICOPHEROUS FOR THE SKIN & HAIR...........	12.00
MEDICINE, BARRY'S TRICOPHEROUS FOR THE SKIN & HAIR, AQUA......	24.00
MEDICINE, BAYER ASPIRIN, SCREW TOP, MACHINE MADE, CLEAR........	3.00
MEDICINE, BEACH & CLARRIDGE CHEMISTS, BLOWN IN MOLD, CLEAR.....	2.00

MEDICINE,AMBER,ROUND,6 IN

MEDICINE,AQUA,6 IN

```
MEDICINE,BEEBE'S WHITE PINE & TAR,CLEAR......................    4.00
MEDICINE,BELL-ANS..........................................    1.50
MEDICINE,BENJAMIN GREEN APOTHECARY,BLOWN IN MOLD,AMETHYST...    2.00
MEDICINE,BENJAMIN GREEN APOTHECARY,CLEAR............ 1.50 TO    2.00
MEDICINE,BENNET'S MAGIC CURE,COBALT.................COLOR..   30.00
MEDICINE,BERLINER KUMMEL,GAL................................    4.00
MEDICINE,BEVEL CORNERS,WIDE MOUTH,OPEN PONTIL,EMBOSSED IA,
  SQUARE...................................................   10.95
MEDICINE,BIRD'S LUNG CURE,AQUA.............................    6.00
MEDICINE,BLOWN IN MOLD,AMBER...............................    1.00
MEDICINE,BLOWN IN MOLD,AMETHYST............................    2.00
MEDICINE,BLOWN IN MOLD,AQUA........................ 1.00 TO    3.00
MEDICINE,BLOWN IN MOLD,BLUE........................ 1.50 TO    2.00
MEDICINE,BLOWN IN MOLD,BROWN...............................    1.75
MEDICINE,BLOWN IN MOLD,CLEAR....................... 1.00 TO    2.25
MEDICINE,BLOWN IN MOLD,COBALT BLUE.........................    1.00
MEDICINE,BLOWN IN MOLD,SHORT BALL NECK,AQUA................    1.00
MEDICINE,BLOWN IN MOLD,SQUARE BASE,CLEAR...................    2.50
MEDICINE,BLOWN IN MOLD,STRAP SIDE,CLEAR....................    1.50
MEDICINE,BLOWN IN MOLD,WHITTLE,AQUA................ 2.00 TO    3.50
MEDICINE,BLOWN IN MOLD,WHITTLE,BLUE........................    1.25
MEDICINE,BLOWN IN MOLD,WHITTLE,CLEAR.......................    2.50
MEDICINE,BLOWN IN MOLD,3 1/2 IN. TALL,CLEAR................    1.00
MEDICINE,BLOWN IN MOLD,3 3/4 IN. TALL,AQUA.................    1.00
MEDICINE,BLOWN IN MOLD,4 3/8 IN. TALL,AQUA.................    1.00
MEDICINE,BLOWN IN MOLD,5 1/4 IN. TALL,BROWN................    1.00
MEDICINE,BLOWN IN MOLD,7 1/4 IN. TALL,AMBER................    2.00
MEDICINE,BLOWN IN MOLD,7 1/4 IN. TALL,AQUA.................    2.00
MEDICINE,BLOWN IN MOLD,7 1/2 IN. TALL,COBALT BLUE..........    3.00
MEDICINE,BLOWN IN MOLD,7 1/2 IN. TALL,GREEN........ 2.00 TO    3.00
MEDICINE,BLOWN IN MOLD,8 1/2 IN. TALL,AQUA.................    2.25
MEDICINE,BLOWN IN MOLD,10 IN. TALL,AQUA....................    2.25
MEDICINE,BLOWN IN MOLD,10 3/4 IN. TALL,AMBER...............    3.50
MEDICINE,BOARDMAN & NORTON,BLOWN IN MOLD,CLEAR.............    1.50
MEDICINE,BOERICKE & SCHRECK,AMBER.................. 1.50 TO    2.50
MEDICINE,BOERICKET & RUNYON CO.,CLEAR......................    3.00
MEDICINE,BOGLE'S HYPERION FLUID FOR THE HAIR,OVAL,AQUA.....   15.00
MEDICINE,BONPLAND'S FEVER & AGUE REMEDY....................   20.00
MEDICINE,BOSCHEES,DR.A.GERMAN SYRUP,LONG NECK,AQUA.........    3.00
MEDICINE,BROMO CAFFEINE,BLUE...............................    4.00
MEDICINE,BROMO SELTZER,APPLIED LIP.........................    1.50
MEDICINE,BROMO SELTZER,SCREW TOP,COBALT............ 1.00 TO    3.00
MEDICINE,BROMO SELTZER,2 1/2 IN. TALL,MACHINE MADE,COBALT...   2.00
MEDICINE,BROMO SELTZER,4 IN. TALL,MACHINE MADE,ROUND,COBALT.   2.00
MEDICINE,BROMO SELTZER,4 3/4 IN. TALL,MACHINE MADE,COBALT...   2.00
```

```
MEDICINE,BROMO SELTZER,5 IN. TALL,ROUND,COBALT.............    4.00
MEDICINE,BROMO SELTZER,6 1/2 IN. TALL,MACHINE MADE,COBALT...    3.00
MEDICINE,BROMO SELTZER,8 IN. TALL,MACHINE MADE,COBALT.......    4.00
MEDICINE,BROOKS LEMOS AUSTRALIA,AQUA.......................   15.00
MEDICINE,BROWNELL IRON,STUBBY,COBALT.......................   35.00
MEDICINE,BUCHAN'S HUNGARIAN BALSAM OF LIFE,KIDNEY CURE,GREEN    5.00
MEDICINE,BUCKINGHAM,WHISKER DYE,BROWN......................    4.00
MEDICINE,BURNETT BOSTON SMELLING SALTS.....................    5.50
MEDICINE,BURNETT,BOSTON....................................    1.50
MEDICINE,BURNETT'S COCAINE.................................    5.00
MEDICINE,BURNETT'S COCAINE,AQUA............................    3.00
MEDICINE,BURNETT'S COCAINE,8 PANEL.........................    7.50
MEDICINE,BURNHAM'S BEEF,WINE & IRON,SLOPED SHOULDERS,OLIVE
  GREEN...................................................    2.75
MEDICINE,BYTHINIA WATER,EMBOSSED,AMBER.....................   12.00
MEDICINE,C.C.C.LIGHTBODY'S COUGH SYRUP,BLOWN IN MOLD,BROWN..    2.00
MEDICINE,C.C.C.LIGHTBODY'S COUGHS,COLDS,GREEN..............    2.50
MEDICINE,C.DAMSCHINSKY HAIR DYE,AQUA............... 2.00 TO    3.00
MEDICINE,C.HEIMSTREET,TROY,N.Y.,COBALT BLUE................   65.00
MEDICINE,C.K.MAGEE'S EMULSION,AQUA,10 IN............ILLUS..    5.00
MEDICINE,CALCINED MAGNESIA,SQUARE,WIDE MOUTH,PONTIL,WHITTLED   12.00
MEDICINE,CALDWELL'S LAXATIVE...............................    3.50
MEDICINE,CALDWELL'S PEPSIN.................................    5.00
MEDICINE,CALDWELL'S SENNA,BLACK............................    3.50
MEDICINE,CALDWELL'S SYRUP PEPSIN,AQUA.;............. 1.00 TO    2.00
MEDICINE,CALDWELL'S SYRUP PEPSIN,EMBOSSED,CORKER...........    2.00
MEDICINE,CALDWELL'S SYRUP PEPSIN,RECTANGULAR,AQUA..........    4.00
MEDICINE,CALIFORNIA FIG SYRUP,CLEAR................. .50 TO    2.00
MEDICINE,CAMPHORMENTH ADS,MILK GLASS................ILLUS..    2.00
MEDICINE,CAPUDINE FOR HEADACHE,OVAL,AMBER..................    2.00
MEDICINE,CARBONA PRODUCTS CO.,HAIR DRESSING,AQUA...........    3.00
MEDICINE,CARBONA PRODUCTS CO.,HAIR OIL,AQUA................    2.00
MEDICINE,CARBONA,PANELED,AQUA..............................    5.00
MEDICINE,CARBONA,12 PANELS,MACHINE MADE....................    5.00
MEDICINE,CARDUI,GREEN......................................    5.00
MEDICINE,CASCARA AROMATIC,CLEAR,7 1/2 IN............ILLUS..    5.00
MEDICINE,CASTOR OIL,PURE,2 OZ.,FRANK TEA & CO.,FLASK,CLEAR..    8.00
MEDICINE,CASTOR OIL,ROUND,COBALT BLUE......................   12.00
MEDICINE,CASTORIA,AQUA,NEW YORK.....................ILLUS..   12.00
MEDICINE,CASTORINE,HERVAY CHEMICAL CO.,LABEL........ILLUS..    4.50
MEDICINE,CASWELL HANAND & CO.,CHEMISTS,SQUARE,COBALT.......    8.00
MEDICINE,CENTAUR LINIMENT..................................    6.00
MEDICINE,CENTOUR LINIMENT,3 1/2 IN. TALL,AQUA.............    2.00
MEDICINE,CENTOUR LINIMENT,5 IN. TALL,ROUND,AQUA...........    3.00
MEDICINE,CHAMBERLAIN'S COLIC CHOLERA & DIARRHEA REMEDY,AQUA.    4.00
MEDICINE,CHAMBERLAIN'S COLIC CHOLERA REMEDY,EMBOSSED,CORKER.    2.00
```

MEDICINE,C.K.MAGEE'S
EMULSION,AQUA,10 IN

MEDICINE,
CAMPHORMENTH ADS,
MILK GLASS

MEDICINE,CASCARA
AROMATIC,CLEAR,7 1/2 IN

MEDICINE,CASTORIA,
AQUA,NEW YORK

MEDICINE,CASTORINE,
HERVAY CHEMICAL CO.,LABEL

```
MEDICINE,CHAMBERLAIN'S COLIC,AQUA...........................     5.00
MEDICINE,CHAMBERLAIN'S COUGH REMEDY,BLACK...................     3.50
MEDICINE,CHAMBERLAIN'S COUGH REMEDY,RECTANGULAR,AQUA........     4.00
MEDICINE,CHAMBERLAIN'S COUGH REMEDY,RECTANGULAR,CLEAR.......     4.00
MEDICINE,CHAMBERLAIN'S LIQUID PEARL........................     4.50
MEDICINE,CHAMBERLAIN'S PAIN BALM,RECTANGULAR,AQUA..........     4.00
MEDICINE,CHAMBERLAIN'S,MACHINE MADE........................     2.00
MEDICINE,CHAMPLIN'S LIQUID PEARL,MILK GLASS................    12.50
MEDICINE,CHAS.H.PHILLIPS CHEMICAL CO.,BLOWN IN MOLD,CLEAR...     2.00
MEDICINE,CHATTANOOGA MEDICINE,CO.,AMBER....................     2.00
MEDICINE,CHEMICAL CO.D.D.,N.Y.,SQUARE,AMBER................     2.00
MEDICINE,CHESEBOROUGH MFG.CO.VASELINE......................     3.50
MEDICINE,CHRISTIE'S AQUE BALSAM,BIMAL..............ILLUS..       7.00
MEDICINE,CITRATE OF MAGNESIA,DOUBLE RING TOP,7 IN. TALL,AQUA     6.00
MEDICINE,CITRATE MAGNESIA,SCRIPT ON BOTTOM,8 IN. TALL,
   AMETHYST.................................................     2.00
MEDICINE,CITRATE MAGNESIA,SCRIPT,CLEAR.............ILLUS..       3.00
MEDICINE,CITY DRUG STORE,TEXAS,RECTANGULAR,AMETHYST.........     2.00
MEDICINE,CLARKE & WHITE,O.G................................    20.00
MEDICINE,CLARKS & WHITE,NEW YORK,QUART,GREEN...............    25.00
MEDICINE,COBALT BLUE........................... 1.00 TO         1.50
MEDICINE,COD LIVER OIL-FISH,MADE IN ITALY..................    10.00
MEDICINE,COD LIVER OIL,SCREW TOP,MACHINE MADE,ROUND,AMBER...     4.00
MEDICINE,COD LIVER OIL,SCREW TOP,MACHINE MADE,SQUARE,AMBER..     4.00
MEDICINE,COE KONNG TILLY,RED & BLUE........................     2.50
MEDICINE,COLTSFOOTE EXPECTORANT............................     3.00
MEDICINE,COMBAUT'S CAUSTIC BALM............................     4.00
MEDICINE,COMPOUND LITHIA TABLETS,CLEAR,3 IN.........ILLUS..      2.00
```

MEDICINE,
CHRISTIE'S AQUE BALSAM,BIMAL

MEDICINE,CITRATE
MAGNESIA SCRIPT,CLEAR

MEDICINE,COMPOUND LITHIA TABLETS,CLEAR,3 IN

```
MEDICINE,CONGER'S MAGIC REGULATOR,OPEN PONTIL,AQUA..........    10.00
MEDICINE,COOLEY,HARTFORD,CONN.................................   37.50
MEDICINE,COOPER'S NEW DISCOVERY,BLOWN IN MOLD,AQUA..........     4.00
MEDICINE,CORNUCOPIA,PINT......................................   60.00
MEDICINE,CORNUCOPIA,1/2 PINT..............................?....  65.00
MEDICINE,COSMOLINE JELLY,C.1930.......................ILLUS..     2.00
MEDICINE,CRAIG'S KIDNEY & LIVER CURE,AMBER.................      32.00
MEDICINE,CRAMER'S KIDNEY CURE,SAMPLE.........................     7.00
MEDICINE,CRANITONIC HAIR FOOD,LONG NECK......................     5.50
MEDICINE,CREOMULSION FOR COUGHS DUE TO COLDS,AMETHYST.......      4.00
MEDICINE,CREOMULSION FOR COUGHS DUE TO COLDS,CLEAR..........      4.00
MEDICINE,CRISSWELL'S HEADACHE CURE...........................     4.00
MEDICINE,CROWN PERFUMERY CO.SMELLING SALTS...................     7.50
MEDICINE,CURTIS & PERKINS CRAMP & PAIN KILLER,BANGOR,ME.....     10.00
MEDICINE,CURTIS & PERKINS,AQUA...............................     2.00
MEDICINE,CUTICURA SYSTEM,BIMAL...............................     5.00
MEDICINE,CUTICURA TREATMENT,POTTER DRUG & CHEM.CO.,BOSTON,
AQUA.........................................................    10.00
MEDICINE,CUTICURA,CONSTITUTIONAL HUMORS,AQUA........ 5.00 TO      8.00
MEDICINE,D.D.CHEMICAL CO.,N.Y.,AMBER.........................     2.00
MEDICINE,D.D.D.,MACHINE MADE,CLEAR...........................     5.00
MEDICINE,D.D.D.,SQUARE,3 1/2 IN. TALL,AMETHYST..............      6.00
MEDICINE,D.D.D.,SQUARE,5 1/2 IN.,AMETHYST....................     6.00
MEDICINE,D.D.D.EMBOSSED,CORKER...............................     2.00
MEDICINE,D.EVANS CAMOMILE PILLS,OPEN PONTIL..................     7.00
MEDICINE,DAVIONIAN,EMBOSSED & LABELS,AMBER...................    25.00
MEDICINE,DAVIS VEGETABLE COMPOUND............................     4.00
MEDICINE,DAVIS VEGETABLE PAIN KILLER,AQUA...........ILLUS..       3.50
MEDICINE,DAVIS VEGETABLE PAIN KILLER,DATED 1854,AQUA........      3.95
MEDICINE,DAVIS,PAIN KILLER,AQUA..............................     4.00
MEDICINE,DAVIS,SUNKEN PANEL FRONT,BLUE.......................     4.00
MEDICINE,DEAD STUCK,FOR BUGS,NONPOISONOUS,AQUA..............     12.00
MEDICINE,DEEP ROCK,OSWEGO,N.Y.,QUART.........................    22.00
MEDICINE,DEPOSE,RIODINE ORGANIC ASSIMILABE IODINE,
50 CAPSULES..................................................     6.00
MEDICINE,DERWILLO,FOR THE COMPLEXION,SQUARE,CLEAR...........      2.00
MEDICINE,DEWITT'S COLIC & CHOLERA CURE,BLOWN IN MOLD,AQUA...      3.00
MEDICINE,DEWITT'S SOOTHING SYRUP,CHICAGO,ROUND,AMETHYST.....      6.00
MEDICINE,DIABETES CURE,WARNER'S SAFE,BLOB TOP...............     18.00
MEDICINE,DIAMOND OIL,RECTANGULAR,AQUA........................     4.00
MEDICINE,DICKEY'S,JOHN R.,OLD RELIABLE EYE WATER,ROUND,AQUA.      4.00
MEDICINE,DILLS COUGH SYRUP...................................     3.00
MEDICINE,DODSON'S,LIVERTONE,RECTANGULAR,AMETHYST............      4.00
MEDICINE,DODSON'S,LIVERTONE,RECTANGULAR,AQUA.................     4.00
MEDICINE,DR.A.BOSCHEE'S GERMAN SYRUP,CLEAR..........ILLUS..       4.00
```

MEDICINE,
COSMOLINE JELLY,
C.1930

MEDICINE,DAVIS
VEGETABLE PAIN
KILLER,AQUA

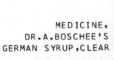

MEDICINE,
DR.A.BOSCHEE'S
GERMAN SYRUP,CLEAR

```
MEDICINE,DR.BAKER'S PAIN PANACEA,AQUA,6 IN..........ILLUS..    5.00
MEDICINE,DR.BAKER'S PAIN PANACEA,SMALL......................   16.00
MEDICINE,DR.BAKER'S PAIN RELIEF,AQUA........................    5.00
MEDICINE,DR.BAXTER'S,PALE SMOKY GREEN.......................   11.00
MEDICINE,DR.CALDWELL'S SYRUP PEPSIN.........................    2.00
MEDICINE,DR.CALDWELL'S SYRUP OF PEPSIN......................    3.00
MEDICINE,DR.CKK.DONNELL'S INDIAN REMEDIES...................    3.00
MEDICINE,DR.COOPER'S ELECTRIC COUGH BALSAM...........ILLUS..   15.00
MEDICINE,DR.COX BARB WIRE LINIMENT..........................    3.00
MEDICINE,DR.CROOKS WINE OF TAR,K IN RECESSED BASE,GREEN.....   10.00
MEDICINE,DR.CUMMING'S VEGETINE,AQUA,9 1/2 IN.........ILLUS..    8.00
MEDICINE,DR.D.JAYNE'S ALTERNATIVE,AQUA......................   13.50
MEDICINE,DR.D.JAYNE'S EXPECTORANT.AQUA...............ILLUS..   14.00
```

MEDICINE,
DR.BAKER'S PAIN
PANACEA,AQUA,6 IN

MEDICINE,
DR.COOPER'S
ELECTRIC
COUGH BALSAM

MEDICINE,
DR.CUMMING'S
VEGETINE,AQUA,
9 1/2 IN

MEDICINE,
DR.D.JAYNE'S
EXPECTORANT,AQUA

```
MEDICINE,DR.D.JAYNE'S EXPECTORANT,PHILA.,TUBULAR PONTIL,AQUA   20.00
MEDICINE,DR.DANIELS'FEVER DROPS.....................ILLUS..    4.50
MEDICINE,DR.DANIELS GOLDEN LINIMENT.........................    1.00
MEDICINE,DR.DANIELS VETERINARY COLIC CURE,NO.1,CLEAR........    1.50
MEDICINE,DR.DANIELS VETERINARY COLIC DROPS,NO.2,CLEAR.......    1.50
MEDICINE,DR.DRAKE'S GERMAN CROUP REMEDY,AQUA................    5.00
MEDICINE,DR.DUNCAN WORM SYRUP...............................    5.00
MEDICINE,DR.E.C.BALM,AQUA...................................   20.00
MEDICINE,DR.FAHRNEY'S HEALTH RESTORER,AMBER.................    6.00
MEDICINE,DR.FENNER,EMBOSSED,CORKER..........................    2.00
MEDICINE,DR.FENNER'S KIDNEY & BACKACHE CURE....... 25.00 TO   35.00
MEDICINE,DR.FENNER'S KIDNEY & BACKACHE CURE,AMBER...........   25.00
MEDICINE,DR.GEORGE PIERCES INDIAN RESTORATIVE BITTERS.......   15.00
MEDICINE,DR.GUNN'S ONION SYRUP,EMBOSSED.....................    4.95
MEDICINE,DR.H.S.THACHER'S DIARRHEA REMEDY,TENN.,SQUARE,
  AMETHYST..................................................    5.00
MEDICINE,DR.H.S.THACHER'S WORM SYRUP,AQUA........... 2.00 TO    5.00
MEDICINE,DR.H.S.THACHER'S WORM SYRUP,CLEAR...........ILLUS..    4.50
MEDICINE,DR.HAND'S TEETHING LOTION,CLEAR............ILLUS..    5.50
MEDICINE,DR.HOBSON'S VEGETABLE PRESCRIPTION.........ILLUS..    3.50
MEDICINE,DR.HUNTER'S EXPECTORANT,APPLIED LIP................    6.00
MEDICINE,DR.J.H.MC LEAN,AMBER...................... 1.00 TO    2.00
MEDICINE,DR.J.H.MC LEAN'S VOLCANIC OIL LINIMENT,SQUARE,AQUA.    6.00
MEDICINE,DR.J.MILLER'S VEGETABLE EXPECTORANT,12 PANELS,AQUA.    3.00
MEDICINE,DR.JAYNE'S ALTERATIVE,AQUA.........................   13.00
MEDICINE,DR.JAYNE'S AMERICAN HAIR DYE.......................   16.00
MEDICINE,DR.JAYNE'S CARMINATIVE BALSAM......................   15.00
MEDICINE,DR.JAYNE'S INDIAN EXPECTORANT,GREEN................   23.00
MEDICINE,DR.JAYNE'S TONIC VERMIFUGE,EMBOSSED,CORKER.........    2.00
MEDICINE,DR.JAYNE'S TONIC VERMIFUGE,OVAL....................   15.00
```

MEDICINE,DR.H.S.THACHER'S
WORM SYRUP,CLEAR

MEDICINE,
DR.HAND'S
TEETHING
LOTION,CLEAR

MEDICINE,
DR.HOBSON'S
VEGETABLE
PRESCRIPTION

MEDICINE,
DR.DANIELS'
FEVER DROPS

MEDICINE,DR.JAYNE'S TONIC VERMIFUGE,SQUARE...................	12.00
MEDICINE,DR.JAYNES ALTERNATIVE,84 CHEST ST.,PHILA.,PONTIL...	14.50
MEDICINE,DR.JAYNES EXPECTORANT...................... 2.75 TO	14.50
MEDICINE,DR.JAYNES EXPECTORANT,PONTIL,EMBOSSED..............	18.00
MEDICINE,DR.KENNEDY'S MEDICAL DISCOVERY,AQUA........ 3.00 TO	4.00
MEDICINE,DR.KENNEDY'S PRAIRIE WEED..........................	14.00
MEDICINE,DR.KENNEDY'S RHEUMATIC DISSOLVENT,8 3/4 IN. TALL, AQUA..	4.00
MEDICINE,DR.KILMER & CO.,BLOWN IN MOLD,AQUA.................	7.00
MEDICINE,DR.KILMER SWAMP ROOT KIDNEY,LIVER & BLADDER REMEDY.	4.00
MEDICINE,DR.KILMER'S AUTUMN LEAF EXTRACT....................	14.00
MEDICINE,DR.KILMER'S HERBAL EXTRACT FOR UTERINE INJECTION, AQUA..	8.00
MEDICINE,DR.KILMER'S KIDNEY & LIVER CURE,LONDON,E.C.,SAMPLE.	15.00
MEDICINE,DR.KILMER'S KIDNEY & LIVER CURE,SAMPLE.............	4.00
MEDICINE,DR.KILMER'S LIVER & KIDNEY........................	3.50
MEDICINE,DR.KILMER'S OCEAN WEED HEART REMEDY,EMBOSSED VERTICAL..	12.00
MEDICINE,DR.KILMER'S OCEANWEED,EMBOSSED HEART,AQUA..........	18.00
MEDICINE,DR.KILMER'S SWAMP-ROOT CURE,7 1/2 IN........ILLUS..	4.50
MEDICINE,DR.KILMER'S SWAMP ROOT KIDNEY CURE,N.Y.,AQUA, 3 1/4 IN...	4.00
MEDICINE,DR.KILMER'S SWAMP ROOT KIDNEY REMEDY,CYLINDER,AQUA.	7.50
MEDICINE,DR.KILMER'S SWAMP ROOT KIDNEY,LIVER & BLADDER CURE, AQUA..	·3.00
MEDICINE,DR.KILMER'S SWAMP ROOT REMEDY............. 5.00 TO	10.00
MEDICINE,DR.KILMER'S SWAMP ROOT REMEDY,AQUA..........ILLUS..	8.00

MEDICINE,DR.KILMER'S
SWAMP-ROOT CURE,7 1/2 IN

MEDICINE,DR.KILMER'S
SWAMP ROOT REMEDY,AQUA

```
MEDICINE,DR.KILMER'S SWAMP ROOT,RECTANGULAR,AQUA............        3.00
MEDICINE,DR.KILMER'S,AMETHYST................................       5.00
MEDICINE,DR.KILMER'S,SAMPLE,EMBOSSED LONDON,AQUA.............       4.00
MEDICINE,DR.KILMSIS INDIAN COUGH CURE.......................        8.00
MEDICINE,DR.KING'S DISCOVERY FOR CONSUMPTION,AQUA...........        3.00
MEDICINE,DR.KING'S NEW DISCOVERY FOR CONSUMPTION............        1.00
MEDICINE,DR.KING'S NEW DISCOVERY FOR COUGHS & COLDS,CLEAR...        4.00
MEDICINE,DR.KING'S NEW DISCOVERY,RECTANGULAR,AQUA...........        4.00
MEDICINE,DR.KING'S NEW LIFE PILLS,SQUARE,CLEAR..............        3.00
MEDICINE,DR.LEPPER'S MOUNTAIN TEA,AQUA......................       10.00
MEDICINE,DR.M.A.SIMMONS LIVER,ROLLED LIP....................        5.00
MEDICINE,DR.MC LEAN'S LIVER & KIDNEY BALM,OVAL FLASK,AQUA...        4.00
MEDICINE,DR.MC MUNN'S ELIXIR OF OPIUM,AQUA..................        1.90
MEDICINE,DR.MC MUNN'S ELIXIR OF OPIUM,CYLINDER,PONTIL,AQUA..        7.50
MEDICINE,DR.MCLANE'S LIVER PILLS,BOX........................        3.00
MEDICINE,DR.MILES HEART CURE................................       12.00
MEDICINE,DR.MILES HEART TREATMENT,AQUA.............. 2.00 TO        3.00
MEDICINE,DR.MILES LABORATORIES INC..........................        1.50
MEDICINE,DR.MILES MEDICAL CO................................        2.50
MEDICINE,DR.MILES MEDICAL CO.,RECTANGULAR,AQUA..............        3.00
MEDICINE,DR.MILES NERVINE,RECTANGULAR,AQUA..................        3.00
MEDICINE,DR.MILES NEW HEART CURE............................        6.00
MEDICINE,DR.MILES NEW HEART CURE,AQUA,8 IN.........ILLUS..         6.00
MEDICINE,DR.MILES NEW HEART CURE,AQUA,8 IN.........ILLUS..        12.00
MEDICINE,DR.MILES NEW HEART CURE,GREEN......................        6.00
MEDICINE,DR.MILES RESTORATIVE NERVINE,AQUA.......... 3.00 TO        5.00
MEDICINE,DR.MITCHELS IPECAC SYRUP,GREEN.....................       10.00
MEDICINE,DR.NEBIR'S MONNOEPA................................        5.00
MEDICINE,DR.NORTON'S TASTELESS WORM DESTROYER,AMBER.........        9.00
MEDICINE,DR.NORTON'S TASTELESS WORM DESTROYER,HONEY AMBER,
   4 IN.....................................................        5.00
```

MEDICINE,   MEDICINE,
DR.MILES NEW HEART CURE,AQUA,8 IN   DR.MILES NEW HEART CURE,AQUA,8 IN

```
MEDICINE,DR.P.FAHRNEY,CLEAR,9 1/2 IN.................ILLUS..        4.00
MEDICINE,DR.PARCIE GOLDEN MEDICAL DISCOVERY,AQUA............        4.00
MEDICINE,DR.PETER FAHRNEY & SONS CO.,CLEAR..........ILLUS..         5.00
MEDICINE,DR.PETER'S KURILO,SQUARE,PANELED,AMETHYST..........        4.00
MEDICINE,DR.PIERCE FAVORITE PRESCRIPTION,EMBOSSED,CORKER....        2.00
MEDICINE,DR.PIERCE SMART-WEED...............................       12.50
MEDICINE,DR.PIERCE'S ANURIC TABLE,AQUA.............. 2.00 TO        3.50
MEDICINE,DR.PIERCE'S ANURIC,SAMPLE..........................        4.50
MEDICINE,DR.PIERCE'S EXTRACT OF SMARTWEED,AQUA..............        6.00
MEDICINE,DR.PIERCE'S FAVORITE PRESCRIPTION.......... 5.00 TO        7.00
MEDICINE,DR.PIERCE'S FAVOURITE PRESCRIPTION,RECTANGULAR,AQUA        4.00
MEDICINE,DR.PIERCE'S GOLDEN MEDICAL DISCOVERY....... 2.00 TO        4.00
MEDICINE,DR.S.& H.& CO.P.R.REGISTERED,ROUND,AMETHYST........       10.00
MEDICINE,DR.S.& H.& CO.P.R.REGISTERED,ROUND,AQUA............       10.00
MEDICINE,DR.S.A.TUTTLE,BLOWN IN MOLD,12 PANELS,BLUE.........        3.00
MEDICINE,DR.S.A.TUTTLE,BLOWN IN MOLD,12 PANELS,GREEN........        3.00
MEDICINE,DR.S.N.THOMAS ELECTRIC OIL,BLUE....................        6.00
MEDICINE,DR.S.PITCHER'S CASTORIA,BLOWN IN MOLD,BLUE.........        1.50
MEDICINE,DR.S.PITCHER'S,CASTORIA,RECTANGULAR,AQUA...........        4.00
MEDICINE,DR.S.S.FITCH & SONS,AQUA...........................        3.00
```

MEDICINE,DR.P.FAHRNEY,CLEAR,9 1/2 IN

MEDICINE,DR.PETER FAHRNEY & SONS CO.,CLEAR

```
MEDICINE,DR.S.S.FITCH,OPEN PONTIL,SHEARED NECK..............   22.00
MEDICINE,DR.SAGES,BUFFALO,CATARRH REMEDY,DR.PRICE PROPR.....    8.00
MEDICINE,DR.SANFORD'S LIVER INVIGORATOR....................     6.00
MEDICINE,DR.SCHENK'S PULMONIC SYRUP........................     7.00
MEDICINE,DR.SEELYE'S MAGIC CURE....................COLOR..     18.00
MEDICINE,DR.SHILOH'S SYSTEM VITALIZER,AQUA.................     10.00
MEDICINE,DR.SHOOP'S CATARRH REMEDY.........................     3.75
MEDICINE,DR.SHOOP'S FAMILY,BLOWN IN MOLD,AQUA....... 3.00 TO    4.00
MEDICINE,DR.SYKES SPECIFIC BLOOD MEDICINE,CLEAR............     3.00
MEDICINE,DR.SYKES SURE CURE FOR CATARRH,AQUA...............     4.00
MEDICINE,DR.SYKES SURE CURE FOR CATARRH,ROUND,AQUA.........     6.00
MEDICINE,DR.TAFT'S ASTHMALENE,N.Y.,RECTANGULAR,AQUA........     4.00
MEDICINE,DR.THACHER'S LIVER & BLOOD SYRUP,TENN.,RECT.,AMBER.    5.00
MEDICINE,DR.THACHER'S VEGETABLE SYRUP,TENN.,RECT.,AMETHYST..    2.00
MEDICINE,DR.THACHER'S VEGETABLE SYRUP,7 IN...........ILLUS..    4.00
MEDICINE,DR.THACHER'S WORM SYRUP,AMBER...............ILLUS..    3.00
MEDICINE,DR.THACHER'S WORM SYRUP,CLEAR,4 IN.........ILLUS..     2.00
MEDICINE,DR.THATCHER'S LIVER & BLOOD SYRUP,TENN.,SAMPLE,
   AMBER....................................................    4.00
MEDICINE,DR.THOMPSON'S EYE WATER,CONN.,ROUND,AQUA...........    2.00
MEDICINE,DR.TICHENOR'S,ANTISEPTIC,RECTANGULAR,AQUA.........     2.00
MEDICINE,DR.TOWNSEND'S STAIN...............................    45.00
MEDICINE,DR.TRUE'S ELIXIR,BIMAL,AQUA.......................     1.50
MEDICINE,DR.W.B.CALDWELL'S SYRUP...........................     4.00
MEDICINE,DR.W.B.CALDWELL'S SYRUP PEPSIN,CORK TOP,CLEAR......     2.50
MEDICINE,DR.W.B.CALDWELL'S SYRUP PEPSIN,PEPSIN SYRUP CO.,
   AQUA...................................................      4.00
```

MEDICINE,DR.THACHER'S
VEGETABLE SYRUP,7 IN

MEDICINE,DR.THACHER'S
WORM SYRUP,AMBER

MEDICINE,DR.THACHER'S
WORM SYRUP,CLEAR,4 IN

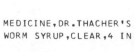

```
MEDICINE,DR.WARREN'S PURE GINGER BRANDY,AMBER...............      25.00
MEDICINE,DR.WILLIAMS PINK PILLS FOR PALE PEOPLE......ILLUS..      16.00
MEDICINE,DR.WISTAR'S BALSAM.................................       5.00
MEDICINE,DR.WISTAR'S BALSAM OF WILD CHERRY.......... 8.00 TO      10.00
MEDICINE,DR.WISTAR'S BALSAM OF WILD CHERRY.............ILLUS..     15.00
MEDICINE,DR.WISTAR'S BALSAM OF WILD CHERRY,AQUA.............       4.50
MEDICINE,DR.WISTAR'S BALSAM OF WILD CHERRY,CLEAR...........       10.00
MEDICINE,DR.WISTAR'S BALSAM,OPEN PONTIL....................       20.00
MEDICINE,DR.WOOD'S CHILL CURE,AQUA.........................        6.00
MEDICINE,DR.Y.Y.B.CALDWELL'S,MONTICELLO,ILLINOIS,AQUA......        3.00
MEDICINE,DRAKE'S CROUP REMEDY,EMBOSSED,CORKER..............        2.00
MEDICINE,DRAKES PALMETTO WINE..............................       18.00
MEDICINE,DUFFY'S MALT LIQUOR...............................        4.00
MEDICINE,DYOTTVILLE GLASS WORKS,3 MOLD.....................       14.00
MEDICINE,E.HARTSHORN & SONS,BLOWN IN MOLD,CLEAR............        3.00
MEDICINE,E.R.SQUIBB,CRUDE LIP,GREEN........................       10.00
MEDICINE,EAU DENTIFRICE DU DOCTEUR JEAU-PARIS,AMETHYST.....        3.00
MEDICINE,EAU DENTIFRICE DU DOCTEUR,JEAU-PARIS,CLEAR........        3.00
MEDICINE,EGYPTIAN CHEMICAL CO.,BOSTON,MASS.................        4.00
MEDICINE,ELEPIZONE CURE FOR FITS & EPILEPSY,AQUA...........       20.00
MEDICINE,ELIXIR ALIMENTAIRE................................        5.00
MEDICINE,ELIXIR OF THE PHOSPHATES,AQUA.....................        5.00
MEDICINE,ELIXIR PARAGORIC..................................        5.00
MEDICINE,ELLENVILLE GLASS WORKS,ROUND,QUART,GREEN..........       20.00
MEDICINE,ELY'S CREAM BALM,APPLIED LIP......................        4.00
MEDICINE,ELY'S CREAM BALM,RECTANGULAR,AMBER................        4.00
MEDICINE,EMBOSSED MAN & FISH,COD LIVER OIL,MACHINE MADE,
  CLEAR...................................................        1.00
MEDICINE,EMERSON DRUG,COBALT...............................        1.00
MEDICINE,ENO'S FRUIT SALT,GLASS LID........................        4.50
MEDICINE,ENO'S FRUIT SALTS,AQUA............................        6.00
MEDICINE,ESKEY FOOD,1/2 GAL.,BROWN.........................        7.75
MEDICINE,ESSENCE OF CHECKERBERRY...........................        8.00
MEDICINE,EVANS CAMOMILE PILLS..............................       10.00
MEDICINE,EXTRACT OF WITCH HAZEL,BLOWN IN MOLD,COBALT BLUE...       16.00
MEDICINE,F.EGNER & CO.,PHARMACEUTICS,CINCINNATI,CLEAR......        1.00
MEDICINE,F.N.BROWN'S ESSENCE OF JAMAICA GINGER,AQUA........        2.00
MEDICINE,F.W.KINSMAN DRUGGIST,BLOWN IN MOLD,STRAP SIDE,AQUA.       2.50
MEDICINE,FAIRCHILD BROS & FOSTER,BLOWN IN MOLD,CLEAR.......        2.00
MEDICINE,FARRAND WILLIAMS & CO.,COBALT,8 IN.........ILLUS..       10.00
MEDICINE,FARRIS HEALING REMEDY,CLEAR.................ILLUS..        2.50
MEDICINE,FATHER JOHN'S.....................................        3.00
MEDICINE,FATHER JOHN'S MEDICINE,BLOWN IN MOLD,BROWN........        4.50
MEDICINE,FAVORITE REMEDY,DR.D.KENNEDY'S,8 1/4 IN. TALL,AQUA.       4.00
MEDICINE,FELLOWS & CO.,CHEMISTS,AQUA................ 2.00 TO       3.00
```

MEDICINE,DR.WILLIAMS
PINK PILLS FOR
PALE PEOPLE

MEDICINE,
FARRAND WILLIAMS &
CO.,COBALT,8 IN

MEDICINE,DR.WISTAR'S
BALSAM OF WILD CHERRY

MEDICINE,FARRIS HEALING REMEDY,CLEAR

```
MEDICINE,FELLOWS SYRUP OF HYPOPHOSPHITS,OVAL,AQUA...........    6.00
MEDICINE,FINKS MAGIC OIL....................................    8.50
MEDICINE,FITCH'S EMULSION,BLOWN IN MOLD,BROWN..............     5.00
MEDICINE,FITCH'S IDEAL DANDRUFF CURE.......................     6.00
MEDICINE,FLAGG'S GOOD SAMARITANS IMMEDIATE RELIEF,AQUA......   10.00
MEDICINE,FLETCHER'S CASTORIA...............................      .50
MEDICINE,FLETCHER'S VEGE-TONIO,SQUARE,AMBER................    15.00
MEDICINE,FOLEY KIDNEY PILLS,FOLEY & CO.,CHICAGO,EMBOSSED,
   CLEAR..................................................      2.50
MEDICINE,FOLEY'S KIDNEY & BLADDER,AMBER....................    12.00
MEDICINE,FOR 40 ISACEN TABLETS,BRASS SCREW CAP,LABEL,
   AMETHYST...............................................     15.00
MEDICINE,FREDERICK STEARNS & CO.,AMBER,10 IN.........ILLUS..    6.00
MEDICINE,FREEMAN BLONDINE..................................     3.50
MEDICINE,FROSTILLA,MACHINE MADE............................     3.00
MEDICINE,FRUITOLA,RECTANGULAR,AQUA.........................     4.00
MEDICINE,G.A.GILKA,OLIVE AMBER.............................    25.00
MEDICINE,GARRETT DRUG CO.,CLEAR............................     2.00
MEDICINE,GAY-U-BA FOR KIDNEY COMPLAINT,W.P.DIGGS & CO.,AQUA.   15.00
MEDICINE,GENUINE ESSENCE,PONTIL............................     8.00
MEDICINE,GENUINE HOME OIL..................................     4.00
MEDICINE,GEO.C.FRYE,BLOWN IN MOLD,CLEAR....................     2.00
MEDICINE,GEO.E.RICHARDS & CO.,BLOWN IN MOLD,CLEAR..........     1.50
MEDICINE,GERMAN FIR COUGH CURE,BLOWN IN MOLD,BALL NECK,AQUA.    2.00
MEDICINE,GIBB'S BONE LINIMENT,6 SIDED,OLIVE GREEN..........   200.00
MEDICINE,GILMAN BROTHER'S,BLOWN IN MOLD,CLEAR..............     1.50
   MEDICINE, GIN, SEE GIN
MEDICINE,GLOVER'S IMPERIAL DISTEMPER REMEDY,NY,LITTLE PET...    1.50
MEDICINE,GLOVER'S IMPERIAL MANGE CURE,BROWN........ 3.50 TO     4.95
MEDICINE,GLOVER'S IMPERIAL MANGE MEDICINE,RECTANGULAR,AMBER.    2.00
MEDICINE,GLOVER'S IMPERIAL MANGE MEDICINE,6 1/2 FL.OZ.,AMBER    3.00
MEDICINE,GLOVER'S IMPERIAL MANGE REMEDY,BLOWN IN MOLD,BROWN.    3.50
MEDICINE,GLOVER'S MANGE REMEDY,AMBER.......................     3.00
MEDICINE,GLYCEROLE,APPLIED RING TOP,AQUA...................     2.00
MEDICINE,GLYCOTHYMOLINE,1 LB.,OVAL,AMETHYST................     5.00
MEDICINE,GLYCOTHYMOLINE,3 OZ.,OVAL,AMETHYST................     3.00
MEDICINE,GOFF'S INDIAN VEGETABLE COUGH SYRUP & BLOOD
   PURIFIER...............................................      9.00
MEDICINE,GOFF'S LINIMENT,EMBOSSED,CORKER...................     2.00
MEDICINE,GOLDEN'S LIQUID BEEF TONIC,CHAMPAGNE TYPE,GREEN....    8.00
MEDICINE,GOMBAULTS J.E.,CAUSTIC BALSAM,RECTANGULAR,AQUA.....    4.00
MEDICINE,GRAENFENBERG CO.CHILDREN'S PANACEA................     5.00
MEDICINE,GRANDMA SHUPES CANKER MEDICINE....................     4.95
MEDICINE,GRANDPA'S PAIN KILLER.............................     3.00
MEDICINE,GREAT SEAL,EMBOSSED,CORKER........................     2.00
MEDICINE,GREELEY'S COPPER,PUCE............................    165.00
MEDICINE,GREEN,PANELS,8 3/4 IN.....................ILLUS..      2.50
MEDICINE,GREEN'S AUGUST FLOWER FOR DYSPEPSIA...............     4.00
MEDICINE,GROVE'S TASTILESE CHILL TONIC,OVAL,AMETHYST.......     3.00
MEDICINE,GROVE'S TASTILESE CHILL TONIC,OVAL,CLEAR..........     3.00
MEDICINE,GUILFORD VT,QUART,GREEN...........................    20.00
MEDICINE,GUYSER SPRING SPOUTING SPRING,PINT,AQUA...........    30.00
MEDICINE,H.H.H.HORSE MEDICINE..............................     3.00
MEDICINE,H.H.H.HORSE,AQUA......................... 4.00 TO     5.00
MEDICINE,H.K.MULFORD CHEMIST,AMBER.........................     4.00
MEDICINE,H.K.WAMPOLE CO.,PHILADELPHIA,AMBER................     5.00
MEDICINE,H.LAKE INDIAN SPECIFIC,RAISED PANELS,NECK BULGE,
   AQUA...................................................     90.00
MEDICINE,HAGAN'S MAGNOLIA BALM,BIMAL,MILK GLASS............     9.00
MEDICINE,HAGEE'S CORDIAL,EMBOSSED,CORKER...................     2.00
MEDICINE,HAIR PRESERVATIVE & BEAUTIFIER,PONTIL,7 IN.,AQUA...   15.00
MEDICINE,HALL'S BALSAM FOR THE LUNGS,RECTANGULAR,AQUA.......    6.00
MEDICINE,HALL'S CATARRH CURE...............................     3.00
MEDICINE,HALL'S CATARRH CURE,AQUA.................. 3.00 TO     4.00
MEDICINE,HALL'S CURE,EMBOSSED,CORKER.......................     2.00
```

```
MEDICINE,HALL'S HAIR RENEWER,PEACOCK BLUE...................   22.50
MEDICINE,HALL'S HAIR RESTORER,BLUE..........................   35.00
MEDICINE,HAMILTON'S OLD ENGLISH BLACK OIL............ILLUS..    2.50
MEDICINE,HAMLIN'S WIZARD OIL,CHICAGO,RECTANGULAR,AQUA.......    3.00
MEDICINE,HAMLIN'S WIZARD OIL,6 IN.,TEAL BLUE...............     7.00
MEDICINE,HANCE BROTHERS & WHITE.............................    1.50
MEDICINE,HANSON & CO.,BLOWN IN MOLD,CLEAR...................    3.00
MEDICINE,HARRIS COUGH REMEDY,ROUND,AQUA.....................    3.50
MEDICINE,HARRIS COUGH REMEDY,SAMPLE.........................    4.00
MEDICINE,HASKEN'S NERVINE,AQUA..............................    6.00
MEDICINE,HASKEN'S NERVINE,LABEL.............................    6.50
MEDICINE,HATHORN,QUART......................................   20.00
MEDICINE,HATTIE & MYLIUS EPIDERMA FOR THE SKIN..............   12.00
MEDICINE,HAY'S HAIR HEALTH,EMBOSSED,CORKER..................    2.00
MEDICINE,HAY'S HAIR RENEWER,COBALT BLUE.....................   16.00
MEDICINE,HAY'S HEALING COMPOUND,APPLIED LIP.................    6.00
MEDICINE,HAYWOOD'S NUBIAN HAIR DYE..................ILLUS..     5.00
MEDICINE,HEALTH SPECIALIST SPROULE,BLOWN IN MOLD,CLEAR......    2.50
MEDICINE,HEALY & BIGELOW INDIAN SAGWA,EMBOSSED INDIAN.......   10.00
```

MEDICINE,FREDERICK STEARNS
& CO.,AMBER,10 IN

MEDICINE,GREEN,
PANELS,8 3/4 IN

MEDICINE,HAMILTON'S OLD
ENGLISH BLACK OIL

MEDICINE,HAYWOOD'S NUBIAN
HAIR DYE

```
MEDICINE,HEALY & BIGELOW INDIAN SAGWA,EMBOSSED INDIAN,AQUA..    8.00
MEDICINE,HEALY & BIGELOW KICKAPOO INDIAN OIL........ 3.50 TO    7.00
MEDICINE,HECEMAN & CO.,CHEMISTS,N.Y.,AQUA...................    8.00
MEDICINE,HERBINE,ST.LOUIS,HERBINE CO.,RECTANGULAR,CLEAR.....    3.00
MEDICINE,HESS HAIR MILK,AMBER,7 1/2 IN.,LABEL........ILLUS..    3.00
MEDICINE,HIBBARDS RHEUMATIC SYRUP,AMBER.....................   26.00
MEDICINE,HIMALYA,NATURES CURE FOR ASTHMA,AMBER...... 8.00 TO   10.00
MEDICINE,HINDS HONEY & ALMOND CREAM,MACHINE MADE,SCREW CAP..    2.00
MEDICINE,HOBO MED.CO.,REG.TRADEMARK HB,RECTANGULAR,CLEAR....    5.00
MEDICINE,HOFF'S GERMAN LINIMENT,AQUA................ 3.00 TO    5.00
MEDICINE,HOLLAND DRUG CO.,USP,RECTANGULAR,AMETHYST..........    2.00
MEDICINE,HOLTON'S ELECTRIC OIL,ROUND,AMETHYST...............    4.00
MEDICINE,HOPKINS'PHARMACY,BLOWN IN MOLD,CLEAR...............    1.50
MEDICINE,HOT SPRINGS LINIMENT...............................    7.95
MEDICINE,HOWARD DRUGS & MEDICINE CO.,FRIXIE HAIR OIL,
    AMETHYST................................................    4.00
MEDICINE,HOWARD DRUGS & MEDICINE CO.,FRIXIE HAIR OIL,CLEAR..    4.00
MEDICINE,HUMPHREYS NO.7,COLDS,GRIP..................ILLUS..     1.50
MEDICINE,HYGERIA WILD CHERRY PHOSPHATE,AQUA.................   10.00
MEDICINE,INDIAN COUGH SYRUP,WARM,SPRINGS,ORE................    7.00
MEDICINE,INDIAN ROOT BEER EXTRACT...........................    3.00
MEDICINE,INFLAMMACINE,BLOWN IN MOLD,1 1/2 IN. TALL,WHITE....    1.00
MEDICINE,IODINE PETROGEN,JOHN WYETH,AMBER...........ILLUS..     3.50
MEDICINE,J.D.KNOWLTON DRUGGIST,BLOWN IN MOLD,CLEAR..........    1.50
```

MEDICINE, HESS HAIR MILK,
AMBER, 7 1/2 IN., LABEL

MEDICINE,
HUMPHREYS NO.7, COLDS, GRIP

MEDICINE, IODINE PETROGEN,
JOHN WYETH, AMBER

MEDICINE, J.S.P., GREEN.............................. 10.00 TO   15.00
MEDICINE, JAMES FOLSOM, SHIP'S APOTHECARY, BOSTON, SQUARE, 1880..   9.50
   MEDICINE, JAYNES, SEE ALSO BITTERS, DR.JAYNE'S
MEDICINE, JAYNES, DR.D.EXPECTORANT, PONTIL, AQUA.................   15.00
MEDICINE, JAYNES, DR.D.TONIC VERMIFUGE, RECTANGULAR, AQUA.......   3.00
MEDICINE, JOHN RYAN CITRATE OF MAGNESIA, ROUND, AQUA...........   10.00
MEDICINE, JOHN WYETH & BRO., MEASURE, COBALT...................   7.75
MEDICINE, JOHN WYETH, DOSE CAP, COBALT.........................   5.00
MEDICINE, JOHNSON ANODYNE, AQUA................................   2.00
MEDICINE, JOHNSON'S AMERICAN ANODYNE LINIMENT.................   5.00
MEDICINE, JOHNSON'S AMERICAN ANODYNE LINIMENT, BLOWN IN MOLD,
   AQUA..   3.00
MEDICINE, JUG, POISON, AMBER...................................   4.25
MEDICINE, KALOPEAN HAIR DYE, OPEN PONTIL.......................   10.00
MEDICINE, KATHAIRON FOR THE HAIR..............................   6.00
MEDICINE, KATZ & BESTHOIF PHARMACISTS, PINK........... 2.50 TO   3.50
MEDICINE, KEASBEY & MATTISON CO.CHEMISTS, RECTANGULAR, BLUE....   3.00
MEDICINE, KEMP'S BALSAM, EMBOSSED, CORKER.....................   2.00
MEDICINE, KEMP'S COUGH BALSAM, BLOWN IN MOLD, AQUA.............   1.50
MEDICINE, KENDALL'S SPAVIN CURE, AMBER........................   6.50
MEDICINE, KENDALL'S SPAVIN FOR HUMAN FLESH, AQUA..............   4.50
MEDICINE, KENDALL'S SPAVIN TREATMENT, 12 PANELED, AMBER........   5.00
MEDICINE, KICKAPOO INDIAN OIL, AQUA.................... 3.50 TO   6.00
MEDICINE, KILMER'S SWAMP ROOT, KIDNEY, LIVER & BLADDER CURE....   3.50
MEDICINE, KNOWN THROUGHOUT ALASKA MC INTOCH & KUBON
   PRESCRIPTION..   8.00
MEDICINE, KOLD-CARDINETTE, 8 PANEL SHOULDERS, 4 PANEL NECK,
   AMBER..   7.50
MEDICINE, KONJOLA MOSBY MED.CO., RECTANGULAR, CLEAR............   2.00
MEDICINE, KUROKOL CARDIU......................................   3.00
MEDICINE, L.DAMMANN & KORDES, GREEN...........................   15.00
MEDICINE, L.M.GREEN, PROP., BLOWN IN MOLD, CLEAR...............   2.50
MEDICINE, L.PAUTAUBERGE PHARMACIEU, PARIS, SQUARE, COBALT.......   12.00
MEDICINE, L.ROSE & CO., DOUBLE COLLAR.........................   9.00
MEDICINE, LACTOPEPTINE..   3.00
MEDICINE, LACTOPEPTINE FOR ALL DIGESTIVE AILMENTS, GREEN......   6.50
MEDICINE, LARKIN SOAP CO.SMELLING SALTS.......................   4.50
MEDICINE, LAXOL, COBALT BLUE.......................... 8.00 TO   10.00
MEDICINE, LAXOL, TRIANGULAR, COBALT BLUE......................   7.00
MEDICINE, LAXOL, TRIANGULAR, COBALT BLUE.............. 8.50 TO   10.00
MEDICINE, LICORICE ROOT, CLEAR, 3 1/2 IN..............ILLUS..   1.50
MEDICINE, LIEBIGS BEEF WINE & IRON, BLOWN IN MOLD, AQUA........   3.00
MEDICINE, LIGHTNING HOT DROPS, BLACK..........................   4.50
MEDICINE, LIQUID OPODELDOC, AQUA..............................   10.00
MEDICINE, LIQUOZONE, BROWN............................ 1.50 TO   2.50

```
MEDICINE,LIQUOZONE,EMBOSSED,CORKER.........................   2.00
MEDICINE,LISTERINE,BLOWN IN MOLD,CLEAR.....................   1.50
MEDICINE,LISTERINE,CORK TOP,CLEAR..........................   2.00
MEDICINE,LISTERINE,LAMBERT CO.,AMETHYST....................   4.00
MEDICINE,LISTERINE,LAMBERT CO.,CLEAR.......................   4.00
MEDICINE,LIVER INVIGERATOR,FROM PANAMA CANAL,50 YEARS OLD...  25.00
MEDICINE,LOAN'S,LABEL,METAL CAP............................   2.50
MEDICINE,LOCKPORT GARGLING OIL,BLUE........................  10.00
MEDICINE,LOCKPORT GARGLING OIL,GREEN.............. 7.00 TO    8.00
MEDICINE,LOCKPORT GARGLING OIL,TEAL........................  10.00
MEDICINE,LOG CABIN COUGH & CONSUMPTION REMEDY,AMBER.........  90.00
MEDICINE,LONG NECK,GREEN KICK-UP & PONTIL,9 IN.TALL........   18.95
MEDICINE,LORILLARD JAR.....................................   8.00
MEDICINE,LOU WISHART'S PINE TREE TAR CORDIAL,AMBER..........  15.00
MEDICINE,LOUIS DANDELIN CO.BLOOD WINE,GREEN................   5.00
MEDICINE,LQC WISHART'S PINE TREE TAR CORDIAL,AMBER..........  15.00
MEDICINE,LUYTIES TRITURATION TABLETS,HONEY AMBER...........   5.00
MEDICINE,LYDIA E.PINKHAM'S VEGETABLE COMPOUND........ILLUS..   3.50
MEDICINE,LYDIA E.PINKHAM'S,GREEN................... 1.50 TO   2.50
MEDICINE,LYDIA PINKHAM VEGETABLE COMPOUND,AQUA.............   3.00
MEDICINE,LYDIA PINKHAM,FROM PANAMA CANAL,50 YEARS OLD.......  25.00
MEDICINE,LYDIA PINKHAM'S BLOOD PURIFIER,AQUA........ 4.00 TO  0.00
MEDICINE,LYNCH & CLARK,PONTIL..............................  80.00
MEDICINE,LYONS HATAIRON FOR THE HAIR.......................  15.00
MEDICINE,LYSOL,CORK TOP,AMBER..............................   3.00
MEDICINE,M.F.& CO.,CLEAR........................... 10.00 TO  15.00
MEDICINE,M.M.FENNER KIDNEY PILLS,PAPER LABEL.........ILLUS.. 10.00
MEDICINE,MACHINE MADE,STRAP SIDED,AMBER....................   1.50
MEDICINE,MACHINE MADE,8 IN. TALL,AMBER.....................   1.25
MEDICINE,MADAM KYOWLIN,RING MOUTH,GREEN....................  18.00
MEDICINE,MAGEE'S EMULSION,BLOWN IN MOLD,AQUA...............   4.00
MEDICINE,MAGNETIC LINIMENT,A.C.GRANT,GERMAN................  12.00
MEDICINE,MAJOR'S CEMENT....................................   2.00
MEDICINE,MALARIAL CHILL REMEDY.............................   3.00
MEDICINE,MALTINE MFG CO.CHEMISTS,BLOWN IN MOLD,BROWN.......   4.00
MEDICINE,MAN-A-LIN REMEDY,AQUA.............................  12.95
MEDICINE,MARIA FARINA,GERMAN,CLEAR,4 IN.............ILLUS..   7.50
MEDICINE,MATHIS QUARTERDOLLAR FAMILY LINIMENT,OVAL,AQUA.....  6.00
MEDICINE,MC ALLISTER'S MOCKING BIRD FOOD,PINT,GROUND TOP....  5.00
MEDICINE,MC ELREE'S CARDUI.................................   5.00
```

MEDICINE,LICORICE ROOT,
CLEAR,3 1/2 IN

MEDICINE,
LYDIA E.PINKHAM'S
VEGETABLE
COMPOUND

MEDICINE,
M.M.FENNER
KIDNEY PILLS,
PAPER LABEL

MEDICINE,MARIA FARINA,
GERMAN,CLEAR,4 IN

```
MEDICINE,MELLIN'S FOOD,EMBOSSED,TIN LID,3 IN.X 6 IN.TALL,
   AQUA.................................................................   3.50
MEDICINE,MELLIN'S INFANT'S FOOD,LARGE LETTERS........ILLUS..   6.00
MEDICINE,MELLIN'S INFANT'S FOOD,SMALL LETTERS........ILLUS..   6.50
MEDICINE,MELLIN'S,LABELED LID..............................   6.00
MEDICINE,MENTHOLATUM REG.TRADE MARK,MACHINE MADE,WHITE......    .75
MEDICINE,MEXICAN MUSTANG LINIMENT.................... 3.00 TO  15.00
MEDICINE,MEXICAN MUSTANG LINIMENT,ROUND,PONTIL,AQUA.........  10.00
MEDICINE,MICROBE KILLER,QUART,AMBER.........................  50.00
MEDICINE,MIDDLETOWN HEALING,QUART,AMBER.....................  20.00
MEDICINE,MILES MEDICAL CO.,EMBOSSED,CORKER..................   2.00
MEDICINE,MILES RESTORATIVE NERVINE,EMBOSSED,CORKER..........   2.00
MEDICINE,MILK OF MAGNESIA,BLUE..............................   9.50
MEDICINE,MILK OF MAGNESIA,EMBOSSED,COBALT.......... 3.00 TO   9.50
MEDICINE,MILK OF MAGNESIA,U.S.PAT.AUGUST 21,1906,COBALT.....   2.50
MEDICINE,MILK'S EMULSION,AMBER..............................   1.50
MEDICINE,MILKS EMULSION,LARGE MOUTH,BROWN...................   3.50
MEDICINE,MINARD'S LINIMENT,BLOWN IN MOLD,CLEAR TO YELLOW....   2.00
MEDICINE,MISSION DRY SPARKLING,BLACK........................   3.00
MEDICINE,MODAK INDIAN OIL.......................... 8.00 TO   9.00
MEDICINE,MORESE'S CELEBRATED SYRUP,PROV.R.I.,OVAL..........  66.00
MEDICINE,MORGANS GOLDEN EXTRACT FOR HAIR,OPEN PONTIL........  15.00
MEDICINE,MORSE'S CELEBRATED SYRUP...........................  45.00
MEDICINE,MORSE'S CELEBRATED SYRUP WATER,GREEN.............. 110.00
MEDICINE,MOTHER'S FRIEND,EMBOSSED,CORKER....................   2.00
MEDICINE,MOTHER'S FRIEND,GREEN..............................   3.50
MEDICINE,MOXIE NERVE FOOD.......................... 3.00 TO   5.00
MEDICINE,MOXIE NERVE FOOD,BLOB TOP,QUART........... 7.00 TO   7.50
MEDICINE,MOXIE NERVE FOOD,BLOWN IN MOLD,AQUA................   4.00
MEDICINE,MOXIE NERVE FOOD,CRUDE,BLOB TOP,AQUA...............   7.50
MEDICINE,MOXIE NERVE FOOD,ROUND,10 1/2 IN.,BLUE-AQUA........   8.50
MEDICINE,MOXIE NERVE FOOD,TRADEMARK.........................   4.00
MEDICINE,MOXIE NERVE,PORCELAIN TOP,AQUA.....................   8.00
MEDICINE,MOXIE,7 OZ.,AQUA...................................   8.00
MEDICINE,MRS.M.M.GARDNER'S INDIAN BALSAM OF LIVERWORT.......  19.00
MEDICINE,MRS.POTTER'S HYGIENIC SUPPLY CO.,AMBER.............   2.50
MEDICINE,MRS.POTTER'S WALNUT TINT HAIR STAIN.........ILLUS..   3.00
MEDICINE,MRS.S.A.ALLEN'S WORLD HAIR BALSAM,AQUA.............  16.00
MEDICINE,MRS.S.A.ALLEN'S WORLD HAIR RESTORER,AMBER..........  15.00
MEDICINE,MRS.WINSLOW'S SOOTHING SYRUP.......................   2.00
MEDICINE,MRS.WINSLOW'S SOOTHING SYRUP,ROUND,AQUA............   4.00
MEDICINE,MRS.WINSLOW'S SOOTHING SYRUP,ROUND,PONTIL,AQUA.....   4.00
MEDICINE,MRS.WINSLOW'S SOOTHING SYRUP,8 SIDED,AQUA..........   1.50
MEDICINE,MRS.WINSLOW'S SOOTHING SYRUPS,AQUA........ 3.50 TO  12.00
MEDICINE,MUEGGE THE DRUGGIST,GREEN................ 15.00 TO  20.00
MEDICINE,MULFORD'S DIGESTIVE MALT EXTRACT,EMBOSSED,AMBER....   8.00
```

MEDICINE,
MELLIN'S INFANT'S
FOOD,LARGE
LETTERS

MEDICINE,
MELLIN'S
INFANT'S
FOOD,SMALL
LETTERS

MEDICINE,MRS. POTTER'S
WALNUT TINT HAIR STAIN

```
MEDICINE,MULFORD'S PRE-DIGESTED BEEF........................      3.50
MEDICINE,MULLIN'S FOOD,AQUA.................................      2.00
MEDICINE,MUNYON'S PAW PAW,RECTANGULAR,AMBER.................     14.00
MEDICINE,MUSTANG LINIMENT FOR MAN AND BEAST.................      3.00
MEDICINE,MUSTANG LINIMENT,OPEN PONTIL.......................     10.00
MEDICINE,MUSTEROLE CLEVELAND,MACHINE MADE,WHITE.............       .75
MEDICINE,N.K.BROWN'S AROMATIC ESSENCE OF GINGER,AQUA........      3.00
MEDICINE,N.K.BROWN'S AROMATIC ESSENCE OF JAMAICA GINGER.....      1.50
MEDICINE,N.Y.PHARMACAL ASSOCIATION,BLOWN IN MOLD,CLEAR......      2.00
MEDICINE,N.Y.PHARMACAL ASSOCIATION,COBALT..................      8.00
MEDICINE,N.Y.PHARMACAL ASSOCIATION,LACTOPEPTINE,COBALT......     12.00
MEDICINE,N.WOOD & SON,BLOWN IN MOLD,BLUE....................      3.50
MEDICINE,NADINOLA BLEACHING CREAM,1/4 OZ....................      5.00
MEDICINE,NADINOLA BLEACHING CREAM,1/2 OZ....................      5.00
MEDICINE,NATHAN WOOD & SON,BLOWN IN MOLD,CLEAR...... 2.00 TO      2.50
MEDICINE,NATHAN WOOD & SON,BLOWN IN MOLD,WHITTLE,AQUA.......      1.50
MEDICINE,NATIONAL REMEDY CO.,BLACK..........................      3.50
MEDICINE,NATIONAL REMEDY CO.,EMBOSSED,CORKER................      2.00
MEDICINE,NERVITA RESTORES VITALITY,LOST VIGOR........ILLUS..     12.00
MEDICINE,NEW HAMPSHIRE STATE BOARD OF HEALTH,BLOWN IN MOLD,
  CLEAR.....................................................      1.50
MEDICINE,NEWBRO'S HERPICIDE OF THE SCALP.............ILLUS..      3.00
MEDICINE,NEWBRO'S HERPICIDE,FOR DANDRUFF,CLEAR...... 1.00 TO      2.50
MEDICINE,NEWTON'S PANACEA PURIFIER OF THE BLOOD,GOLD AMBER..    190.00
MEDICINE,NOAH'S LINIMENT,MAN OR BEAST.......................      4.00
MEDICINE,NOXZEMA,MACHINE MADE,COBALT BLUE...................      1.00
MEDICINE,NYAL'S EMULSION OF COD LIVER OIL,AMBER.............      4.00
MEDICINE,NYAL'S LINIMENT,RING NECK,AMBER....................      4.00
MEDICINE,O'NEILL'S GENUINE RHEUMATIC DECOCTION,QUART,GREEN..    100.00
MEDICINE,OD CHEM.CO.,N.Y.,AMBER.............................      2.00
MEDICINE,OIL ORIGANUM,ROCHESTER,N.Y.,CLEAR...........ILLUS..      1.50
MEDICINE,OIL SPIKE LINIMENT,GIBSON-SNOW CO...........ILLUS..      1.50
MEDICINE,OLD EYE,MARKED WYETH CO.,STOPPER IS EYECUP,COBALT
  BLUE......................................................      5.00
MEDICINE,OLD GLOVER'S IMPERIAL MANGE.......................      4.95
MEDICINE,OLD SACHEM BITTERS & WIGWAM TONIC.................     80.00
MEDICINE,OMEGA OIL CHEMICAL CO.,N.Y.,FLARED TOP,GREEN.......      6.00
MEDICINE,OPIUM VIAL,AQUA....................................      7.50
MEDICINE,OPIUM,SQUARE,DECORATED,TAPERED,FROSTED.............      4.00
MEDICINE,OPIUM,1/2 OZ.,AMETHYST.............................      8.00
MEDICINE,OPIUM,1 DROP,AMETHYST..............................      8.00
MEDICINE,OPIUM,1 DROP,CLEAR.................................      8.00
MEDICINE,OPODEL DOC LIQUID..................................      5.00
MEDICINE,ORIENTAL CREAM,GOURAUDS,SQUARE,AMETHYST............      3.00
MEDICINE,ORIENTAL CREAM,GOURAUDS,SQUARE,CLEAR...............      3.00
MEDICINE,OSGOOD'S INDIA CHOLAGOGUE,AQUA.....................     16.00
```

MEDICINE,
NERVITA RESTORES
VITALITY,LOST VIGOR

MEDICINE,NEWBRO'S
HERPICIDE OF THE SCALP

MEDICINE,
OIL ORIGANUM,
ROCHESTER,
N.Y.,
CLEAR

MEDICINE,
OIL SPIKE LINIMENT,
GIBSON-SNOW CO

```
MEDICINE,OWL DRUG CO.,EMBOSSED,COBALT BLUE.......... 2.50 TO    3.50
MEDICINE,OWL DRUG STORE,EMBOSSED OWL,CLEAR..................    6.00
MEDICINE,OWL DRUG,ORANGE LABEL,4 1/4 IN.,CLEAR.............     3.75
MEDICINE,OWL,CLEAR........................................     3.50
MEDICINE,OWL,DRUG,12 IN. HIGH,BEVELED CORNER,COBALT.........   81.00
MEDICINE,OWL,GLASS EYES,RED...............................    12.00
MEDICINE,OZOMULSION,AMBER.................................     4.00
MEDICINE,P.F.HEVRING,KØBENHAUN BASE,WHITTLED...............     5.00
MEDICINE,P.F.HEERING,RED AMBER............................    18.00
MEDICINE,PAINE'S CELERY COMPOUND,AMBER...............ILLUS..    9.50
MEDICINE,PAINE'S CELERY COMPOUND,BLOWN IN MOLD,AMBER........    4.50
MEDICINE,PARKER DRUG STORE,BLOWN IN MOLD,CLEAR.............     1.50
MEDICINE,PARKER'S HAIR BALSAM,AMBER.......................     2.50
MEDICINE,PARKERS HEADACHE CURE............................     5.00
MEDICINE,PARMALU DYSPEPSIA KIDNEY & LIVER CURE,LABEL & BOX..   13.00
MEDICINE,PATTERSON & BRAZEAU VICHY WATER,N.Y.,GREEN.........   10.00
MEDICINE,PAUL B.ELDER CO.,OHIO,AQUA,9 1/2 IN.........ILLUS..    4.50
MEDICINE,PAUL'S SAFETY,PINT,SQUATTY,BLUE AQUA..............    15.00
MEDICINE,PAYNE CELERY COMPOUND,SQUARE,AMBER................     5.00
MEDICINE,PE-RU-NA-TONIC...............................ILLUS..   2.00
MEDICINE,PEACH & HONEY,GAL................................     3.00
MEDICINE,PEARL'S WHITE GLYCERINE,COBALT BLUE...............    26.00
MEDICINE,PEPERAZINE EFFERVESCENTE MEDY,3 VERTICAL LINES,
  AMBER...................................................     4.00
MEDICINE,PEPTENZYME,REED & CARNICK,JERSEY CITY,N.J.,COBALT..    6.00
MEDICINE,PEPTO MANGAN GUDE,BLOWN IN MOLD,6 PANELS,AQUA......    3.00
MEDICINE,PEPTONIZED COD LIVER OIL & MILK,BLOWN IN MOLD,BROWN    6.00
MEDICINE,PEPTONOIDS,ARLINGTON CHEMICAL CO.,AMBER...........     4.50
MEDICINE,PERRIGO WORM SYRUP...............................    23.00
MEDICINE,PRESTON OF NEW HAMPSHIRE SMELLING SALTS...........     5.50
MEDICINE,PRESTON OF NEW HAMPSHIRE SMELLING SALTS,LABEL......    7.50
MEDICINE,PRICKLY ASH......................................    25.00
MEDICINE,PROF.I.HUBERT'S MALVINA LOTION,COBALT BLUE.........   21.00
MEDICINE,PROFESSOR DEAN'S KING CACTUS OIL,EMBOSSED..........  125.00
MEDICINE,PROFESSOR WOOD'S HAIR RESTORATIVE DEPOTS,AQUA......   18.00
MEDICINE,PROFESSOR WOOD'S HAIR RESTORATIVE DEPOTS,OPEN
  PONTIL..................................................    16.00
MEDICINE,PRESCRIPTION BOTTLE,OUNCES ON SIDE..........ILLUS..    1.00
MEDICINE,PHELP'S RHEUMATIC ELIXIR,AQUA....................     8.50
MEDICINE,PHILADELPHIA,U.S.A.,BLOWN IN MOLD,AMBER..........     1.00
MEDICINE,PHILLIPS MILK OF MAGNESIA,BLOWN IN MOLD,BLUE.......    2.50
MEDICINE,PHILLIPS MILK OF MAGNESIA,DATE 1873,PINT..........     5.00
MEDICINE,PHILLIPS MILK OF MAGNESIA,MACHINE MADE,COBALT BLUE.    1.25
MEDICINE,PHOENIX NERVE BEVERAGE CO.,BOSTON,CLEAR...........     3.95
MEDICINE,PIERCE GOLDEN MED.DISCOVERY,EMBOSSED,CORKER.......     2.00
MEDICINE,PILL,PLAIN,OVAL,SHEAR TOP,SCREW TOP,CLEAR.........     6.00
MEDICINE,PINEX,EMBOSSED,CORKER............................     2.00
MEDICINE,PISO'S CURE FOR CONSUMPTION,AQUA.................     5.50
MEDICINE,PISO'S CURE,GREEN................................     5.00
MEDICINE,PITCHERS LIVURA..................................     8.50
MEDICINE,PLUTO WATER,DEVIL & PLUTO,ROUND,CLEAR.............     4.00
MEDICINE,PLUTO WATER,DEVIL & PLUTO,ROUND,GREEN.............     4.00
MEDICINE,PLUTO WATER,ENGRAVED PLUTO WATER AMERICA'S PHYSIC..    8.00
MEDICINE,PLUTO WATER,MACHINE MADE.........................     2.00
MEDICINE,POISON,B.P.CO.,COBALT BLUE.......................    10.50
MEDICINE,POISON,TINCTURE IODINE,SKULL & CROSS BONES,OVAL,
  AMBER...................................................    10.00
MEDICINE,POND'S EXTRACT,EMBOSSED,CORKER...................     2.00
MEDICINE,POOR MAN'S FAMILY................................    15.00
MEDICINE,PORTER'S PAIN KING,CLEAR.........................     2.00
MEDICINE,PRE-DIGESTED FOOD CO.,EMBOSSED PINEAPPLE,AMBER.....    4.50
MEDICINE,PROTER'S PAIN KING...............................     4.00
MEDICINE,QUININE,GROUND STOPPER,COBALT....................     7.50
MEDICINE,R.R.R.RADWAY & CO.,AQUA................... 2.00 TO    3.00
MEDICINE,R.R.R.RADWAY & CO.,NEW YORK,BLUE.................     6.00
MEDICINE,R.S.HALE & CO.,DRUGGISTS,CLEAR...................     3.00
```

MEDICINE,PAINE'S CELERY
COMPOUND,AMBER

MEDICINE,PAUL B.ELDER
CO.,OHIO,AQUA,9 1/2 IN

MEDICINE,
PE-RU-NA-TONIC

MEDICINE,PRESCRIPTION BOTTLE,
OUNCES ON SIDE

MEDICINE,R.V.PIERCE,N.D.,N.Y.,RECTANGULAR,AQUA.............	2.00
MEDICINE,RADAMS MICROBE KILLER,EMBOSSED...................	45.00
MEDICINE,RAINEY'S CHILL REMEDY...........................	2.00
MEDICINE,RAMON'S RELIEF,BLOWN IN MOLD,AQUA...............	2.00
MEDICINE,RAWLEIGH'S.....................................	2.50
MEDICINE,RAWLEIGH'S TRADE MARK,8 IN.,AQUA...........ILLUS..	2.50
MEDICINE,RED CROSS COUGH CURE,AQUA......................	5.00
MEDICINE,RED STAR COUGH CURE,EMBOSSED,AQUA..............	5.00
MEDICINE,REED & CARNRICH PHARMACISTS,PEPTOMZMO,AMBER........	6.00
MEDICINE,REED & CARNRICH,PEPTOM7MO,RING TOP,COBALT..........	12.00
MEDICINE,REES REMEDY FOR PILES,CRUDE PONTIL,AQUA............	60.00
MEDICINE,REGISTERED PUREOXIA,DIMAL,TORPEDO SHAPE,AQUA.......	3.50
MEDICINE,RENNES' MAGIC OIL,AQUA,6 IN................ILLUS..	6.00

MEDICINE,
RAWLEIGH'S TRADE MARK,8 IN.,AQUA

MEDICINE,RENNES' MAGIC OIL,AQUA,6 IN

MEDICINE,REPRODUCTION,TAIWAN,AQUA,OCTAGONAL..........ILLUS..	1.50
MEDICINE,REPRODUCTION,TAIWAN,BROWN...................ILLUS..	1.50
MEDICINE,REPRODUCTION,TAIWAN,CLEAR...................ILLUS..	1.50
MEDICINE,REPRODUCTION,TAIWAN,SQUARE,BROWN............ILLUS..	1.50
MEDICINE,RETONGA TONIC..................................	3.00
MEDICINE,REVOLUTIONARY WAR,MARKED BRITISH BROAD ARROW,BLOWN.	25.00
MEDICINE,RIGHTER'S PAIN EXPELLER,FLUTED NECK,AQUA...........	7.50
MEDICINE,RIKER-JAYNES DRUG STORES,BLOWN IN MOLD,CLEAR.......	3.00
MEDICINE,RIKER'S DEODOR,MILK GLASS................. 4.75 TO	5.00
MEDICINE,RISLEY'S WITCH HAZEL,BIMAL,AQUA...................	2.50
MEDICINE,RIVER SWAMP CHILL AND FEVER CURE,AMBER......COLOR..	50.00

MEDICINE, REPRODUCTION,
TAIWAN, AQUA, OCTAGONAL

MEDICINE,
REPRODUCTION,
TAIWAN, BROWN

MEDICINE,
REPRODUCTION,
TAIWAN, CLEAR

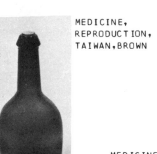

MEDICINE, REPRODUCTION,
TAIWAN, SQUARE, BROWN

MEDICINE, ROBERT TURLINGTON...................................   5.00
MEDICINE, ROBERT TURLINGTON FOR HIS INVENTED BALSAM OF LIFE.. 14.00
MEDICINE, ROBERT TURLINGTON, BALSAM OF LIFE, PEAR SHAPE........   8.00
MEDICINE, ROCK & RYE, WITH GLYCERINE FOR COUGHS & COLDS, GAL...   3.00
MEDICINE, RODERIC WILD CHERRY COUGH BALSAM, BLOWN IN MOLD,
   CLEAR..   1.50
MEDICINE, ROHRER'S EXPECTORANT, IRON PONTIL................... 115.00
MEDICINE, ROHRER'S WILD CHERRY TONIC, AMBER..........120.00 TO 135.00
MEDICINE, ROUND TABLET, BLOWN IN MOLD, AQUA..................   1.00
MEDICINE, RUB—MY—TISM, CLEAR.............................ILLUS..   6.00
MEDICINE, RUBIFOAM FOR THE TEETH, E.W.HOYTH & CO., AMETHYST....   4.00
MEDICINE, RUBIFOAM FOR THE TEETH, E.W.HOYTH & CO., CLEAR.......   4.00
MEDICINE, RUMFORD CHEMICAL WORKS, BLOWN IN MOLD, 8 PANELS, BLUE.   8.00
MEDICINE, RUMFORD CHEMICAL, TEAL..................... 5.00 TO   7.00
MEDICINE, RUMFORD CHEMICALS, BIMAL, BLUE GREEN................   6.00
MEDICINE, RUSSIAN HAIR DYE NO.1, AQUA.........................   7.00
MEDICINE, S.A.RICHMOND M.D., ST.JOSEPH, MO., SAMARITAN NERVINE..   5.00
MEDICINE, S.A.RICHMOND, M.D., AQUA, 8 1/2 IN.............ILLUS..   6.00
MEDICINE, S.B.GOFF'S COUGH SYRUP, C.1920, CLEAR.........ILLUS..   3.00
MEDICINE, S.O.RICHARDSONS, PONTILED, AQUA..................... 15.00
MEDICINE, S.S.S., THE GREAT HORSE REMEDY, AMBER...............   6.00
MEDICINE, SABROOK COUGH SYRUP..........................ILLUS..   3.50
MEDICINE, SAFETY VALVE, CLOUDY................................ 10.00
MEDICINE, SALVATION OIL, RECTANGULAR..........................   6.00
MEDICINE, SALVE, BLOWN IN MOLD, AMBER.........................   1.00
MEDICINE, SALVE, BLOWN IN MOLD, AMETHYST......................   1.00
MEDICINE, SANDERSON'S BLOOD RENOVATOR, AQUA................... 65.00
MEDICINE, SANFORD'S RADICAL CURE, COBALT BLUE........ 12.00 TO 28.00
MEDICINE, SANFORD'S RADICAL CURE, 80 PERCENT LABEL............ 25.00
MEDICINE, SANITAS JAR...   2.00
MEDICINE, SANITOL FOR THE TEETH, STOPPER, MILK GLASS..........   8.50
MEDICINE, SANITOL, FOR THE TEETH, 3 CORNER PANELS, MILK GLASS... 12.00
MEDICINE, SARATOGA CONGRESS & EMPIRE, PINT.................... 20.00
MEDICINE, SARATOGA CONGRESS & EMPIRE, QUART, C................ 20.00
MEDICINE, SARATOGA CONGRESS & EMPIRE, QUART, E................ 20.00
MEDICINE, SASPARILLIAN RESOLVENT RADWAYS, AQUA................ 25.00
MEDICINE, SCHENKS PULMONIC SYRUP, 8 SIDED, AQUA............... 25.00
MEDICINE, SCHENKS SEAWEED TONIC, SQUARE, AQUA................. 15.00
MEDICINE, SCHLOTTERBECK & FLOSS CO., BLOWN IN MOLD, BROWN......   2.50
MEDICINE, SCOTT'S EMULSION COD LIVER OIL, AQUA........ 1.50 TO   3.50
MEDICINE, SCOTT'S EMULSION COD LIVER OIL, WHIT LIME & SODA,
   AQUA...   4.00

MEDICINE,
RUB-MY-TISM,
CLEAR

MEDICINE,
S.B.GOFF'S
COUGH SYRUP,
C.1920,CLEAR

MEDICINE,
SABROOK
COUGH SYRUP

MEDICINE,S.A.RICHMOND,
M.D.,AQUA,8 1/2 IN

```
MEDICINE,SCOTT'S EMULSION,AMBER,7 1/2 IN..............ILLUS..      4.00
MEDICINE,SCOTT'S EMULSION,COD LIVER OIL,FISHERMAN WITH FISH,
    AQUA........................................................      2.75
MEDICINE,SCOTT'S EMULSION,GREEN.....................  3.00 TO       5.00
MEDICINE,SEEBER & KENYON DRUGIST...........................       1.00
MEDICINE,SHARP & DOHME,AMBER.....................  1.50 TO       2.50
MEDICINE,SHEPARD'S FLY GUARD VETERINARY LINIMENT...........       4.00
MEDICINE,SHILOH COUGH SYRUP,S.C.WELLS & CO...........ILLUS..       7.50
```

MEDICINE,SCOTT'S EMULSION,
AMBER,7 1/2 IN

MEDICINE,SHILOH COUGH
SYRUP,S.C.WELLS & CO

```
MEDICINE,SHILOH'S CONSUMPTION CURE..................  3.00 TO       7.50
MEDICINE,SHILOH'S CONSUMPTION CURE,AQUA......................       5.00
MEDICINE,SHUPTXINE,DRUGGIST,PAT.,GREEN......................      12.00
MEDICINE,SIMMON'S LIVER REGULATOR,CLEAR.............  3.00 TO       5.00
MEDICINE,SLOAN'S LINIMENT,BLOWN IN MOLD,3 OZ.,CLEAR.........       2.00
MEDICINE,SLOAN'S LINIMENT,MACHINE MADE......................       1.00
MEDICINE,SLOAN'S SURE COLIC CURE,BLOWN IN MOLD,AQUA.........       1.75
MEDICINE,SLOCUM'S COD LIVER OIL,AQUA,10 IN...........ILLUS..       4.00
MEDICINE,SLOCUM'S COLTSFOOT EXPECTORANT.............  4.00 TO       5.00
MEDICINE,SLOCUM'S COLTSFOOT EXPECTORANT,EMBOSSED BASE.......       5.00
MEDICINE,SMELLING SALTS,LARKIN SOAP CO.,BLOWN IN MOLD,GREEN.       5.00
MEDICINE,SNAKE OIL LINIMENT.................................       4.00
```

```
MEDICINE,SNAPPS IRON PONTIL,GREEN.........................    25.00
MEDICINE,SOLOMONS CO.,SCRIPT,BRANCH DRUG STORE,GA.,AMETHYST.   4.00
MEDICINE,SOLOMONS CO.,SCRIPT,BRANCH DRUG STORE,GA.,AQUA.....   4.00
MEDICINE,SOLOMONS CO.,SCRIPT,BRANCH DRUG STORE,GA.,COBALT...   8.00
MEDICINE,SPARKS PERFECT HEALTH FOR KIDNEY & LIVER DISEASES,
  ROUND...................................................    6.00
MEDICINE,SPENCER MED.CO.,NUBIAN TEA,GOLDEN.................    6.00
MEDICINE,SPENCER MED.CO.,NUBIAN TEA,TRADE MARK,SQUARE,AMBER.   6.00
MEDICINE,SQUARE,APPLIED TOP,PONTIL,AQUA....................   12.00
MEDICINE,SQUARE,WOLF HEAD ON BASE,DOUBLE COLLAR LIP,GREEN...   5.00
MEDICINE,ST.JAKOB'S OIL,AQUA...............................   4.50
MEDICINE,STAR SPRING,QUART,AMBER...........................   30.00
MEDICINE,STERLING'S AMBROSIA FOR THE HAIR,AQUA.............   4.00
MEDICINE,SUCCUS ALTERANS,LILLY,AMBER,8 IN...........ILLUS..   3.50
MEDICINE,SUTHERLAND SISTERS HAIR GROWER,PEA GREEN..........   8.00
MEDICINE,SWAIM'S PANACEA,AQUA..............................   75.00
MEDICINE,SWAIM'S PANACEA,PANELED,OLIVE GREEN...............   62.00
MEDICINE,SWAN & CO.,ROUND,COBALT...........................   5.00
MEDICINE,SYLVESTER BRAND HAARLEM OIL................ILLUS..   3.00
MEDICINE,SYRUP OF HYPOPHOSPHITES,COBALT....................   9.00
MEDICINE,SYRUP OF SQULLIS,OPEN PONTIL......................   5.00
MEDICINE,TABLETS,BLOWN IN MOLD,CLEAR.......................   1.50
MEDICINE,TENILINE FOR SORE THROATS,GIRAFFE FRONT,AQUA......   5.00
MEDICINE,THE CUTICURA SYSTEM OF CURING CONSTITUTIONAL HUMORS  6.00
MEDICINE,THE GREAT DR.KILMER'S SWAMP ROOT..................   6.00
MEDICINE,THE NAME ST.JOSEPH ASSURES PURITY.................   9.00
MEDICINE,THE RELIABLE OLD TIME PREPARATION FOR HOME USE,
  CLEAR...................................................    3.00
```

MEDICINE,
SLOCUM'S COD LIVER OIL,AQUA,10 IN

MEDICINE,SUCCUS ALTERANS,LILLY,
AMBER,8 IN

MEDICINE,SYLVESTER BRAND HAARLEM OIL

```
MEDICINE,THOMPSON'S BEEF,WINE & IRON,LABEL.................   9.00
MEDICINE,THOMPSON'S WILD CHERRY PHOSPHATE,AQUA.............   7.50
MEDICINE,THREAD BOTTLE,EMBOSSED PAT.DATE,LABEL,AMBER.......   7.50
MEDICINE,THRIFT JAR........................................   6.00
MEDICINE,TOMPKINS CHEMISTS,271 WASHINGTON ST.,BOSTON,MILK
  GLASS...................................................   18.00
MEDICINE,TONIC VERMIFUGE,AQUA..................... 1.50 TO    2.00
MEDICINE,TOOTH POWDER,BLOWN IN MOLD,3 1/2 IN. TALL,CLEAR....   1.00
MEDICINE,TRADE MARK,VASELINE,MACHINE MADE,BROWN............   1.00
MEDICINE,TRASK'S LINIMENT..................................   7.50
MEDICINE,TREATMENT OF CHOLERA,1832,PHOENIX,WOODEN BOX,13.... 130.00
MEDICINE,TRIALOIDS,COBALT..................................   3.50
MEDICINE,TRUE'S WORM ELIXIR FOR HORSES,AMBER...............   5.50
MEDICINE,TURLINGTON BALSAM OF LIFE.........................   5.00
MEDICINE,TUTTLE'S ELIXIR CO.,BLOWN IN MOLD,12 PANELS,BLUE...   3.00
MEDICINE,TUTTLE'S ELIXIR CO.,BLOWN IN MOLD,12 PANELS,CLEAR..   2.50
```

MEDICINE,U.S.A.HOSP.DEPT.,3 PIECE MOLD,WHITTLE,AMBER........	15.00
MEDICINE,UDOLPHO WOLFES AROMATIC SCHNAPPS,SCHIEDAM,AMBER....	12.00
MEDICINE,UDOLPHO WOLFES AROMATIC SCHNAPPS,SCHIEDAM,OLIVE....	12.00
MEDICINE,UNCLE SAM SPECIAL ELIXIR..........................	1.50
MEDICINE,UNITED DRUG CO.,BOSTON,MASS.......................	10.00
MEDICINE,VAN,DUNCK'S COACHMAN MEDICINE,AMBER...............	135.00
MEDICINE,VASELINE,BLOWN IN MOLD,AMBER......................	2.50
MEDICINE,VASELINE,BLOWN IN MOLD,AMETHYST............ 2.50 TO	3.00
MEDICINE,VASELINE,CHESEBROUGH NEW YORK,AMETHYST............	4.00
MEDICINE,VASELINE,CHESEBROUGH NEW YORK,CLEAR...............	4.00
MEDICINE,VASELINE,MACHINE MADE,CLEAR......................	1.00
MEDICINE,VAUGHNS VEGETABLE LITHONTRIPTIC MIXTURE,PINT,AQUA..	25.00
MEDICINE,VAUGHNS VEGETABLE LITHONTRIPTIC MIXTURE,QUART,AQUA.	18.00
MEDICINE,VEGETABLE PULMONARY BALSAM,AQUA........... 8.50 TO	12.00
MEDICINE,VEGETABLE PULMONARY BALSAM,OPEN PONTIL............	6.00
MEDICINE,VERMIFUGE,AQUA...............................ILLUS..	18.00
MEDICINE,VICKS DROPS,MACHINE MADE,COBALT BLUE..............	1.50
MEDICINE,VICKS DROPS,SCREW TOP,MACHINE MADE,COBALT.........	4.00
MEDICINE,VIMALT HEALTH TONIC,AMBER,9 IN...............ILLUS..	3.50
MEDICINE,W.H.BULL'S HERBS & IRON..........................	10.00
MEDICINE,W.J.EVANS REGISTERED,BLOWN IN MOLD,CLEAR..........	1.50
MEDICINE,WAKELEE'S CAMELLINE,COBALT BLUE............ 5.00 TO	6.00
MEDICINE,WARNER'S COMPOUND A DIURETIC,LABEL,CONTENTS,7 IN.,	
AMBER..	20.00
MEDICINE,WARNER'S COUGH & CONSUMPTION REMEDY,LOG CABIN......	60.00
MEDICINE,WARNER'S DIABETES CURE,BLOB......................	32.00
MEDICINE,WARNER'S KIDNEY & LIVER REMEDY............. 9.00 TO	18.00
MEDICINE,WARNER'S NERVINE,CLEAR...........................	6.00
MEDICINE,WARNER'S SAFE CURE,BLOB TOP......................	2.75
MEDICINE,WARNER'S SAFE CURE,ROCHESTER,N.Y.,ENGLAND,CANADA,	
AMBER..	60.00
MEDICINE,WARNER'S SAFE DIABETES REMEDY,AMBER....... 17.50 TO	52.00
MEDICINE,WARNER'S SAFE KIDNEY & LIVER CURE.......... 9.00 TO	35.00
MEDICINE,WARNER'S SAFE KIDNEY & LIVER CURE...........ILLUS..	20.00
MEDICINE,WARNER'S SAFE KIDNEY & LIVER CURE,DOUBLE COLLAR,	
AMBER..	20.00
MEDICINE,WARNER'S SAFE KIDNEY & LIVER CURE,REDDISH AMBER....	7.50
MEDICINE,WARNER'S SAFE KIDNEY & LIVER CURE,SAFE HINGES......	35.00
MEDICINE,WARNER'S SAFE KIDNEY & LIVER,AMBER......... 7.50 TO	10.00
MEDICINE,WARNER'S SAFE NERVINE,AMBER......................	25.00
MEDICINE,WARNER'S SAFE NERVINE,AMBER............... 30.00 TO	33.00
MEDICINE,WARNER'S SAFE PILLS.............................	7.00
MEDICINE,WARNER'S SAFE REMEDIES,AQUA......................	17.00
MEDICINE,WARNER'S SAFE RHEUMATIC CURE.............. 34.00 TO	40.00
MEDICINE,WARNER'S SAFE RHEUMATIC CURE,AMBER...............	12.00
MEDICINE,WARNER'S SAFE,ROUND COLLAR,AMBER.................	10.00
MEDICINE,WAVENLOCK FOR HAIR & SCALP,8 IN.............ILLUS..	8.00
MEDICINE,WAW-WAW...	8.00
MEDICINE,WAYNE'S DIURETIC ELIXIR,SQUARE,AMBER.............	15.00
MEDICINE,WEEDON DRUG CO.,FLA.,AMETHYST....................	4.00
MEDICINE,WEEDON DRUG CO.,FLA.,CLEAR.......................	4.00
MEDICINE,WHEELER'S TISSUE PHOSPHATES,BEVELED CORNERS,AQUA...	8.00
MEDICINE,WHITTEMORE,AQUA........................... 1.50 TO	2.50
MEDICINE,WILD CHERRY EXPECTORANT,DEVILS SLIDE UTAH,AMBER....	5.00
MEDICINE,WILLIAM RADMUS MICROBE KILLER,AMBER..............	55.00
MEDICINE,WILLIAM'S WHITE PINE,HONEY & TAR.................	3.00
MEDICINE,WINE ELIXIR TONIC GENTIN,3 PIECE MOLD,OLIVE......	8.50
MEDICINE,WINE OF CARDUI,AQUA....................... 2.00 TO	2.50
MEDICINE,WINSLOWS SOOTHING SYRUP,OPEN PONTIL..............	10.00
MEDICINE,WISDON'S ROBERTINE,COBALT.......................	5.00
MEDICINE,WISTAR,CIRCA 1730,7 1/4 IN.,OLIVE GREEN..........	95.00
MEDICINE,WM.RADAM MICROBE KILLER,EMBOSSED MAN,SKELETON,AMBER	40.00
MEDICINE,WM.RADAMS MICROBE KILLER,2 GAL.JUG...............	15.00
MEDICINE,WRIGHTS SMOKE FLAVOR,AMBER......................	1.50
MEDICINE,WYETH & BRO.,AMETHYST..................... 2.50 TO	3.50

MEDICINE, VERMIFUGE, AQUA

MEDICINE, VIMALT
HEALTH TONIC,
AMBER, 9 IN

MEDICINE, WARNER'S
SAFE KIDNEY &
LIVER CURE

MEDICINE, WAVENLOCK FOR
HAIR & SCALP, 8 IN

```
MEDICINE, WYETH & BRO., BLOWN IN MOLD, COBALT BLUE.............      5.00
MEDICINE, WYETH COLYRRIUM, EYE CUP STOPPER, COBALT............      7.50
MEDICINE, WYETH DOSE WITH CUP, COBALT.................. 6.00 TO      8.00
MEDICINE, WYETH 1, BLOWN IN MOLD, CLEAR.......................      2.00
MEDICINE, WYETH 3 BRO., BLOWN IN MOLD, FLASK, STRAP SIDE, CLEAR..      3.50
MEDICINE, WYETH, BLOWN IN MOLD, CLEAR........................      2.00
MEDICINE, WYETH, LIQ.EXT.MALT, AMBER........................      4.50
MEDICINE, 12 PANELS, BROKEN PONTIL, CLEAR....................     10.00
MEDICINE, 12 SIDED, ROUND, PONTIL...........................     10.00
METAXA, GREEK GUARD........................................     17.95
```

```
    MILK BOTTLES WERE FIRST USED IN THE 1880'S.  THE
    CHARACTERISTIC SHAPE AND PRINTED OR EMBOSSED WORDING
    IDENTIFY THESE BOTTLES FOR COLLECTORS.
MILK, ALTAMONT CREAMERY, ALTAMONT, ILL., CLEAR.................      2.50
MILK, AMBER.......................................... 2.50 TO      8.00
MILK, BABY FACE, QUART.....................................      5.50
MILK, BABY FACE, 1/2 PINT..................................      4.50
MILK, BENNINGTON MILK EXCHANGE, CREAM, EMBOSSED..............      1.75
MILK, BERGREN'S, QUART, AMBER..............................      4.50
MILK, BORDEN, GAIL BORDEN SIGNATURE, QUART, AMBER....... 1.75 TO      8.00
MILK, BORDEN, 2 QUART, AMBER..............................      6.00
MILK, BORDEN'S CONDENSED, BABY BRAND, 8 SIDED, MILK GLASS COVER.      5.00
MILK, BORDON SIGNATURE & PICTURE, 1/2 GAL., AMBER..............      2.00
MILK, CARIBOU FARMS, EMBOSSED, QUART....................ILLUS..      6.00
MILK, CARRIGANS NIAGARA, 1 PINT, EMBOSSED HEAD OF BOY..........      3.00
MILK, CEREAL, GROUND MOUTH, AMBER.........................      3.50
MILK, CLOVERLEAF DAIRY, BLACK PRINT, QUART..............ILLUS..      5.00
MILK, CREAM TOP, QUART.................................ILLUS..      5.00
MILK, DOUBLE BABY FACE....................................      5.00
MILK, DURANGO, COLO., SQUARE, GREEN LETTERING................      1.50
MILK, EMBOSSED BABY FACE & LETTERS, QUART....................     14.00
MILK, EMBOSSED 56MM, 1/4 PINT.............................      1.50
MILK, FAIRMONTS, SOUR CREAM, 1/2 PINT......................      1.25
MILK, GROVE DAIRY, 1/2 PINT, EMBOSSED, OHIO..............ILLUS..      3.00
MILK, HARTMAN FARM, EMBOSSED, QUART....................ILLUS..      3.00
MILK, HAWAII, 1/2 PINT, FROSTED, SILVERSFORD PLANT & HALEAKALA
  DAIRY...................................................      2.00
MILK, HOME DAIRY, 1/2 PINT, EMBOSSED, CREAM TOP..........ILLUS..      5.00
```

MILK,CARIBOU FARMS,EMBOSSED,QUART

MILK,CLOVERLEAF DAIRY,
BLACK PRINT,QUART

MILK,CREAM TOP,
QUART

MILK,GROVE DAIRY,
1/2 PINT,EMBOSSED,
OHIO

MILK,HARTMAN FARM,
EMBOSSED,QUART

MILK,
HOME DAIRY,
1/2 PINT,
EMBOSSED,
CREAM TOP

```
MILK,LAND-O-PINES,PRINTED IN GREEN,TREE,1/2 PINT,CLEAR......      1.50
MILK,PLAIN,PINT......................................ILLUS..      2.00
MILK,PLAIN,1/2 PINT..................................ILLUS..      1.50
MILK,POLK'S,IT WHIPS,CREAM TOP,QUART.................ILLUS..      3.00
MILK,QUART,PLUG CAP,AMBER...................................      2.50
MILK,SQUARE,QUART,AMBER.....................................      5.00
MILK,STORE BOTTLE,5 CENTS,1/2 PINT...................ILLUS..      1.50
MILK,TIN CAP & HANDLE,PAT.1898,QUART........................     10.00
MILK,TIN HOLDER.............................................     35.00
MILK,WARDS MILK PRESERVING JAR,CIRCA 1890-92,45 WORDS.......    140.00
MILK,1/4 PINT,EMBOSSED......................................      1.50
MILK GLASS,MENTHOLATUM,SCREW TOP.....................ILLUS..      1.00
MILK GLASS,METAL SCREW TOP...........................ILLUS..      1.50
MILK GLASS,MUSTEROLE,SCREW TOP.......................ILLUS..      2.00
MILK GLASS,SCREW TOP.................................ILLUS..      1.50
MILK GLASS,SHAVO CREAM...............................ILLUS..      6.00
MILK GLASS,TOILET WATER,SATIN FINISH,PAIR,WHITE.............     46.00
MILK GLASS,WORLD'S FAIR 1939...............................      6.50
MILK GLASS,WORLD'S FAIR,1939,EMBOSSED MAP..................      8.00
MILKS EMULSION,LARGE MOUTH,BROWN...........................      3.50
```

MILK,PLAIN,PINT

 MILK,PLAIN,1/2 PINT

 MILK,POLK'S,IT WHIPS, CREAM TOP,QUART

 MILK, STORE BOTTLE, 5 CENTS,1/2 PINT

 MILK GLASS. MENTHOLATUM,SCREW TOP

 MILK GLASS,METAL SCREW TOP

MILK GLASS, MUSTEROLE, SCREW TOP

 MILK GLASS,SCREW CAP

 MILK GLASS,SHAVO CREAM

MINERAL SPRING, CONGRESS & EMPIRE SPRING CO., WHITTLED, GREEN, QUART	22.50
MINERAL SPRING, GETTYSBURG KATALYSINE WATER, OLIVE GREEN, QUART	30.00
MINIATURE, ALE, PABST, GREEN, 4 IN....ILLUS..	3.00
MINIATURE, ANCIENT URN, DELFT	5.00
MINIATURE, ANISETTE, ZACKS BUDAPEST	10.00
MINIATURE, ARDO NUBIAN	5.00
MINIATURE, ARDO PAESTUM	6.00
MINIATURE, ARDO VENUS DE MILO	7.00
MINIATURE, ARSON'S VIKING SHIP, CHINA	14.00
MINIATURE, BALLANTINE JUG, SCOTLAND	8.00
MINIATURE, BARD'S TOWN, VIOLIN SHAPE, 5 IN....ILLUS..	6.00
MINIATURE, BEER, BUDWEISER, AMBER, 4 1/4 IN....ILLUS..	3.00
MINIATURE, BEER, PABST, AMBER, 4 IN....ILLUS..	3.00
MINIATURE, BEER, ROCK CITY, AMBER, 3 3/4 IN....ILLUS..	3.00
MINIATURE, BEER, SCHLITZ, AMBER, 4 IN....ILLUS..	4.00
MINIATURE, BEER, TIPTOP, AMBER, 3 IN....ILLUS..	9.50
MINIATURE, BENEAGLES, BURNS HOMESTEAD	5.00
MINIATURE, BENEAGLES, CURLING STONE	5.00
MINIATURE, BENEAGLES, EDINBURGH CASTLE	5.00

MINIATURE, ALE, PABST, GREEN, 4 IN

MINIATURE, BARD'S TOWN,
VIOLIN SHAPE, 5 IN

MINIATURE, BEER, BUDWEISER,
AMBER, 4 1/4 IN

MINIATURE, BEER,
PABST, AMBER, 4 IN

MINIATURE, BEER,
ROCK CITY,
AMBER, 3 3/4 IN

MINIATURE,
BEER, TIPTOP,
AMBER, 3 IN

MINIATURE, BEER,
SCHLITZ, AMBER, 4 IN

```
MINIATURE,BENEAGLES,PHEASANT................................    5.00
MINIATURE,BENEAGLES,SCOTCH BARREL,THISTLE...................    5.00
MINIATURE,BENEAGLES,TROUT...................................    5.00
MINIATURE,BITTERS,HARTWIG KANTOROWICZ,MILK GLASS............   75.00
MINIATURE,BLOWN,BLUE........................................    3.00
MINIATURE,BORGHINI,BLACK CAT................................    5.00
MINIATURE,BORGHINI,CANDLE LAMP..............................    6.00
MINIATURE,BORGHINI,CANDLEHOLDER.............................    7.00
MINIATURE,BORGHINI,CAT,BLACK................................    5.00
MINIATURE,BORGHINI,FRUIT BOWL...............................    6.00
MINIATURE,BORGHINI,MAN ON WINE CASK.........................    6.00
MINIATURE,BORGHINI,PENGUIN..................................    5.00
MINIATURE,BORGHINI,RED BIRD.................................    5.00
MINIATURE,BORGHINI,WINE CASK,OLD MAN........................    6.00
MINIATURE,BOURBON BLEND.....................................    1.00
MINIATURE,BRONTE JUG........................................    2.00
MINIATURE,BROWN FORMAN,1870,4 IN.....................ILLUS..    4.00
MINIATURE,CANADIAN CLUB,4 IN.........................ILLUS..    3.50
MINIATURE,CASTELWOOD,DUCK PIN,CALIFORNIA,MUSCATEL...........    6.00
MINIATURE,CHARLES JACQUN ET CIE INC.,3 IN............ILLUS..    8.00
MINIATURE,CHIANTI CASTIEVECCHIO,4 IN.,1949...........ILLUS..    2.00
```

MINIATURE, BROWN FORMAN,
1870, 4 IN

MINIATURE,
CANADIAN
CLUB, 4 IN

MINIATURE, CHARLES
JACQUN ET CIE
INC., 3 IN

MINIATURE, CHIANTI
CASTIEVECCHIO,
4 IN., 1949

```
MINIATURE,CHIVAS REGAL,GREEN,3 3/4 IN................ILLUS..    4.50
MINIATURE,CHURN,DELFT.......................................    5.00
MINIATURE,COCA COLA,GOLD....................................     .49
MINIATURE,COCA COLA,PLASTIC,1940............................     .10
MINIATURE,COCA COLA,1923,2 1/2 IN. HIGH.....................    4.00
MINIATURE,COCA COLA,3 IN. TALL..............................     .75
MINIATURE,COCA COLA,3 IN. TALL,CAPPED,FULL..................    1.00
MINIATURE,COCA COLA,3 IN. TALL,TRADE MARKED ON 2 SIDES......    1.00
MINIATURE,COGNAC TURISTA,MEXICO.............................    6.00
MINIATURE,COURVOISIER,CANNON................................    3.00
MINIATURE,COURVOISIER,4 1/2 IN.......................ILLUS..    2.00
MINIATURE,CREME DE CACAO,MELSON,1937........................    4.00
MINIATURE,CREME DE CACAO,3 IN........................ILLUS..    4.00
MINIATURE,CRESTA BLANCA,1934................................    4.00
MINIATURE,CUSENIER APRICOT LIQUEUR BUENOS AIRES,1935........    8.00
MINIATURE,CUSENIER CREME DE CACAO VANILLAN,BUENOS AIRES,
  1936......................................................    8.00
MINIATURE,CUSENIER,FRANCE,CERAMIC...........................   10.00
MINIATURE,D.O.M.BENEDICTINE,GREEN,3 1/2 IN...........ILLUS..    4.00
MINIATURE,DR.KILMER.........................................    2.50
MINIATURE,DR.SPOOR..........................................    2.50
MINIATURE,DRIOLI CAT........................................    8.00
```

MINIATURE,CHIVAS REGAL,
GREEN,3 3/4 IN

MINIATURE,
COURVOISIER,4 1/2 IN

MINIATURE,
CREME DE CACAO,3 IN

MINIATURE,D.O.M.BENEDICTINE,
GREEN,3 1/2 IN

```
MINIATURE,DRIOLI DOG...........................................    8.00
MINIATURE,DRIOLI DUCK..........................................    8.00
MINIATURE,DRIOLI MOUSE.........................................    8.00
MINIATURE,DRIOLI,MEN,SET OF 6..................................   14.00
MINIATURE,DU BOUCHETT,CREME DE MENTHE,1948,....................    3.50
MINIATURE,DUFFY MALT,PAT.AUG.24,1886,ROUND,AMBER...............   10.00
MINIATURE,E.ALDABO HAVANA CUBA 1934............................    6.00
MINIATURE,EARLY TIMES,4 3/4 IN. HIGH,ROUND CLEAR...............    2.00
MINIATURE,EASTSIDE BEER........................................    3.00
MINIATURE,ELK'S WHISKEY,EAR OF CORN WITH EAR OF CORN STOPPER    120.00
MINIATURE,ELY'S CREAM BALM.....................................    2.50
MINIATURE,EMBOSSED CHELSEY'S JOCKEY CLUB.......................  500.00
MINIATURE,EXTRA SEC CUSENIER,BUENOS AIRES,1937.................    8.00
MINIATURE,FIGURAL,GLASS HORSE & RIDER,FRANCE.........ILLUS..     15.00
MINIATURE,FIGURAL,GLASS HORSE & RIDER,O.J............ILLUS..      6.00
MINIATURE,FIGURAL,TARBABY,HAND DECORATED,GERMAN CIRCA 1915..      1.50
MINIATURE,FOUR ROSES,EMBOSSED,AMBER............................    1.50
MINIATURE,FOUR ROSES,EMBOSSED,CORK TOP.........................    1.50
MINIATURE,FOUR ROSES,4 IN............................ILLUS..      8.00
MINIATURE,FRANZIA,CALIFORNIA PORT..............................    2.00
MINIATURE,FRUIT JAR,BALL PERFECT MASON,1939 WORLD'S FAIR....      5.00
MINIATURE,GALLIANO.............................................    2.25
MINIATURE,GARNIER,FRANCE,1934..................................    7.50
MINIATURE,GARNIER,SOLDIER,4 1/2 IN...................ILLUS..     13.00
MINIATURE,GILBEY'S VODKA,5 IN. HIGH,SQUARE,CLEAR...............    2.00
```

MINIATURE,FIGURAL,
GLASS HORSE &
RIDER,FRANCE

MINIATURE, FOUR
ROSES,4 IN

MINIATURE,FIGURAL,
GLASS HORSE &
RIDER,O.J.

MINIATURE,
GARNIER,SOLDIER,
4 1/2 IN

```
MINIATURE,GIN...........................................    1.00
MINIATURE,GLASS ANIMAL,CAMEL,4 IN....................ILLUS..    6.00
MINIATURE,GLASS ANIMAL,CAT,2 IN......................ILLUS..    5.00
MINIATURE,GLASS ANIMAL,DACHSHUND,1 1/2 IN............ILLUS..    5.00
MINIATURE,GLASS ANIMAL,DEER,BLACK ANTLERS............ILLUS..    4.50
MINIATURE,GLASS ANIMAL,DEER,BUDDING BUCK,2 IN........ILLUS..    4.50
MINIATURE,GLASS ANIMAL,DEER,DOE,1 1/2 IN.............ILLUS..    4.50
MINIATURE,GLASS ANIMAL,DEER,1 IN.....................ILLUS..    4.50
MINIATURE,GLASS ANIMAL,DOG,1 IN......................ILLUS..    5.00
MINIATURE,GLASS ANIMAL,HORSE,1 1/2 IN................ILLUS..    4.50
MINIATURE,GLASS ANIMAL,PELICAN,WHITE BILL............ILLUS..    5.00
MINIATURE,GLASS ANIMAL,PELICAN,2 1/2 IN..............ILLUS..    5.00
MINIATURE,GLASS ANIMAL,PELICAN,4 IN..................ILLUS..    6.00
MINIATURE,GLASS ANIMAL,PIG,4 IN......................ILLUS..    6.00
MINIATURE,GORDONS DRY GIN,4 1/2 IN. HIGH,RECTANGULAR,CLEAR..    4.00
MINIATURE,GRAND GIFFARD,PITCHER,BLUE.......................    9.95
MINIATURE,GRAND GIFFARD,PITCHER,RED........................    9.95
MINIATURE,GRAND GIFFARD,TEAPOT,BLACK.......................    9.95
```

MINIATURES,GLASS ANIMALS

DEER,
BUDDING BUCK,2 IN

DEER,1 IN DEER,
BLACK ANTLERS HORSE,
1 1/2 IN DEER,DOE,
1 1/2 IN

DACHSHUND.
1 1/2 IN PELICAN,
2 1/2 IN

CAT,2 IN DOG,1 IN PELICAN,
WHITE BILL

MINIATURES, GLASS ANIMALS

PELICAN, 4 IN   CAMEL, 4 IN   PIG, 4 IN

```
MINIATURE,GREEN RIVER,4 IN..............................ILLUS..      4.00
MINIATURE,HAIG & HAIG,4 IN..............................ILLUS..      3.00
MINIATURE,HAIG AND HAIG,WIRE...................................      4.00
MINIATURE,HARVARD RYE,CLEAR....................................      4.00
MINIATURE,HIGH BUTTON SHOE.....................................     18.00
MINIATURE,HIRAM WALKER,CREME DE MENTHE..................ILLUS..      3.50
MINIATURE,HIRAM WALKER,THREADED,AMBER..........................      1.50
MINIATURE,HIS MASTERS BREOTH,POTTERY,JAPAN.............ILLUS..       8.00
```

MINIATURE,
GREEN RIVER, 4 IN

MINIATURE,
HIRAM WALKER,
CREME DE MENTHE

MINIATURE,
HAIG &
HAIG, 4 IN

MINIATURE,
HIS MASTERS BREOTH,
POTTERY, JAPAN

```
MINIATURE,HOUSE OF KOSHU,RAINBOW...............................      3.50
MINIATURE,HUFELAND,SAN FRANCISCO,1930..........................      7.50
MINIATURE,HUNTER,4 1/2 IN...............................ILLUS..      3.50
MINIATURE,IRISH MIST SOLDIER...................................      7.00
MINIATURE,J.G.B.SIEGERT........................................      5.00
MINIATURE,JAPAN,BLUE JUG,NEW,3 IN.......................ILLUS..      1.50
MINIATURE,JUG,DELFT............................................      5.00
MINIATURE,JUG,MOHAWK PEACH LIQUEUR,4 IN.................ILLUS..      3.00
MINIATURE,KEASBEY & MATTISON...................................      2.50
MINIATURE,KELLER STRAUSS.......................................      7.50
MINIATURE,KEMP'S COUGH BALSAM..................................      2.50
MINIATURE,KENTUCKY BEAM,4 IN. HIGH,RECTANGULAR,CLEAR...........      2.00
MINIATURE,KING'S RANSOM,3 IN............................ILLUS..      3.00
MINIATURE,KLM DELFT,2 STORY HOUSE..............................     12.00
MINIATURE,KORD,HORSEHEAD.......................................      3.50
```

MINIATURE, HUNTER,
4 1/2 IN

MINIATURE,
JAPAN,
BLUE JUG,
NEW, 3 IN

MINIATURE, JUG,
MOHAWK PEACH
LIQUEUR, 4 IN

MINIATURE, KING'S RANSOM,
3 IN

```
MINIATURE, LAMP, BLUE CURACAO, 4 IN......................ILLUS..     11.00
MINIATURE, LAMP, RUM CARIOCA, 6 IN........................ILLUS..      8.00
MINIATURE, LARSENS COGNAC, FRANCE, GLASS VIKING SHIP...........       9.00
MINIATURE, LARSENS COGNAC, FRANCE, LIMOGES CHINA, VIKING SHIP...     12.00
MINIATURE, LEGENDRE HERBSAINT, FRANCE 1932....................       5.00
MINIATURE, LUXARDO, GAMBIA....................................       1.75
MINIATURE, LUXARDO, NUBIAN....................................       1.75
MINIATURE, MAC NAUGHTON, 5 IN. HIGH, ROUND AMBER..............       3.00
MINIATURE, MAISON COINTREAU, FRANCE...........................       6.00
MINIATURE, MARIE BRIZARD, BORDEAUX, 1930......................      10.00
MINIATURE, MARQUIS DE MONTESQUIEU.............................       9.00
MINIATURE, MARTIN'S SHERRY, AMBER, 5 1/2 IN............ILLUS..       2.50
MINIATURE, MASSON, RARE TAWNY PORT, 1940......................       3.00
MINIATURE, MAZARINE CORDIAL, 3 IN.....................ILLUS..       3.50
MINIATURE, MC LECH, BARREL OF KINDNESS, HAMILTON, STEWART, GORDON    2.50
MINIATURE, MC LECH, DOE HEAD..................................       5.00
MINIATURE, MC LECH, ELF.......................................       2.50
MINIATURE, MC LECH, GOLF BALL.................................       2.50
MINIATURE, MC LECH, OLD PUB BARRELS, LONDON SCENES............       2.50
MINIATURE, MC LECH, RABBIT....................................       2.50
MINIATURE, MC LECH, ROBERT BURNS, WHITE BUST..................       5.00
MINIATURE, MC LECH, SHIP LANTERNS, PORT & STARBOARD, PAIR.......      4.50
MINIATURE, MC LECH, TAM O'SHANTER, YE OLDE PUB PUMP HANDLE.....       4.00
MINIATURE, MC LECH, TOBY JUG, FOOTBALL........................       3.00
```

MINIATURE, LAMP,
BLUE CURACAO, 4 IN

MINIATURE,
LAMP, RUM
CARIOCA,
6 IN

MINIATURE,
MARTIN'S SHERRY,
AMBER, 5 1/2 IN

MINIATURE,
MAZARINE
CORDIAL, 3 IN

```
MINIATURE,MEIER'S,BASEBALL,2 1/2 IN..................ILLUS..    11.00
MINIATURE,MEIER'S,FOOTBALL,2 1/2 IN..................ILLUS..    11.00
MINIATURE,MONNET COGNAC,FRANCE,1932..........................    6.00
MINIATURE,MOULIN ROUGE BRANDY,3 1/2 IN. HIGH,RECTANGULAR,
  CLEAR......................................................    4.00
MINIATURE,O'SHAUGHNESSEY,4 3/4 IN. HIGH,SQUARE,CLEAR........    2.50
MINIATURE,OIL LAMP,DELFT...................................    5.00
MINIATURE,OLD ANGUS,AMBER,5 IN.......................ILLUS..    2.00
MINIATURE,OLD MR.BOSTON,4 IN.........................ILLUS..    4.00
MINIATURE,PABST BLUE RIBBON BEER..........................    3.00
MINIATURE,PAUL BONES,4 IN............................ILLUS..    6.00
MINIATURE,PAUL JONES,BLOWN................................   13.00
MINIATURE,PAUL JONES,EMBOSSED,CORK TOP....................    1.50
MINIATURE,PAUL MASSON,AMBER,3 1/2 IN.................ILLUS..    3.00
MINIATURE,PEPTENZYME,COBALT...............................    5.00
MINIATURE,PRINA VISTA,ENGLAND,1934........................    4.00
MINIATURE,PRIVATE MOULD EMBOSSED,VINOL SHAPE,AMBER.........    5.00
MINIATURE,PURE ANISE EXTRACT,NEW ORLEANS..................    5.00
MINIATURE,RAILROAD,GIN,CONTINENTAL,PHILA..................    4.75
MINIATURE,RHUM NEGRITA,FRANCE,1937........................    7.50
MINIATURE,RIEMEISCHMID,COFFEEPOT..........................    3.00
MINIATURE,RIEMEISCHMID,EARTHENWARE JUG....................    3.00
MINIATURE,RIEMEISCHMID,FLASK..............................    3.00
MINIATURE,RIEMEISCHMID,JUG................................    3.00
MINIATURE,RUM CARIOCA,MAN & CART,5 IN................ILLUS..   15.00
MINIATURE,RUM CARIOCA,5 IN...........................ILLUS..    3.00
```

MINIATURE,MEIER'S,
BASEBALL,2 1/2 IN

MINIATURE,MEIER'S,
FOOTBALL,2 1/2 IN

MINIATURE,
OLD MR.BOSTON,4 IN

MINIATURE,OLD ANGUS,
AMBER,5 IN

MINIATURE,
PAUL BONES,
4 IN

MINIATURE,
PAUL MASSON,
AMBER,3 1/2 IN

MINIATURE,
RUM CARIOCA,
MAN & CART,
5 IN

MINIATURE,
RUM CARIOCA,
5 IN

MINIATURE,RYENBENDE CANDLESTICK.............................. 6.00
MINIATURE,RYENBENDE CANDLESTICK,DELFT,BLUE.................... 5.00
MINIATURE,RYENBENDE CHURN..................................... 6.00
MINIATURE,RYENBENDE CRUET..................................... 6.00
MINIATURE,RYENBENDE OIL LAMP.................................. 6.00
MINIATURE,RYENBENDE SHOE...................................... 6.00
MINIATURE,SAN MIGUEL BEER,MANILA,PHILIPPINES.................. 2.00
MINIATURE,SANFORD DRUGGIST,CHESTERTOWN,N.Y.,CCCC............. 2.50
MINIATURE,SCHENLEY,CORK TOP,EMBOSSED,AMBER................... 1.50
MINIATURE,SCHENLEY,EMBOSSED,AMBER............................ 1.50
MINIATURE,SCOTCH... 1.00
MINIATURE,SEAL BOTTLE,AQUA,5 IN.....................ILLUS.. 1.00
MINIATURE,SET,3 BOTTLES,SOUTHERN SALES,3 IN...........ILLUS.. 7.50
MINIATURE,SHOE,DELFT... 5.00
MINIATURE,SIPHON,METAL TOP,GREEN,WEIL PARFUM.........ILLUS.. 12.00
MINIATURE,SIPHON,METAL TOP,6 IN.,CLEAR..............ILLUS.. 12.00
MINIATURE,SLOPPY JOE'S CUBA,HAVANA,1936...................... 5.00
MINIATURE,SODA,FANTA... .50
MINIATURE,SODA,SPRITE,3 IN. TALL............................. .50
MINIATURE,SODA,UNCLE JO,AMBER................................ 3.00

MINIATURE,SEAL BOTTLE,   MINIATURE,SET,3 BOTTLES,
AQUA,5 IN   SOUTHERN SALES,3 IN

MINIATURE,SIPHON,
METAL TOP,GREEN,   MINIATURE,
WEIL PARFUM   SIPHON,METAL TOP,6 IN.,CLEAR

MINIATURE,SPANISH LADY,CREMA CACAO,6 IN..............ILLUS.. 15.00
MINIATURE,SPRITE,GREEN....................................... 1.50
MINIATURE,TOREADOR,CREMA CACAO,6 IN..................ILLUS.. 15.00
MINIATURE,TULLAMORE DEW,JUG,IRELAND.......................... 5.00
MINIATURE,USHER'S,5 IN. HIGH,ROUND,CLEAR.................... 3.00
MINIATURE,VAT 69,GREEN,4 IN..........................ILLUS.. 4.00
MINIATURE,VICENTE BOSCH,BADALONA............................. 4.00
MINIATURE,VICENTE BOSCH,BADALONA,EMBOSSED MEXICO 1932........ 7.00
MINIATURE,VODKA.. 1.00
MINIATURE,WAMPOLE'S ANAEMIOL................................. 2.50
MINIATURE,WHISKEY,BLACK HORSE,3 IN...................ILLUS.. 2.00
MINIATURE,WHISKEY,ICE BUCKET,6 BOTTLE,4 IN...........ILLUS.. 4.00
MINIATURE,WHISKEY,KENTUCKY PERFECTION,3 IN...........ILLUS.. 2.00
MINIATURE,WHITE LABEL,5 IN. HIGH,ROUND CLEAR................ 2.00
MINIATURE,WINDMILL,DELFT..................................... 5.00
MINIATURE,WINE,THIN NECK,4 IN.,BLUE-GREEN.................... 2.50
MINIATURE,ZWACK,BUDAPEST,1934,CORDIAL BITTERS............... 15.00
MONOGRAM,STERLING SCREW TOP,GREEN............................ 3.50
MOONWALK,MIDLAND'S AMERICAN SHERRY........................... 9.95
MOSER,DECANTER,SIGNED,PANEL CUT............................. 63.00
MOSER,PERFUME,6 PANEL,SIGNED,SMOKY TOPAZ.................... 50.00
MOXIE,DRINK MOXIE,PRINTED............................ILLUS.. 7.00
MOXIE,NO DEPOSIT,8 IN................................ILLUS.. .50
MOXIE,TRADEMARK NERVE FOOD,AQUA,10 1/2 IN.............ILLUS.. 8.50
MOXIE,702,CROWN CAP,8 IN.............................ILLUS.. 3.00

MINIATURE,
SPANISH LADY,
CREMA CACAO,
6 IN

MINIATURE,
TOREADOR,
CREMA CACAO,
6 IN

MINIATURE, WHISKEY,
BLACK HORSE, 3 IN

MINIATURE, VAT 69,
GREEN, 4 IN

MINIATURE, WHISKEY,
ICE BUCKET, 6 BOTTLE, 4 IN

MINIATURE, WHISKEY,
KENTUCKY PERFECTION,
3 IN

MOXIE, NO DEPOSIT, 8 IN

MOXIE, DRINK MOXIE,
PRINTED

MOXIE, TRADEMARK NERVE FOOD,
AQUA, 10 1/2 IN

MOXIE, 702, CROWN CAP, 8 IN

MR.BOSTON,BOB WHITE.. 12.50
MR.BOSTON,GUITAR.. 7.95
MR.BOSTON,THIN MAN,MINIATURE.. 2.50
MT.WASHINGTON,COLOGNE,ENAMELED FLORAL............................... 26.00
MT.WASHINGTON,PERFUME,STERLING EMBOSSED COVER,SIGNED................ 46.00
MYAL QUALITY,BUBBLES,AMBER.. 6.00
MYERS ROCK ROSE,NEW HAVEN,COLLARED MOUTH,IRON PONTIL................ 30.00
NAILSEA,DECANTER,13 IN. HIGH,BLUE,WHITE LOOPINGS.................... 101.00
NAILSEA,DOUBLE GEMEL,PINT,WHITE,RED LOOPINGS........................ 47.00
NAILSEA,PERFUME,CLEAR,WHITE LOOPINGS................................ 31.00
NAVEL JELLY... 14.95

NURSING BOTTLES WERE FIRST USED IN THE SECOND HALF OF
THE 19TH CENTURY. THEY ARE EASILY IDENTIFIED BY THE
UNIQUE SHAPE AND THE MEASURING UNITS THAT ARE OFTEN
MARKED ON THE SIDES.

NURSING,BLUE & WHITE POTTERY.. 35.00
NURSING,EMPIRE,WHITALL,TATUM & CO................................... 35.00
NURSING,EUREKA,8 OZ.,2 VIEWS...............................ILLUS.. 9.00
NURSING,LAYS FLAT,TURNED UP STRETCHED TOP,THE SEASIDE............... 6.50
NURSING,MOTHER,BABY,ROCKING CHAIR,EMBOSSED MOTHER'S PET,
　GREEN.. 35.00
NURSING,OVAL,ONE SIDE IS FLAT,OUNCE SCALE,EIGHT-POINT STAR,
　ACME... 9.00
NURSING,RAISED NECK,OVAL,H.WOOD & SONS.............................. 9.00
NURSING,SUNNY BABE,SPRAWLED ON LENGTH OF ONE SIDE,EMBOSSED,
　8 OZ... 7.00
NURSING,TEMP-GUARD,6 1/2 IN................................ILLUS.. 5.00
NURSING,THE JEWEL FEEDING BOTTLE,GOOSE NECK,AQUA.................... 6.00
NURSING,VIOLIN SHAPE,BURRS PAT.1872,AQUA,6 IN...................... 20.00
OBR,BALLOON,RED... 5.95 TO 13.25
OBR,NATIONAL HOCKEY LEAGUE SERIES,BOSTON BRUINS..................... 14.95
OBR,NATIONAL HOCKEY LEAGUE SERIES,CHICAGO BLACK HAWKS............... 14.95
OBR,NATIONAL HOCKEY LEAGUE SERIES,DETROIT RED WINGS................. 14.95

NURSING,EUREKA,
8 OZ.,2 VIEWS

NURSING,TEMP-GUARD,
6 1/2 IN

OBR,NATIONAL HOCKEY LEAGUE SERIES,MINNESOTA NORTH STARS..... 14.95
OBR,NATIONAL HOCKEY LEAGUE SERIES,NEW YORK RANGERS.......... 14.95
OBR,NATIONAL HOCKEY LEAGUE SERIES,ST.LOUIS BLUES............ 14.95
OBR,PIERCE ARROW.................................. 7.95 TO 11.95
OBR,PRAIRIE SCHOONER.............................. 7.95 TO 11.95
OBR,RIVER QUEEN................................... 4.95 TO 8.95
OBR,TITANIC.. 13.50
OIL,MOTOR,SHELL-PENN,OWENS ILLINOIS GLASS CO.,MACHINE MADE,
　CLEAR... 3.00
OIL,STANDARD,INDIANA,POLARINE JAR,QUART,CLEAR.............. 18.00
OIL,THOMAS EDISON BATTERY OIL,FLAT,WHITE................... 1.50

```
OIL,THOMAS EDISON BATTERY OIL,ROUND,WHITE....................    1.50
OIL,THOMAS ELECTRIC OIL,INTERNAL & EXTERNAL.................     3.00
OIL,3 IN 1,MACHINE MADE.....................................     1.50
OLD CROW DISTILLERY,TURN MOLD,12 IN. TALL,OLIVE GREEN.......     5.00
OLD CROW,CHESSMAN..........................................     10.95
OLD CROW,ROYAL DOULTON,CIRCA 1958..........................     75.00
OLD CROW,WARLY.............................................     60.00
OLD FITZGERALD,BIRD DOG....................................      7.95
OLD FITZGERALD,CABIN STILL,BLARNEY.................. 6.95 TO    11.00
OLD FITZGERALD,CABIN STILL,CALIFORNIA......................     11.00
OLD FITZGERALD,CABIN STILL,CANDLELIGHT,PAIR,1956...........     17.00
OLD FITZGERALD,CABIN STILL,DEER BROWSING............ 4.95 TO     6.00
OLD FITZGERALD,CABIN STILL,DOG,POINTING SETTER.............     14.00
OLD FITZGERALD,CABIN STILL,DUCK..................... 7.95 TO     9.00
OLD FITZGERALD,CABIN STILL,FISH............................      4.00
OLD FITZGERALD,CABIN STILL,FLAGSHIP................. 5.00 TO     6.49
OLD FITZGERALD,CABIN STILL,FLEUR DE LIS............ 12.00 TO    17.00
OLD FITZGERALD,CABIN STILL,FLORENTINE.............. 7.95 TO     10.00
OLD FITZGERALD,CABIN STILL,FOUR SEASONS....................      5.00
OLD FITZGERALD,CABIN STILL,GOLD COASTER............ 12.95 TO    14.00
OLD FITZGERALD,CABIN STILL,GOLD WEB........................     18.00
OLD FITZGERALD,CABIN STILL,HILLBILLY,PINT........... 27.50 TO   30.00
OLD FITZGERALD,CABIN STILL,HILLBILLY,QUART,'54.......ILLUS..    40.00
OLD FITZGERALD,CABIN STILL,HILLBILLY,1956..................     39.50
OLD FITZGERALD,CABIN STILL,HILLBILLY,1969............ILLUS..     7.50
OLD FITZGERALD,CABIN STILL,LEPRECHAUN............... 6.00 TO    10.00
OLD FITZGERALD,CABIN STILL,LEPRECHAUN,GOD........... 19.00 TO   24.95
OLD FITZGERALD,CABIN STILL,LEXINGTON.......................      5.00
```

OLD FITZGERALD,
CABIN STILL,HILLBILLY,
1969

OLD FITZGERALD,
CABIN STILL,
HILLBILLY,QUART, '54

```
OLD FITZGERALD,CABIN STILL,MASTERPIECE.....................     40.00
OLD FITZGERALD,CABIN STILL,PHEASANT,RISING.................     15.00
OLD FITZGERALD,CABIN STILL,QUAIL................... 4.00 TO      7.95
OLD FITZGERALD,CABIN STILL,REBEL YELL HORSE................     15.00
OLD FITZGERALD,CABIN STILL,RIP VAN WINKLE,'71........ILLUS..     7.50
OLD FITZGERALD,CABIN STILL,SONS OF ERIN............ 7.95 TO      9.00
OLD FITZGERALD,CABIN STILL,SOUTH CAROLINA..................     11.00
OLD FITZGERALD,CABIN STILL,TOURNAMENT.............. 12.95 TO    14.00
OLD FITZGERALD,CABIN STILL,TREE OF LIFE............ 8.95 TO     10.00
OLD FITZGERALD,CABIN STILL,VENETIAN........................      5.00
```

```
OLD FITZGERALD,CANDLELIGHT,1956...............................      5.95
OLD FITZGERALD,CANDLESTICK,1961................................      5.95
OLD FITZGERALD,COAT OF ARMS....................................      2.00
OLD FITZGERALD,COLONIAL........................................      4.95
OLD FITZGERALD,CROWN...........................................      6.95
OLD FITZGERALD,DIAMOND,1961....................................      9.95
OLD FITZGERALD,JEWEL...........................................      7.95
OLD FITZGERALD,LEXINGTON.......................................      4.95
OLD FITZGERALD,MONTICELLO,DECANTER.............................      6.45
OLD FITZGERALD,POINTING SETTER,1965............................     12.95
OLD STYLE COLONY WINERY,DER BRUDER,BROTHER...........ILLUS..     14.95
OLD STYLE COLONY WINERY,DIE SCHWESTER,SISTER..................     14.95
   OLD TAYLOR, SEE WHISKEY, OLD TAYLOR
ORANGE CRUSH,JULY 1920.........................................      2.00
ORANGE CRUSH,29 RIDGES,CLEAR...................................      2.50
PALMER'S,GREEN,5 IN............................................      5.00
PANELED,SAYS SMILE,DATED 1922,18 IN.HIGH.......................     45.00
PAPER LABEL,NICE OLD PORT,BOSTON,AMBER,QUART...................      5.00
PAPER LABEL,OLD WAVERLY PROCESS,AMBER,QUART...................      5.00
PEACHBLOW,GUNDERSON,DECANTER,STOPPER...........................    186.00
PEACHBLOW,WEBB,SCENT,GOLD DECOR,SILVER MOUNT,DATE 1885.......    376.00
PEACHBLOW,WHEELING,SNUFF.......................................     56.00
PEPPERSAUCE,AMETHYST................................. 15.00 TO     20.00
PEPPERSAUCE,AQUA.....................................  8.00 TO     12.00
PEPPERSAUCE,BIRD,PAPER LABEL,AQUA,9 IN...............ILLUS..     18.00
PEPPERSAUCE,BLOWN IN MOLD,CLEAR................................      6.00
```

OLD STYLE COLONY
WINERY,DER BRUDER,
BROTHER

OLD FITZGERALD,CABIN
STILL,RIP VAN WINKLE,'71

PEPPERSAUCE,
BIRD,PAPER LABEL,
AQUA,9 IN

```
PEPPERSAUCE,BLOWN IN MOLD,GREEN...............................     15.00
PEPPERSAUCE,CATHEDRAL,AQUA....................................     25.00
PEPPERSAUCE,CATHEDRAL,6 PANELS,2 WINDOWS,AQUA.................     18.00
PEPPERSAUCE,CATHEDRAL,6 SIDED,AQUA.................. 15.00 TO     40.00
PEPPERSAUCE,EMBOSSED..........................................     45.00
PEPPERSAUCE,EVANGELINE,ST.MARTINVILLE,LA.,SCREW TOP..........      3.00
PEPPERSAUCE,FLUTED,10 IN.,AQUA...............................     12.00
PEPPERSAUCE,PANELED BODY,3 ROWS DIAMONDS,SWIRLED NECK........     25.00
PEPPERSAUCE,RITTER...........................................      1.50
PEPPERSAUCE,6 SIDED,RIDGY,AQUA...............................     12.00
PEPPERSAUCE,18 RING,OVAL,MM,CLEAR............................      6.00
PEPPERSAUCE,20 RING,OVAL,CLEAR...............................      8.00
```

```
PEPPERSAUCE,20 RINGS,ROUND,AQUA..............................  12.00
PEPPERSAUCE,20 RINGS,ROUND,CLEAR.............................  12.00
PEPPERSAUCE,22 RINGS,OVAL,AQUA...............................  12.00
PEPPERSAUCE,22 RINGS,OVAL,CLEAR..............................  12.00
PEPPERSAUCE,24 RING,ROUND,S.C.A..............................  10.00
PEPSI COLA,BIRMINGHAM,AMBER..................................  15.00
PERFUME,AMETHYST QUARTZ,GOLD,DIAMOND,CABOCHON SAPPHIRE,
   RUSSIA...................................................1,000.00
PERFUME,ATOMIZER,CUT GLASS,PEWTER TOP........................  10.00
PERFUME,BACCARAT,PANELED,GROUND STOPPER......................   6.00
PERFUME,BACCARAT,SIGNED,STOPPER,PAIR.........................  45.00
PERFUME,BALL SHAPE,HARVARD CUT,EMBOSSED SILVER CAP,CUT GLASS   16.00
PERFUME,BELL SHAPE,FLARED BASE,HANDLE,CORK,NICKEL CAP,
   6 IN.TALL................................................   9.00
PERFUME,BIEDERMEIER,TRIPLE PLATE,STOPPER..................... 190.00
PERFUME,BLACK AMETHYST,CUBE SHAPE,MARKED GUERLAIN,PARIS,
   FRANCE...................................................  10.00
PERFUME,BLOWN IN MOLD,AMETHYST...............................   1.50
PERFUME,BLOWN IN MOLD,GLASS STOPPER,CLEAR........... 1.00 TO   1.50
PERFUME,BLOWN IN MOLD,6 IN. TALL,CLEAR.......................   1.25
PERFUME,BLUE MILK GLASS STOPPER,OPALESCENT...................  22.50
PERFUME,BULBOUS,STERLING SILVER OVERLAY,STOPPER,7 IN.HIGH...  60.00
PERFUME,BULBOUS,STOPPER,HOBSTARS & GEOMETRICS................  28.00
PERFUME,BURMESE,STOPPER...................................1,200.00
PERFUME,C.H.SELICK,AMETHYST......................... 2.00 TO   2.50
PERFUME,CAMBRIDGE HELIO,ATOMIZER,BLACK & GOLD DECOR.........  48.00
PERFUME,CENTURY FILL TO THIS LINE,BLOWN IN MOLD,CLEAR.......   1.50
PERFUME,CHAPOTEAUT PARIS,BLOWN IN MOLD,10 PANELS,CLEAR......   2.00
PERFUME,CITRON WEBB CAMEO,LAY DOWN,WHITE FLOWERS............ 175.00
PERFUME,COLGATE & CO.,BLOWN IN MOLD,BALL NECK,CLEAR.........   2.00
PERFUME,COLGATE & CO.,N.Y.,AMETHYST..........................   3.00
PERFUME,COLGATE & CO.,N.Y.,CLEAR.............................   3.00
PERFUME,COLGATE & CO.,N.Y.,RECTANGULAR,AMETHYST..............   4.00
PERFUME,COLGATE & CO.,N.Y.,SQUARE,CLEAR......................   2.00
PERFUME,CREAMY GROUND,MAROON FLORAL,METAL RIM,SIGNED RICHARD 150.00
PERFUME,CRYSTAL,SILVER OVERLAY,FLORAL,BIRD,PANELS,GORHAM....  59.50
PERFUME,CUT CRYSTAL,GOLD TOP,BIRD,LEATHER CASE,3 3/4 IN.HIGH  95.00
PERFUME,CUT GLASS,FLORAL CUT,CLOISONNE TOP..................  12.00
PERFUME,CUT GLASS,OVERALL HARVARD CUT,SILVER TOP,FACETED
   STOPPER..................................................  15.00
PERFUME,CUT GLASS,SERIAL NO. ON BOTTLE & STOPPER.............  49.50
PERFUME,CUT GLASS,STOPPER,9 1/2 IN. TALL....................  27.50
PERFUME,CUT GLASS,VIAL,BRASS LID.............................   8.50
PERFUME,DAYBROOKS DETROIT,AMETHYST...........................   6.00
PERFUME,DAYBROOKS DETROIT,CLEAR..............................   6.00
PERFUME,DIAMONDS,SUNBURSTS,BALL STOPPER,CUT GLASS,SET OF
   FOUR.....................................................  21.00
PERFUME,DISK-SHAPED BODY,STOPPER,DABBER,AMBERINA,LALIQUE,
   WORTH....................................................  32.00
PERFUME,EMBOSSED STORK,STAR,MOON,BIMAL,CLEAR................   4.00
PERFUME,ENGRAVED,CYLINDER,GRAPE & LEAF DESIGN,GROUND STOPPER  37.00
PERFUME,FANCY,4 SIDES,RING VASE TYPE BODY,RING TOP.........  10.00
PERFUME,FLOWERS,2 DANCING FIGURES MAKE GLASS STOPPER,SATIN
   GLASS....................................................  60.00
PERFUME,FRASER,EMBOSSED,RECTANGULAR,PURPLE...................  15.00
PERFUME,FRY FOVAL,JADE FOOT & STOPPER........................  45.00
PERFUME,FRY FOVAL,PEARL WARE BODY,DELFT BLUE PEDESTAL BASE..  69.00
PERFUME,GLASS STOPPER,STERLING SILVER OVERLAY,CHASED DESIGN.  24.00
PERFUME,GOLD GILT EDGING,PATTERN & FLOWERS,STOPPER,4 1/2 IN.  10.00
PERFUME,GOLD ORMOLU FRAME,PAIR..............................  10.00
PERFUME,GREEN,4-FOOTED ORMOLU HOLDER,40 STONES ON BASE,
   STOPPER..................................................  55.00
PERFUME,GROUND TOP,OVAL......................................   6.00
PERFUME,HOYT,F & CO.,ROUND,AMETHYST..........................   3.00
PERFUME,HOYT'S COLOGNE,BIMAL.................................   1.50
```

PERFUME,HUDNUT,RICHARD,N.Y.,SQUARE,AMETHYST.................. 4.00
PERFUME,LALIQUE,RECTANGULAR,3 IN. TALL...................... 25.00
PERFUME,LALIQUE,SET OF 5,SIGNED,DORE........................ 200.00
PERFUME,LAVENDER SACHET,GLASS STOPPER,PAPER LABELS.......... 10.00
PERFUME,LAZZELL'S,BIMAL,CLEAR............................... 2.00
PERFUME,LEMON,LEAF SPRAYS,DOUBLE POINT TOP,PORCELAIN,FRANCE. 9.50
PERFUME,LUTZ,PEDESTAL BASE,SWIRLED BLUE ON CLEAR,GOLD
 STOPPER.. 20.00
PERFUME,MARKED GERMANY,PORCELAIN,HANDPAINTED,WHITE.......... 5.00
PERFUME,MINIATURE,NUDES,PORCELAIN,GERMANY,MARKED,PAIR....... 20.00
PERFUME,OPALESCENT,FOOTED,ENAMELED,YELLOW................... 23.00
PERFUME,OPALESCENT,HOBNAIL,STOPPER IS SMALL VASE............ 6.50
PERFUME,OPALINE,BRONZE ORMOLU LACY TRIM,CAMEO INSERT,GREEN.. 86.00
PERFUME,OVAL,INVERTED RIBBING,EMBOSSED FLORAL,CRYSTAL,SILVER
 LID... 13.00
PERFUME,PAIRPOINT,GRADUATED KNOPS & SPIRAL RIBBINGS......... 25.00
PERFUME,PAIRPOINT,HEAVY RIBBING,STOPPER,7 1/4 IN.,CLEAR
 CRYSTAL... 15.00
PERFUME,PAIRPOINT,PAPER LABEL,BUBBLE STOPPER,8 PANELS....... 25.00
PERFUME,PAIRPOINT,SIGNED,MELON SHAPED,CRYSTAL............... 40.00
PERFUME,PAIRPOINT,8 RIBBED BASE,STEEPLE STOPPER............. 19.00
PERFUME,PALMER,AMETHYST..................................... 4.00
PERFUME,PALMER,CLEAR.. 4.00
PERFUME,PALMER,IN SCRIPT,RING TOP........................... 12.00
PERFUME,PALMER,IN SCRIPT,RING TOP,OVAL,GREEN................ 10.00
PERFUME,PALMER,SOLON PALMER PERFUMER,GLASS STOPPER,GREEN.... 12.00
PERFUME,PALMER,SOLON PALMER PERFUMER,RIBBED,GREEN........... 12.00
PERFUME,PAPERWEIGHT,PINK ROSE IN BOTTLE & STOPPER,WHITTEMORE 160.00
PERFUME,PELICAN,GERMANY,MARKED,PORCELAIN.................... 10.00
PERFUME,PRESSED GLASS,STOPPER,DAISY & BUTTON,5 1/2 IN.HIGH,
 PAIR.. 15.00
PERFUME,PURPLE GRAPE,GREEN LEAF TRIM,PORCELAIN,FRANCE,
 4 1/4 IN.. 8.50
PERFUME,RICKSECKER PERFUMER,N.Y.,PORCELAIN,PINK,BLUE,CUPID.. 30.00
PERFUME,RICKSECKER,BLOWN IN MOLD,GREEN...................... 2.00
PERFUME,RUBINA CRYSTAL,STOPPER.............................. 50.00
PERFUME,SANDWICH GLASS,PEWTER TOP,COBALT BLUE............... 36.00
PERFUME,SANDWICH GLASS,STAR,PAIR,AMETHYST................... 151.00
PERFUME,SAWTOOTH SIDES,GROUND STOPPER....................... 5.00
PERFUME,SILVER FILIGREE,3 1/2 IN.TALL....................... 12.50
PERFUME,SILVER OVERLAY,STOPPER,CLEAR........................ 20.00
PERFUME,STERLING SILVER OVERLAY,LEAF DECOR,BALL STOPPER,
 2 3/4 IN.. 12.00
PERFUME,STERLING SILVER OVERLAY,MONOGRAM,PAIR............... 27.50
PERFUME,STERLING SILVER,PURSE............................... 2.50
PERFUME,STERLING,SHELL SHAPE,POINTED RED STONE............. 6.50
PERFUME,STEUBEN SIGNED,GREEN & BLACK........................ 42.50
PERFUME,STEUBEN,SIGNED F.CARDER,CLEAR....................... 110.00
PERFUME,SWEET BYE & BYE,LANTERN SHAPE,1890.................. 12.00
PERFUME,THOUSAND-EYE,BULBOUS,5 1/2 IN.TALL.................. 12.50
PERFUME,VASELINE GLASS,FOOTED............................... 10.00
PERFUME,VIAL,LAY DOWN,NOTCHES,GROUND STOPPER,GOLD........... 7.00
PERFUME,VOGN IN SCRIPT,PERFUMERY CO.NEW YORK,CLEAR.......... 6.00
PERFUME,WEBB,CAMEO,PURSE SIZE,BUTTERFLY & FLORAL,CRANBERRY.. 151.00
PERFUME,WHITE ROSE,MUTUAL MFG.CO.....................ILLUS.. 3.00
PERFUME,YELLOW ROSES,PAPERWEIGHT,STOPPER,WHITTEMORE......... 150.00
PERUNA.. 4.00
PICKLE,AQUA... 2.00
PICKLE,BLOWN IN MOLD,BALL NECK,AQUA......................... 2.00
PICKLE,BLOWN IN MOLD,BLUE........................... 1.75 TO 2.50
PICKLE,BLOWN IN MOLD,CLEAR.......................... 1.50 TO 4.00
PICKLE,BLOWN IN MOLD,GLASS STOPPER,CLEAR.................... 1.75
PICKLE,BLOWN IN MOLD,7 1/4 IN. TALL,CLEAR................... 2.00
PICKLE,BUNKER HILL PICKLES,HONEY AMBER,7 3/4 IN............. 18.00
PICKLE,BUNKER HILL,PINT,HONEY AMBER................. 9.00 TO 18.00

Lionstone, Camp Cook

Lionstone, Renegade Trader

Elephant, Nixon, Agnew

Donkey, Humphrey, Muskie

WHEATON NULINE CAMPAIGN SERIES

Flask, For Pike's Peak, c. 1872

Jack Daniel, Jug, Lynchburg, Tennessee

Jack Daniel's, Decanter, Gold Medal, Old No. 7

Jack Daniel, Jug, Old No. 7

Jack Daniels, Gold Medal Old No. 7, Nineteenth Century

Ketchup, 1889-1910

Keystone Ketchup, Jug

Preserved Sweet Pickles

Gherkins

H. J. Co., Apple Butter, Basket, 1885

Chutney, 1895-1900

Bellows, Eighteenth Century

Whiskey,
Peacock Distiller

Whiskey,
Old Guckenheimer, c. 1890

Figural, George Washington

Bitters, Drake's Plantation
Fish
Brown's Celebrated Indian Herb
Warner's Safe Cure

Flask, Mc Kearin
G I-96, Benjamin Franklin

WHITE

BLACK

Back & White Scotch, Scotty

Medicine, Dr. Seelye's
Magic Cure

Medicine, The River
Swamp Chill and Fever
Cure, Amber

Medicine, Bennet's
Magic Cure, Cobalt

sk, Mc Kearin G I-112, Frigate, Mississippi
sk, Sailing Ship, Man O' War, Yankee

Flask, Early Nineteenth
Century

Flask, Mc Kearin G I-80,
De Witt Clinton, 1825

Whiskey, U.S.S. Constitution,
1852, Paper Label

Whiskey,
Carlton,
Pure Rye

Decanter, Douglas Club; Whiskey, Burke's; Decanter, Paul Jones; I. W. Harper, Circa 1910;
Decanter, Rye, Wm. H. Lee & Co., St. Louis

Whiskey, Tucker, 1900

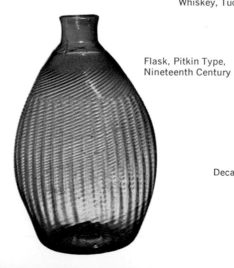

Flask, Pitkin Type,
Nineteenth Century

Decanter, Lakewood Rye,
Silver and Glass

PERFUME,WHITE ROSE,MUTUAL MFG.CO

```
PICKLE,BUNKER HILL,QUART,AQUA..................................    10.00
PICKLE,BUNKER HILL,QUART,HONEY AMBER........................    22.75
PICKLE,CATHEDRAL,EMERALD GREEN..............................   100.00
PICKLE,CATHEDRAL,FOUR DOORS,I.G.CO.,AQUA,WOODEN PEG,
  8 3/4 IN...................................................    10.00
PICKLE,CATHEDRAL,SQUARE,APPLIED RING & LIP,SQUARE,AQUA......    30.00
PICKLE,CATHEDRAL,SQUARE,COBALT..............................    25.00
PICKLE,CATHEDRAL,1/2 GAL.,AQUA..............................    17.50
PICKLE,CATHEDRAL,6 PANELS,13 IN.HIGH,AQUA...................    48.00
PICKLE,CATHEDRAL,13 1/2 IN.TALL,6 SIDED,GREEN...............    75.00
PICKLE,CATHEDRAL,13 3/4 IN.TALL,6 SIDED,AMETHYST............    60.00
PICKLE,EAST INDIA,RIBBED SIDES,APPLIED LIP..................    10.00
PICKLE,H.J.HEINZ CO.59,PAT'D JUNE 9,1891,CLEAR.............     2.00
PICKLE,HEINZ,PLAIN,PAT.APR.4,1882,AQUA......................     6.00
PICKLE,I.G.CO.,BLOWN IN MOLD,CLEAR..........................     2.00
PICKLE,PANELED CORNER,PLAIN,SQUARE,YELLOW...................    15.00
PICKLE,PATENT OCT.9,1900,BLOWN IN MOLD,CLEAR................     2.50
PICKLE,TIME TO RELISH,EMBOSSED CLOCK........................     5.00
```

POISON BOTTLES WERE USUALLY MADE WITH RAISED DESIGNS SO
THE USER COULD FEEL THE DANGER IN THE DARK. THE MOST
INTERESTING POISON BOTTLES WERE MADE FROM THE 1870'S TO
THE 1930'S.

```
POISON,AMBER.......................................  4.00 TO     5.00
POISON,BLOWN IN MOLD,CLEAR..................................     1.25
POISON,BRITISH,SLATTED,MOLDED,NOT TO BE TAKEN,COBALT BLUE...     5.00
POISON,BROWN,3-SIDED........................................     2.00
POISON,CLEAR,EARLY..........................................    45.00
POISON,COBALT BLUE,SQUARE,CORRUGATED ON TWO SIDES,
  2 1/4 IN.HIGH.............................................     4.00
POISON,EMBOSSED,HEXAGONAL,GROUND STOPPER,COBALT,
  5 3/4 IN.TALL.............................................    17.50
POISON,EMBOSSED,NOT TO BE TAKEN,USE WITH CAUTION,COBALT.....    20.00
POISON,HB CO.,3 3/4 IN. TALL,COBALT.........................     6.00
POISON,HB CO.,6 1/2 IN. TALL,COBALT.........................     8.00
POISON,IRREGULAR DIAMOND SHAPE,AMBER........................     6.00
POISON,JTM & CO.,MILLIKEN'S,AMBER...........................     6.00
POISON,LATTICE,POINTS,USPHS,BUBBLES,COBALT,1/2 GAL..........    90.00
POISON,LATTICED,3 SIDED,COBALT..............................     4.00
POISON,LETTERED POISON,ATROPHINE SULPHATE,JOHN WYETH,COBALT
  BLUE......................................................     9.00
POISON,NOBBED ON 3 SIDES,ROUND BACK.........................    12.00
POISON,ON EACH SIDE PANEL,4 CORNERS,NOBBED,AMBER............     6.00
POISON,ON EACH SIDE,ROUND BACK,MACHINE MADE,AMBER...........     6.00
POISON,OWL DRUG,COBALT,2 3/4 IN.............................    12.50
POISON,SKELETON IN SHROUD,FIGURAL,LETTERED POISON,MAJOLICA..    15.00
```

```
POISON,SKULL & CROSSBONES,EMBOSSED POISON ON 2 SIDES........    23.00
POISON,SKULL,CROSSBONES,ROUND,RING TOP,PAT.APPL'D FOR,COBALT    25.00
POISON,SQUARE,COBALT.......................................     4.00
POISON,THREE-SIDED,AMBER...................................     2.50
POISON,TRI-SEPS,MILLIKEN,3 SIDES,RING TOP...................     6.00
POISON,TRIANGULAR,BIMAL,AMBER..............................     3.50
POISON,TRILOIDS,TRIANGULAR,COBALT..........................     6.00
POISON,VAPO CRESOLENE,S IS REVERSED,DATED JULY 23,1894,
   4 IN.HIGH...............................................     4.50
POISON,WYETH,COBALT,1 1/2 IN.DIAMETER,2 1/2 IN.HIGH........     3.75
POISON,2 PLAT SIDES,ROUNDED,FRONT,EMBOSSED,APPLIED NECK,
   CA.1880................................................     41.00
POISON,3 SIDED,LETTERED POISON,AMBER.......................     4.00
POISON,6 SIDED,EMBOSSED BE CAREFUL,AMBER...................    15.00
POP,AGATE SEALER...........................................    15.00
POP,PALMER COX BROWNIE.....................................     6.50
POP,POTTERY,ENGRAVED CALIFORNIA,PONTIL,OCT.29,72...........    35.00
POP,RUBBER GASKET & WIRE LOOP INSIDE NECK,HAND BLOWN,
   HUTCHINSON..............................................     4.00
POP,WIRE LOOP CONTROLLED RUBBER GASKET IN NECK,HUTCHINSON,
   AQUA...................................................      4.00
POP,WORD SMILE ON TWO SIDES,MESH-DESIGNED PANELS,
   PAT.7-11-1922...........................................     3.50
PORTER LABEL,LONDON,SEALED,GREEN...........................    16.00
PORTER,LONG LADY'S LEG TYPE NECK,LATE 18TH CENTURY.........   125.00
PORTER,LONG NECK,OPEN PONTIL,FREE BLOWN,BLACK GLASS,CIRCA
   1750...................................................     38.00
PORTER,3 MOLD,PONTIL,BLACK.................................     10.00
RUM,FREE BLOWN,10 3/4 IN. TALL,OLIVE GREEN.................     25.00
RUM,IMPRESSED OBER-SELTENS,NASSAU,HANDLE,LABEL,EARTHENWARE..     12.00
RUM,JAMAICA,IMPORTED,GAL............................ 3.60 TO     4.00
RUM,JAMAICA,IMPORTED,QUART.................................       .90
RUM,MEDFORD RUM,GAL........................................     3.00
RUM,NEW ENGLAND,GAL........................................     3.00
RUM,NEW ENGLAND,QUART......................................      .80
RUM,ST.CROIX,IMPORTED,GAL..................................     4.00
RUM,WILD CHERRY BOUNCE,14 YEAR OLD,GAL.....................     3.98
RUM,WILD CHERRY BOUNCE,14 YEAR OLD,QUART...................     1.00
RUMFORD,EMBOSSED,BLUE,4 1/2 IN.............................     4.00
RUMFORD,GREEN,EMBOSSED,4 1/2 IN............................     4.00
S.O.DUNBAR,HALF PINT,AQUA..................................     9.50
SAKE JUG,PINCHED SIDES,APPLIED DANCING FIGURE,1850,BIZENWARE    38.00
SALTZMAN,SWIRL NECK,AMBER..................................     7.00
SALTZMAN,SWIRL NECK,CLEAR..................................     5.00
SAMSON,IMPROVED,BATTERY,QUART,AQUA.........................    12.50
SAMURAI,ABRAHAM LINCOLN,KIKUKAQA PLUM WINE.................     11.99
SAMURAI,DAIMYO,KIKUKAWA PLUM WINE..........................    13.99
SAMURAI,DWIGHT EISENHOWER,KIKUKAWA PLUM WINE...............    11.99
SAMURAI,GENERAL,KIKUKAWA PLUM WINE.........................    18.49
SAMURAI,GEORGE WASHINGTON,KIKUKAWA PLUM WINE...............    11.99
SAMURAI,JOHN KENNEDY,KIKUKAWA PLUM WINE....................    11.99
SAMURAI,SAMURAI,KIKUKAWA PLUM WINE.........................    21.99
SAMURAI,THEODORE ROOSEVELT,KIKUKAWA PLUM WINE..............    11.99


        SARSAPARILLA BOTTLES MUST BE MARKED WITH THE WORD
        SARSAPARILLA TO BE COLLECTED.  MOST DATE FROM
        1840 TO 1900.
SARSAPARILLA,ALLEN'S.......................................     7.00
SARSAPARILLA,ALLENS,OVAL,AQUA..............................    21.00
SARSAPARILLA,AUNT DINAH....................................     5.00
SARSAPARILLA,AYER'S COMPOUND EXTRACT,CONCENTRATED,AQUA......    26.00
SARSAPARILLA,AYER'S,AQUA............................. 3.00 TO    10.00
SARSAPARILLA,AYER'S,BIMAL,AQUA.............................     4.00
```

```
SARSAPARILLA,AYER'S,CIRCA 1900,AQUA.....................    5.00
SARSAPARILLA,AYER'S,COMPOUND EXT.,AQUA...................    3.00
SARSAPARILLA,BABCOCK'S,AQUA..............................   36.00
SARSAPARILLA,BRISTOL'S EXTRACT,OPEN PONTIL...............   28.00
SARSAPARILLA,BRISTOL'S,GENUINE SARSAPARILLA,AQUA.........    6.00
SARSAPARILLA,BROWN'S,AQUA................................    8.00
SARSAPARILLA,BROWNS,AQUA,PINT..................... 10.00 TO 12.00
SARSAPARILLA,BULL'S,AQUA.................................   66.00
SARSAPARILLA,CABIN.......................................   55.00
SARSAPARILLA,DALTON,LABEL................................   18.00
SARSAPARILLA,DALTON,LABEL & CONTENTS,AQUA.......... 8.00 TO 10.00
SARSAPARILLA,DANA'S,AQUA.......................... 5.00 TO 10.00
SARSAPARILLA,DANA'S,BELFAST ME.,AQUA.....................    6.00
SARSAPARILLA,DANA'S,BLOWN IN MOLD,AQUA...................    8.00
SARSAPARILLA,DE WITTS,AQUA...............................   21.00
SARSAPARILLA,DOLTON'S,AQUA...............................   11.00
SARSAPARILLA,DR.BELDING MEDICINE CO.,WILD CHERRY,AQUA....   25.00
SARSAPARILLA,DR.BELDING'S WILD CHERRY,AQUA...............   12.00
SARSAPARILLA,DR.GREENE'S,AMETHYST........................   25.00
SARSAPARILLA,DR.GREENE'S,CLEAR...........................   11.00
SARSAPARILLA,DR.GREENE'S,LABEL,AQUA......................   10.00
SARSAPARILLA,DR.GREENES',AMETHYST........................   25.00
SARSAPARILLA,DR.GUYSOTTS,BARNES & PARK,N.Y.,AQUA.........   48.00
SARSAPARILLA,DR.J.H.MC LEAN'S............................   18.00
SARSAPARILLA,DR.J.TOWNSENDS,WHITTLE,GRAPHITE,GREEN.......   95.00
SARSAPARILLA,DR.JAMES',CLEAR.............................   35.00
SARSAPARILLA,DR.TOWNSEND'S,CRUDE,OPEN PONTIL,OLIVE AMBER.   80.00
SARSAPARILLA,DR.TOWNSEND'S,FLASK,ALBANY,N.Y.,OLIVE.......   55.00
SARSAPARILLA,DR.TOWNSEND'S,ROUGH PONTIL,BLACK............   25.00
SARSAPARILLA,DR.TOWNSEND'S,SHORT BODY,LONG NECK,GREEN....  100.00
SARSAPARILLA,DR.TOWNSENDS,EMERALD GREEN..................   65.00
SARSAPARILLA,DR.TOWNSENDS,GRAPHITE PONTIL GREEN..........   15.00
SARSAPARILLA,DR.WOOD'S WILD CHERRY BITTERS,FLASK,GREEN...   40.00
SARSAPARILLA,DR.WOOD'S WILD CHERRY BITTERS,OPEN PONTIL,AQUA. 75.00
SARSAPARILLA,GRAEFENBERG CO.,COMPOUND,LABEL,CONTENTS,AQUA.  25.00
SARSAPARILLA,HALL'S COMPOUND,9 1/2 IN.,AQUA........ILLUS..    4.50
SARSAPARILLA,HAUTHAWAY PEERLESS GLOSS,GREEN..............    7.00
SARSAPARILLA,HELMBALD'S,LABEL............................   11.00
SARSAPARILLA,HOOD,J.C.,LOUISVILLE,KY.,AQUA..............    46.00
SARSAPARILLA,HOOD'S COMPOUND EXTRACT,MACHINE MADE,AQUA...    3.50
SARSAPARILLA,HOOD'S,AQUA.......................... 2.00 TO  3.50
SARSAPARILLA,HOOD'S,AQUA,9 IN......................ILLUS..    4.00
SARSAPARILLA,HOOD'S,BLOWN IN MOLD,AQUA...................    4.50
SARSAPARILLA,JOHN D.PARK,TAPERED TOP,GRAPHITE PONTIL,AQUA.  25.00
SARSAPARILLA,JOY'S,AQUA..................................   22.00
SARSAPARILLA,LEON'S,AQUA.................................   21.00
SARSAPARILLA,LOG CABIN,90 PERCENT LABEL,HONEY AMBER......  110.00
```

SARSAPARILLA,
HALL'S COMPOUND,9 1/2 IN.,AQUA

SARSAPARILLA, HOOD'S, AQUA, 9 IN

```
SARSAPARILLA,MANNERS DOUBLE EXTRACT.........................    10.00
SARSAPARILLA,RADWAY'S RESOLVENT,AQUA........................    11.00
SARSAPARILLA,RADWAY'S,AQUA..................................    20.00
SARSAPARILLA,RADWAYS,ENTD.ACCORD TO ACT OF CONGRESS,1/2 PINT    12.00
SARSAPARILLA,RUSH'S,AQUA....................................    11.00
SARSAPARILLA,RUSH'S,MISSPELLED..............................    21.00
SARSAPARILLA,RUSHS MISSPELLED SASPARILLA,AQUA...............     9.00
SARSAPARILLA,RUSHS SARSAPARILLA & IRON,AQUA.................    12.00
SARSAPARILLA,SANA'S,AQUA....................................     4.00
SARSAPARILLA,SAND'S,NEW YORK,GREEN..........................    22.50
SARSAPARILLA,SANDS,QUART,AQUA...............................    25.00
SARSAPARILLA,SARATOGA,QUART,C,GREEN.........................    25.00
SARSAPARILLA,SARATOGA,QUART,E,GREEN.........................    25.00
SARSAPARILLA,SKODA'S DISCOVERY,AMBER.............. 23.00 TO     25.00
SARSAPARILLA,WEST'S,AQUA....................................    20.00
SCENT,BLOWN,FLASK SHAPE,GOLD,BLACK..........................    35.00
SCENT,BLUE,ELONGATED ROSETTE DESIGN,SANDWICH GLASS,2 3/4 IN.    44.00
SCENT,DUCK-BILL,CARVED,WHITE OVER CITRON,LAY-DOWN,CAMEO,
  ENGLAND...................................................   450.00
SCENT,OPAQUE,STEIGEL........................................    25.00
SCENT,PEACHBLOW,COIN GOLD DECORATED,SILVER MOUNT,1885.......   375.00
SCENT,STEIGEL,AMETHYST......................................    35.00
SCENT,SULFIDE,FRENCH,5 IN.............................ILLUS..   375.00
SCENT,SULFIDE,3 3/8 IN................................ILLUS..   200.00
SCENT,WHITE FLOWER,ACORN;SILVER BALL-SHAPED TOP,5 IN........   300.00
SELTZER,ANTONS PALISADES PARK,N.J.,SAPPHIRE BLUE............     8.00
```

SCENT,SULFIDE,
FRENCH,5 IN

SCENT,SULFIDE,
3 3/8 IN

```
SELTZER,BLUE-GREEN.........................................     3.00
SELTZER,DAISY & BUTTON,LABEL G.W.HAZELTON,1885.............    20.00
SELTZER,DR.PEPPER,HEX-SIDED,BROWN..........................    13.00
SELTZER,ETCHED,1900........................................    12.00
SELTZER,MAE WEST,BLUE,SIPHON TUBE,PEWTER TOP,12 IN.TALL.....    15.00
SELTZER,METAL CASINGS,SIPHON...............................     7.50
SELTZER,PEWTER TOP & SIPHON TUBE,COCA COLA,GREEN...........    17.50
SELTZER,PEWTER TOP & SIPHON TUBE,CZECHOSLOVAKIA,BLUE.......     6.50
SELTZER,PEWTER TOP & SIPHON TUBE,MADE IN AUSTRIA,GREEN.....     8.50
SELTZER,PEWTER TOP & SIPHON TUBE,TAPERED,BLUE..............    15.00
SELTZER,PEWTER TOP & SIPHON TUBE,10 SIDED,CRYSTAL CLEAR.....     7.00
SELTZER,PEWTER TOP & SIPHON TUBE,10 SIDED,GREEN............     7.50
SELTZER,SIPHON,ETCHED WESTERN SODA WORKS...................     5.00
SELTZER,SIPHON,PEWTER TOP & TUBE,TAPERED,BLUE..............    15.00
SHOE POLISH,ALBRECHT ALL-BRIGHT,CLEAR,7 1/2 IN.......ILLUS..     1.50
SHOE POLISH,BAIRD BROS.& CO.,CLEAR,OHIO..............ILLUS..     6.00
SHOE POLISH,BARREL..................................ILLUS..     4.00
SHOE POLISH,BARREL,HUB SHOE DRESSING.................ILLUS..     6.00
```

SHOE POLISH,
ALBRECHT ALL-BRIGHT,
CLEAR, 7 1/2 IN

SHOE POLISH,
BAIRD BROS.& CO.,
CLEAR, OHIO

SHOE POLISH,
BARREL

SHOE POLISH, BARREL,
HUB SHOE DRESSING

```
SHOE POLISH,BIXBY,CONE TYPE,PAT.MAR.6-83,AQUA................    4.00
SHOE POLISH,EAGLE BRAND,5 IN..........................ILLUS..    2.00
SHOE POLISH,EVERETT & BARRON CO.,R.I.,OVAL,CLEAR............     2.00
SHOE POLISH,FRENCH SATIN GLOSS,1890'S,GREEN..........ILLUS..     4.50
SHOE POLISH,MASON'S WHITE DRESSING,CLEAR,4 IN........ILLUS..     4.00
SHOE POLISH,PAT'D MAR.6,83,BLOWN IN MOLD,AQUA...............     3.00
SHOE POLISH,PEE-CHEE WHITE CLEANER,6 IN..............ILLUS..     1.50
SHOE POLISH,RUSSET DRESSING FOR LEATHER..............ILLUS..     5.50
```

SHOE POLISH,
EAGLE BRAND, 5 IN

SHOE POLISH, FRENCH SATIN GLOSS,
1890'S, GREEN

SHOE POLISH,
MASON'S WHITE
DRESSING, CLEAR,
4 IN

SHOE POLISH, PEE-CHEE
WHITE CLEANER, 6 IN

SHOE POLISH, RUSSET
DRESSING FOR LEATHER

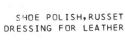

```
SHOOFLY FLASK,BIMAL...........................................    3.00
SHOOFLY,CLEAR,QUART...........................................   12.00
SHOOFLY,EMBOSSED STAR,AMBER...................................    8.00
SHOOFLY,TEAL BLUE,QUART.......................................   15.00
SIPHON,ETCHED WESTERN SODA WORKS..............................    5.00
SMELLING SALTS,STERLING SILVER OVERLAY & TOP,GREEN GLASS....     6.50
SMELLING,STIEGEL-TYPE.........................................   45.00
SMELLING,STIEGEL-TYPE,DIAMOND DESIGN,SHEARED LIP,ROUGH
   PONTIL.....................................................   65.00
SMIRNOFF,BEAR,WHITE...........................................   12.00
```

SNUFF BOTTLES HAVE BEEN MADE SINCE THE EIGHTEENTH
CENTURY. GLASS, METAL, CERAMIC, IVORY, AND PRECIOUS
STONES WERE ALL USED TO MAKE PLAIN OR ELABORATE SNUFF
HOLDERS.

```
SNUFF,AGATE,FISH FORM,BROWN,MALACHITE STOPPER,CHIEN LUNG
   MARK......................................................    70.00
SNUFF,AGATE,ORIENTAL,PEANUT BOTTLE,BROWN.....................   801.00
SNUFF,AMBER,CARVED,WOMAN HOLDING FAN,ATTENDANTS,TREES,CHINA.   130.00
SNUFF,BLUE OVERLAY,PAINTED SCENES INSIDE,GREEN TOP..........    30.00
SNUFF,BLUE,PAINTED INSIDE,ORIENTAL MAN & WOMAN,MARKED CHINA.   27.50
SNUFF,BLUE,WHITE,PORCELAIN,2 3/4 IN.........................    80.00
SNUFF,CAMEO CARVED,WHITE OVERLAY,COBALT,GREEN STOPPER.......    29.00
SNUFF,CARVED WOMAN,BRIDGE,CORAL STOPPER.............ILLUS..    625.00
SNUFF,CHINESE CARVED IVORY,PAIR JOINED,HIS & HERS...........    25.00
SNUFF,CHINESE CHARACTER WRITING & CARVING,IVORY,2 3/4 IN....    21.50
SNUFF,CHINESE,IVORY,CARVED TREES............................    81.00
SNUFF,CHINESE,IVORY,SCRIPT ONE SIDE,MAN OTHER...............    51.00
SNUFF,CHINESE,IVORY,4 PANELS,BAMBOO TREES,MAN,WOMAN.........    86.00
SNUFF,CHINESE,PEKING GLASS,RED CARVED ON WHITE..............    51.00
SNUFF,CHINESE,PEKING GLASS,5 COLOR BIRDS & FLOWERS,JADE
   STOPPER...................................................    76.00
SNUFF,CHLOROMELANITE,FORM OF CUCUMBER,CORAL TOAD STOPPER,
   CHINA.....................................................    40.00
SNUFF,CLOISONNE,CHINESE DRAGONS.............................    91.00
SNUFF,CORAL,CARVED,TWO BOYS,BATS,CORAL STOPPER..............   150.00
SNUFF,CORAL,DRAGON & PHOENIX HANDLES,BOYS,FLORAL,FU LION
   STOPPER...................................................   230.00
SNUFF,CRYSTALLINE GREEN CORUNDUM,RUBY & BLACK MOTTLE........   275.00
SNUFF,DEEP RED,CYLINDRICAL,JADE STOPPER,2 IN................    50.00
SNUFF,DOUBLE BOTTLE OF MALACHITE & SILVER WITH INLAID STONES   90.00
SNUFF,DR.MARSHALL'S CATARRH.................................    18.00
SNUFF,EMBOSSED,2 PIECE MOLD,AMBER...........................    25.00
SNUFF,ENAMEL ON GLASS,OVOID,GOLD GROUND,FLORAL..............   141.00
SNUFF,ENAMELED GLASS,PEKING.........................ILLUS..    130.00
SNUFF,ENAMELED GLASS,PEKING.........................ILLUS..    60.00
SNUFF,FIGURAL,MONKEY,PEACH TREE ON SIDE,HORN,STOPPER,CHINA..  100.00
SNUFF,FISH,SHELL,WAVES,CARVED,AMETHYST,BUBBLE STOPPER.......   135.00
SNUFF,FRUIT-FORM,19TH CENTURY,AMBER.........................   575.00
SNUFF,GARRETT,AMBER,SQUARE..................................     1.50
SNUFF,GILDED METAL,18TH-19TH CENTURY........................   475.00
SNUFF,GLASS PAINTED INSIDE,SCENIC,CLOU LO YUAN..............    76.00
SNUFF,GOURD SHAPE,CARVED FLOWERS,CINNABAR...................   126.00
SNUFF,HELMES RAILROAD MILLS.................................    11.00
SNUFF,INSIDE LANDSCAPE,PEKING GLASS,3 1/4 IN................    19.50
SNUFF,IVORY,CARVED MAN,TREE,ETCHED DEER,BIRD,TEAK STAND,
   2 3/4 IN..................................................    37.50
SNUFF,JADE STOPPER,18TH-19TH CENTURY,AMBER..................   700.00
SNUFF,JADE,MUTTONFAT,3 IN...................................   125.00
SNUFF,JAPANESE,LACQUE-BURGAUTE..............................   525.00
SNUFF,KEENE,GREEN...........................................    95.00
SNUFF,LABEL,AMBER,GLASS.....................................      .50
SNUFF,LACQUER,ORIENTAL FIGURES,RED,BLACK,WHITE & IVORY......    78.00
```

SNUFF, CARVED WOMAN, BRIDGE, CORAL STOPPER

SNUFF, ENAMELED
GLASS, PEKING

SNUFF, ENAMELED
GLASS, PEKING

```
SNUFF,LAPIS LAZULI,BLUE,GRAY & GOLD FLECKS,TURQUOISE STOPPER    185.00
SNUFF,LAPIS LAZULI,CARVED,CORAL STOPPER...............ILLUS..   300.00
SNUFF,LAPIS LAZULI,HEART SHAPE,BLUE,TURQUOISE STOPPER.......    160.00
SNUFF,LAQUE BURGUATE,MOTHER-OF-PEARL INLAY,HEXAGONAL,STAND..    180.00
SNUFF,MALACHITE,UPRIGHT CARP RESTING ON TAILFINS............    175.00
SNUFF,MAN,LADY,CARVED,CHINA,PAIR...........................    145.00
SNUFF,MOLDED,CORKED,ORIGINAL LABEL & SNUFF,SQUARE,AMBER.....     18.50
SNUFF,MOSS AGATE,AVENTURINE STOPPER,PEKING GLASS............     45.00
SNUFF,MOTHER-OF-PEARL,CARVED DRAGONS.......................    145.00
SNUFF,MOTHER-OF-PEARL,CARVED INSECT DECOR..................     95.00
SNUFF,MOTHER-OF-PEARL,EIGHTEEN LOHAN FIGURES,DRAGON,CARVED..     60.00
SNUFF,MOTHER-OF-PEARL,GOLD,SILVER INLAY,JADE STOPPER,CHIEN
  LUNG.....................................................    175.00
SNUFF,MOTHER-OF-PEARL,19TH CENTURY,,,,,,,,,,,,,,,,,,,,,,,,,    400.00
SNUFF,MOTTLED GREEN-BEIGE JADE,JADE STOPPER,2 3/4 IN........    250.00
SNUFF,MOUNTAIN SCENE ON ONE SIDE,BIRD,BRANCH ON OTHER,CHINA.     35.00
SNUFF,O.G.,RECTANGULAR,PONTIL..............................     36.00
SNUFF,OLIVE GREEN..........................................      7.00
SNUFF,OPAL,BAT,CLOUD MOTIFS,CARVED,CORAL STOPPER,WOODEN
  STAND....................................................    250.00
SNUFF,OPAL,CORAL STOPPER...........................ILLUS..     475.00
SNUFF,OPAL,VARIEGATED,PREDOMINATE GREEN,CARVED DRAGONS,LAPIS
  TOP......................................................    400.00
```

SNUFF, LAPIS LAZULI, CARVED, CORAL STOPPER

SNUFF, OPAL, CORAL STOPPER

```
SNUFF,OPEN PONTIL,FREE-BLOWN,OLIVE GREEN...................    45.00
SNUFF,P.LORILLARD..........................................    16.00
SNUFF,PAINTED INSIDE.......................................    32.00
SNUFF,PEKING ENAMEL,RESERVES OF WOMEN IN GARDEN,YELLOW
   GROUND.................................................    90.00
SNUFF,PEKING GLASS,RED CARVED ON WHITE MILK GLASS..........    76.00
SNUFF,PEKING GLASS,RED,WHITE,TIGER'S-EYE STOPPER...........   150.00
SNUFF,PINK,URN SHAPE,GREEN STOPPER.........................    30.00
SNUFF,PLAIN,BEVELED CORNERS,CRUDE NECK,OLIVE...............    25.00
SNUFF,PLAIN,RING NECK,AMBER................................     6.00
SNUFF,PLAIN,SQUARE,BEVELED CORNER,CRUDE TOP,AMBER..........    12.00
SNUFF,PLAIN,SQUARE,BEVELED CORNER,PONTIL,AMBER.............    25.00
SNUFF,PONTIL,RECTANGULAR,GREEN.............................    25.00
SNUFF,PORCELAIN,RECLINING WOMAN.....................ILLUS..   140.00
SNUFF,PORCELAIN,TIGER EYE STOPPER,IVORY PICK,WHITE,BLUE....   111.00
SNUFF,RECTANGULAR,SMOOTH BASE,GREEN........................    15.00
SNUFF,ROBED LADIES,SCENERY,PAGODA,CARVED,IVORY,SIGNED......    20.00
SNUFF,ROCK CRYSTAL,INTERIOR-PAINTED........................   700.00
SNUFF,ROCK CRYSTAL,QUARTZ STOPPER..........................   150.00
SNUFF,ROSE TOURMALINE,1850-1920............................   700.00
SNUFF,RUBY MATRIX,1800-1900................................   750.00
SNUFF,SAPPHIRE MATRIX,AMETHYSTINE QUARTZ STOPPER...........   125.00
SNUFF,SHADES OF BLUE,BROWN,GOLD,CLOISONNE..................    75.00
SNUFF,SILVER INLAY OF DRAGON AMONG CLOUDS,STOPPER,
   2 3/4 IN.HIGH..........................................    99.50
SNUFF,SMOKE CRYSTAL,INTERIOR-PAINTED.......................   350.00
SNUFF,TAO KUANG,FIGURES IN FAMILLE ROSE,AGATE STOPPER,
   PORCELAIN..............................................   200.00
SNUFF,THREE DOTS,AMBER.....................................     3.00
SNUFF,TOURMALINE,ROSE-PINK.................................   451.00
SNUFF,TURQUOISE,FISH FORM,SCROLLING WAVES,MATCHING STOPPER..   130.00
SNUFF,TURQUOISE,FLATTENED HEART SHAPE,CORAL STOPPER........   100.00
SNUFF,TWIN ROCK CRYSTAL,FEI TS'UI JADE STOPPER.............   125.00
SNUFF,WHITE JADE,CARVED BOTH SIDES,CARNELIAN TOP,STAND,
   3 3/4 IN...............................................   265.00
SNUFF,WHITE JADE,CARVED,TWO PEACHES,CORAL STOPPER,2 1/4 IN..   160.00
SNUFF,1800-1860,AQUAMARINE.................................   301.00
SNUFF,19TH C.,ORIENTAL,AMBER...............................   601.00
SNUFF,4 1/2 IN. TALL,AMBER.................................     4.00


   SODA BOTTLES HELD SODA POP OR COCA-COLA OR OTHER
   CARBONATED DRINKS.  MANY SODA BOTTLES HAD A
   CHARACTERISTIC BLOB TOP.  HUTCHINSON STOPPERS AND CODD
   BALL STOPPERS WERE ALSO USED.
   SODA, SEE ALSO WATER
SODA WATER,EMBOSSED STAR,PINCHED NECK,MARBLE STOPPER INSIDE
   NECK...................................................     6.00
SODA WATER,PIP,SUNKEN & PINCHED NECK,MARBLE STOPPER,AQUA....    10.00
SODA WATER,RUBBER GASKET,WIRE LOOP INSIDE NECK,HUTCHINSON,
   AQUA...................................................     4.00
SODA,A.PALMTAG & CO.,AMBER.......................... 5.00 TO    6.00
SODA,ABM MISSION ORANGE,BLACK..............................     2.50
SODA,ANDREWS & WOOD,BLOWN IN MOLD,CLEAR....................     4.50
SODA,BARQ'S................................................     2.00
SODA,BEAR MOUNTAIN SPRING..................................     3.50
SODA,BELFAST,PLAIN FLAT BOTTOM,AQUA........................     4.00
SODA,BLOB TOP,A.J.WINTLE & SONS,BILL MILLS NR ROSS,LEMON
   YELLOW.................................................    15.00
SODA,BLOB TOP,A.KRUMENAKER,N.Y.,REG.,AQUA..................     6.00
SODA,BLOB TOP,AMOS GORDON,TANNERSVILLE,N.Y.,WIRE PLUNGER,
   CLAMP..................................................     4.00
SODA,BLOB TOP,D.G.HALL,IRON PONTIL,BUBBLES,GREEN...........    30.00
SODA,BLOB TOP,EMBOSSED.............................. 2.00 TO    6.50
```

SNUFF, PORCELAIN, RECLINING WOMAN

```
SODA,BLOB TOP, GEO.DOHLEN,AQUA.........................................    6.00
SODA,BLOB TOP, IRON PONTIL,P.PAUL,HONESDALE P.A.,GREEN.......             50.00
SODA,BLOB TOP,J.NEY,NEW YORK,GREEN.............................          20.00
SODA,BLOB TOP,OWEN CASSEY EAGLE SODA WORKS SAC CITY,CODALT
  BLUE.......................................................            15.00
SODA,BLOB TOP,ROUND BOTTOM.....................................           5.50
SODA,BLOB TOP,WHITTLED,GRAPHITE PONTIL,GREEN..................           15.00
SODA,BLOB TOP,WM DEAN NEWARK,N.J.,TEAL GREEN..................           18.00
SODA,BLOWN IN MOLD,AMETHYST....................................           2.00
SODA,BLOWN IN MOLD,AQUA............................ 2.50 TO              3.00
SODA,BLOWN IN MOLD,C.BERRY & CO.,GREEN.........................          6.00
SODA,BLOWN IN MOLD,E.WAGNER MANCHESTER,N.H.,AQUA..............           3.50
SODA,BLOWN IN MOLD,WHITTLE MARK,GREEN..........................          3.00
SODA,BLOWN IN MOLD,6 3/4 IN. TALL,AQUA.........................          3.50
SODA,BLOWN IN MOLD,6 3/4 IN. TALL,GREEN........................          4.00
SODA,BLOWN IN MOLD,7 IN. TALL,AQUA.............................          3.50
SODA,BRIDGETON GLASS WORKS,N.J.,AQUA...........................         12.00
SODA,BROWNELL,IRON PONTIL,COBALT...............................         41.00
SODA,BUDWINE,EMBOSSED MAKES YOU GLAD YOU'RE THIRSTY..........            2.00
SODA,BUFFALO GINGER ALE,BUFFALO HEAD ON 2 SIDES..............            8.00
SODA,C.A.COLE,OPEN PONTIL,CODD PIG,MARBLE IN NECK,BLUE......             6.00
SODA,C.O.D.SODA WORKS,BAKERSFIELD,PINT.............. 3.00 TO             4.00
SODA,CALIFORNIA BOTTLING CO.,AQUA.................... 4.00 TO            5.00
SODA,CALVERT BOTTLE WORKS,TEXAS,AQUA...........................          4.00
SODA,CANADA DRY,RED,GOLD,BEADED,CARNIVAL GLASS................          10.00
SODA,CELEBRATED CLICQUOT CLUB,BLOWN IN MOLD,CLEAR............            3.50
SODA,CHERO COLA................................................          3.00
SODA,CHERO COLA BOTT. CO.,TEXAS,RAISED SQUARE X PATTERN,AQUA            2.00
SODA,CLEAR....................................... 2.50 TO               3.00
SODA,CLEBURNE BOTTLING WORK,WIRE POP STOPPER,PANELED........             8.00
SODA,COBALT BLUE................................. 10.00 TO             15.00
SODA,COCHRAN & CO.,BLOWN IN MOLD,AQUA..........................          5.00
SODA,COLES GINGER BEER,DOULTON.................................          7.75
SODA,CONCORD BOTTLING CO.,BLOWN IN MOLD,BLUE..................           4.00
SODA,COSCROUL JAMES,S.C.,AQUA..................................          4.00
SODA,CROWN TOP HIPPO,NOV.21,1926...............................         2.50
SODA,CRYSTAL SPRING BOTTLING CO.,CLEAR.........................          3.00
SODA,DR.PEPPER KING OF BEVERAGES,TEXAS,AMETHYST..............            5.00
SODA,DR.PEPPER,KING OF BEVERAGES,TEXAS,REGISTERED,AMETHYST..             6.00
SODA,DRINK PYROK WATER EMBOSSED,CHAS.HIRES,CLEAR.............            5.00
SODA,E.H.EDDY & CO.,BLOWN IN MOLD,AMETHYST....................           3.00
SODA,E.MOYLE,BLOB TOP,1880,AQUA................................          6.00
SODA,E.OTTENVILLE,BLOB TOP,COBALT..............................         35.00
```

```
SODA,E.OTTENVILLE,EMBOSSED DIAGONALLY,SQUAT,BLOB TOP,AMBER..        35.00
SODA,EAGLE SODA WATER,BLOB,COBALT BLUE......................       125.00
SODA,EASTERN N.Y. EMBOSSED,HUTCHINSON.......................         4.50
SODA,EEL RIVER VALLEY SODA WORKS,AQUA.............. 10.00 TO         15.00
SODA,EMBOSSED,BLOB TOP......................................         4.40
SODA,EMBOSSED,PATENTED PALMER COX TILE,P.F.K.GERMANY,
  BROWNIES.................................................         11.00
SODA,EMERSON & CO. BOTTLERS,BLOWN IN MOLD,AQUA..............         3.50
SODA,EXCELSIOR SODAWORKS,SAVANNAH,GEO.,1866,BLOB TOP,COBALT
  BLUE....................................................         18.00
SODA,EYE-SE,GILMER,TEXAS,ROUND,AQUA.........................         4.00
SODA,FARGO BOTTLING WORKS CO.,N.DAK.,GREEN.......... 3.00 TO         4.00
SODA,G.EBBERWEIN GINGER ALE,AMBER.................. 15.00 TO         25.00
SODA,G.W.TALLMAN,TELLURIDE,COLO.,AQUA.............. 10.00 TO         15.00
SODA,GEMUNDEN EAGLE,GRAPHITE PONTIL,BLOB TOP,GREEN..........         37.00
SODA,GINGER ALE,ALBERT VON HARTEN,BLOB TOP,GREEN... 15.00 TO         20.00
SODA,GINGER ALE,BARQ'S BEVERAGES OF BILOXI,MS.,1939,7 OZ.,
  GREEN...................................................          .75
SODA,GINGER ALE,BARQ'S BEVERAGES OF BILOXI,MS.,1939,12 OZ.,
  GREEN...................................................         1.00
SODA,GINGER ALE,BARQ'S BEVERAGES OF BILOXI,MS.,1939,32 OZ.,
  GREEN...................................................         1.50
SODA,GINGER ALE,CIRCLE,ROUND,AQUA...........................         4.00
SODA,GINGER ALE,EDWARD MOYLE,SAVANNAH,GA.,AMBER.............         20.00
SODA,GINGER ALE,G.EBBERWEIN,BLOB TOP,AMBER..................         30.00
SODA,GINGER ALE,G.EBBERWEIN,SAVANNAH,GEO.,BLOB TOP,BLUE.....         18.00
SODA,GINGER,OLD ENGLISH STONEWARE,SCREW IN STOPPER..........         3.50
SODA,GRAPE SMASH,GLASS LABEL,12 IN.,CLEAR.............ILLUS..         6.00
SODA,GRAPHITE PONTIL,EMBOSSED PHILADELPHIA XX PORTER & ALE,
  GREEN..................................................         37.00
SODA,GRATTAN & CO.,ORIGINAL MAKERS OF GINGER ALE,BLOB TOP,
  AQUA...................................................         5.50
SODA,GREEN..........................................2.50 TO         3.00
SODA,HEMPSTEAD BOTTLING WORK,FLUTED BOTTOM,AMETHYST.........         4.00
SODA,HENRY KUCK,BLOB TOP,AQUA...............................         10.00
SODA,HENRY KUCK,CIRCLE SLUGPLATE,GREEN......................         22.00
SODA,HENRY LUBS,1885,BLOB TOP...............................         11.50
SODA,HERBE CO.,BLOWN IN MOLD,AQUA...........................         2.00
SODA,HIPPLER & BRICKSON,TELLURIDE,COLO.,AQUA....... 10.00 TO         15.00
SODA,HIPPO SIZE,ALAMO BOTTLING WKS.,NOV.2,1926,CLEAR........         4.00
SODA,HIRE'S CARBONATED BEVERAGES............................         3.50
SODA,HIRE'S ROOT BEER..................................50            4.50
SODA,HIRE'S ROOT BEER,MACHINE MADE..........................         1.00
SODA,HIRES RASPBERRYADE,PAPER LABEL,9 IN.............ILLUS..         8.50
SODA,HORLOCK,R.A.CO.,ROUND,AMETHYST.........................         3.00
SODA,HOSKINS QUALITY........................................         4.00
SODA,HOUCK & DIETER,6 CATHEDRAL PANELS,CROWN TOP,AQUA.......         7.00
SODA,HUTCHINSON,BOONEVILLE MINERAL SPRINGS,AMBER............         12.50
SODA,HUTCHINSON,WIRE LOOP CONTROLS RUBBER GASKET INSIDE
  NECK,AQUA..............................................         4.00
SODA,IDAN-HA,IDAHO,BROWN....................................         12.00
SODA,IDAN-HA,SODAWATER,IDAHO,GREEN..........................         6.00
SODA,INGALLS BROS.,BLOWN IN MOLD,AQUA.......................         4.50
SODA,JACKSON'S NAPA SODA,CLEAR..................... 10.00 TO         15.00
SODA,JAMES RAY,GINGER ALE,BLOB,COBALT BLUE......... 25.00 TO         29.00
SODA,JAS.RAY,IRIDESCENT,AQUA,7 1/2 IN................ILLUS..         5.00
SODA,JOHN HESSLER BOTTLING WORKS,AQUA................ILLUS..         4.00
SODA,JOHN RYAL,1852 EXCELSIOR,GINGER ALE,AMBER.............         20.00
SODA,JOHN RYAN JAMAICA GINGER,AQUA..........................         8.00
SODA,JOHN RYAN 1859,2 IN. LETTERS,BLOB TOP,COBALT BLUE......         35.00
SODA,JOHN RYAN 1866,CIDER,AMBER.............................         15.00
SODA,JOHN RYAN 1866,COBALT..................................         14.00
SODA,JOHN RYAN 1866,EXCELSIOR SODAWORKS,BLUE................         25.00
SODA,JOHN RYAN 1866,EXCELSIOR SODAWORKS,COBALT..............         25.00
SODA,JOHN RYAN 1866,EXCELSIOR SODAWORKS,GREEN...............         25.00
```

SODA,GRAPE SMASH,
GLASS LABEL,12 IN.,CLEAR

SODA,HIRES
RASPBERRYADE,
PAPER LABEL,9 IN

SODA,JAS.RAY,
IRIDESCENT,
AQUA,7 1/2 IN

SODA,JOHN HESSLER
BOTTLING WORKS,AQUA

SODA,JOHN RYAN 1866,EXCELSIOR SODAWORKS,OLIVE...............	25.00
SODA,JOHN RYAN 1866,EXCELSIOR SODAWORKS,RED..................	25.00
SODA,JOHN RYAN,2 IN. LETTERS,GRAPHITE PONTIL,ICE BLUE.......	38.00
SODA,JOSEPH KERN & CO.,BLOWN IN MOLD,CLEAR..................	4.00
SODA,JURGENS & PRICE BOTTLERS,MONT.,GREEN.......... 10.00 TO	15.00
SODA,KALOLA CO.,AMERICAN CLUB GINGER ALE....................	3.50
SODA,KALOLA CO.,SAVANNAH,GA................................	3.50
SODA,KNICKERBOCKER,7 IN.,COBALT BLUE.......................	70.00
SODA,KUCA NOLA,AMBER.......................................	6.00
SODA,KUHLMAN BREWING,BLOB LIP..............................	3.00
SODA,LARKIN CO.,BUFFALO EMBOSSED...........................	2.00
SODA,LIME COLA...	3.00
SODA,M.T.QUINNAN,1884,BLOB TOP,COBALT BLUE.................	25.00
SODA,MEINCKE & EBBERWEIN,1882,BLOB TOP,COBALT BLUE.........	24.00
SODA,MEINCKE & EBBERWEIN,1882,GINGER ALE,BLOB TOP,AMBER.....	15.00
SODA,MERRILL SODA WORKS,MERRILL,ORE.,CLEAR.................	15.00
SODA,MILTON AERATED WATERWORKS,AQUA,8 IN.............ILLUS..	8.00
SODA,MISSION DRY,BLACK.....................................	3.00
SODA,N.J.,BLOB TOP,EMBOSSED................................	3.50
SODA,NU GRAPE,6 OZ.,AQUA,1920,7 1/2 IN...............ILLUS..	3.50
SODA,OLD ENGLISH,APPLIED LIP,SCREW IN STOPPER,AQUA..........	5.00
SODA,ORANGE CRUSH,AMBER....................................	2.00
SODA,ORANGE CRUSH,JULY 1920................................	2.00
SODA,ORANGE CRUSH,1920 DATE ON SIDE,EMBOSSED,CLEAR..........	5.00
SODA,ORANGE JULEP,GLASS LABEL,12 IN.,CLEAR...........ILLUS..	6.00
SODA,PABLO & CO.,BLOB,AQUA.................................	22.50
SODA,PEPSI COLA,CROWN TOP,AQUA.............................	6.00
SODA,PEPSI COLA,CROWN TOP,CLEAR............................	6.00
SODA,PEPSI COLA,EMBOSSED,AMBER.............................	22.50
SODA,PEPSI COLA,TRADEMARK,REG.2322,CROWN TOP,AMBER..........	25.00
SODA,PEPSI COLA,6 OZ.,AQUA.................................	4.00
SODA,PHILIPSBURG BOTTLING WORKS,MONT.,AQUA......... 10.00 TO	15.00
SODA,PHOENIX BOTTLING WORKS,10 PANELS,BLUE.................	8.00
SODA,PIEDMONT BOTTLING WORKS,EMBOSSED,AMBER................	10.00
SODA,PIONEER SODA WORKS,RENO,NEVADA,LIGHT GREEN............	5.00
SODA,PIONEER SODA WORKS,SAN FRANCISCO,AQUA......... 10.00 TO	15.00
SODA,POP,OPALESCENT,PLAIN,AQUA.............................	5.00
SODA,PORTER & ALE,1866,BLOB TOP,COBALT BLUE................	33.00
SODA,QARER,WELLER SARATOGA SPRINGS,BLOB TOP,AQUA...........	8.00
SODA,QUART,SOUTH RANGE BOTTLING,AQUA.......................	1.50
SODA,QUART,SOUTH RANGE BOTTLING,CLEAR......................	1.50
SODA,REGISTERED,BLOWN IN MOLD,CLEAR................. 3.00 TO	4.00

SODA, MILTON AERATED
WATERWORKS, AQUA, 8 IN

SODA, NU GRAPE, 6 OZ.,
AQUA, 1920, 7 1/2 IN

SODA, ORANGE JULEP, GLASS LABEL, 12 IN., CLEAR

SODA, REGISTERED, CLARK & ROBERTS, BLOWN IN MOLD, CLEAR.........	2.50
SODA, REGISTERED, J.L.EPPLER GERMANIA HOUSE, BLOWN IN MOLD, CLEAR...	3.50
SODA, REGISTERED, MICHAEL CONNOR SONS, BLOWN IN MOLD, CLEAR.....	3.00
SODA, REGISTERED, ROBINSON BROS., BLOWN IN MOLD, AMETHYST.......	4.50
SODA, REGISTERED, STILLMAN BOTTLING CO., BLOWN IN MOLD, AQUA....	2.00
SODA, ROMMENEY BOTTLING CO., BLOWN IN MOLD, AQUA...............	4.00
SODA, ROOT BEER, MASONS, AMBER........................ 3.00 TO	6.00
SODA, ROUND BOTTOM................................... 2.00 TO	3.00
SODA, ROUND WHITE..	2.00
SODA, RUSSELL, AQUA...	8.00
SODA, SAYS SMILE, LIGHT BLUE, DATED 1922, 20 IN.................	32.00
SODA, SEVEN-UP, AMBER.......................................	9.00
SODA, SEVEN-UP, BUBBLE GIRL.................................	2.00
SODA, SEVEN-UP, CROWN TOP, SQUAT, BROWN......................	8.00
SODA, SEVEN-UP, LABEL, QUART, BROWN.........................	4.50
SODA, SOUTH RANGE BOTTLING, QUART, AQUA.....................	1.50
SODA, SOUTH RANGE BOTTLING, QUART, SPRING STOPPER, CLEAR........	1.50
SODA, SPRING STOPPER, BLUFF CITY BOTTLING CO.................	8.00
SODA, SQUARE, GREEN...	2.25
SODA, SQUARE, WHITE...	2.25
SODA, SQUAT, SLUGPLATE, GRAPHITE PONTIL, GREEN................	20.00
SODA, ST.JAKOBS OEL EMBOSSED...............................	2.00
SODA, STEGMALER, AMBER.....................................	3.00
SODA, STRAFORD'S SPRINGS, BLACK.............................	3.50
SODA, TAYLOR & CO., VALPARAISO CHILE, GRAPHITE PONTIL, TEAL GREEN..	34.00
SODA, TEARDROP, THOMPSTONES CELEBRATED SODAWATER, GREEN........	24.00
SODA, TELLURIDE BOTTLING CO., COLO., AQUA.............. 3.00 TO	4.00
SODA, THE PROPERTY OF THE HAAS CO., CHICAGO, AQUA.............	8.00
SODA, THOMAS MAHER, DYOTTVILLE GLASS WORKS, SQUAT, GREEN........	35.00
SODA, THOS MAHER, SLUGPLATE, GRAPHITE PONTIL, BLOB TOP, GREEN....	18.00
SODA, TORPEDO, BLOB TOP, AQUA...............................	3.00
SODA, TORPEDO, 3 MOLD, GREEN...............................	17.50
SODA, TRY IT, KENMORE, OHIO, CLEAR, 9 IN................ILLUS..	6.00
SODA, UNION BOTTLING WORKS, CENTRALIA, ILL., GREEN.............	2.50
SODA, VERNOR'S GINGER ALE, EMBOSSED SEAL, RED.................	8.00
SODA, VIRGINIA FRUIT JUICE CO., NORFOLK VA., PARTIAL TORPEDO...	2.00
SODA, VON HARTEN & GROGEN, GREEN...........................	14.00
SODA, VON HARTEN, ALBERT, GINGER ALE, BLUE-GREEN.............	31.00
SODA, WAGNER & MATTHES, BLOB TOP, DARK AMBER.................	4.00
SODA, WAIALUA SODA WORKS LTD., HAWAII, CLEAR...... 10.00 TO	15.00
SODA, WATKIN'S, CLEAR.............................. 1.50 TO	2.50

SODA,TRY IT,KENMORE,OHIO,CLEAR,9 IN

SODA,WHISTLE,ALTOONA,PA.,EMBOSSED............................ 2.50
SODA,WHITTLE MOLD,AQUA............................... 8.00 TO 12.00
SODA WATER,PIP,SUNKEN & PINCHED NECK,MARBLE STOPPER,AQUA.... 10.00
SOUTHERN COMFORT,GENERAL LEE................................ 500.00
SPARKS,MINER... 12.50
SPIRIT,FOUR PARTS BLOWN INTO ONE........................... 35.00
SPIRITS,FOUR PARTS,FRANCE.................................. 44.00
STEIGEL TYPE,ENAMEL,18TH CENTURY........................... 75.00
STONEWARE GINGER BEER,SIGNED J C IN COBALT................. 8.00
STONEWARE,MARKED S.TABOR,JR.ROOT BEER,10 3/4 IN.HIGH....... 10.00
STRIKOW,FERTILITY GODDESS.................................. 17.50
STRIKOW,TOTEM POLE... 15.90
STRIKOW,WATER JUG.. 24.90
SWIRLED WHITE ON CLEAR STRIPES,POLISHED PONTIL,BLOWN,
  12 1/4 IN... 38.00
SYRUP,OCTAGON,PULMONIC SYRUP WRITTEN IN RELIEF,CIRCA 1800... 45.00
TANTALUS,LOCK & KEY PATTERN,CUT STOPPERS,3 BOTTLES.......... 135.00
TEAR,PRESSED SWIRL DESIGN,CUT NOTCHES ON SIDES,ENAMEL DECOR. 18.00
THE BONHERU CO.,INC.,MACHINE MADE,CLEAR.................... 4.00
THREE PART MOLD,EMPRONE PORTAL KICKUP,DARK OLIVE........... 12.00
THREE PART MOLD,OPEN PONTIL,WHITTLED,AQUA.................. 10.00
THREE PIECE MOLD,PATENT ON SHOULDER,ROUND,AMBER........... 4.00
THREE-PIECE MOLD,BLACK GLASS,PINT.......................... 3.00
THREE-PIECE MOLD,BLACK GLASS,QUART......................... 5.00
THREE SIDED,ENAMELED PANSIES,CLEAR TO CRANBERRY,PAIR....... 125.00
TIFFANY,GOURD SHAPE,SIGNED & NUMBERED,SATIN IRIDESCENCE,GOLD 151.00
TOILET,SQUARE,HANDPAINTED,ENAMELED,PEROXIDE,POND'S EXTRACT,
  PAIR.. 9.00
TOM SIMS,APOLLO.. 7.95
TOM SIMS,ASTRONAUT.. 7.95
TSUNDURU,RED BUCKET.. 17.50
TSUNDURU,RED BUCKET,MINIATURE.............................. 10.00
TULLAMORE,JUG.. 4.95
TWO-MOLD TOP,THREE-MOLD BASE,OLIVE-AMBER,10 IN............. 10.00
VANDENBURG,BLOB & PAPER SEAL............................... 60.00
VERRE DE SOIE,FLAT STAND OUT RIM,SIGNED.................... 36.00
VERRE DE SOIE,PERFUME,GREEN STOPPER....................... 48.00
VERRE DE SOIE,PERFUME,SQUATTY,PINK BUD STOPPER............. 76.00
VIARENGO,CHICKEN ON NEST................................... 12.00
VIARENGO,CLOWN... 8.50
VIARENGO,SKIER... 8.50
VINAIGRETTE,CHASED SPIRALS ON BODY,GREEK KEY BORDER,OVAL,
  GOLD.. 120.00
VINEGAR,APPLE PIE,RIDGE.................................... 4.00
VINEGAR,CLEAR,HEISEY,SIGNED,5 IN........................... 10.00
VINEGAR,ETCHED,DATED....................................... 12.00
VINEGAR,LIGHTHOUSE,SCREW TOP,CLEAR......................... 5.00

```
VINEGAR,SAMPLE,DIAMOND EMBOSSED,CLEAR......................   12.00
VINEGAR,SAMPLE,DIAMOND EMBOSSED,CLEAR......................   10.00
VINEGAR,WHITE HOUSE,EMERALD GREEN..........................    6.00
VINEGAR,WHITE HOUSE,LID....................................    6.00
VINEGAR,WHITE HOUSE,PAT.1909,EMBOSSED,QUART................    3.50
VINEGAR,WHITE HOUSE,PINT...................................    2.00
VINEGAR,WINE...............................................    5.00
VINEGAR,WORLD'S FAIR,CLEAR.................................    8.00
   WATER, SEE ALSO SODA
WATER,ABILENE NATURAL CATHARTIC WATER,AMBER................    5.00
WATER,ABILENE NATURAL CATHARTIC WATER,BROWN................    5.00
WATER,ALBURCH SPRINGS VT.MINERAL WATER,QUART...............   75.00
WATER,B&G SAN FRANCISCO SUPERIOR MINERAL,COBALT BLUE.......   61.00
WATER,BALLSTON SPA,EMBOSSING,PINT,GREEN....................   32.00
WATER,BLOUNT SPRINGS NATURAL SULPHUR,BLOB TOP,COBALT.......   30.00
WATER,BOLEN WAACK & CO.,N.Y.,SARATOGA MINERAL..............   18.00
WATER,BUFFALO LITHIA SPRING................................    4.00
WATER,BUFFALO LITHIA,AQUA,10 IN.....................ILLUS..   11.00
WATER,BUFFALO LITHIA,GREEN.................................   21.00
WATER,BUFFALO MINERAL SPRINGS,1/2 GAL......................    3.50
WATER,C.CLARK ON FRONT,MINERAL WATER ON BACK,PONTIL,OLIVE...  20.00
WATER,CANTRELL & COCHRAN'S AERATED,DUBLIN & BELFAST,AQUA....    6.00
WATER,CHALEYBEATE WATER OF THE AMERICAN SPA SPRING CO.,GREEN  40.00
WATER,CLARK & WHITE IN U,MINERAL WATER,OLIVE GREEN.........   10.00
WATER,CLARK & WHITE,N.Y.,QUART,OLIVE GREEN.................   21.00
WATER,CONGRESS & E.E.EMPIRE,QUART,GREEN....................   40.00
WATER,CUT GLASS,HOBSTAR ROSETTES & LACY,COLLAR CUT BASE....   40.00
WATER,D.A.KNOWLTON,QUART,OLIVE GREEN.......................   41.00
WATER,DR.BURNSIDE PURIFIED BUFFALO.........................   11.00
WATER,EMPIRE MINERAL,C IN CENTER,PINT......................   10.00
WATER,EMPIRE WATER,QUART...................................   21.00
WATER,EXCELSIOR SPRINGS,SARATOGA,QUART,GREEN...............   45.00
WATER,FLORIDA,MURRAY & LANMAN DRUGGISTS,AQUA...............    6.00
WATER,FLORIDA,WHITTLE,AQUA.................................    5.00
WATER,FLORIDA,6 IN.,AQUA...................................    3.50
WATER,GETTYSBURY KATALIPINE,WHITTLED,GREEN.................   35.00
WATER,GEYER SPRING,PINT,AQUA...............................   21.00
WATER,HAT HORN SPRING,SARATOGA,N.Y.,QUART,BLACK............   65.00
WATER,HAYTHORN SPRING,QUART,AMBER..........................   17.00
WATER,JOHNSON LIVERPOOL MINERAL,GREEN............... 8.00 TO  10.00
WATER,MAGNETIC SPRINGS,HENNIKER,N.H.,QUART,AMBER...........   55.00
WATER,MIDDLETON HEALING SPRINGS,VT.,QUART,AMBER............   45.00
```

MINERAL WATER WAS FIRST BOTTLED ABOUT 1828 IN THE
UNITED STATES. EMBOSSED BOTTLES THAT HELD MINERAL
SPRING WATERS ARE USUALLY THE ONLY ONES INCLUDED IN
THIS CATEGORY.
  MINERAL WATER BOTTLES HELD THE FRESH NATURAL SPRING
WATERS FAVORED FOR HEALTH AND TASTE. MOST OF THE
BOTTLES COLLECTED TODAY DATE FROM THE 1850-1900 PERIOD.
MANY OF THESE BOTTLES HAVE BLOB TOPS.

```
WATER,MINERAL,ADIRONDACK SPRING,WESTPORT,N.Y.,EMERALD.......  65.00
WATER,MINERAL,BUFFALO SPRINGS,APPLIED LIP,EMBOSSED LADY.....  11.00
WATER,MINERAL,BUFFALO SPRINGS,1/2 GAL......................    3.50
WATER,MINERAL,C.EBBERWEIN,AQUA,8 IN.................ILLUS..    5.00
WATER,MINERAL,CHAMPION SPOUTING SPRINGS,BLOWN IN MOLD,AQUA..  10.00
WATER,MINERAL,CLARK & CO.,IRON PONTIL,GREEN................   90.00
WATER,MINERAL,CLARK & WHITE................................   22.00
WATER,MINERAL,CLARK & WHITE IN HORSESHOE,OLIVE GREEN.......   10.00
WATER,MINERAL,CLARK & WHITE,IRON PONTIL,PINT...............   35.00
WATER,MINERAL,CLARK & WHITE,PINT,OLIVE BLACK...............   26.00
WATER,MINERAL,CLARK & WHITE,QUART..........................   20.00
WATER,MINERAL,CLARK & WHITE,QUART,OLIVE BLACK..............   26.00
```

WATER,BUFFALO LITHIA,AQUA,10 IN

WATER,MINERAL,C.EBBERWEIN,AQUA,8 IN

```
WATER,MINERAL,CLARKE & WHITE,QUART,OLIVE GREEN..............     26.00
WATER,MINERAL,CONGRESS & E.C.CONGRESS,QUART,AMBER...........     35.00
WATER,MINERAL,CONGRESS & E.E.EMPIRE,PINT...................      18.00
WATER,MINERAL,CONGRESS & EMPIRE CO.,N.Y.,PINT,GREEN........      15.00
WATER,MINERAL,CONGRESS & EMPIRE SPRING CO.,EMERALD GREEN....     15.00
WATER,MINERAL,CONGRESS & EMPIRE SPRING CO.,N.Y.,BLUE GREEN..     10.00
WATER,MINERAL,CONGRESS & EMPIRE SPRING CO.,QUART,GREEN......     24.00
WATER,MINERAL,CONGRESS & EMPIRE SPRING CO.,SARATOGA,PINT,
   GREEN......................................................   22.50
WATER,MINERAL,CONGRESS & EMPIRE SPRING CO.,WHITTLED,QUART,
   GREEN......................................................   22.50
WATER,MINERAL,CONGRESS & EMPIRE SPRING,QUART,LONG NECK,GREEN     46.00
WATER,MINERAL,CONGRESS & EMPIRE SPRINGS,PINT,GREEN..........      2.00
WATER,MINERAL,CONGRESS SPRING CO.,BLOB TOP,GREEN... 10.00 TO     17.00
WATER,MINERAL,CONGRESS SPRING CO.,LARGE C..................      18.00
WATER,MINERAL,CONGRESS SPRING CO.,N.Y.,QUART,GREEN.........      15.00
WATER,MINERAL,CONGRESS SPRING CO.,SARATOGA SPRINGS,
   CYLINDRICAL...............................................    14.00
WATER,MINERAL,CONGRESS SPRING CO.,2 QUART,.................      31.00
WATER,MINERAL,CONGRESS,SARATOGA,PINT,EMERALD GREEN..........     25.00
WATER,MINERAL,CONGRESS,SARATOGA,QUART,EMERALD GREEN........      25.00
WATER,MINERAL,CONSUMERS ICE CO.,HYGEIA WATER,MEMPHIS,TENN...      5.00
WATER,MINERAL,CROWN ON SHOULDER,BEER TYPE,OLIVE GREEN.......      8.00
WATER,MINERAL,CRYSTAL SPRING,N.Y.,QUART,GREEN..............      10.00
WATER,MINERAL,FREDERICK MEINCHE,1882,COBALT................      18.00
WATER,MINERAL,FRIEDRICHSHALL COPPEL & CO.,FROM ENGLAND,QUART     20.00
WATER,MINERAL,G.EBBERWEIN,SAVANNAH,GEO.,BLOB TOP,AMBER......     20.00
WATER,MINERAL,G.EBBERWEIN,SAVANNAH,GEO.,BLOB TOP,AQUA.......     10.00
WATER,MINERAL,G.EBBERWEIN,SAVANNAH,GEO.,BLOB TOP,BLUE.......     12.00
WATER,MINERAL,G.EBBERWEIN,SAVANNAH,GEO.,BLOB TOP,DARK BLUE..     20.00
WATER,MINERAL,GETTYSBURG KATALYSINE,GREEN..................      35.00
WATER,MINERAL,GETTYSBURG KATALYSINE,QUART,GREEN.............     35.00
WATER,MINERAL,GEYSER SPRING,SARATOGA SPRINGS,QUART,BLUE.....     15.00
WATER,MINERAL,GUILFORD.....................................      30.00
WATER,MINERAL,GUILFORD SPRINGS,GUILFORD,VT.,BUBBLES,QUART,
   GREEN......................................................   32.00
WATER,MINERAL,GUILFORD SPRINGS,9 1/2 IN....................      19.50
WATER,MINERAL,HATHORN SPRINGS,PINT,BROWN...................      20.00
WATER,MINERAL,HENRY HURTEN'S,POTTERY,BROWN.................       8.00
WATER,MINERAL,HIAWATHA SPRING,1883,APPLIED HANDLE,AMBER.....     13.50
WATER,MINERAL,HOLMES & CO.,AQUA............................      20.00
WATER,MINERAL,HUNYADI-JANOS BUDAI KESERUVIZ..........ILLUS..      9.00
WATER,MINERAL,J.MANKE & CO.,BLOB TOP,AQUA..................      10.00
WATER,MINERAL,JOHN RYAN,EXCELSIOR,COBALT BASE..............      25.00
WATER,MINERAL,JOHN RYAN,GROUND PONTIL,COBALT...............      24.00
WATER,MINERAL,M.T.QUINAN,1884,BLOB TOP,COBALT..............      18.00
WATER,MINERAL,MEINCKE & EBBERWEIN,1882,BLOB TOP,COBALT......     30.00
```

WATER,MINERAL,HUNYADI-JANOS BUDAI KESERUVIZ

```
WATER,MINERAL,MISSISQUOI SPRINGS,QUART,AMBER................     30.00
WATER,MINERAL,PLUTO WATER,AMERICA'S PHYSIC,EMBOSSED,AQUA....      2.50
WATER,MINERAL,POLAND SPRINGS,MAINE,HIRAM RICKER.............     35.00
WATER,MINERAL,POTTERY................................ 8.00 TO     10.00
WATER,MINERAL,QUART,3 MOLD,OLIVE AMBER.....................     18.00
WATER,MINERAL,SAXLEHNER BITTERQUELLE HUNYADI JANOS,GREEN....      7.00
WATER,MINERAL,SPRING SARATOGA CO.,PINT.....................     40.00
WATER,MINERAL,SPRING,GETTYSBURG KATALYSINE,QUART,OLIVE GREEN    30.00
WATER,MINERAL,T.LAUGHTON SCARBOROUGH,CROWN INSIDE THREAD,
   GREEN....................................................      6.50
WATER,MINERAL,UTE CHIEF,COLO.,CROWN TOP,CLEAR..............      6.00
WATER,MINERAL,UTE CHIEF,COLO.,CROWN TOP,PURPLE.............      6.00
WATER,MINERAL,VERONICA,SQUARE,AMBER........................      4.00
WATER,MINERAL,VERONICA,SQUARE,CLEAR........................      4.00
WATER,MINERAL,WASHINGTON SPRING,BLOWN IN MOLD,GREEN........     15.00
WATER,MINERAL,1859,GRAPHITE PONTIL,COBALT BLUE.............     27.00
WATER,MINERAL,6 PANELS,IMPROVED PONTIL,GREEN...............     18.00
WATER,MISSIQUOI A SPRINGS,MINERAL,QUART....................     32.00
WATER,MISSIQUOI A SPRINGS,QUART,GREEN......................     45.00
WATER,MISSIQUOI SPRINGS,VERMONT,AMBER......................    100.00
   WATER, MOSES SEE ALSO FIGURAL, MOSES  WHISKEY, HIRAM
   RICKER
WATER,MOSES,POLAND SPRINGS,CLEAR...........................     35.00
WATER,OAK ORCHARD ACID SPRING,BLUE GREEN...................     40.00
WATER,OLNEY SODA,OLNEY,ILL.,CLEAR..........................      2.50
WATER,P.H.CRYSTAL SPRING WATER CO.,N.Y.,10 IN.,AQUA........      5.00
WATER,PAVILION & UNITED STATES SPRING......................     41.00
WATER,PURE FOOD SODA,CENTRALIA,ILL.,CLEAR.......... 2.00 TO      2.50
WATER,QUALITY BEVERAGE,MURPHYBORO,ILL.,CLEAR...............      2.50
WATER,SARATOGA EMPIRE WATER,PINT,GREEN.....................     31.00
WATER,SARATOGA LINCOLN,PORCELAIN STOPPER,AMBER.............     20.00
WATER,SARATOGA RED SPRING,PINT.............................     31.00
WATER,SARATOGA STAR SPRING,QUART,AMBER.....................     20.00
WATER,SARATOGA STAR SPRINGS,BACKWARDS S IN SPRINGS,QUART,
   AMBER...................................................     31.00
WATER,SARATOGA,C.W.WESTON & CO.,PINT,DARK GREEN............     27.00
WATER,SAXLEHNERS BITTERQUELLE MINERAL WATER................      6.00
WATER,SPRING,CLYSMIC,LABEL,BLOB TOP,QUART,GREEN............     12.00
WATER,STAR SPRINGS CO.,SARATOGA,N.Y.,PINT,GOLD AMBER.......     30.00
WATER,STAR SPRINGS CO.,SARATOGA,N.Y.,PINT,RED AMBER........     40.00
WATER,STRAWBERRY,DIAMOND,FAN,CUT GLASS.....................     22.50
WATER,SUPERIOR MINERAL WATER,COBALT BLUE...................     80.00
WATER,TATE SPRINGS NATURAL MINERAL,ROUND,1/2 GAL.,AMBER....     15.00
WATER,VICHY,PATTERSON & BRAZEAU,PINT,OLIVE.................     25.00
WATER,WEDDING BAND.........................................     21.50
WATER,WITTER SPRINGS MINERAL,AMBER.........................      5.00
WATER,1 GAL.,15 IN. HIGH,CIRCA 1900,AQUA...................      7.00
WEEKS & POTTER,BOSTON,EMBOSSED,3 PIECE MOLD,SCREW TOP......     20.00
```

WHEATON COMPANY WAS ESTABLISHED IN 1888. THE FIRM MADE
HAND-BLOWN AND PRESSED GLASSWARE. IN 1938 AUTOMATIC
EQUIPMENT WAS ADDED AND MANY MOLDED GLASS ITEMS WERE
MADE. WHEATON-NULINE NOW MAKES ALL TYPES OF CONTAINERS
FOR PHARMACEUTICALS AND COSMETICS AND FOODS, AS WELL AS
GIFT SHOP ANTIQUE-STYLE BOTTLES.

WHEATON NULINE,APOLLO XI	COLOR..	15.00
WHEATON NULINE,APOLLO XII	COLOR..	15.00
WHEATON NULINE,APOLLO XIII	COLOR..	5.00
WHEATON NULINE,DONKEY,HUMPHREY,MUSKIE	COLOR..	16.00
WHEATON NULINE,DWIGHT D.EISENHOWER	COLOR..	20.00
WHEATON NULINE,EDISON,THOMAS ALVA	COLOR..	10.00
WHEATON NULINE,EISENHOWER,GENERAL	COLOR..	15.00
WHEATON NULINE,ELEPHANT,NIXON,AGNEW	COLOR..	16.00
WHEATON NULINE,FRANKLIN D.ROOSEVELT	COLOR..	20.00
WHEATON NULINE,FRANKLIN,BENJAMIN	COLOR..	5.00
WHEATON NULINE,GRAHAM,BILLY	COLOR..	5.00
WHEATON NULINE,JEFFERSON,THOMAS	ILLUS..	50.00
WHEATON NULINE,JOHN F.KENNEDY	COLOR..	25.00
WHEATON NULINE,KELLER,HELEN	ILLUS..	50.00
WHEATON NULINE,KENNEDY,ROBERT	COLOR..	18.00
WHEATON NULINE,KING,MARTIN LUTHER	COLOR..	18.00
WHEATON NULINE,LEE,ROBERT E	COLOR..	10.00
WHEATON NULINE,LINCOLN,ABRAHAM	COLOR..	18.00
WHEATON NULINE,LINDBERGH,CHARLES	COLOR..	10.00
WHEATON NULINE,MACARTHUR,DOUGLAS	COLOR..	14.00
WHEATON NULINE,PAUL REVERE,SYRUP,1970	ILLUS..	1.50
WHEATON NULINE,ROGERS,WILL	COLOR..	5.00
WHEATON NULINE,ROOSEVELT,THEODORE	COLOR..	5.00
WHEATON NULINE,ROSS,BETSY	COLOR..	5.00
WHEATON NULINE,WASHINGTON,GEORGE	COLOR..	4.95
WHEATON NULINE,WILSON,WOODROW	COLOR..	13.00
WHIMSEY,DOG,BLOWN,THREADED NECK,CLEAR		25.00
WHIMSEY,HAT,BLOWN,CLEAR		5.00
WHIMSEY,MUG,APPLIED EAR HANDLE,CLEAR		2.00
WHIMSEY,PIG,BLOWN,THREADED NECK,CLEAR		25.00

WHEATON NULINE, HELEN KELLER

WHEATON NULINE,
THOMAS JEFFERSON

WHEATON NULINE,PAUL REVERE,
SYRUP,1970

WHISKEY BOTTLES CAME IN ASSORTED SIZES AND SHAPES
THROUGH THE YEARS. ANY CONTAINER FOR WHISKEY IS
INCLUDED IN THIS CATEGORY.

WHISKEY,A MERRY CHRISTMAS & A HAPPY NEW YEAR	COLOR..	XX.XX
WHISKEY,A MERRY CHRISTMAS & A HAPPY NEW YEAR	COLOR..	XX.XX
WHISKEY,A MERRY CHRISTMAS AND A HAPPY NEW YEAR,1/2 PINT		30.00

```
WHISKEY,A.M.BININGER & CO.,GIN,SQUARE,AMBER.................    45.00
WHISKEY,A.VAN HOBOKEN & CO.,10 IN.,GREEN.............ILLUS..     8.00
WHISKEY,AINSLIE'S,10 IN.,OLIVE GREEN......................    30.00
WHISKEY,ALTAMONT FINEST AMERICAN.........................    16.00
WHISKEY,ALTSCHUL DISTILLING CO.,SPRINGFIELD,OHIO,AMBER......    15.00
WHISKEY,AMBER............................................    40.00
WHISKEY,AMBER,GLASS SCREW TOP,PAT.1861,PINT..............     6.00
WHISKEY,AMERICAN PICON PHILLIPPEVILLE,EMBOSSED,3 MOLD.......    15.00
WHISKEY,AMERICUS CLUB PURE,AMETHYST......................    10.00
WHISKEY,AMERICUS CLUB PURE,CLEAR.........................    10.00
WHISKEY,AMETHYST.........................................     3.00
WHISKEY,ANTIQUE,1/2 PINT.........................ILLUS..     4.00
WHISKEY,BAILEY'S,HUEY & CHRIST,PHILA.....................    26.00
  WHISKEY, BALLANTINE, SEE BALLANTINE
  WHISKEY, BEAM, SEE BEAM
WHISKEY,BELL SCOTCH,BELL,1970,REGAL..................ILLUS..    13.00
WHISKEY,BELL SCOTCH,BELLRINGER.....................:....ILLUS..    14.00
WHISKEY,BELL,GOLDEN WEDDING,MARIGOLD,PINT................    12.00
WHISKEY,BELLE OF ANDERSON,EMBOSSED FIVE-POINT STAR,MILK
  GLASS.................................................    36.50
```

WHISKEY,A. VAN HOBOKEN &
CO.,10 IN.,GREEN

WHISKEY,
ANTIQUE,
1/2 PINT

WHISKEY,
BELL
SCOTCH,
BELL,
1970,
REGAL

WHISKEY,BELL SCOTCH,
BELLRINGER

```
WHISKEY,BELLE OF ANDERSON,MILK GLASS.....................    96.00
WHISKEY,BINNINGER'S REGULATOR,CLOCK SHAPE,AMBER............   396.00
WHISKEY,BINSWANGER & BRO.,AMETHYST.......................     4.00
WHISKEY,BINSWANGER & BRO.,CLEAR..........................     4.00
  WHISKEY, BLACK & WHITE, SEE BLACK & WHITE
WHISKEY,BLANKENHEYM & NOLET,CASE GIN,OLIVE GREEN...........    17.50
WHISKEY,BLOWN IN MOLD,STRAP SIDE,AQUA....................     2.50
WHISKEY,BLOWN IN MOLD,STRAP SIDE,CLEAR...................     2.00
WHISKEY,BONNIE BROS.,LOUISVILLE,KY.......................    16.00
WHISKEY,BONNIE BROS.,PINK................................    20.00
WHISKEY,BONNIE BROS.,QUART,CLEAR.........................     5.00
WHISKEY,BOOZ,E.C.,OLD CABIN......................COLOR..    XX.XX
WHISKEY,BOOZ,E.C.,OLD CABIN,1940,CIRCULAR DEPRESSION.......    75.00
WHISKEY,BOOZ,E.G.,CABIN,19TH CENTURY,AMBER...............   301.00
WHISKEY,BOOZ,1840,BROWN,REPRODUCTION.....................     8.50
WHISKEY,BOURBON,ROUND,AMBER..............................    25.00
WHISKEY,BROOK SUNNY,PURE FOOD,ST.LOUIS 1904,AMETHYST......    12.00
WHISKEY,BROOK SUNNY,PURE FOOD,ST.LOUIS 1904,CLEAR........    12.00
WHISKEY,BROWN FORMAN CO.,LOUISVILLE,KY.,AMETHYST.........     4.00
WHISKEY,BROWN FORMAN CO.,LOUISVILLE,KY.,CLEAR...........     4.00
WHISKEY,BRUNSING,TOLLE & POSTEL,INC.,QUART,AMBER............    20.00
WHISKEY,BUCHANANS BLACK & WHITE,GREEN....................    10.00
```

```
WHISKEY,BURKE'S.........................................COLOR..    XX.XX
WHISKEY,BURNETT,SIR R.& CO.,LONDON,ENGLAND,12 IN.TALL,AQUA..        6.00
WHISKEY,BURNETT,SIR R.& CO.,LONDON,ENGLAND,12 IN.TALL,CLEAR.        6.00
WHISKEY,C.O.TAYLOR. REGISTERED TRADE MARK,3 PIECE MOLD,AMBER.       6.00
WHISKEY,CABIN COTTAGE BRAND RYE JUG,AQUA...................       116.00
WHISKEY,CAMBRIDGE NEAR CUT,32 OZ.,CLEAR....................        38.00
WHISKEY,CANADIAN CLUB DUMMY................................         3.00
WHISKEY,CANADIAN MIST,MOUNTY...............................        18.50
WHISKEY,CARLTON,PURE RYE............................COLOR..        XX.XX
WHISKEY,CHARLES LONDON,CORDIAL,GIN,GREEN...................        40.00
WHISKEY,CHAS.S.GOVE CO.,BOSTON.............................        10.00
WHISKEY,CHATTANOOGA DISTILLERY,TENN.,PINT..................        16.00
WHISKEY,CHESLEY'S JOCKEY CLUB,AMETHYST.....................       100.00
WHISKEY,CHESLEY'S JOCKEY CLUB,CLEAR........................       100.00
WHISKEY,CHESTNUT GROVE,C.W..........................COLOR..        XX.XX
WHISKEY,CHESTNUT GROVE,HANDLED,CHESTNUT,OPEN PONTIL,AMBER...       135.00
WHISKEY,CHESTNUT GROVE,HANDLED,JUG.........................       176.00
WHISKEY,CHESTNUT GROVE,PINT................................       126.00
WHISKEY,CIACOMINI & BOYD,AMBER.............................        15.00
WHISKEY,CLARKE & WHITE,NEW YORK,GREEN......................        21.50
WHISKEY,COCA MARIANI,PARIS,WHITTLE MOLD,GREEN..............         6.00
WHISKEY,COCA MARIANI,PARIS,WHITTLE,LONG NECK,GREEN..........        5.00
WHISKEY,COLUMBIAN KENTUCKY BOURBON,AMBER,..................       100.00
WHISKEY,CORN SHAPE,OLD ELK..........................COLOR..        XX.XX
WHISKEY,COTT'S,AMBER GREEN.................................         7.00
WHISKEY,CRABFELDERS,AMBER,5 3/4 IN.........................         4.75
WHISKEY,CROW,CHESSMAN......................................         7.53
WHISKEY,CROWN DISTILLERIES CO.,ROUND,SAMPLE,AMETHYST.......         4.00
WHISKEY,CROWN DISTILLERIES CO.,ROUND,SAMPLE,CLEAR..........         4.00
WHISKEY,CROWN DISTILLERIES,AMBER...........................        20.00
WHISKEY,CROWN DISTILLERY,INSIDE THREAD WITH CORK...........        13.50
WHISKEY,CYRUS NOBLE,AMBER..................................        20.00
WHISKEY,DALLEMAND & CO.,CREAM RYE,AMBER....................         4.00
WHISKEY,DALLEMAND & CO.,ROUND,QUART,AMBER..................        31.00
   WHISKEY, DANI, SEE DANT
WHISKEY,DAWSON,BLACK.......................................        12.00
WHISKEY,DE TURK...........................................        10.00
WHISKEY,DEEP SPRING TENN.WHISKEY,QUART,AMBER...............        15.00
WHISKEY,DEEP SPRING,TENN.,3 MOLD...........................        16.00
WHISKEY,DIAMOND PATTERN,8 IN........................ILLUS..         6.50
WHISKEY,DIAMOND PATTERN,9 1/2 IN....................ILLUS..         6.00
WHISKEY,DOUBLE SPRINGS,PEASANT MAN.........................         6.95
WHISKEY,DOUBLE SPRINGS,PEASANT WOMAN.......................         6.95
```

WHISKEY,DIAMOND PATTERN,8 IN

WHISKEY,DIAMOND PATTERN,9 1/2 IN

```
WHISKEY,DUFF'S MALT,AMBER.....................................   5.75
WHISKEY,DUFFY MALT WHISKEY CO.,ROCHESTER,GREEN...... 8.00 TO    10.00
WHISKEY,DUFFY MALT WHISKEY,AMBER..............................   5.00
WHISKEY,DUFFY MALT,AMBER......................................   2.50
WHISKEY,DUFFY MALT,MD.,PAT.AUG.24'86,AMBER...................  15.00
WHISKEY,DUFFY MALT,N.Y.,PAT.AUG.24,1886,ROUND,AMBER.........   6.00
WHISKEY,DUFFY MALT,PAT.AUG.24,1886,ROUND,MACHINE MADE,AMBER.   3.00
WHISKEY,DUFFY MALT,PAT.AUG.24'86,BALTIMORE,MD.,MACHINE MADE.   4.00
WHISKEY,DUFFY MALT,PAT.AUG.24'86,PINT,AMBER.................  20.00
WHISKEY,DUFFY MALT,PAT.AUG.24'86,QUART,BALTIMORE,MD.,AMBER..   8.00
WHISKEY,DUFFY MALT,PAT.AUG.24'86,SAMPLE,MACHINE MADE,MD.,
  AMBER......................................................  10.00
WHISKEY,DUFFY MALT,PAT.AUG.24'86,1/2 PINT...................  20.00
WHISKEY,DUFFY'S MALT..........................................   1.00
WHISKEY,DUNSTER BOTTLING CO.,BOSTON,SQUARE,QUART,AMBER......   5.00
WHISKEY,DURHAM.............................................1,200.00
WHISKEY,DYOTTEVILLE GLASS WORKS,3 PIECE MOLD,BUBBLES,YELLOW.  35.00
WHISKEY,DYOTTVILLE,MARKED ON BOTTOM,QUART,GREEN.............  65.00
WHISKEY,E.E.GRAY & CO.,BLOWN IN MOLD,AQUA...................   3.00
WHISKEY,EAR OF CORN,AMBER....................................  75.00
WHISKEY,EARLY TIMES,PROHIBITION,BOTTLE..............COLOR..  XX.XX
WHISKEY,EARLY TIMES,PROHIBITION,CAN.................COLOR..  XX.XX
WHISKEY,EG.LYONS & RAAS SF,CALIFORNIA,CYLINDER,PURPLE.......  12.00
WHISKEY,EMBOSSED FEATHERS,CLEAR,9 IN................ILLUS..   2.50
WHISKEY,ENAMELED BOURBON,FLUTES CUT IN NECK & BASE,BLACK....  18.00
  WHISKEY, EZRA BROOKS, SEE EZRA BROOKS
WHISKEY,F.CHEVALIER CO.,CASTLE,AMBER.........................  25.00
WHISKEY,F.HERRING,AMBER......................................  15.00
WHISKEY,FERNBERGER BROS.,PHILA,AMBER.........................  18.50
WHISKEY,FIFTH,RIBS ON SHOULDER & BOTTOM,AMETHYST............   6.00
WHISKEY,FIFTH,RIBS ON SHOULDER & BOTTOM,CLEAR..............   6.00
WHISKEY,FLEISCHMANN,PINT,EMBOSSED COAT OF ARMS,AMBER......  14.00
WHISKEY,FLORA TEMPLE HARNESS TROT....................COLOR..  XX.XX
WHISKEY,FOUR ROSES,AMBER.....................................   7.00
WHISKEY,FOUR ROSES,DECANTER,POTTERY,TRAIN...........ILLUS..  15.00
```

WHISKEY,EMBOSSED FEATHERS,CLEAR, 9 IN

WHISKEY,FOUR ROSES,DECANTER,
POTTERY,TRAIN

```
WHISKEY,FRED RASCHEN........................................  16.00
WHISKEY,FRIEDENWALD,J.H.,FAMILY WINE & LIQUOR,BALTIMORE.....  23.00
WHISKEY,G.O.BLAKE'S RYE & BOURBON,BLOWN IN MOLD,CLEAR.......   6.00
WHISKEY,G.O.BLAKE'S RYE & BOURBON,EMBOSSED.................   6.00
WHISKEY,G.O.BLAKE'S,CLEAR..................................  25.00
WHISKEY,G.O.BLAKES RYE & BOURBON,EMBOSSED BARREL...........   4.50
WHISKEY,GAELIC OLD SMUGGLER,3 PIECE MOLD,OLIVE.............  12.00
```

```
WHISKEY,GANNYMEDE 76,RECTANGULAR,AMBER......................    16.00
WHISKEY,GENUINE IRISH,GAL.................................     6.00
WHISKEY,GENUINE SCOTCH,GAL................................     6.00
WHISKEY,GEO.BENZ & SONS,AMBER.............................    30.00
WHISKEY,GEO.H.GOODMAN CO.,EMBOSSED,PADUCAH,KY.............     6.00
WHISKEY,GEO.WISSEMAN,SACRAMENTO,GREEN.....................    20.00
WHISKEY,GIBBONS...................................COLOR..     XX.XX
WHISKEY,GILKA,AMBER.......................................    10.00
WHISKEY,GIN,A.V.H.,GREEN..................................    30.00
WHISKEY,GIN,CASE,CRUDE....................................    12.50
WHISKEY,GIN,CASE,OLIVE GREEN..............................     8.00
WHISKEY,GIN,OPEN PONTIL...................................    25.00
WHISKEY,GIN,PONTIL,GREEN..................................    35.00
WHISKEY,GIN,TAPERED PONTIL,GREEN..........................    28.00
WHISKEY,GIN,200 YEARS OLD,BLACK...........................    75.00
WHISKEY,GLENMORE,POTTERY JUG..............................     2.75
WHISKEY,GOLD & WHITE DECOR,ENAMEL,BLOWN,FLINT,HANDLE,GREEN..   65.00
WHISKEY,GOLD DUCT KENTUCKY BOURBON,AMETHYST...............   100.00
WHISKEY,GOLD DUCT KENTUCKY BOURBON,CLEAR..................   100.00
WHISKEY,GOLDEN WEDDING,AMBER..............................     6.00
WHISKEY,GOLDEN WEDDING,CARNIVAL GLASS.....................    15.00
WHISKEY,GOLDEN WEDDING,CARNIVAL,FEDERAL LAW PROHIBITS.......   11.00
WHISKEY,GOLDEN WEDDING,CLEAR,EMBOSSED,PINT................     7.50
WHISKEY,GOLDEN WEDDING,PINT,DATE 1910,CLEAR...............     8.00
WHISKEY,GORDON'S DRY GIN,AQUA.............................     2.00
WHISKEY,GORDON'S DRY GIN,LONDON,ENGLAND...................     6.50
WHISKEY,GORDON'S GIN,LINDEN,N.J. .........................     3.00
WHISKEY,GORDON'S GIN,LONDON,ENGLAND.......................     5.00
WHISKEY,GORDON'S LONDON GIN...............................     7.00
WHISKEY,GRANT'S STAND FAST,THREE-SIDED,PAISLEY,SCOTLAND....     4.00
WHISKEY,GRANT'S,DRUMMOND,BOY.......................ILLUS..    20.00
WHISKEY,GRANT'S,LAMOND,GIRL........................ILLUS..    20.00
WHISKEY,GREEN,9 IN.,MODERN.........................ILLUS..     2.00
WHISKEY,GUARANTEED FULL 1/2 PINT,BLOWN IN MOLD,AMBER......     1.50
WHISKEY,GUARANTEED FULL 1/2 PINT,BLOWN IN MOLD,CLEAR......     2.00
WHISKEY,GUARANTEED FULL 1/2 PINT,P.DEMPSEY & CO.,CLEAR.....     2.00
```

WHISKEY,
GREEN,9 IN.,MODERN

WHISKEY,GRANT'S,
DRUMMOND,BOY

WHISKEY,GRANT'S,
LAMOND,GIRL

```
WHISKEY,GUND,CLEVELAND,OHIO........................ILLUS..        2.00
WHISKEY,H.B.KIRK & CO.,N.Y.,BLOWN IN MOLD,AMBER............        4.00
WHISKEY,HAIG & HAIG,STERLING SILVER,BAMBOO OVERLAY.........       32.00
WHISKEY,HALL,LUHRS & CO.,CLEAR............................       20.00
WHISKEY,HALL,LUHRS & CO.,SACRAMENTO,AMBER..................       25.00
WHISKEY,HANNIS DIST.CO.,AMBER.............................       30.00
WHISKEY,HARDY,MILTON J.,OLD BOURBON,EMBOSSED EAGLE,AMBER....       76.00
WHISKEY,HART,JOHN & CO.,FIGURAL,AMBER......................       26.00
WHISKEY,HARVARD RYE,PINT,CLEAR............................        4.00
WHISKEY,HARVARD RYE,QUART,CLEAR...........................        5.00
WHISKEY,HARVARD RYE,SELECT STOCK,KLEIN BROS.,CINN.,O.,
  C.1895.................................................        9.00
WHISKEY,HARVARD RYE,1/2 PINT,CLEAR........................        4.00
WHISKEY,HARVARD,B EMBOSSED OVER A K,RYE IN CIRCLE BIMAL,
  CLEAR.................................................       20.00
WHISKEY,HARVEST KING,AMETHYST BIMAL.......................        8.00
WHISKEY,HASBROOK.........................................       10.00
WHISKEY,HAYNER DISTILLERY,TROY,OHIO,1897,BIMAL............        8.00
WHISKEY,HAYNER DISTILLING CO.,DAYTON,ST.LOUIS,PINT,CLEAR...       21.00
WHISKEY,HAYNER WHISKEY DISTILLERY,NOV.30,1897,ROUND,AMETHYST      14.00
WHISKEY,HAYNER,PAT.1897,CLEAR.............................        3.95
WHISKEY,HAYNER,TROY,OHIO,DATED 1897.......................        9.00
WHISKEY,HEATHER DEW,POTTERY JUG......................ILLUS..       15.00
WHISKEY,HENRY ELIKINS SIR................................        7.00
WHISKEY,HERMAN JANSEN SCHIEDAM,OLIVE GREEN................       42.50
WHISKEY,HEWITT CO.,ST.LOUIS BIMAL........................        9.00
WHISKEY,HIGHLAND,LAMBRETH DOULTON JUG,BROWN TO TAN,GREEN....       45.00
WHISKEY,HILDEBRANDT POSNER & CO.,GREEN....................       20.00
WHISKEY,HILL AND HILL,1920,CLEAR,7 IN................ILLUS..        9.00
WHISKEY,HIRAM RICKER,FACSIMILE POLAND WATER..........ILLUS..       35.00
```

WHISKEY,GUND,CLEVELAND,OHIO

WHISKEY,
HEATHER DEW,
POTTERY JUG

WHISKEY,
HILL AND
HILL,
1920,
CLEAR,
7 IN

WHISKEY,HIRAM RICKER,
FACSIMILE POLAND WATER

```
WHISKEY,HOLIHAN BROS.MAIL ORDER LIQUOR DEALERS LAWRENCE,
  MASS................................................       16.00
WHISKEY,HOLLYWOOD,EMBOSSED,QUART,AMBER....................        8.50
WHISKEY,HOLLYWOOD,QUART,AMBER.............................        6.00
WHISKEY,HOLLYWOOD,QUART,CIRCA 1900,AMBER..................        7.50
WHISKEY,HOLLZEUMAN'S,2 SIDED CABIN ROOF...................      476.00
WHISKEY,I.E.GOLDBERG,NEW YORK,N.Y.,AMBER..................        8.00
  WHISKEY, I.W.HARPER SEE I.W.HARPER
WHISKEY,IRISH MIST,SOLDIER...............................       12.50
WHISKEY,IRISH MIST,SOLDIER...............................       15.00
  WHISKEY, JACK DANIEL SEE JACK DANIEL
WHISKEY,J.C.ZCHNELL,BACKWARD Z,KILN DRIED GRAIN...........       25.00
WHISKEY,J.E.BRENNAN,GRAPHITE PONTIL......................       60.00
```

WHISKEY,J.F.CUTTER,AMBER	15.00
WHISKEY,J.RIEGER & CO.,PINK	20.00
WHISKEY, J.W.DANT, SEE DANT	
WHISKEY,J.W.PALMER,KY.,POTTERY JUG,HANDLE,BROWN & TAN	6.00
WHISKEY,JACKMAN,PINT,CARNIVAL GLASS YELLOW	8.00
WHISKEY,JACKMAN,1/2 PINT,CARNIVAL GLASS YELLOW	8.00
WHISKEY,JAMES KANE......COLOR..	XX.XX
WHISKEY,JESSE MOORE & CO.,OLD BOURBON,AMBER	35.00
WHISKEY,JESSE MOORE & CO.,RYE,AMBER	35.00
WHISKEY, JIM BEAM, SEE BEAM	
WHISKEY,JO-JO-MONOGRAM,PINT	101.00
WHISKEY,JOE GIDEON,PINT	4.00
WHISKEY,JOHN & JAMES BUCHANAN'S WHITE LABEL,3 PIECE MOLD,	
GREEN	8.00
WHISKEY,JOHN H.WALSH & CO.,BLOWN IN MOLD,11 1/2 IN. TALL,	
CLEAR	3.50
WHISKEY,JOHN SCHWEYER & CO. DISTILLERS CHICAGO	7.00
WHISKEY,JOS.A.MAGUS & CO.,PINT,AMBER	5.00
WHISKEY,JOS.A.MAGUS & CO.,PINT,SQUARE,CLEAR	4.00
WHISKEY,JOS.A.MAGUS & CO.,1/2 PINT,AMBER	4.0C
WHISKEY,JOS.A.MAGUS & CO.,1/2 PINT,RIBBED,CLEAR	4.0C
WHISKEY,JOS.A.MAGUS & CO.,1/2 PINT,SQUARE,CLEAR	3.00
WHISKEY,JOS.A.MAGUS & CO.,5TH,SQUARE RIBBED,CLEAR	10.00
WHISKEY,JOS.M.FREY,COR.,EMBUSSED,BUBBLES,AMETHYST	10.00
WHISKEY,JUG,POTTERY,GREEN	12.00
WHISKEY,JUNIPER BERRY GIN,QUININE WH.,DIURETIC,QUART,GREEN..	18.50
WHISKEY,KELLERSTRAUS DISTILLING CO.,ST.LOUIS,AMETHYST	26.00
WHISKEY,KELLERSTRAUS,D.C.,BIMAL,QUART,CLEAR	16.50
WHISKEY,KEWANEE,RACER CAR,GREEN	3.50
WHISKEY,KEYSTONE,SAN JOSE,CALIFORNIA	32.50
WHISKEY,KUMMEL BEAR,GREEN,LABEL IN RUSSIAN WRITING	50.00
WHISKEY,L.T.& CO.,AMBER	20.00
WHISKEY,LABELS,CUSHING PROCESS,BOSTON,LIGHTHOUSE,AMBER,QUART	5.00
WHISKEY,LEVAGGI CO.,SAN FRANCISCO,AMBER	15.00
WHISKEY,LILIENTHAL & CO.,AMBER	15.00
WHISKEY, LIONSTONE, SEE LIONSTONE	
WHISKEY,LIQUOR DEL DIVAU,DEVIL'S HEAD,QUART,AMBER	201.00
WHISKEY,LONDON JOCKEY CLUBHOUSE GIN,BLACK	900.00
WHISKEY,LOUIS TAUSSIG & CO.,CLEAR	20.00
WHISKEY,MAIL BOX RYE,PAT.DATE 1891,FIGURAL,QUART	91.00
WHISKEY,MAJOR GRAY	50.00
WHISKEY,MALLARD DISTILLING,BALTIMORE & NEW YORK,VIOLIN	
SHAPED	21.00
WHISKEY,MBR ON BASE,BULBOUS TOP & BOTTOM,SQUARE BIMAL	8.50
WHISKEY,MC KEARIN G I-16,HANDLE,AMBER	175.00
WHISKEY,MC KEARIN G V-10,BINNINGER,HANDLE,AMBER	195.00
WHISKEY,MCLEOD & HATJE,AMBER	25.00
WHISKEY,MEEHAN'S MALT	4.00
WHISKEY,MELL,W.H.,TOLEDO,O.,ROUND,QUART,COBALT BLUE	226.00
WHISKEY,MELLOW AS MOONLIGHT,MOON & CLOUDS	7.00
WHISKEY,MERRY CHRISIMAS & HAPPY NEW YEAR,CLEAR	20.00
WHISKEY,MIDDLETOWN WHEAT 1825,BLOB SEAL,1/2 GAL.,AMBER	91.00
WHISKEY,MILLER'S GAME COCK,BOSTON	11.00
WHISKEY,MOORE,JESSIE,FIFTH,AMBER	41.00
WHISKEY,MOUNT VERNON PURE RYE,MARCH 25,1890,AMBER	20.00
WHISKEY,MT.VERNON,AMBER	9.00
WHISKEY,NEALS AMBROSIA,BLUE	100.00
WHISKEY,OAKLAND CANADIAN MALT,LABEL,CLEAR	6.50
WHISKEY,OLD BOURBON,FOR MEDICINAL PURPOSES,GREEN	10.00
WHISKEY,OLD BUSHMILL EST.1784	15.00
WHISKEY,OLD BUSHMILLS DISTILLERY,DATED 1784,QUART	9.50
WHISKEY,OLD CHARTER PURE RYE,P.& B.,ATLANTA,3 PIECE MOLD....	10.00
WHISKEY, OLD CROW, SEE OLD CROW	
WHISKEY,OLD DRIOLI,PITCHER,NATIVE ON FRONT,TOTEM POLE ON	
BACK	32.50

```
WHISKEY,OLD DRUM...............................................    5.00
    WHISKEY, OLD FITZGERALD, SEE OLD FITZGERALD
WHISKEY,OLD FORESTER,PERSONALIZED,AMBER,1950.........ILLUS..       5.00
WHISKEY,OLD GILT EDGE BOURBON,FIFTH,AMBER.................     101.00
WHISKEY,OLD GUCKENHEIMER,C.1890......................COLOR..      XX.XX
WHISKEY,OLD HICKORY...........................................    12.50
WHISKEY,OLD JERSEY...........................................     2.75
WHISKEY,OLD JUDGE KENTUCKY WHISKEY,AMBER...................      50.00
WHISKEY,OLD KENTUCKY CO.,DISTILLERS,KY.,QUART,CLEAR.....         10.00
WHISKEY,OLD KENTUCKY VALLEY,LITHOGRAPH LABEL.........ILLUS..      18.00
WHISKEY,OLD LEXINGTON CLUB,EMBOSSED,AMBER.................       22.50
WHISKEY,OLD MAID,GALLON JUG,AMETHYST......................       10.00
WHISKEY,OLD MONONGAHELA RYE,ROUND,AMBER...................       18.00
WHISKEY,OLD MR.BOSTON........................................     7.00
WHISKEY,OLD QUAKER,EMBOSSED..................................     4.00
WHISKEY,OLD QUAKER,EMBOSSED ANCHOR BOTTOM,PINT,CLEAR.....        26.00
WHISKEY,OLD QUARTER CENTURY,WELLER...................COLOR..      XX.XX
WHISKEY,OLD RAVEN............................................    22.50
WHISKEY,OLD SACHEM..........................................    125.00
WHISKEY,OLD SCHLOTTERBECK & FOSS..........................        4.95
WHISKEY,OLD SETTLER,PEORIA,ILL.,LABEL,AMBER..............        12.00
WHISKEY,OLD TAYLOR CASTLE...................................     14.00
WHISKEY,OLD TAYLOR,CASTLE,1967.....................ILLUS..       14.00
WHISKEY,OLD TIMES BOURBON,8 YEARS OLD,GAL.................        3.50
WHISKEY,OLD TIMES BOURBON,10 YEARS OLD,GAL................        4.00
WHISKEY,OLD TIMES BOURBON,12 YEARS OLD,GAL................        5.00
WHISKEY,OLD TIMES BOURBON,18 YEARS OLD,GAL................        8.00
```

WHISKEY,OLD TAYLOR,
CASTLE,1967

WHISKEY,OLD FORESTER,
PERSONALIZED,AMBER,1950

WHISKEY,OLD KENTUCKY VALLEY,
LITHOGRAPH LABEL

```
WHISKEY,OLD TIMES RYE,8 YEAR OLD,GAL.........................     3.50
WHISKEY,OLD TIMES RYE,10 YEAR OLD,GAL........................     4.00
WHISKEY,OLD TIMES RYE,12 YEARS OLD,GAL.......................     5.00
WHISKEY,OLD TIMES RYE,18 YEARS OLD,GAL.......................     8.00
WHISKEY,OLD TIMES WHITE CORN WHISKEY,8 YEARS OLD,GAL........      3.50
WHISKEY,OLD TIMES WHITE WHEAT WHISKEY,8 YEARS OLD,GAL.......      3.50
WHISKEY,OLD TUCKER RESERVE,PROHIBITION...............COLOR..      XX.XX
WHISKEY,OLD 49 MARYLAND RYE,C.1915,9 IN..............ILLUS..      15.00
WHISKEY,OREGON IMPORTING CO.,AMBER.........................      15.00
WHISKEY,ORENE PARKER CO.,JUG,GAL.,AMETHYST...................    20.00
WHISKEY,P.DAWSON DUFFTOWN GLENLIVET,10 IN.,SQUATTY,OLIVE
    GREEN...................................................     12.00
WHISKEY,PALMER,GREEN.........................................     5.00
WHISKEY,PARKER RYE,6 PANELS ON NECK,FLAY TOP,CLEAR...........     6.00
WHISKEY,PARKER RYE,6 PANELS,FANCY,CLEAR......................    10.00
WHISKEY,PAROLE PURE RYE,HORSE IN CENTER,5TH,SQUAT,AMBER.....    100.00
```

WHISKEY,OLD 49 MARYLAND RYE,C.1915,9 IN

```
WHISKEY,PAUL JONES PURE RYE,BLOB SEAL........................    15.00
WHISKEY,PAUL JONES PURE RYE,BLOB SEAL,ROUND,AMBER...........    14.00
WHISKEY,PAUL JONES WHISKEY,BLOB SEAL,ROUND,AMBER...........    14.00
WHISKEY,PAUL JONES,AMBER...................................    25.00
WHISKEY,PAUL JONES,APPLIED SEAL...........................    12.00
WHISKEY,PAUL JONES,BLOB SEAL,AMBER........................     6.00
WHISKEY,PAUL JONES,BLOB SEAL,RED AMBER....................    10.00
WHISKEY,PAUL JONES,DATED 1906.............................     5.00
WHISKEY,PAUL JONES,FLASK,EMBOSSED S.C.,AMBER..............     7.00
WHISKEY,PAUL JONES,HEAD,SHIPS.............................     7.00
WHISKEY,PEACOCK DISTILLER.........................COLOR..    XX.XX
WHISKEY,PEPPER DISTILLERY,AMBER...........................    30.00
WHISKEY,PETT'S BALD EAGLE,BOSTON,MASS.....................     3.50
WHISKEY,PHILADELPHIA PORT & ALE,XXX,TEA GREEN.............    36.00
WHISKEY,PIG,DRINK WHISKY FROM THIS HOG,EMBOSSED,CLEAR.....    60.00
WHISKEY,PIKE'S PEAK OLD RYE,PITTS.,PA.,PINT,AQUA..........    56.00
WHISKEY,PIKE'S PEAK,OLD RYE,PITTSBURGH,1/2 PINT...........    45.00
WHISKEY,PINCH,QUART,AMBER.................................    10.00
WHISKEY,PINE TREE TAR CORDIAL,GREEN.......................    35.00
WHISKEY,PLAIN,QUART,ROUND,BLOB NECK,AMBER.................    20.00
WHISKEY,PLAIN,QUART,TURNMOLD,GREEN........................    12.00
WHISKEY,PLAIN,RIBBED SHOULDER,PINT,AMBER..................     8.00
WHISKEY,PLAIN,RIBBED SHOULDER,PINT,AMETHYST...............     4.00
WHISKEY,PLAIN,RIBBED SHOULDER,PINT,CLEAR..................     4.00
WHISKEY,PLAIN,RIBBED SHOULDER,QUART,AMBER.................     8.00
WHISKEY,PLAIN,RIBBED SHOULDER,QUART,CLEAR.................     4.00
WHISKEY,PLAIN,SIDE STRAP,UNION OVAL,PINT,AMBER............    12.00
WHISKEY,PLAIN,SIDE STRAP,UNION OVAL,PINT,CLEAR............    12.00
WHISKEY,PLAIN,SIDE STRAP,UNION OVAL,PINT,GREEN............    12.00
WHISKEY,PLAIN,SIDE STRAP,UNION OVAL,QUART,AMBER...........    12.00
WHISKEY,PLAIN,SIDE STRAP,UNION OVAL,QUART,CLEAR...........    12.00
WHISKEY,PLAIN,SIDE STRAP,UNION OVAL,QUART,GREEN...........    12.00
WHISKEY,PLAIN,SIDE STRAP,UNION OVAL,1/2 PINT,AMBER........    12.00
WHISKEY,PLAIN,SIDE STRAP,UNION OVAL,1/2 PINT,CLEAR........    12.00
WHISKEY,PLAIN,SIDE STRAP,UNION OVAL,1/2 PINT,GREEN........    12.00
WHISKEY,PLATTE VALLEY MISSOURI STRAIGHT CORN,PINT,POTTERY...     6.00
WHISKEY,POLAND SPRINGS,GIN,GREEN..........................     1.70
WHISKEY,PONTIL CHECK,AMBER................................    65.00
WHISKEY,PREACHER,1/2 PINT,CURVED,OFF CENTER NECK,AMETHYST...    20.00
WHISKEY,PREACHER,1/2 PINT,CURVED,OFF CENTER NECK,CLEAR......    20.00
WHISKEY,QUAKER MAID,AMBER.................................    24.00
WHISKEY,QUAKER MAID,PINT..................................    12.00
WHISKEY,QUART,AMBER.......................................     1.00
WHISKEY,QUART,BIMAL,PURPLE................................     6.50
WHISKEY,QUART,BLOWN IN MOLD,12 IN. TALL,AMBER.............     4.00
WHISKEY,QUART,EMBOSSED,3 MOLD,GREEN.......................    20.00
WHISKEY,RARE OLD PRIVATE STOCK EXPORT.....................     8.49
```

WHISKEY,REBEL YELL.. 14.95
WHISKEY,RED AMBER.. 5.00
WHISKEY.RICKETTS,BRISTOL,CIRCA 1810.MORRIS L.MILLER
    MEDALLION.. 100.00
WHISKEY,ROTH & CUTTER... 8.00
WHISKEY,ROYAL SOCIETY X RYE,10 YEAR OLD,GAL................... 2.98
WHISKEY,ROYAL SOCIETY XX RYE,12 YEAR OLD,GAL.................. 3.49
WHISKEY,ROYAL SOCIETY XXX RYE,13 YEAR OLD,GAL................. 3.98
WHISKEY,ROYAL SOCIETY XXXX RYE,14 YEAR OLD,GAL............... 3.98
WHISKEY,ROYAL SOCIETY XXXXX RYE,18 YEAR OLD,GAL.............. 5.49
WHISKEY,RUTHERFORD & KAY,AMBER................................ 6.00
WHISKEY,RYE & FLORAL DESIGN ETCHED ON FRONT................... 5.00
WHISKEY,S.C.BOEHM & CO.,SHEAF OF WHEAT & 1876 IN SHIELD..... 8.00
WHISKEY,S.ROSENTHAL & CO.,6 SIDED,EMBOSSED,AMBER............. 17.50
WHISKEY,SAMPLER,BLOWN IN MOLD,AMBER........................... 4.00
WHISKEY,SAMPLER,BLOWN IN MOLD,BROWN........................... 4.00
WHISKEY,SAMPLER,BLOWN IN MOLD,CLEAR........................... 3.00
WHISKEY,SAMPLER,BLOWN IN MOLD,WHITTLE,OPEN PONTIL,AQUA...... 15.00
WHISKEY,SANDMAN,WEDGWOOD,LEFT................................. 11.95
WHISKEY,SANDMAN,WEDGWOOD,RIGHT................................ 11.95
WHISKEY,SAYS FELS WHISKEY,KANSAS CITY,INSIDE IS WELL,ROPE,
    BUCKET.. 30.00
WHISKEY,SCHENLEY,EMPIRE STATE FIGURAL,CLEAR.................. 35.00
WHISKEY,SCHENLEY,FLOWERS ON FRONT............................ 7.00
WHISKEY,SCOTCH,HAND-DECORATED,GOLD,HANDLE,STOPPER,PORCELAIN. 24.00
WHISKEY,SEAL,BLACK,A.S.C.R................................... 75.00
WHISKEY,SECOR,PRIVATE STOCK,DECANTER,STOPPER.........ILLUS.. 10.00

WHISKEY,SECOR,PRIVATE STOCK,DECANTER,STOPPER

WHISKEY,SHEEHAN'S MALT,CLEAR.................................. 5.00
WHISKEY,SHOOFLY,AMETHYST...................................... 4.00
WHISKEY,SHOOFLY,MERRY XMAS,SWIRLED,CLEAR..................... 10.50
WHISKEY,SIEBE BROS.& PLAGEMAN,CLEAR.......................... 20.00
WHISKEY,SIGNED HAWKES,19TH HOLE,CLUBHOUSE,FAIRWAYS,GREENS... 65.00
WHISKEY,SILVER DOLLAR,CLEAR,EMBOSSED,PINT.................... 7.50
WHISKEY,SPIDER WEB,EMBOSSED SPIDER........................... 13.00
WHISKEY,SQUARE,COPPER WHEEL CUT,DEER,9 IN. TALL............. 32.00
WHISKEY,ST.REMI BRANDY....................................... 10.00
WHISKEY,STAR JUG,OPEN PONTIL,AMBER........................... 126.00
WHISKEY,STRAUS BROS CHICAGO,BIMAL............................ 8.00
WHISKEY,STRAUS BROS.CO.,CHICAGO,U.S.A.,GREEN,WHITTLED....... 20.00
WHISKEY,T.& J.SLINEY,BLOWN IN MOLD,CLEAR..................... 2.25
WHISKEY,TAYLOR & WASHINGTON,8 IN............................. 2.75
WHISKEY,TAYLOR & WILLIAMS,KY.,RING TOP,CLEAR................ 6.00
WHISKEY,TAYLOR & WILLIAMS,KY.,ROUND,RING TOP,AMETHYST....... 6.00
WHISKEY,TEAKETTLE OLD BOURBON,AMBER.......................... 100.00
WHISKEY,TEXAS QUART,FLASK,TAPERED TOP,CLEAR................. 10.00
WHISKEY,THREE PIECE MOLD,BULBOUS NECK,GREEN................. 7.00
WHISKEY,THREE PIECE MOLD,FIFTH,CLEAR......................... 4.00

```
WHISKEY,THREE PIECE MOLD,WHITTLE MARKED,12 1/8 IN. TALL,
   CLEAR.........................................................    4.00
WHISKEY,THREE-MOLD,BROWN........................................    4.00
WHISKEY,THREE-MOLD,GREEN........................................    4.00
WHISKEY,TUCKER,1900....................................COLOR..   XX.XX
WHISKEY,TURN MOLD,AMBER.........................................    5.00
WHISKEY,TURN MOLD,GREEN.........................................    5.00
WHISKEY,TURN MOLD,QUART,GRASS GREEN.............................   21.00
WHISKEY,TURN MOLD,SQUAT,QUART,AMBER.............................   10.00
WHISKEY,TURN MOLD,11 IN. TALL,EMERALD GREEN.....................    3.00
WHISKEY,TURN MOLD,11 1/2 IN. TALL,BROWN.........................    2.50
WHISKEY,TWO-MOLD,DOUBLE COLLAR NECK,WHITTLED,BLUE-GREEN.....   10.00
WHISKEY,UDOLPHO WOLFE SCHNAPPS,HONEY-AMBER,QUART............    7.00
WHISKEY,USS CONSTITUTION,1852,PAPER LABEL............COLOR..   XX.XX
WHISKEY,VALALPHO WOLFE'S AROMATIC SCHNAPPS,HONEY AMBER......    8.00
WHISKEY,VOGT APPLEGATE CO.,3 PIECE MOLD,AMBER...............    5.00
WHISKEY,VOLDNERS AROMATIC SCHNAPPS,GRAPHITE PONTIL,BLACK....   30.00
WHISKEY,W.C.FIELDS..............................................   18.50
WHISKEY,W.H.HOOKER,COBALT BLUE..................................    5.00
WHISKEY,W.J.VAN SCHUYVER & CO.,GREEN...........................   20.00
WHISKEY,WALKER'S KILMARROCK,CORKER,AQUA,10 1/2 IN............   17.50
WHISKEY,WALKERS DLC,DUMMY.......................................    3.00
WHISKEY,WARNER'S ENGLISH IMPORTED GIN,1860,AQUA.............   30.00
WHISKEY,WARRANTED FLASK,BLOWN IN MOLD,STRAP SIDE,CLEAR......    5.00
WHISKEY,WARRANTED OVAL,BLOWN IN MOLD,CLEAR.....................    2.50
WHISKEY,WEDDERBURN RYE,LABEL,EMBOSSED,AMBER....................    7.00
WHISKEY,WEEKS & GILSON,QUART,AMBER.............................   65.00
WHISKEY,WEEKS & GILSON,QUART,GOLD AMBER........................   65.00
WHISKEY,WESTHEIMER,FERDINAND & SONS,CINCINNATI,AMBER........    7.00
WHISKEY,WHARTON'S,AMBER.........................................   18.50
WHISKEY,WHITE & MC KAY,BAGPIPE MAN.............................   11.95
WHISKEY,WHITE HORSE,SCREW TOP,AMBER............................    3.00
WHISKEY,WILLIAM GUINAN,EMBOSSED,AMBER..........................   10.00
WHISKEY,WM.H.SPEARS OLD PIONEER,AMBER..........................  100.00
WHISKEY,WM.H.SPEARS OLD PIONEER,CLEAR..........................  100.00
WHISKEY,WRIGHT & TAYLOR DISTILLERS,LOUISVILLE,KY.,QUART,
   AMBER.......................................................   20.00
WHISKEY,WRIGHT & TAYLOR,AMBER..................................    5.00
WHISKEY,YE OLD MOSSROFF BOURBON,CABIN SHAPE,AMBER...........   12.00
WHISKEY,11 1/4 IN.,GOLDEN AMBER................................   15.00
WHITTLE,BUBBLES,GRAPHITE PONTIL, THREE-MOLD,OLIVE AMBER,
   11 IN.HIGH..................................................   20.00
WINE,ANGELICA,FINEST,VINTAGE 1886,IMPORTED,GAL..............    3.00
WINE,ANGELICA,FINEST,VINTAGE 1886,IMPORTED,QUART............     .75
WINE,BARDENHEIERS,GRAPES & LEAVES EMBOSSED.....................    4.50
WINE,BEST SHERRY,PALE,VINTAGE 1886,IMPORTED,GAL.............    3.20
WINE,BEST SHERRY,PALE,VINTAGE 1886,IMPORTED,QUART...........     .80
WINE,BULBOUS PEAR-SHAPED,RED,CLEAR,SUNK HONEYCOMB,
   D.D.ACKERMAN................................................   39.50
WINE,BUNCH OF GRAPES SHAPE,CLEAR...............................    5.00
WINE,C.A.& C. DOS VINHOS DO PORTO,WHITTLE,AMBER.............    8.00
WINE,C.A.& C. DOS VINHOS DO PORTO,WHITTLE,OLIVE.............    8.00
WINE,CHAMPAGNE,BLOWN IN MOLD,9 1/8 IN. TALL,GREEN..........    3.00
WINE,CHAMPAGNE,BLOWN IN MOLD,9 1/8 IN. TALL,OLIVE GREEN.....    3.00
WINE,CHAMPAGNE,BLOWN IN MOLD,9 3/4 IN. TALL,GREEN..........    3.00
WINE,CHAMPAGNE,CYLINDER,INDENTED BOTTOM,GREEN..............    8.00
WINE,CHAMPAGNE,PLAIN,KICK UP,GREEN OPALESCENT...............    3.00
WINE,EMBOSSED,APPLIED HANDLES,CROCKERY,GERMANY.............    4.00
WINE,FIGURAL,BUNCH OF GRAPES,PURPLE,CLEAR STOPPER,PAIR......   22.50
WINE,FISH,GREEN................................................    6.00
WINE,FLINTLOCK PISTOL,PORCELAIN,16 IN.LONG.................    8.50
WINE,FOUR COLUMNS,HAND-BLOWN...................................   16.50
WINE,FREE BLOWN,ROUGH PONTIL,11 3/4 IN. TALL,OLIVE GREEN....   30.00
WINE,FREE BLOWN,11 3/4 IN. TALL,GREEN.........................    8.00
WINE,GARRETT & CO.,BIMAL.......................................    4.50
```

```
WINE,GARRETT & CO.,EST.1835,AMERICAN WINES,QUART,AMETHYST...    8.00
WINE,GARRETT & CO.,EST.1835,AMERICAN WINES,QUART,CLEAR......    8.00
WINE,GARRETT & CO.,EST.1835,AMERICAN WINES,SAMPLE,CLEAR.....    8.00
WINE,GARRETT & CO.,EST.1835,AMERICAN WINES,SAMPLE,AMETHYST..    8.00
WINE,GARRETT & CO.,ST.LOUIS,MO.,CLEAR,12 IN.........ILLUS..     5.00
WINE,GOLD RUSH,TURN MOLD,FRATELLI BRANCE MILANO,GREEN.......    4.75
WINE,H.A.SMITH,WINE MERCHANT,NEWPORT......................    50.00
WINE,HOCK,AMBER.....................................  3.00 TO   4.00
WINE,HOCK,BROKEN OUTSIDE BUBBLE,IMPROVED PONTIL,FREE BLOWN,
  AMBER...................................................   23.50
WINE,HOCK,GREEN............................................    4.50
WINE,HOCK,QUART,BLUE.......................................    5.00
WINE,HOCK,RED AMBER........................................    4.50
WINE,HOCK,TEAL............................................     5.00
WINE,HONEY AMBER,EARLY 18TH CENTURY,6 IN.TALL..............   35.00
WINE,MADEIRA,IMPORTED,GAL.................................     3.00
```

```
WINE,GARRETT & CO.,ST.LOUIS,MO.,CLEAR,12 IN
```

```
WINE,MALAGA, IMPORTED,GAL..................................     3.00
WINE,MODEL T CAR,GREEN....................................      3.50
WINE,MONKEY AROUND,GREEN..................................      5.00
WINE,MONTEBELLO,AMBER.....................................     12.00
WINE,OLD ROYAL PORT,VINTAGE 1886,IMPORTED,GAL.............      3.20
WINE,OLD ROYAL PORT,VINTAGE 1886,IMPORTED,QUART...........       .80
WINE,OLIVE GREEN..........................................      3.00
WINE,ORIENTAL ANIMAL,MONKEY TRIO,SASA PLUM................      5.49
WINE,ORIENTAL ANIMAL,SMOKISAN,SASA PLUM...................      5.99
WINE,PALE SHERRY,IMPORTED,GAL.............................      3.00
WINE,PITCHER,AMBER,GOLD TRIM..............................      5.00
WINE,PITCHER,BLUE.........................................      6.00
WINE,PITCHER,BLUE,GOLD TRIM...............................      5.00
WINE,PLAIN,TURN MOLD,GREEN................................      4.00
WINE,PLAIN,TURN MOLD,JADE GREEN...........................      4.00
WINE,PLAIN,TURN MOLD,OLIVE GREEN..........................      4.00
WINE,ROUGH PONTIL,EARLY 18TH CENTURY......................     45.00
WINE,ROUGH PONTIL,OLIVE GREEN,ELLENVILLE,N.Y.,PINT........     22.00
WINE,ROYAL PORT,IMPORTED,GAL..............................      3.00
WINE,SALZMAN & SEIGLEMAN SHERRY,CROCK JUG,BROWN & CREAM....      5.00
WINE,SWEET CATAWBA,BEST,VINTAGE 1886,IMPORTED,GAL.........      3.00
WINE,SWEET CATAWBA,BEST,VINTAGE 1886,IMPORTED,QUART.......       .75
WINE,TESTER,FREE FLOWN,8 1/2 IN. TALL,GREEN...............     25.00
WINE,TESTER,GREEN.........................................     20.00
WINE,TOKAY,IMPORTED,GAL...................................      3.00
WINE,TRINER'S BITTER WINE,LABEL,AMBER.....................      2.00
WINE,TUCKED UP BOTTOM,GREEN...............................      2.50
WINE,TURN MOLD,11 3/4 IN. TALL,OLIVE GREEN................      2.50
WINE,TURN MOLD,12 IN. TALL,AQUA...........................      3.00
WINE,VASE,WHITE WITH RED ROSES............................      8.00
```

```
WINE,VERMOUTH,TURN MOLD,13 1/4 IN. TALL,OLIVE GREEN.........    3.00
WINE,1/2 GAL.,BLOB LIP,TURN MOLD,GREEN......................    2.50
WINE,11 3/4 IN. TALL,AQUA...................................    1.50
WINE,1720 SHAPE,GREEN.......................................  110.00
WISTAR,OLIVE GREEN,CIRCA 1730,7 1/4 IN......................   95.00
WOLFS MT.CARMEL BOTTLING,MT.CARMEL,ILL.,CLEAR...............    2.50
ZELLER SCHWARZE KATZ,MACHINE MADE,GOLDEN CAT,GREEN..........   10.00
ZSOLNAY,PERFUMER,BARREL SHAPE,HANDLE AT TOP,GOLD & TURQUOISE   76.00
```